Louis A. Airoldi

Preface

This text, a revision of *Analytic Geometry and Calculus*, is designed to serve as an introductory course in analytic geometry and calculus for students who have some familiarity with the basic principles of algebra and trigonometry. The book provides sufficient material for classes that meet four or five hours per week for three semesters. The arrangement of the topics, however, facilitates the organization of shorter courses.

Purpose. The basic theory of calculus is developed in this book with a view to giving the student a sound understanding of the fundamental concepts of calculus and a thorough appreciation of its many applied uses. Considerable stress has been placed on the logical structure of the theory in order that students might gain some active experience in making original mathematical developments. To serve this purpose all definitions, theorems, and general procedures are presented in as much detail as the demands of clarity and relative simplicity permit.

Special features. The topics usually covered in a course on analytic geometry have been distributed throughout the text in a manner designed to supplement and augment efficiently the presentation of the basic concepts of the calculus.

The fundamental principles of calculus are clearly stated in precise mathematical terms. Numerous illustrations and illustrative examples are presented to clarify both the theoretical and the applied aspects of the subject.

For the convenience of the many students of calculus who are primarily interested in engineering and other applied fields, the concept of integration and its applications are introduced in the early part of the book. Also, to assist in the computational aspects of calculus, the formulas and curves of more elementary mathematics are given in an Introduction, five numerical tables are given on pp. 569 ff., and the answers to all odd-numbered problems are included in the text. A pamphlet containing the answers to the even-numbered problems is available to instructors.

Revised features. In order to make the text as adaptable as possible to modern needs, the basic material on limits, functions, and continuity has been thoroughly revised with a view to emphasizing modern mathematical techniques. Extensive additions on the theoretical structure of calculus have been made, both in illustrations and exercises, throughout the book.

On the applied side, considerable material has been added to illustrate the many applications of differential equations. Another important addition supplementing the applied work is a chapter on the calculus of vectors. This chapter covers completely the algebra, differentiation, and integration of vectors, including discussions of directional derivatives, line integrals, and surface integrals.

Acknowledgments. The author wishes to take this opportunity to express his appreciation to his many friends and colleagues who have so graciously criticized and assisted in the revision of the text. In particular the author would like to thank the many users of the original edition who have contributed worth-while suggestions for the revision.

T. S. P.

Portland, Oregon
May, 1960

CALCULUS

WITH ANALYTIC GEOMETRY

Introduction

Mathematical Formulas

The following list of mathematical formulas and graphs is given to summarize briefly the computational aspects of more elementary mathematics and to serve as a convenient reference in future work.

GEOMETRY

In the following formulas, r denotes radius, h altitude, l slant height, b base, B area of base, θ central angle expressed in radians.

1. **Triangle.** Area $= \frac{1}{2}bh$.
2. **Rectangle.** Area $= bh$. Diagonal $= \sqrt{b^2 + h^2}$.
3. **Trapezoid.** Area $= \frac{1}{2}h(b_1 + b_2)$.
4. **Circle.** Arc $= r\theta$. Circumference $= 2\pi r$. Area $= \pi r^2$.
5. **Circular sector.** Area $= \frac{1}{2}r^2\theta$.
6. **Circular segment.** Area $= \frac{1}{2}r^2(\theta - \sin\theta)$.
7. **Rectangular parallelepiped.** If a, b, c are the sides

   Volume $= abc$. Diagonal $= \sqrt{a^2 + b^2 + c^2}$.
8. **Prism.** Volume $= Bh$.
9. **Pyramid.** Volume $= \frac{1}{3}Bh$.
10. **Right circular cylinder.** Lateral surface $= 2\pi rh$. Volume $= \pi r^2 h$.
11. **Right circular cone.** Lateral surface $= \pi rl$. Volume $= \frac{1}{3}\pi r^2 h$.
12. **Sphere.** Surface $= 4\pi r^2$. Volume $= \frac{4}{3}\pi r^3$.
13. **Spherical segment.** Volume $= \frac{1}{3}\pi h^2(3r - h)$.
14. **Frustum of a pyramid.** Volume $= \frac{1}{3}h(B_1 + B_2 + \sqrt{B_1 B_2})$.
15. **Frustum of a right circular cone.**

    Lateral surface $= \pi l(r_1 + r_2)$. Volume $= \frac{1}{3}\pi h(r_1^2 + r_2^2 + r_1 r_2)$.
16. **Prismatoid.** Volume $= \frac{1}{6}h(B_1 + 4B_m + B_2)$.

ALGEBRA

17. **Quadratic formula.** If $ax^2 + bx + c = 0$, $a \neq 0$, then

$$x = \frac{-b \pm \sqrt{b^2 - 4ac}}{2a}.$$

18. Properties of logarithms.

(a) $\log(MN) = \log M + \log N$, (b) $\log(M/N) = \log M - \log N$,
(c) $\log M^n = n \log M$, (d) $\log \sqrt[n]{M} = (1/n) \log M$,
(e) $\log_b b = 1$, (f) $\log_b 1 = 0$.

19. Factorial numbers. $n! = 1 \cdot 2 \cdot 3 \cdots (n-1) \cdot n$. $0! = 1$.

20. Binomial expansion.

$$(a+b)^n = a^n + {}_nC_1 a^{n-1}b + {}_nC_2 a^{n-2}b^2 + \cdots + {}_nC_r a^{n-r}b^r + \cdots + b^n,$$

where

$${}_nC_1 = \frac{n}{1}, \quad {}_nC_2 = \frac{n(n-1)}{1 \cdot 2}, \ \ldots, \quad {}_nC_r = \frac{n!}{r!(n-r)!}, \ \ldots.$$

21. Arithmetic progression. If a denotes the first term, d the common difference, n the number of terms, l the last term, and S the sum, then

$$l = a + (n-1)d, \qquad S = \tfrac{1}{2}n(a+l), \qquad S = \tfrac{1}{2}n[2a + (n-1)d].$$

22. Geometric progression. If a denotes the first term, r the common ratio, n the number of terms, l the last term, and S the sum, then

$$l = ar^{n-1}, \qquad S = a\frac{1-r^n}{1-r}, \qquad S = \frac{a-rl}{1-r}.$$

23. Infinite geometric progression. $S = a/(1-r)$, if $r^2 < 1$.

TRIGONOMETRY

24. Radians and degrees. $360° = 2\pi$ radians $= 1$ revolution.
1 radian $= 57.2957\cdots$ degrees. 1 degree $= 0.0174532\cdots$ radian.

25. Values of trigonometric functions for certain angles.

Angle in Degrees	sin	cos	tan	cot	sec	csc	Angle in Radians
0°	0	1	0		1		0
30°	$\frac{1}{2}$	$\frac{1}{2}\sqrt{3}$	$\frac{1}{3}\sqrt{3}$	$\sqrt{3}$	$\frac{2}{3}\sqrt{3}$	2	$\frac{1}{6}\pi$
45°	$\frac{1}{2}\sqrt{2}$	$\frac{1}{2}\sqrt{2}$	1	1	$\sqrt{2}$	$\sqrt{2}$	$\frac{1}{4}\pi$
60°	$\frac{1}{2}\sqrt{3}$	$\frac{1}{2}$	$\sqrt{3}$	$\frac{1}{3}\sqrt{3}$	2	$\frac{2}{3}\sqrt{3}$	$\frac{1}{3}\pi$
90°	1	0		0		1	$\frac{1}{2}\pi$
180°	0	−1	0		−1		π
270°	−1	0		0		−1	$\frac{3}{2}\pi$
360°	0	1	0		1		2π

26. Fundamental identities.

$$\csc x = 1/\sin x, \qquad \sec x = 1/\cos x, \qquad \cot x = 1/\tan x,$$

$$\tan x = \sin x/\cos x, \qquad \cot x = \cos x/\sin x,$$

$$\sin^2 x + \cos^2 x = 1, \qquad 1 + \tan^2 x = \sec^2 x, \qquad 1 + \cot^2 x = \csc^2 x.$$

27. Reduction relations.

Angle	Sine	Cosine	Tangent	Co-tangent	Secant	Cosecant
$-x$	$-\sin x$	$\cos x$	$-\tan x$	$-\cot x$	$\sec x$	$-\csc x$
$90° - x$	$\cos x$	$\sin x$	$\cot x$	$\tan x$	$\csc x$	$\sec x$
$90° + x$	$\cos x$	$-\sin x$	$-\cot x$	$-\tan x$	$-\csc x$	$\sec x$
$180° - x$	$\sin x$	$-\cos x$	$-\tan x$	$-\cot x$	$-\sec x$	$\csc x$
$180° + x$	$-\sin x$	$-\cos x$	$\tan x$	$\cot x$	$-\sec x$	$-\csc x$
$270° - x$	$-\cos x$	$-\sin x$	$\cot x$	$\tan x$	$-\csc x$	$-\sec x$
$270° + x$	$-\cos x$	$\sin x$	$-\cot x$	$-\tan x$	$\csc x$	$-\sec x$
$360° - x$	$-\sin x$	$\cos x$	$-\tan x$	$-\cot x$	$\sec x$	$-\csc x$

28. Formulas for the sum and difference of two angles.

$$\sin (x \pm y) = \sin x \cos y \pm \cos x \sin y,$$

$$\cos (x \pm y) = \cos x \cos y \mp \sin x \sin y,$$

$$\tan (x \pm y) = \frac{\tan x \pm \tan y}{1 \mp \tan x \tan y}.$$

29. Double-angle formulas.

$$\sin 2x = 2 \sin x \cos x, \qquad \cos 2x = \cos^2 x - \sin^2 x,$$

$$\tan 2x = \frac{2 \tan x}{1 - \tan^2 x}.$$

30. Half-angle formulas.

$$\sin \frac{x}{2} = \pm \sqrt{\frac{1 - \cos x}{2}}, \qquad \cos \frac{x}{2} = \pm \sqrt{\frac{1 + \cos x}{2}},$$

$$\tan \frac{x}{2} = \pm \sqrt{\frac{1 - \cos x}{1 + \cos x}} = \frac{1 - \cos x}{\sin x} = \frac{\sin x}{1 + \cos x}.$$

31. Sum formulas.

$$\sin x + \sin y = 2 \sin \tfrac{1}{2}(x + y) \cos \tfrac{1}{2}(x - y),$$
$$\sin x - \sin y = 2 \cos \tfrac{1}{2}(x + y) \sin \tfrac{1}{2}(x - y),$$
$$\cos x + \cos y = 2 \cos \tfrac{1}{2}(x + y) \cos \tfrac{1}{2}(x - y),$$
$$\cos x - \cos y = -2 \sin \tfrac{1}{2}(x + y) \sin \tfrac{1}{2}(x - y).$$

32. Product formulas.

$$\sin x \sin y = \tfrac{1}{2} \cos (x - y) - \tfrac{1}{2} \cos (x + y),$$
$$\sin x \cos y = \tfrac{1}{2} \sin (x - y) + \tfrac{1}{2} \sin (x + y),$$
$$\cos x \cos y = \tfrac{1}{2} \cos (x - y) + \tfrac{1}{2} \cos (x + y).$$

33. Inverse formulas. When $a > 0$,

$$\mathrm{Sin}^{-1}(-a) = -\mathrm{Sin}^{-1} a, \qquad \mathrm{Cot}^{-1}(-a) = \pi - \mathrm{Tan}^{-1}(1/a),$$
$$\mathrm{Cos}^{-1}(-a) = \pi - \mathrm{Cos}^{-1} a, \qquad \mathrm{Sec}^{-1}(-a) = \mathrm{Cos}^{-1}(1/a) - \pi,$$
$$\mathrm{Tan}^{-1}(-a) = -\mathrm{Tan}^{-1} a, \qquad \mathrm{Csc}^{-1}(-a) = \mathrm{Sin}^{-1}(1/a) - \pi,$$
$$\mathrm{Sin}^{-1} a = \mathrm{Cos}^{-1}\sqrt{1 - a^2},$$
$$\mathrm{Cos}^{-1} a = \mathrm{Sin}^{-1}\sqrt{1 - a^2}.$$

When $a > 0$, $b > 0$,

$$\mathrm{Sin}^{-1} a - \mathrm{Sin}^{-1} b = \mathrm{Sin}^{-1}(a\sqrt{1 - b^2} - b\sqrt{1 - a^2}),$$
$$\mathrm{Tan}^{-1} a - \mathrm{Tan}^{-1} b = \mathrm{Tan}^{-1}(a - b)/(1 + ab),$$
$$\mathrm{Cos}^{-1} a + \mathrm{Cos}^{-1} b = \begin{cases} \mathrm{Cos}^{-1}[ab - \sqrt{(1 - a^2)(1 - b^2)}], & \text{if } a^2 + b^2 > 1, \\ \pi/2, & a^2 + b^2 = 1, \\ \pi - \mathrm{Cos}^{-1}[\sqrt{(1 - a^2)(1 - b^2)} - ab], & a^2 + b^2 < 1, \end{cases}$$
$$\mathrm{Tan}^{-1} a + \mathrm{Tan}^{-1} b = \begin{cases} \mathrm{Tan}^{-1}(a + b)/(1 - ab), & \text{if } ab < 1, \\ \pi/2, & ab = 1, \\ \pi - \mathrm{Tan}^{-1}(a + b)/(ab - 1), & ab > 1. \end{cases}$$

34. Formulas for any triangles. Sides, a, b, c; opposite angles, A, B, C; $s = \tfrac{1}{2}(a + b + c)$; radius of circumcircle, R; radius of incircle, r.

Law of sines. $$\frac{a}{\sin A} = \frac{b}{\sin B} = \frac{c}{\sin C} = 2R,$$

Law of cosines. $$a^2 = b^2 + c^2 - 2bc \cos A,$$

$$r = \sqrt{\frac{(s - a)(s - b)(s - c)}{s}},$$

$$\text{Area} = \tfrac{1}{2}ab \sin C$$
$$= \frac{a^2 \sin B \sin C}{2 \sin (B + C)}$$
$$= \sqrt{s(s - a)(s - b)(s - c)}.$$

PLANE ANALYTIC GEOMETRY

35. For two points $P_1(x_1,y_1)$ and $P_2(x_2,y_2)$.

Distance P_1P_2. $d = \sqrt{(x_1 - x_2)^2 + (y_1 - y_2)^2}$.

Slope of P_1P_2. $m = \dfrac{y_1 - y_2}{x_1 - x_2}$.

Mid-point of P_1P_2. $x = \frac{1}{2}(x_1 + x_2),\ y = \frac{1}{2}(y_1 + y_2)$.

36. Angle between two lines with slopes m_1 and m_2.

$$\tan \phi = \frac{m_1 - m_2}{1 + m_1 m_2}.$$

For parallel lines $m_1 = m_2$; for perpendicular lines $m_1 = -1/m_2$.

37. Equations of straight lines.

Point-slope form. $y - y_1 = m(x - x_1)$.

Slope-intercept form. $y = mx + b$.

Two-point form. $\dfrac{y - y_1}{x - x_1} = \dfrac{y_2 - y_1}{x_2 - x_1}$.

Intercept form. $\dfrac{x}{a} + \dfrac{y}{b} = 1$.

Horizontal line. $y = b$.

Vertical line. $x = a$.

38. Distance from $P(x_1,y_1)$ to the line $Ax + By + C = 0$.

$$d = \frac{Ax_1 + By_1 + C}{\pm\sqrt{A^2 + B^2}}.$$

39. Relations between rectangular and polar coordinates.

$$x = r\cos\theta, \qquad r = \pm\sqrt{x^2 + y^2},$$
$$y = r\sin\theta. \qquad \theta = \tan^{-1}(y/x).$$

40. Equation of circle. Center (h,k), radius r.

$$(x - h)^2 + (y - k)^2 = r^2.$$

41. Equation of ellipse. Center (h,k), semimajor axis a, semiminor axis b.

$$\frac{(x-h)^2}{a^2} + \frac{(y-k)^2}{b^2} = 1 \quad \text{or} \quad \frac{(y-k)^2}{a^2} + \frac{(x-h)^2}{b^2} = 1.$$

42. Equation of hyperbola. Center (h,k), semitransverse axis a, semiconjugate axis b.

$$\frac{(x-h)^2}{a^2} - \frac{(y-k)^2}{b^2} = 1 \quad \text{or} \quad \frac{(y-k)^2}{a^2} - \frac{(x-h)^2}{b^2} = 1.$$

Equilateral hyperbola with center at origin $xy = C$.

43. **Equation of parabola.** Vertex (h,k), focal distance p.

$$(y - k)^2 = 4p(x - h) \quad \text{or} \quad (x - h)^2 = 4p(y - k).$$

SOLID ANALYTIC GEOMETRY

44. **For two points $P_1(x_1,y_1,z_1)$ and $P_2(x_2,y_2,z_2)$.**

Distance P_1P_2. $d = \sqrt{(x_1 - x_2)^2 + (y_1 - y_2)^2 + (z_1 - z_2)^2}$.

Direction numbers of P_1P_2. $[x_1 - x_2, y_1 - y_2, z_1 - z_2]$.

Mid-point of P_1P_2. $x = \frac{1}{2}(x_1 + x_2), y = \frac{1}{2}(y_1 + y_2), z = \frac{1}{2}(z_1 + z_2)$.

45. **Angle between two lines whose direction numbers are $[a_1, b_1, c_1]$ and $[a_2, b_2, c_2]$.**

$$\cos\phi = \pm \frac{a_1a_2 + b_1b_2 + c_1c_2}{\sqrt{a_1^2 + b_1^2 + c_1^2}\sqrt{a_2^2 + b_2^2 + c_2^2}}.$$

Parallel lines. $\dfrac{a_1}{a_2} = \dfrac{b_1}{b_2} = \dfrac{c_1}{c_2}$.

Perpendicular lines. $a_1a_2 + b_1b_2 + c_1c_2 = 0$.

46. **Equation of a plane through $P(x_1,y_1,z_1)$ and perpendicular to a line with direction numbers $[A,B,C]$.**

$$A(x - x_1) + B(y - y_1) + C(z - z_1) = 0.$$

47. **Equations of a line through $P(x_1,y_1,z_1)$ with direction numbers $[a,b,c]$.**

$$\frac{x - x_1}{a} = \frac{y - y_1}{b} = \frac{z - z_1}{c}.$$

48. **Distance from $P(x_1,y_1,z_1)$ to the plane $Ax + By + Cz + D = 0$.**

$$d = \frac{Ax_1 + By_1 + Cz_1 + D}{\pm\sqrt{A^2 + B^2 + C^2}}.$$

49. **Relations between rectangular and cylindrical coordinates.**

$$x = r\cos\theta, \qquad y = r\sin\theta, \qquad z = z;$$

$$r = \pm\sqrt{x^2 + y^2}, \qquad \theta = \tan^{-1}(y/x), \qquad z = z.$$

50. **Relations between rectangular and spherical coordinates.**

$$x = r\sin\theta\cos\phi, \qquad y = r\sin\theta\sin\phi, \qquad z = r\cos\theta;$$

$$r = \pm\sqrt{x^2 + y^2 + z^2}, \quad \phi = \tan^{-1}(y/x), \quad \theta = \tan^{-1}(\sqrt{x^2 + y^2})/z.$$

51. Sine curve.

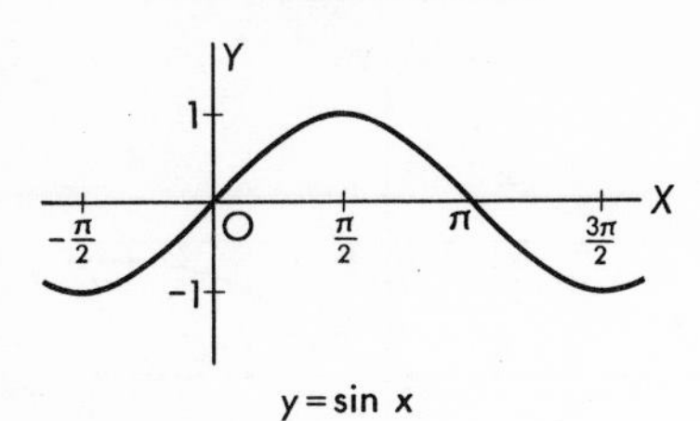

$y = \sin x$

52. Cosine curve.

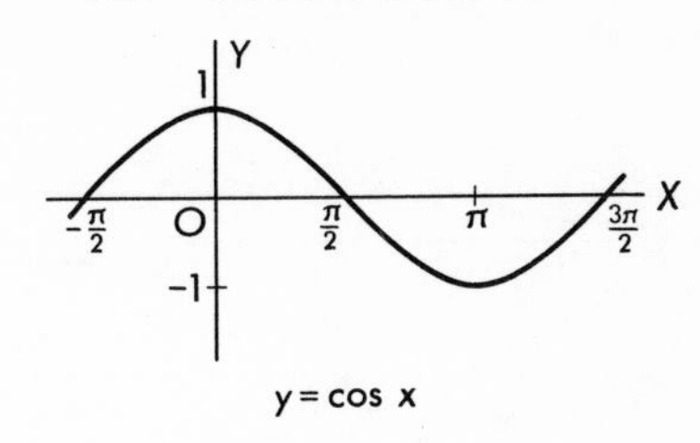

$y = \cos x$

53. Tangent curve.

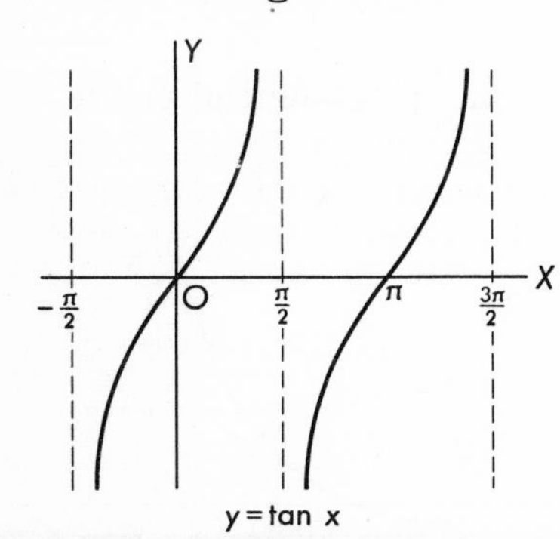

$y = \tan x$

54. Secant curve.

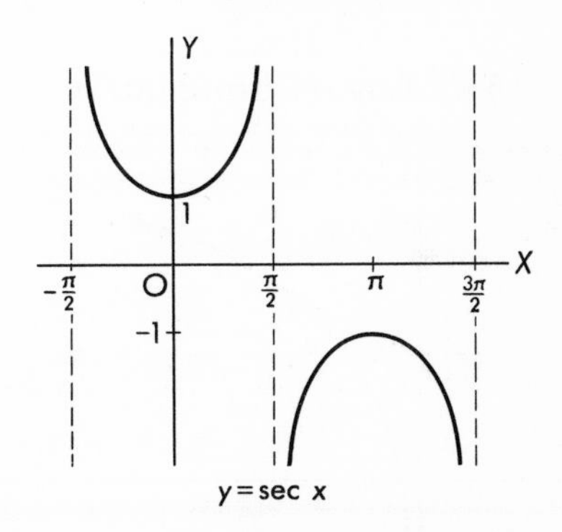

$y = \sec x$

55. Inverse sine curve.

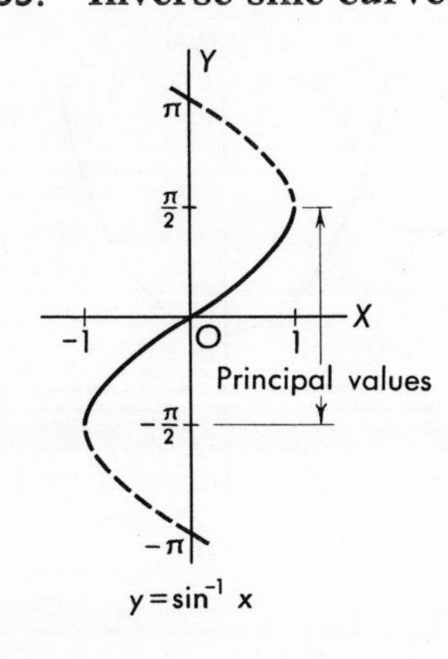

$y = \sin^{-1} x$

56. Inverse cosine curve.

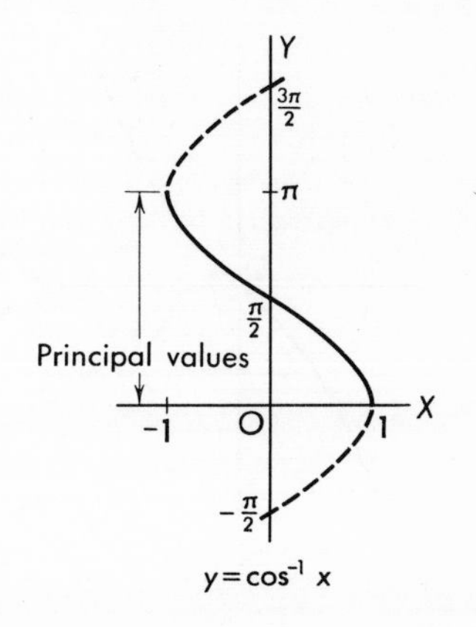

$y = \cos^{-1} x$

57. Inverse tangent curve.

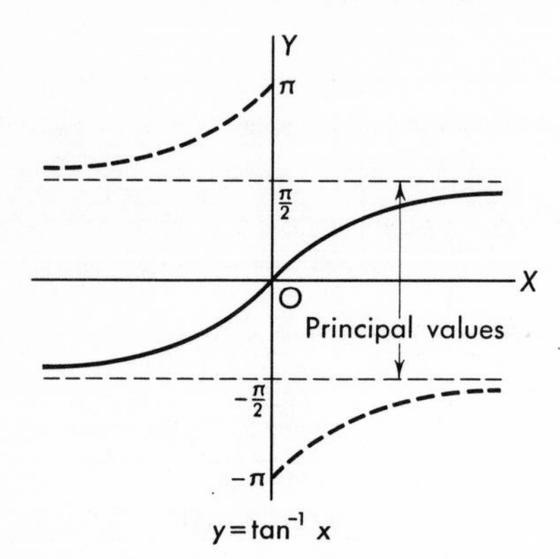

$y = \tan^{-1} x$

58. Inverse secant curve.

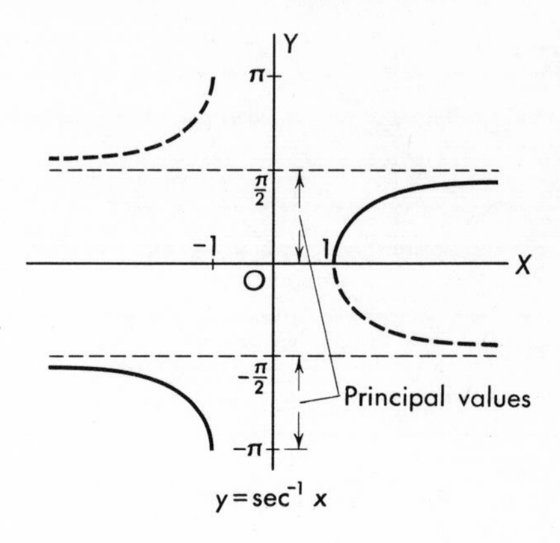

$y = \sec^{-1} x$

59. Logarithmic curve.

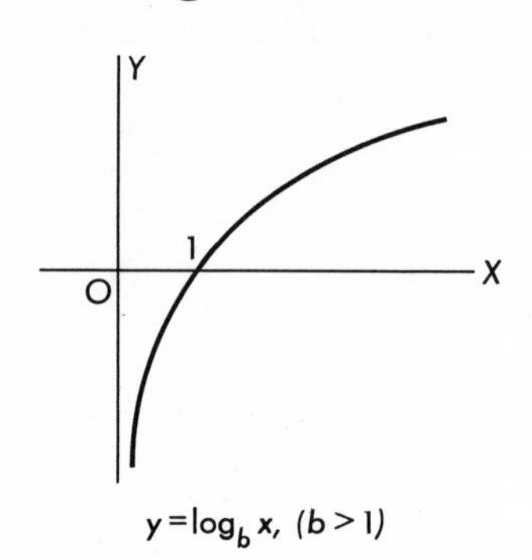

$y = \log_b x, \ (b > 1)$

60. Exponential curve.

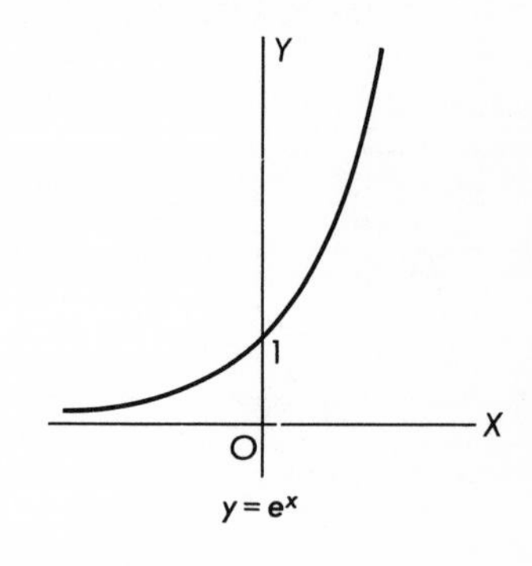

$y = e^x$

61. Hyperbolic sine curve.

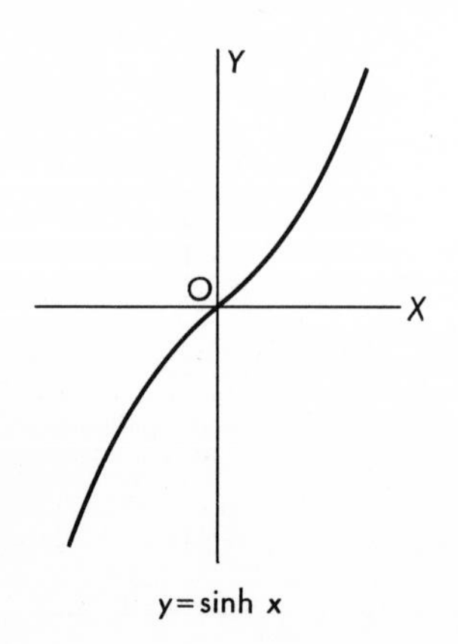

$y = \sinh x$

62. Hyperbolic cosine curve.

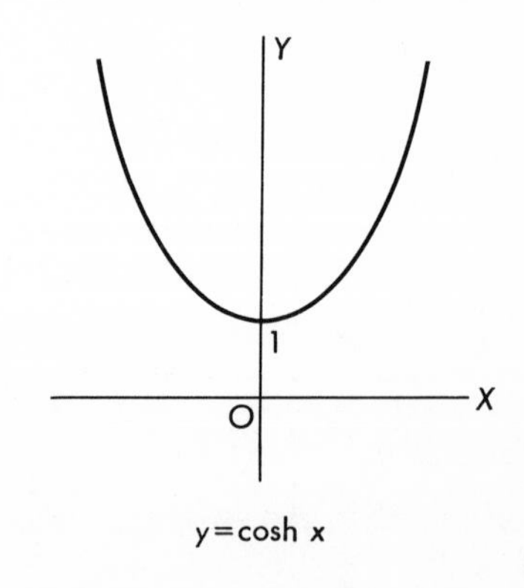

$y = \cosh x$

63. Cubical parabola.

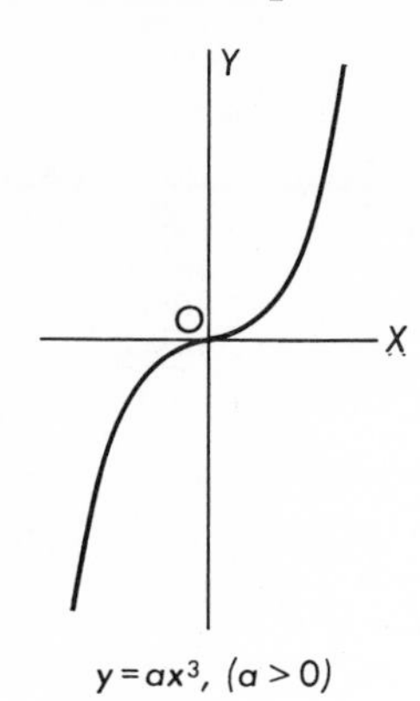

$y = ax^3, \ (a > 0)$

64. Semicubical parabola.

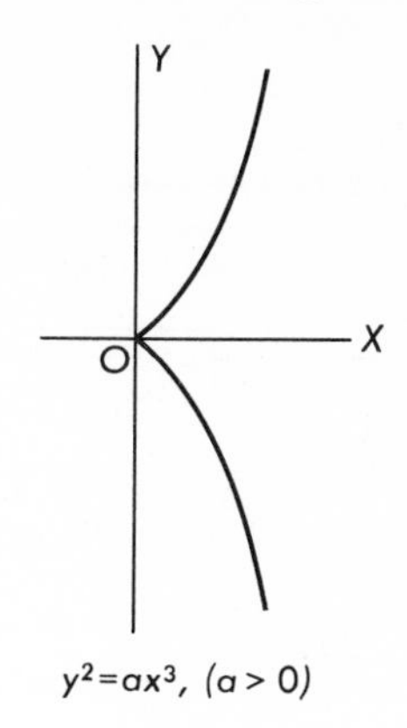

$y^2 = ax^3, \ (a > 0)$

65. Probability curve.

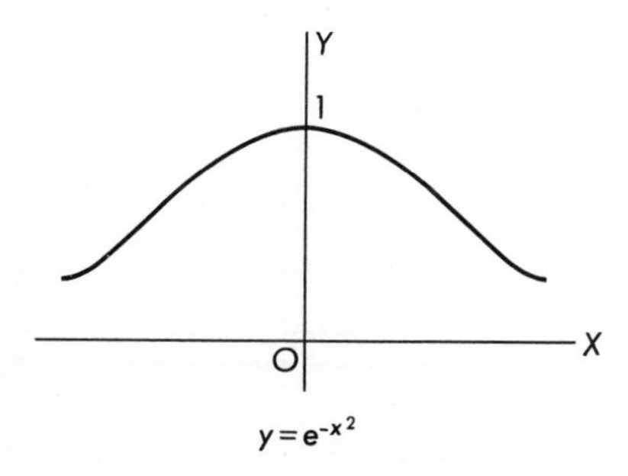

$y = e^{-x^2}$

66. Parabolic arc.

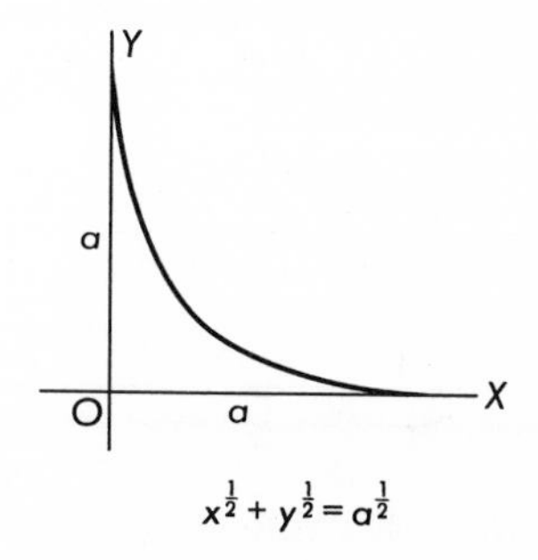

$x^{\frac{1}{2}} + y^{\frac{1}{2}} = a^{\frac{1}{2}}$

67. Folium of Descartes.

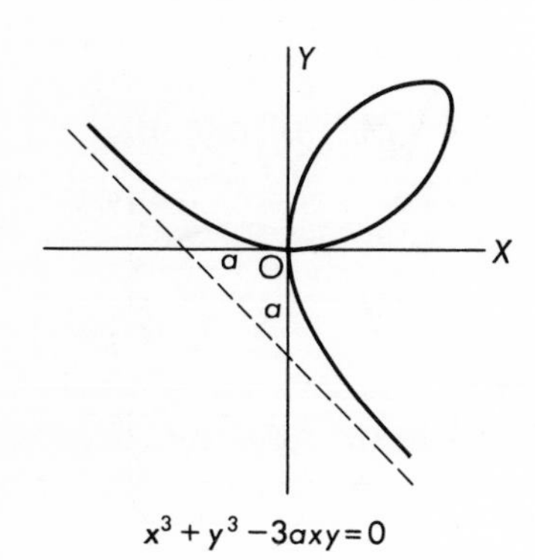

$x^3 + y^3 - 3axy = 0$

68. The cissoid of Diocles.

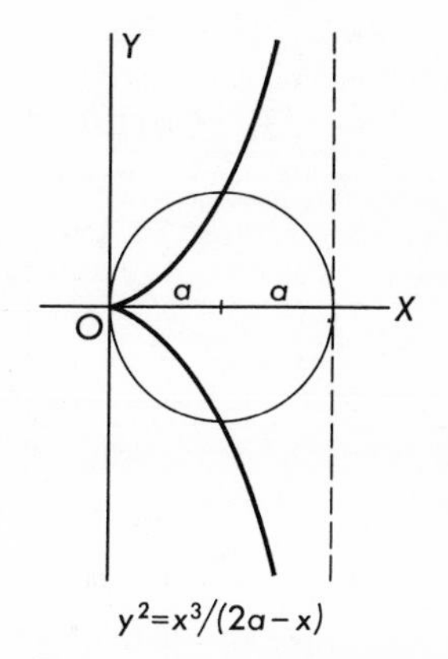

$y^2 = x^3/(2a - x)$

69. Astroid.

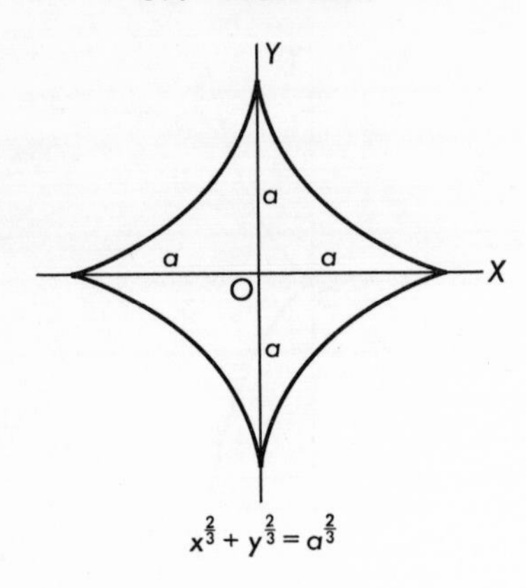

$x^{\frac{2}{3}} + y^{\frac{2}{3}} = a^{\frac{2}{3}}$

70. The witch of Agnesi.

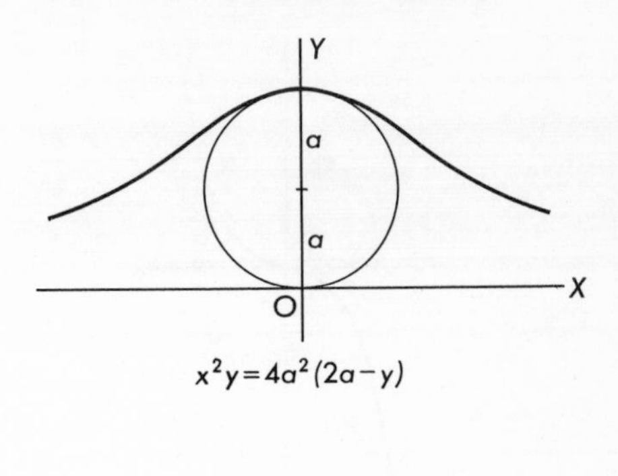

$x^2 y = 4a^2 (2a - y)$

71. Strophoid.

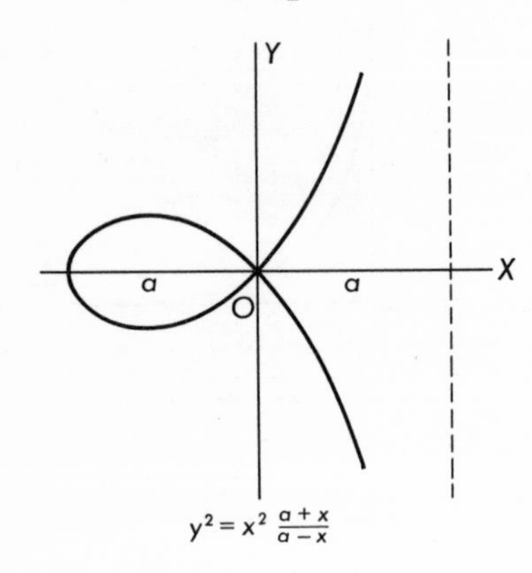

$y^2 = x^2 \frac{a+x}{a-x}$

72. Tractrix.

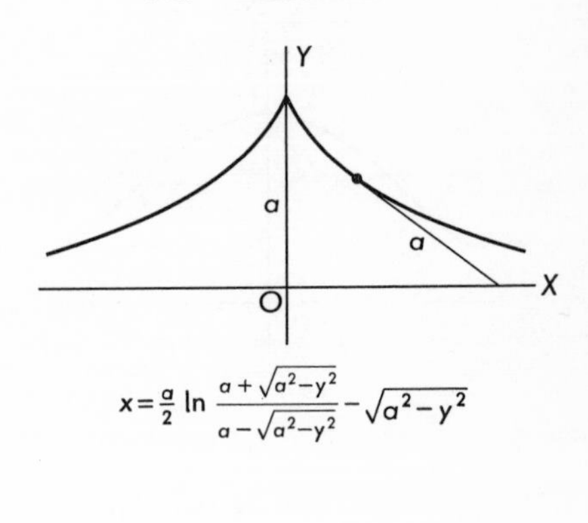

$x = \frac{a}{2} \ln \frac{a + \sqrt{a^2 - y^2}}{a - \sqrt{a^2 - y^2}} - \sqrt{a^2 - y^2}$

73. Cardioid.

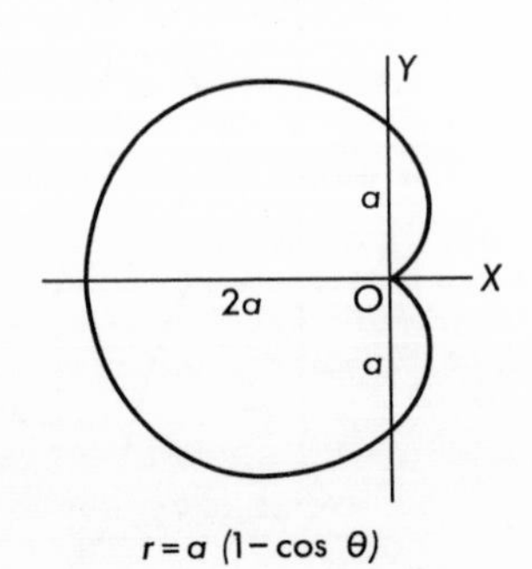

$r = a\ (1 - \cos\ \theta)$

74. Limaçon.

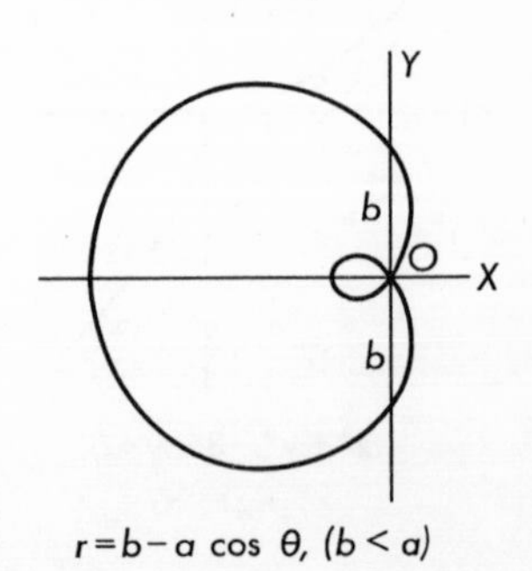

$r = b - a \cos\ \theta,\ (b < a)$

75. Spiral of Archimedes.

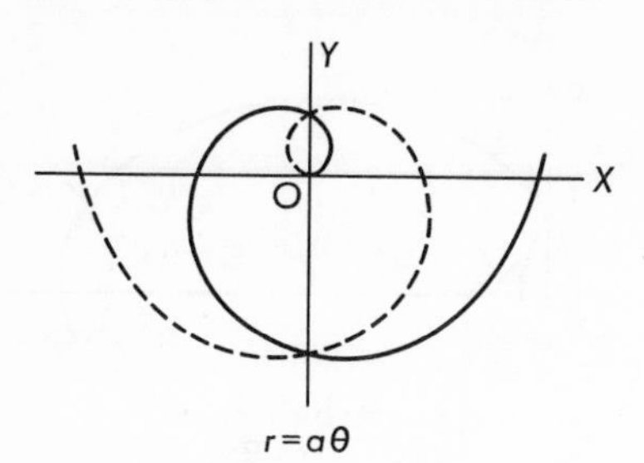

$r = a\theta$

76. Hyperbolic spiral.

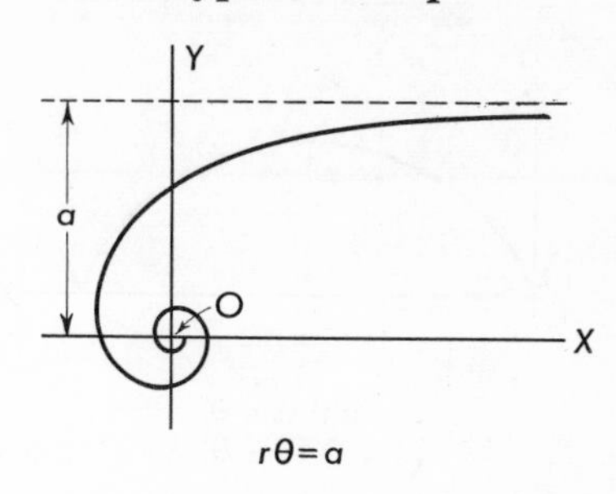

$r\theta = a$

77. The lemniscate of Bernoulli.

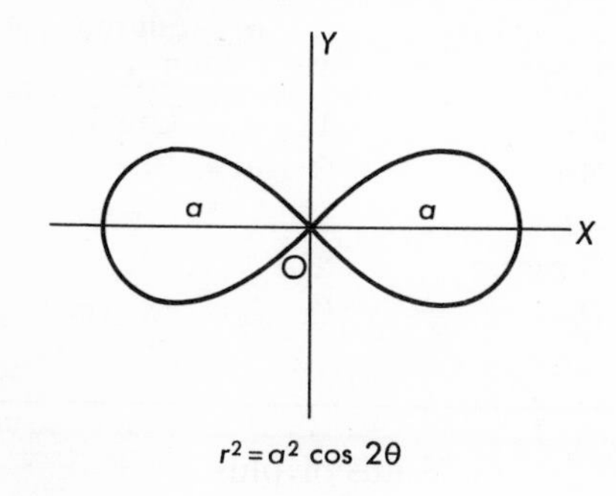

$r^2 = a^2 \cos 2\theta$

78. The conchoid of Nicomedes.

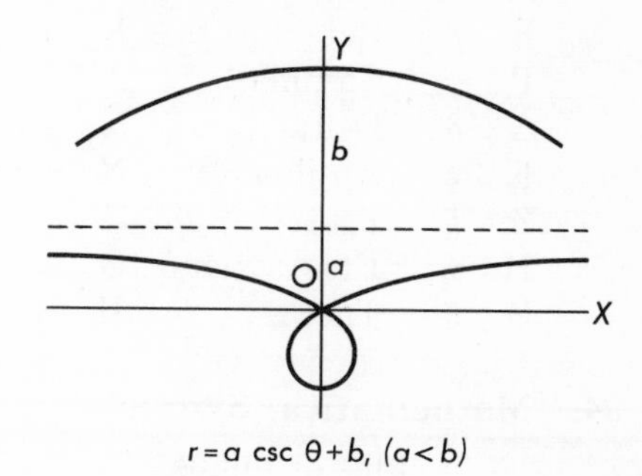

$r = a \csc \theta + b, \ (a < b)$

79. Three-leaved rose.

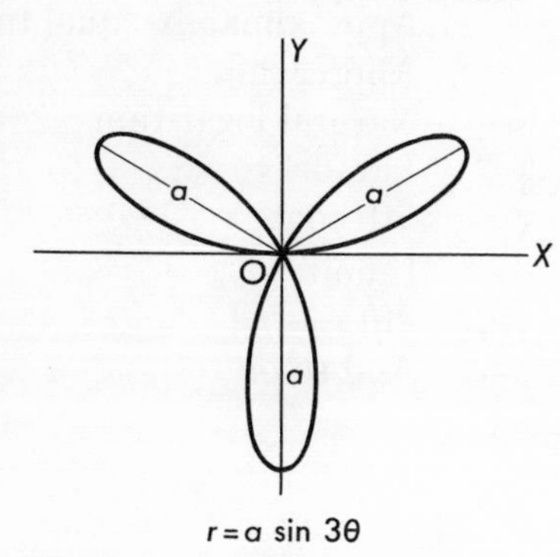

$r = a \sin 3\theta$

80. Four-leaved rose.

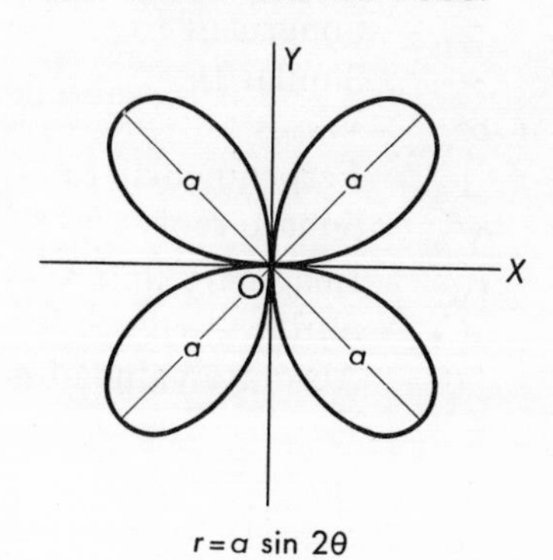

$r = a \sin 2\theta$

81. Cycloid.

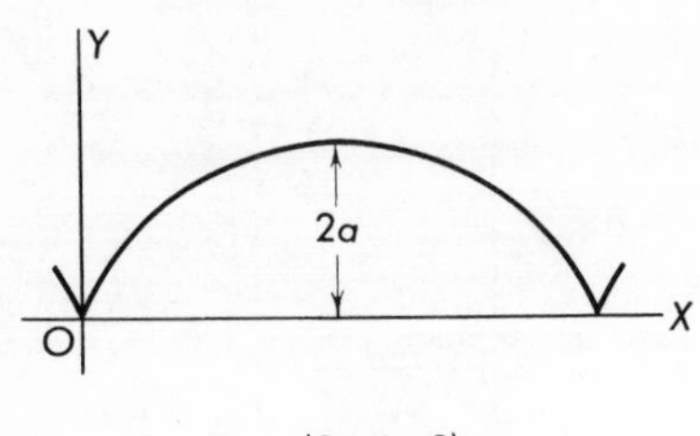

$$\begin{cases} x = a(\theta - \sin\theta), \\ y = a(1 - \cos\theta) \end{cases}$$

82. Trochoid.

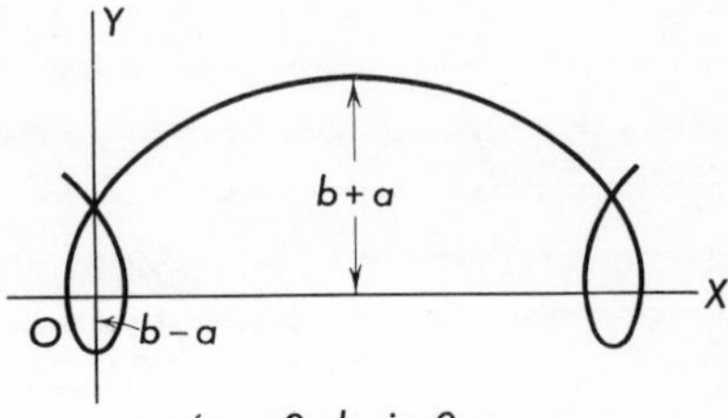

$$\begin{cases} x = a\theta - b\sin\theta, \\ y = a - b\cos\theta, (a < b) \end{cases}$$

83. Greek Alphabet.

Α	α	Alpha	Ι	ι	Iota	Ρ	ρ	Rho
Β	β	Beta	Κ	κ	Kappa	Σ	σ	Sigma
Γ	γ	Gamma	Λ	λ	Lambda	Τ	τ	Tau
Δ	δ	Delta	Μ	μ	Mu	Υ	υ	Upsilon
Ε	ϵ	Epsilon	Ν	ν	Nu	Φ	ϕ	Phi
Ζ	ζ	Zeta	Ξ	ξ	Xi	Χ	χ	Chi
Η	η	Eta	Ο	o	Omicron	Ψ	ψ	Psi
Θ	θ	Theta	Π	π	Pi	Ω	ω	Omega

84. Mathematical Symbols.

$\pm$	Plus or minus	$\mp$	Minus or plus
$=$	Equal to	$\neq$	Not equal to
$\equiv$	Identically equal to	$\not\equiv$	Not identically equal to
$\times$,	Multiplication	$\div$, /	Division
$>$	Greater than	$<$	Less than
$\geqq$	Greater than or equal to	$\leqq$	Less than or equal to
$\cong$	Congruent to	$\approx$	Approximately equal to
$\sim$	Similar to	$\rightarrow$	Approaches
$\propto$	Varies as	ln	Natural logarithm
$\perp$	Perpendicular to	$\parallel$	Parallel to
$\sqrt{\ }$	Square root	$\sqrt[n]{\ }$	nth root
i	Imaginary unit $\sqrt{-1}$	∞	Infinity
${}_nC_r$	$n!/r!(n - r)!$	${}_nP_r$	$n!/(n - r)!$
$\|a\|$	Absolute value of a	$\cdots$	And so on

CHAPTER 1

Coordinates and Lines

1. Introduction

Prior to the year 1600, geometry as developed by the Greeks and algebra as developed by the Hindus, Moslems, and Persians were two completely unrelated mathematical disciplines. They remained so until 1637 when René Descartes (1596–1650), a renowned French mathematician and philosopher, published a treatise *La Geométrie* in which he introduced the concept of coordinate systems. He indicated how, by using coordinates, it was possible to represent geometric configurations by equations, and vice versa. This important discovery made it possible to use algebraic or analytic methods in geometry and as a result led to the development of a far more comprehensive theory of geometry, called *analytic geometry*.

Thirty years after the origin of analytic geometry, two other prominent mathematicians, Sir Isaac Newton (1642–1727) and Gottfried Wilhelm Leibnitz (1646–1716), developed independently another new and revolutionary idea in mathematics. This new concept dealt with the notion of limits, that is, with the values approached by non-finite sequences of numbers. This theory of limits is the basis for what we now call *calculus*.

The advent of these two significant contributions marks the beginning of modern mathematics.

2. Number System

In analytic geometry and calculus we are primarily concerned with real numbers. These numbers can be divided into two groups, the **rational** and **irrational.** The rational numbers consist of zero, the positive and negative integers, and the numbers which can be written as the quotient of two integers, such as $\frac{3}{4}$ and $-\frac{7}{5}$. All other real numbers, such as $\sqrt{2}$ and π, are called irrational numbers.

Note: Remember that division by zero is not defined in mathematics. Thus the expressions $1/x$ and $\cot x$ have no meaning when $x = 0$.

The real numbers can be represented graphically on a straight line by designating an arbitrary point of the line as O, the **origin,** and laying off equal divisions in both directions from O as shown in Figure 1. It is customary to locate the positive numbers to the right of O, and the negative numbers to the left. A scale such as that depicted is called a **real continuum.**

If A and B are any two real numbers, the notation $A < B$ means that A is less than B, or graphically that A is to the left of B on the real continuum. This same relation can also be written as $B > A$, read as "B is greater than A." Observe in both cases that the inequality sign "points" toward the smaller of the two numbers. Certain classes of real numbers can be designated by using inequality signs. Thus $x < A$ means all numbers x to the left of A. The notation $A < x < B$ represents all numbers x *between* A and B, that is, the numbers which are both greater than A and less than B. To represent

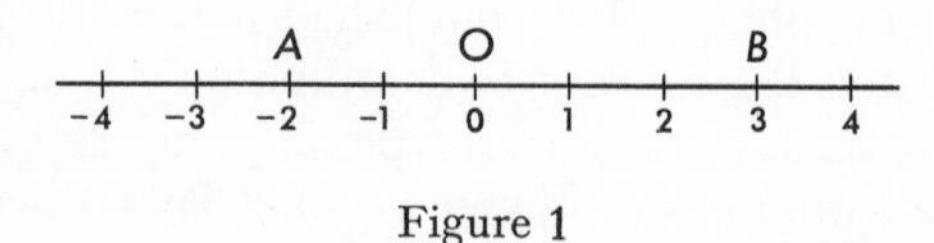

Figure 1

the points of the continuum which lie outside the interval from A to B, it is necessary to write two inequalities $x < A$ or $x > B$. Observe that these two inequalities cannot be written together as $A > x > B$, since this latter expression implies that $A > B$ which is incorrect.

When any line segment is taken in a definite sense from one end point to the other, the segment is said to be **directed.** Thus, in Figure 1, if the segment from A to B is considered to be in a positive direction, then the segment from B to A is negative. Thus we have

$$AB = -BA \qquad \text{or} \qquad AB + BA = 0$$

for all directed line segments.

The absolute or numerical value of a real number a is denoted by $|a|$ and means the magnitude of a regardless of its algebraic sign. Thus, $|\pm 3| = 3$. In accordance with this definition observe that $|x| < 2$ is another way of representing the points in the interval $-2 < x < 2$; and $|x - 1| \leqq 2$ is equivalent to $-2 \leqq x - 1 \leqq 2$ or $-1 \leqq x \leqq 3$. Also, for directed magnitudes, the absolute values $|AB|$ or $|BA|$ are equal and represent the numerical distance between the points A and B.

3. Rectangular Coordinates

In order to describe the position of a point in a plane, we form what is called a system of **rectangular** or **Cartesian coordinates.** First draw a pair of perpendicular reference lines $X'X$ and $Y'Y$. These lines divide the plane into four parts, called **quadrants,** which are numbered as shown in Figure 2. The line $X'X$ is called the ***x* axis,** $Y'Y$ is called ***y* axis,** and together they are known as the **coordinate axes.** Their point of intersection O is called the **origin.**

The position of any point in the plane can be described by giving its distance from these two axes. To measure such distances, we arbitrarily choose some unit of length, and agree that distances measured to the *right* of the y axis shall be *positive,* and those to the *left negative.*

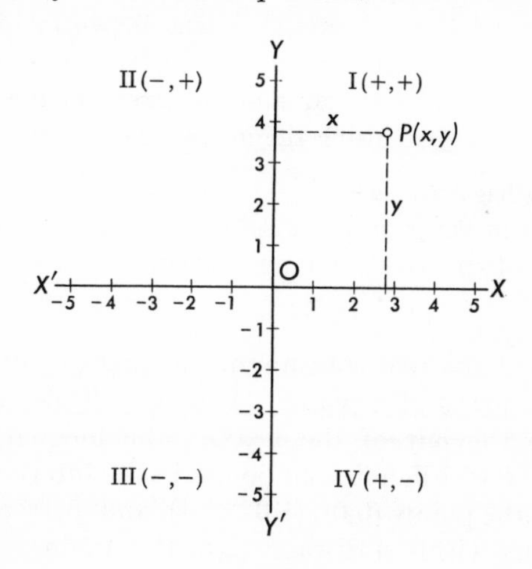

Figure 2

Similarly, distances measured upward from the x axis are *positive* and those below are *negative.*

Let P represent any point of the plane whose distance from the y axis is x and whose distance from the x axis is y. The value x thus obtained is called the **abscissa** or ***x* coordinate** of the point P, and y is called the **ordinate** or ***y* coordinate.** Together these values are called the **rectangular coordinates** of the point P and we write them in the form (x,y). The position of a point is determined if its coordinates are known; conversely, if the position of a point is known, its coordinates can be found by measuring its distance from the two axes. The process of locating points when their coordinates are given is called **plotting** the points.

Example. Draw a line connecting the points $A(-2,3)$ and $B(1,-1)$, and find its length.

Solution: In the notation used for representing points remember that the first number given is the x coordinate, and that the algebraic signs indicate directions.

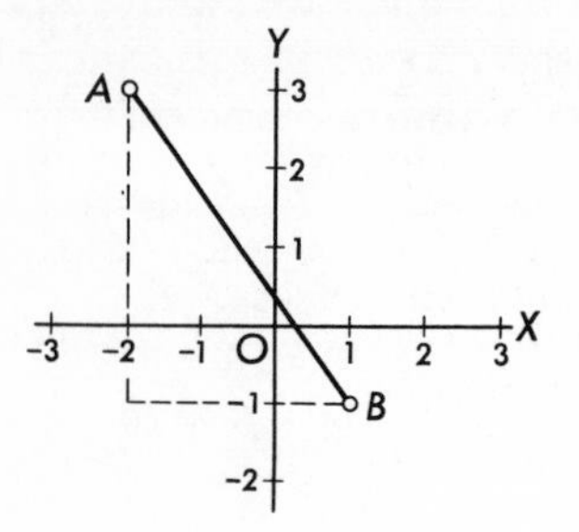

Figure 3

Starting at the origin, to plot the point $(-2,3)$ we move to the left two units and then up three units. To plot $(1,-1)$ we move one unit to the right of the origin and then down one unit.

After connecting these two points with a straight line, we may draw a horizontal and a vertical line as shown in Figure 3. Since the triangle thus formed is a right triangle, we can find the length of the hypotenuse by using the following geometric theorem.

Theorem of Pythagoras. *In any right triangle the square on the hypotenuse is equal to the sum of the squares on the other two sides.*

Since the sides of the above triangle are clearly 3 and 4, we have

$$AB = \sqrt{3^2 + 4^2} = 5.$$

As in the case of the real continuum, inequality signs can be used to describe certain areas of a plane. Thus $x < 0$ means all points in the half plane to the left of the y axis; the inequality $0 < x < 1$ together with $0 < y < 1$ denotes all points in the interior of the square whose vertices are the points (0,0), (1,0), (1,1), and (0,1); and $x^2 + y^2 < 4$ represents all points within a distance 2 of the origin.

EXERCISE I

1. For what values of x is (*a*) $x - 3 = 1$, (*b*) $|x - 3| = 1$?
   Ans. (*a*) 4, (*b*) 2, 4.
2. For what values of x is (*a*) $x^2 - 3 = 1$, (*b*) $|x^2 - 3| = 1$?
3. For what values of x is (*a*) $x^2 < 9$, (*b*) $|x| < 3$? *Ans.* $-3 < x < 3$.
4. What integer n satisfies $|n - 2| < 3/2$ and $|n - 5| < 5/2$?
5. Plot the points $(-1,2)$, $(2,3)$, $(0,-4)$, and $(2\frac{1}{2},0)$.
6. Plot the points $A(-1,5)$, $B(7,5)$, $C(7,-1)$, and $D(-1,-1)$. What kind of figure is $ABCD$? Draw the diagonals AC and BD, and give the coordinates of their point of intersection.
7. Plot the points $A(-6,7)$, $B(2,-3)$, $C(0,8)$, and $D(-3,-1)$. What is the point of intersection of AB and CD? *Ans.* $(-2,2)$.
8. Three vertices of a rectangle are $(2,5)$, $(-3,5)$, and $(2,-1)$. Find the coordinates of the fourth vertex.

9. Find the area of a triangle whose vertices are $(-2,0)$, $(4,0)$, and $(3,3)$. *Ans.* 9.
10. The line from $A(3,4)$ to O is extended through O to B so that $OB = AO$. Find the coordinates of B.
11. The line from O to $A(3,4)$ is extended through A to B so that $AB = OA$. Find the coordinates of B. *Ans.* $(6,8)$.
12. A square of side 4 has its center at the origin and sides parallel to the axes. Find the coordinates of its vertices.
13. The diagonals of a square of side 4 lie on the axes. Find the coordinates of its vertices. *Ans.* $(\pm 2\sqrt{2},0)$, $(0,\pm 2\sqrt{2})$.
14. A regular hexagon of side 6 has its center at the origin and one diagonal along the x axis. Find the coordinates of its vertices.
15. Three vertices of a parallelogram are $(1,3)$, $(0,0)$, and $(4,0)$. Find the three possible locations of the fourth vertex. *Ans.* $(3,-3)$, $(-3,3)$, $(5,3)$.

In accordance with the following conditions, find where the point $P(x, y)$ is located.

16. $x = 2$.
17. $x < 2$.
18. $|x| < 2$.
19. $|y| > 2$.
20. $|y - 2| < 1$.
21. $x < 0, \quad y > 0$.
22. $\begin{cases} 0 \leqq x \leqq 2, \\ 1 \leqq y < 2. \end{cases}$
23. $x < y$.
24. $\begin{cases} |1 - y| = 3, \\ x > -2. \end{cases}$

4. Distance Between Two Points

The distance d between two points $P_1(x_1,y_1)$ and $P_2(x_2,y_2)$ can be expressed in terms of their coordinates by using the theorem of Pythagoras. Thus, as shown in Figure 4, by constructing the line P_1A parallel to OX and P_2A parallel to OY, we have

$$d = \sqrt{P_1A^2 + AP_2^2}.$$

However, the directed lengths P_1A and AP_2 are $x_2 - x_1$ and $y_2 - y_1$, respectively. Hence, by substitution, we obtain

$$\boldsymbol{d = \sqrt{(x_2 - x_1)^2 + (y_2 - y_1)^2}}. \qquad (1)$$

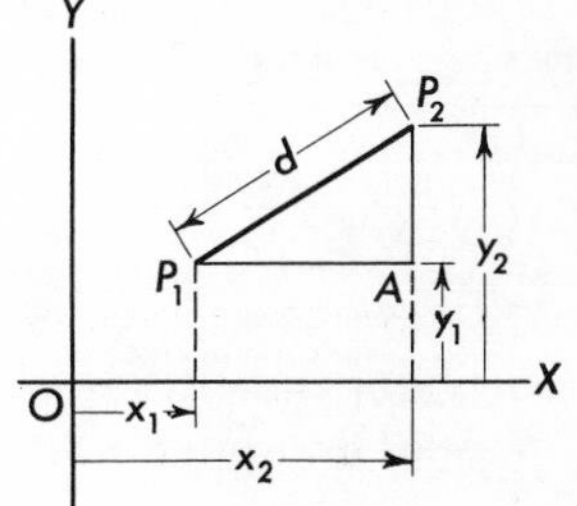

Figure 4

Illustration. The distance between the points $(-3,1)$ and $(3,-2)$, as shown in Figure 5, is by substitution in (1)

$$d = \sqrt{(-3 - 3)^2 + (1 + 2)^2} = 3\sqrt{5}.$$

Observe that the order in which the points are taken is immaterial. Thus, in reversing the order, we find

$$d = \sqrt{(3 + 3)^2 + (-2 - 1)^2} = 3\sqrt{5}.$$

Example. Show that the points $A(-1,2)$, $B(2,1)$, and $C(3,-2)$ are the vertices of an isosceles triangle.

Solution: Finding the sides of the triangle by (1), we have

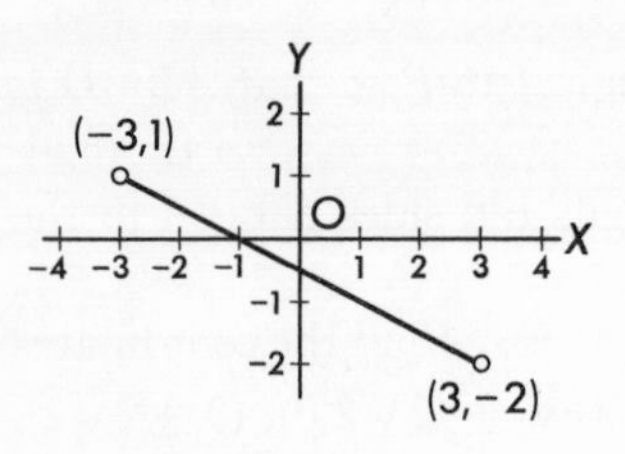

Figure 5

$$AB = \sqrt{(-1-2)^2 + (2-1)^2} = \sqrt{10},$$
$$AC = \sqrt{(-1-3)^2 + (2+2)^2} = \sqrt{32},$$
$$BC = \sqrt{(2-3)^2 + (1+2)^2} = \sqrt{10}.$$

Since the two sides AB and BC are equal in length, the triangle is isosceles.

It is interesting to note here that we have proven a geometric fact without drawing a figure. This illustrates the unusual power of analytic geometry. In spite of this, however, it is probably advisable at first for a student actually to plot the points and construct the figures in order to have a clearer idea of what is taking place, and also to check on the accuracy of the results obtained.

5. Point on the Line Joining Two Points

Let $P(x,y)$ be any point lying on the line joining $P_1(x_1,y_1)$ and $P_2(x_2,y_2)$, and so located that the segment P_1P is a given fraction k of the entire segment P_1P_2; thus

$$P_1P = k \cdot P_1P_2.$$

Constructing P_1A_1, PA, and P_2A_2 parallel to OY, as shown in Figure 6, we find by similar triangles that

$$\frac{A_1A}{A_1A_2} = \frac{P_1P}{P_1P_2} = k \quad \text{or} \quad A_1A = k \cdot A_1A_2.$$

However, $A_1A_2 = x_2 - x_1$; hence it follows that

$$x = OA_1 + A_1A = x_1 + k(x_2 - x_1).$$

A similar result for y is readily derived.

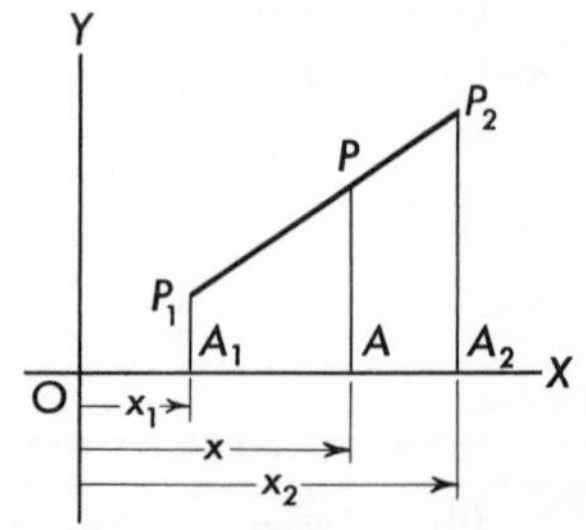

Figure 6

Theorem. *If* $\mathbf{P(x,y)}$ *is a point on the line joining* $\mathbf{P_1(x_1,y_1)}$ *and* $\mathbf{P_2(x_2,y_2)}$*, and if* $\mathbf{P}$ *is located so that* $\mathbf{P_1P = k \cdot P_1P_2}$*, then*

$$\mathbf{x = x_1 + k(x_2 - x_1), \qquad y = y_1 + k(y_2 - y_1).} \tag{1}$$

Illustration 1. If the line in Figure 7 is extended from $A(-2,-1)$ through $B(1, 1)$ to a point $C(x,y)$ so that $AB = BC$, we have $k = 2$,

$x_1 = -2$, $y_1 = -1$, $x_2 = 1$, and $y_2 = 1$. Hence by (1) the coordinates of C are

$$x = -2 + 2[1 - (-2)] = 4,$$
$$y = -1 + 2[1 - (-1)] = 3.$$

Observe also in this case that as we move from A to B the abscissa and the ordinate increase by 3 and 2, respectively. Hence in continuing the same distance from B to C the abscissa and ordinate increase again by the same amounts.

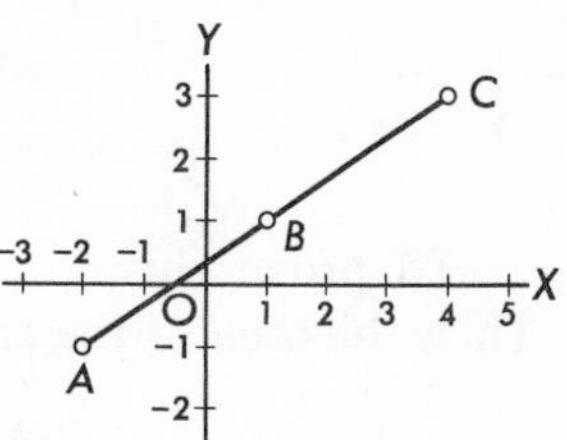

Figure 7

As an important special case of the above theorem, we have the following.

Corollary. *If* $\boldsymbol{P(x,y)}$ *is the mid-point of the segment joining* $\boldsymbol{P_1(x_1,y_1)}$ *and* $\boldsymbol{P_2(x_2,y_2)}$*, then*

$$x = \tfrac{1}{2}(x_1 + x_2), \qquad y = \tfrac{1}{2}(y_1 + y_2).$$

Illustration 2. The mid-point of the segment joining $(2,-5)$ and $(-4,-1)$ is $\left(\frac{2-4}{2}, \frac{-5-1}{2}\right)$ or $(-1,-3)$.

Example. Prove analytically that the diagonals of a parallelogram bisect each other.

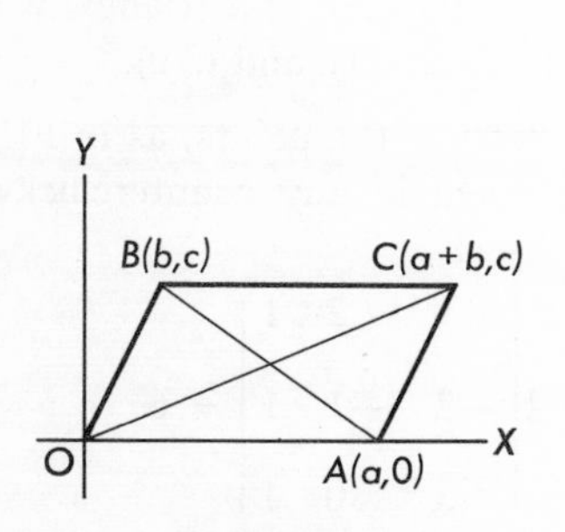

Figure 8

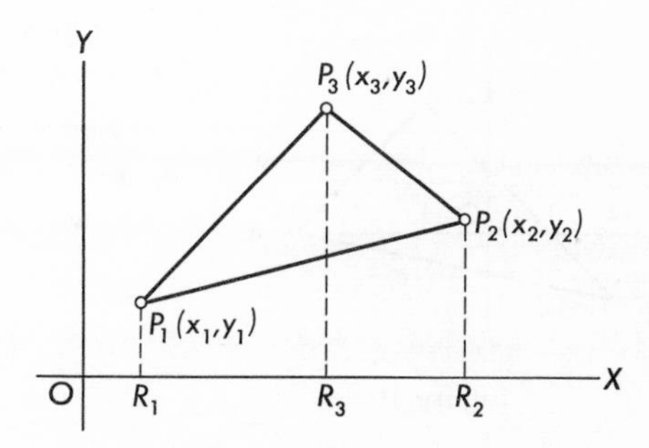

Figure 9

Solution: Place the parallelogram on a coordinate system as shown in Figure 8. If the vertices A and B are located at $(a,0)$ and (b,c), respectively, then the coordinates of C are $(a + b,c)$.

Since the mid-points of OC and AB are both the same point, namely $\left(\frac{a+b}{2}, \frac{c}{2}\right)$, it follows that the diagonals bisect each other.

6. Area of a Triangle

If, as in Figure 9, the vertices $P_1(x_1,y_1)$, $P_2(x_2,y_2)$, and $P_3(x_3,y_3)$ of a triangle are designated in such a way that a point moving from

P_1 to P_2 to P_3 to P_1 traces the boundary of the triangle in a counterclockwise sense, the area of the triangle is given in terms of the coordinates of its vertices by the formula

$$A = \frac{1}{2}\begin{vmatrix} x_1 & y_1 & 1 \\ x_2 & y_2 & 1 \\ x_3 & y_3 & 1 \end{vmatrix}. \tag{1}$$

To prove this, construct P_1R_1, P_2R_2, and P_3R_3 parallel to OY. Then the area of the triangle is

$$A = \text{Area } R_1R_3P_3P_1 + \text{Area } R_3R_2P_2P_3 - \text{Area } R_1R_2P_2P_1.$$

Since each of these trapezoidal areas is the product of one-half the sum of the parallel sides multiplied by their distance apart, we have

$$\begin{aligned} A &= \tfrac{1}{2}(y_1 + y_3)(x_3 - x_1) + \tfrac{1}{2}(y_3 + y_2)(x_2 - x_3) - \tfrac{1}{2}(y_1 + y_2)(x_2 - x_1) \\ &= \tfrac{1}{2}(x_1y_2 + x_2y_3 + x_3y_1 - x_1y_3 - x_2y_1 - x_3y_2), \end{aligned}$$

which is the expanded form of (1).

Example. Find the area of a triangle whose vertices are (1,2), $(-2,-1)$, and (3,0).

Solution: Plotting the points, as in Figure 10, and taking them in any counterclockwise order, we have by (1)

$$A = \frac{1}{2}\begin{vmatrix} 1 & 2 & 1 \\ -2 & -1 & 1 \\ 3 & 0 & 1 \end{vmatrix} = 6.$$

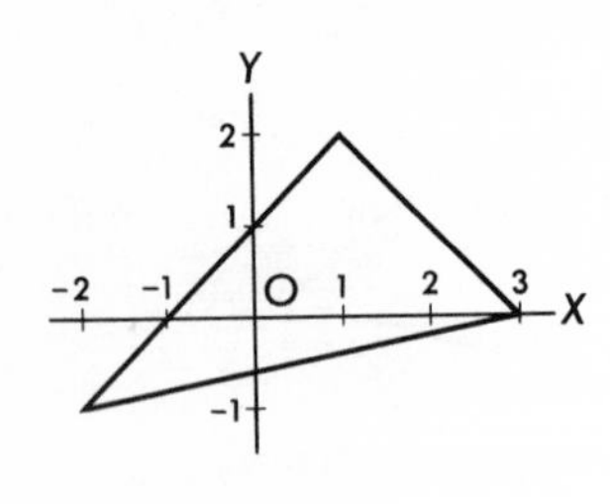

Figure 10

Note: If the points are taken in clockwise order around the boundary, we obtain the *negative* of the area.

By means of the formula (1) it is possible to derive another formula which gives the area of a non-overlapping polygon of n vertices. We shall not attempt here to give the derivation of this formula, but it has the following form. If the vertices P_1 to P_n are chosen in counterclockwise order around the polygon, its area is given by the expression

$$A = \frac{1}{2}\begin{bmatrix} x_1 & x_2 & x_3 & \cdots & x_n & x_1 \\ y_1 & y_2 & y_3 & \cdots & y_n & y_1 \end{bmatrix},$$

where the array of coordinates on the right is defined to have the following numerical value

$$\begin{bmatrix} x_1 & x_2 & x_3 & \cdots & x_n & x_1 \\ y_1 & y_2 & y_3 & \cdots & y_n & y_1 \end{bmatrix} \equiv (x_1y_2 + x_2y_3 + \cdots + x_ny_1) - (y_1x_2 + y_2x_3 + \cdots + y_nx_1).$$

Illustration. The area of the quadrilateral whose vertices in order are (0,0), (3,1), (2,4), and (1,2) is

$$A = \tfrac{1}{2}\begin{bmatrix} 0 & 3 & 2 & 1 & 0 \\ 0 & 1 & 4 & 2 & 0 \end{bmatrix}$$

$$= \tfrac{1}{2}\{(0 + 12 + 4 + 0) - (0 + 2 + 4 + 0)\}$$

$$= 5.$$

EXERCISE 2

Find the distance and mid-point between the following points.

1. (1,2), (5,5). *Ans.* 5, $(3,\frac{7}{2})$.
2. $(-2,-1)$, $(4,-3)$.
3. $(\frac{1}{3},-\frac{1}{2})$, $(-\frac{1}{6},0)$. $\frac{1}{2}\sqrt{2}$, $(\frac{1}{12},-\frac{1}{4})$.
4. $(-1.2,3.4)$, $(1.6,-1.1)$.
5. Find the points which trisect the segment joining the points $(-3,5)$ and (9,2). *Ans.* (1,4), (5,3).
6. If a line is extended from $A(2,3)$ through $B(-2,0)$ to a point C so that $AC = 4AB$, find the coordinates of C.
7. Show that the points $(-2,0)$, (2,3), and $(5,-1)$ are the vertices of a right triangle, and find its area. *Ans.* $12\frac{1}{2}$.
8. Show that the points (1,2), (3,5), and $(-3,9)$ are the vertices of a right triangle, and find its area.
9. Show that the points (5,4), $(-2,1)$, and $(2,-3)$ are the vertices of an isosceles triangle, and find its area. *Ans.* 20.
10. Show that the points $(7,-1)$, (3,5), and $(1,-5)$ are the vertices of an isosceles triangle, and find its area.
11. Show that the points (1,1), (4,5), (0,8), and $(-3,4)$ are the vertices of a square, and find its area. *Ans.* 25.
12. Show that the points $(-1,1)$, $(0,-3)$, (5,2), and (4,6) are the vertices of a parallelogram, and find its area.
13. Find the area of the pentagon connecting the points (3,0), (2,3), $(-1,2)$, $(-2,-1)$, and $(0,-3)$. *Ans.* 18.
14. Determine in two ways whether or not the points $A(-1,-1)$, $B(4,1)$, and $C(12,4)$ lie on a straight line. Is $AB + BC = AC$? Is area ABC zero?
15. If the area of a triangle with vertices (5,2), $(x,4)$, and $(0,-3)$ is $12\frac{1}{2}$, find x. *Ans.* $x = 2$ or 12.

16. For the triangle whose vertices are $A(0,1)$, $B(7,2)$, and $C(3,8)$, find (*a*) its area, (*b*) the length AB, (*c*) the length of the altitude from C on AB.
17. If the mid-point of a segment is (6,3) and one end point is (8,−4), what are the coordinates of the other end? *Ans.* (4,10).
18. For the triangle whose vertices are $A(0,0)$, $B(6,2)$ and $C(2,8)$, find the length of the median from C to AB. *A median* connects a vertex to the mid-point of the opposite side.
19. Determine the vertices of a triangle whose sides have the mid-points (1,0), (2,−1), and (3,1). *Ans.* (2,2), (0,−2), (4,0).
20. Two vertices of a triangle are (0,−6) and (4,0), and the medians intersect at (0,−2). Find the third vertex of the triangle.
21. Prove analytically that the diagonals of a rectangle are equal.
22. Prove analytically that the mid-point of the hypotenuse of a right triangle is equidistant from the three vertices.
23. If the point $P(x,y)$ divides the segment from $P_1(x_1,y_1)$ to $P_2(x_2,y_2)$ in the ratio $r_1{:}r_2$, show that

$$x = \frac{r_1x_2 + r_2x_1}{r_1 + r_2}, \qquad y = \frac{r_1y_2 + r_2y_1}{r_1 + r_2}.$$

24. For a triangle whose vertices are (x_1,y_1), (x_2,y_2), and (x_3,y_3), show that the medians (see Problem 18) intersect at a point whose coordinates are

$$x = \tfrac{1}{3}(x_1 + x_2 + x_3), \qquad y = \tfrac{1}{3}(y_1 + y_2 + y_3).$$

25. Prove analytically that the sum of the squares of the medians of a triangle is equal to three-fourths of the sum of the squares of the sides.
26. Prove analytically that the lines joining the mid-points of the opposite sides of a quadrilateral bisect each other.

7. Inclination and Slope

If a line drawn on a coordinate system (Figure 11) intersects the x axis, we define the **inclination** of the line to be the least counterclockwise angle θ through which the x axis must be rotated about the point of intersection in order to bring it into coincidence with the line. The inclination of a line parallel to the x axis is by definition zero.

The **slope** of a line, usually denoted by m, is defined as the tangent of the inclination, that is, $m = \tan\theta$. The slope of a line can be expressed in terms of the coordinates of any two of its points in the following way.

Construct the triangle shown in Figure 12 so that P_1A and P_2A are parallel to the x and y axes, respectively. Since the lengths of the segments P_1A and P_2A are $x_2 - x_1$ and $y_2 - y_1$, respectively, it follows from $m = \tan\theta$ that

$$\boldsymbol{m = \frac{y_2 - y_1}{x_2 - x_1},} \tag{1}$$

If the given line is parallel to the x axis so that $y_2 = y_1$, (1) gives the correct slope, namely, $m = 0$. If the given line is parallel to the y axis so that $x_2 = x_1$, (1) is meaningless and the slope is not defined. With the coordinate axes in their usual position, we see that a line sloping

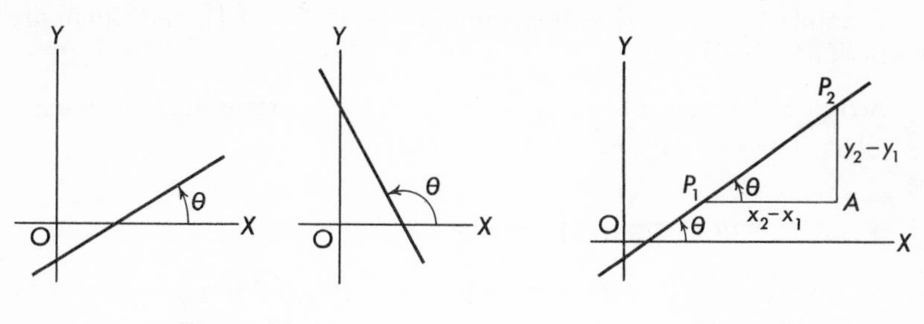

Figure 11

Figure 12

upward to the right has *positive* slope and a line sloping downward to the right has *negative* slope.

Illustration. The slope of the line joining $(2,-1)$ and $(-3,4)$ is $m = \frac{(-1)-(4)}{(2)-(-3)} = \frac{-5}{5} = -1$. Observe that interchanging the order of the points does not alter the value of the slope.

8. Parallel and Perpendicular Lines

If two lines are parallel, they have equal inclinations and hence have equal slopes. Lines parallel to the y axis are excluded, since their slopes are undefined. Conversely, if two lines have equal slopes they have equal inclinations, and hence are parallel.

Theorem I. *Two lines are parallel, if, and only if, their slopes are equal, that is,* $m_1 = m_2$.

If two lines are perpendicular, the inclination of one is 90° more than that of the other. Thus, as in Figure 13, $\theta_2 = \theta_1 + 90°$. By means of a trigonometric reduction formula (see **27,** page 3), we obtain

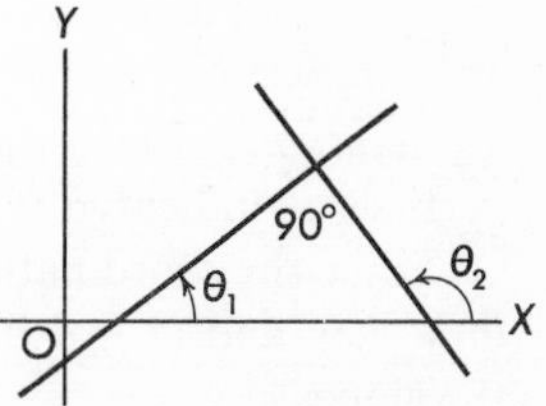

Figure 13

$$\tan \theta_2 = \tan (\theta_1 + 90°) = -\cot \theta_1 = -\frac{1}{\tan \theta_1}.$$

Hence

$$m_2 = -\frac{1}{m_1}.$$

Since the converse can be proven by reversing the above argument, we have the following result.

Theorem 2. *Two lines are perpendicular, if, and only if, the slope of one is the negative reciprocal of the slope of the other, that is,* $m_2 = -1/m_1$.

Example 1. Prove that the points $A(3,-1)$, $B(-1,1)$, and $C(0,3)$ are the vertices of a right triangle.

Solution: Figure 14 indicates that if there is a right angle, it must be at B. The slopes of AB and BC are respectively

$$m_{AB} = \frac{-1-1}{3-(-1)} = -\frac{1}{2}, \qquad m_{BC} = \frac{1-3}{-1-0} = 2.$$

Hence, by Theorem 2, AB is perpendicular to BC, and triangle ABC is a right triangle.

Example 2. Prove that the line segments joining the mid-points of adjacent sides of a quadrilateral form a parallelogram.

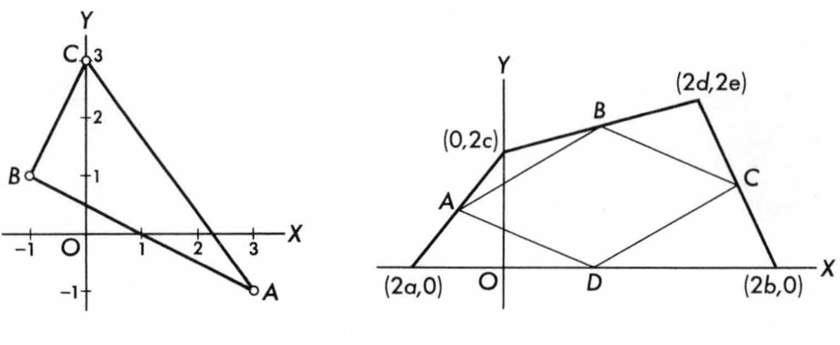

Figure 14 Figure 15

Solution: Place the quadrilateral on a coordinate system and label the vertices as indicated in Figure 15.

Since the coordinates of the mid-points A, B, C, and D are (a,c) $(d,c+e)$, $(b+d,e)$, and $(a+b,0)$, respectively, we find that the sides of $ABCD$ have the slopes

$$m_{AB} = \frac{e}{d-a}, \qquad m_{BC} = -\frac{c}{b}, \qquad m_{CD} = \frac{e}{d-a}, \qquad m_{DA} = -\frac{c}{b}.$$

Thus, since AB is parallel to CD and BC is parallel to DA, the quadrilateral $ABCD$ is a parallelogram.

9. Angle Between Two Lines

A line L_2 intersecting a line L_1 forms two supplementary angles, either of which may be considered as the angle between the lines. To avoid ambiguity, however, we shall define the angle that L_2 makes with L_1 to be the least counterclockwise angle through which L_2 must be rotated to bring it into coincidence with L_1. Thus in Figure 16 ϕ is the angle that L_2 makes with L_1. In Figure 16 we also observe that $\phi = \theta_1 - \theta_2$. Hence it follows that

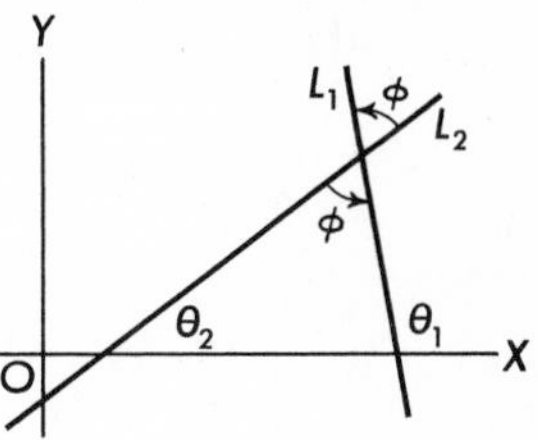

Figure 16

$$\tan \phi = \tan (\theta_1 - \theta_2) = \frac{\tan \theta_1 - \tan \theta_2}{1 + \tan \theta_1 \tan \theta_2}$$

or

$$\tan \phi = \frac{m_1 - m_2}{1 + m_1 m_2}.$$

Theorem. *If* $\boldsymbol{\phi}$ *is the counterclockwise angle formed in rotating line* $\mathbf{L}_2$ *to* $\mathbf{L}_1$*, then*

$$\tan \boldsymbol{\phi} = \frac{\mathbf{m}_1 - \mathbf{m}_2}{1 + \mathbf{m}_1\mathbf{m}_2}, \tag{1}$$

where $\mathbf{m}_1$ *and* $\mathbf{m}_2$ *are the respective slopes of the lines.*

If either of the given lines is parallel to the y axis, formula (1) is meaningless. In this case, however, one of the inclinations is 90°, say $\theta_1 = 90°$. Under this assumption, ϕ can be determined directly in terms of θ_2. Observe also that if $1 + m_1 m_2$ is zero, formula (1) is meaningless. This condition, written as $m_2 = -1/m_1$, indicates, however, that the given lines are perpendicular; hence in this case $\phi = 90°$.

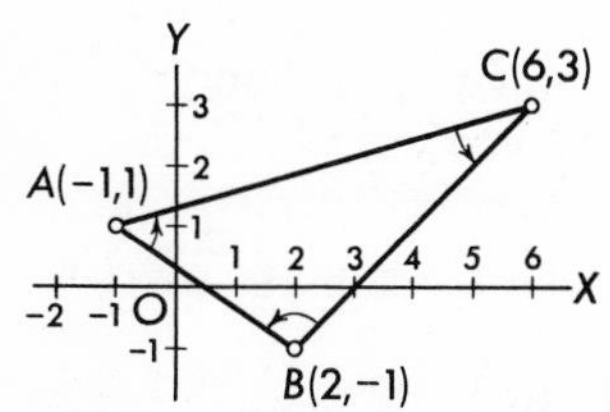

Figure 17

Example. Find the angles of the triangle whose vertices are $A(-1,1)$, $B(2,-1)$, and $C(6,3)$.

Solution: First finding the slope of each side, we have

$$m_{AB} = -\tfrac{2}{3}, \qquad m_{BC} = 1, \qquad m_{AC} = \tfrac{2}{7}.$$

If the angles of the triangle are considered in a counterclockwise sense, as shown in Figure 17, we obtain, using formula (1),

$$\tan A = \frac{m_{AC} - m_{AB}}{1 + m_{AC}m_{AB}} = \frac{\frac{2}{7} + \frac{2}{3}}{1 - \frac{4}{21}} = \frac{20}{17},$$

$$\tan B = \frac{m_{AB} - m_{BC}}{1 + m_{AB}m_{BC}} = \frac{-\frac{2}{3} - 1}{1 - \frac{2}{3}} = -5,$$

$$\tan C = \frac{m_{BC} - m_{AC}}{1 + m_{BC}m_{AC}} = \frac{1 - \frac{2}{7}}{1 + \frac{2}{7}} = \frac{5}{9}.$$

Solving, we find $A = 49.6°$, $B = 101.3°$, $C = 29.1°$, and as a check we observe that the sum of the angles is 180°. The accuracy of the above values of the tangents can also be checked by using the trigonometric relation

$$\tan A + \tan B + \tan C = \tan A \tan B \tan C.$$

Thus, for the above example, we have

$$\frac{20}{17} - 5 + \frac{5}{9} = \left(\frac{20}{17}\right)(-5)\left(\frac{5}{9}\right)$$

$$-\frac{500}{153} = -\frac{500}{153}.$$

EXERCISE 3

Find the slope of the line joining the following points.

1. $(4,-3)$, $(-1,3)$. *Ans.* $-\frac{6}{5}$.
2. $(3,4)$, $(-4,-2)$.
3. $(\frac{1}{2},\frac{1}{3})$, $(-\frac{5}{6},\frac{2}{3})$. $-\frac{1}{4}$.
4. $(-1.1,0.3)$, $(2.5,2.1)$.

Find the acute angle between the lines having the following slopes.

5. 2, 5. *Ans.* 15.3°.
6. -3, 2.
7. $\frac{1}{2}$, $-\frac{1}{3}$. 45°.
8. -4.8, -1.5.

Show by means of slopes that the following points lie on a straight line.

9. $(-6,2)$, $(0,-2)$, $(3,-4)$.
10. $(4,2)$, $(1,3)$, $(-\frac{1}{2},3\frac{1}{2})$.
11. A line of slope 3 passes through the point $(7,10)$. If a point on the line has an abscissa 2, find its ordinate. *Ans.* $y = -5$.
12. If a line drawn from the point (a,b) makes an angle of 30° with the y axis, find its slope. Two answers.
13. Show that $(-2,0)$, $(1,-2)$, and $(5,4)$ are vertices of a right triangle.
14. Show that $(2,1)$, $(1,3)$, $(-3,1)$, and $(-2,-1)$ are vertices of a rectangle.
15. Show that $(1,0)$, $(6,1)$, $(4,3)$, and $(-1,2)$ are vertices of a parallelogram.
16. Show that $(4,1)$, $(1,2)$, $(-3,0)$, and $(-4,-3)$ are vertices of an isosceles trapezoid.
17. Show that $(-1,-2)$, $(3,-2)$, $(1,2)$, and $(-1,1)$ are vertices of a quadrilateral having two right angles.
18. Show that the perpendicular bisector of the line segment joining $(-1,2)$ and $(5,-2)$ passes through the point $(6,6)$.

Find the angles of the triangles having the following vertices.

19. $(-1,1)$, $(5,-1)$, $(4,3)$. *Ans.* 40.2°, 57.5°, 82.2°.
20. $(0,-2)$, $(6,4)$, $(3,4)$.
21. Two vertices of an equilateral triangle are $(0,0)$ and $(5,5)$. Find the slopes of the three sides. *Ans.* 1, -0.2679, -3.7321.
22. The slope of the hypotenuse of an isosceles right triangle is 3. What are the slopes of the equal sides?

23. Show that two lines having slopes a and $\frac{1+a}{1-a}$ intersect at 45°.
24. Given the points $A(5,12)$, $B(0,0)$, $C(8,6)$, and $M(7,9)$, show that BM bisects angle ABC.
25. For the triangle whose vertices are $A(0,1)$, $B(2,5)$, and $C(6,3)$ find the slopes of the three medians. *Ans.* $0, \frac{3}{4}, -3$.
26. What is the slope of the line that bisects angle A in the triangle given in Problem 25?
27. Prove analytically that a segment joining the mid-points of two sides of a triangle is parallel to the third side and half as long.
28. Prove analytically that the diagonals of a rhombus are perpendicular.
29. Prove analytically that a quadrilateral whose diagonals bisect each other is a parallelogram.
30. If $ABCD$ is a parallelogram in which points P and Q trisect the diagonal AC, prove analytically that $BPDQ$ is a parallelogram.

10. The Locus of a Point

In mathematics a constant is defined to be a quantity whose value remains the same throughout a given problem, whereas a variable is a quantity that may assume different values in the same problem. For this reason, in analytic geometry we say that a point whose coordinates are fixed is a *constant point,* and a point with at least one variable coordinate is called a *variable point.* For example, the center of a given circle is a constant point, whereas a point on the circumference of the circle is a variable point because of the infinitely many positions it may assume on the circumference.

Note: The coordinates of a variable point are usually taken as x and y, and the coordinates of a constant point are sometimes denoted by x and y with subscripts or with letters which ordinarily denote constants, such as (x_0,y_0) and (x_1,y_1) or (a,b) and (h,k).

With respect to variable points, we have the following definition.

The curve traced by a variable point as it moves in a plane is called the ***locus*** *of the point.*

Thus if a point moves so that its ordinate is always equal to its abscissa, its locus is a line passing through the origin and bisecting the first and third quadrants. For any point (x,y) on this locus, it is evident that the coordinates satisfy the equation

$$y = x. \tag{1}$$

Conversely, any two numbers that satisfy (1) are coordinates of a point on the locus. For this reason (1) is called the **equation of the locus,** and we make the following definition.

The locus of an equation is a curve containing those points, and only those points, whose coordinates satisfy the equation.

Example. Find the equation of the locus of a point which moves so that its distance from the point $C(3,4)$ is always 5.

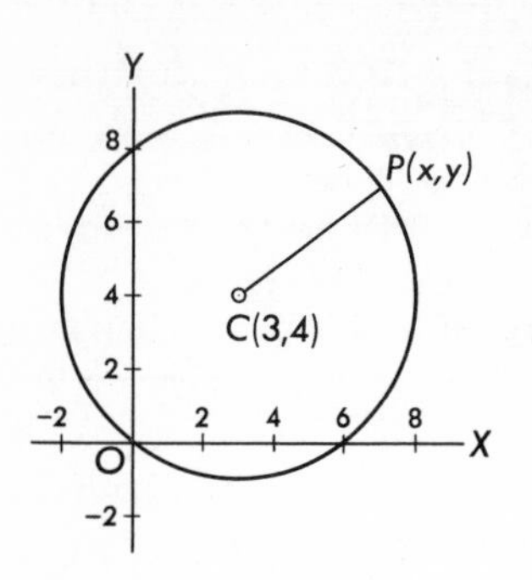

Figure 18

Solution: We know in this case that the locus is a circle with radius 5. Since the center is located at (3,4), we can draw the circle as shown in Figure 18.

Now for any variable point $P(x,y)$ on the locus, it follows from the condition $PC = 5$ that x and y must satisfy

$$\sqrt{(x-3)^2 + (y-4)^2} = 5.$$

Squaring both sides and simplifying, we obtain

$$x^2 + y^2 - 6x - 8y = 0. \tag{2}$$

Thus the coordinates of any point on the locus satisfy (2), and by reversing the steps it can be shown that any pair of values (x_1, y_1) which satisfy (2) are the coordinates of a point 5 units from C.

II. Equation of a Straight Line

A line is a locus of points which has a constant slope. Thus if $P(x,y)$ is any point on a line that crosses the y axis at $(0,b)$ and has a slope m, as shown in Figure 19, the equation of the line is

$$\frac{y-b}{x-0} = m,$$

or

$$y = mx + b. \tag{1}$$

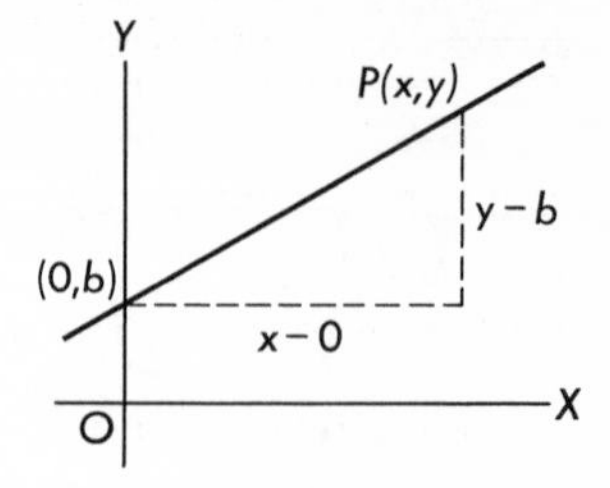

Figure 19

If the given line were parallel to the y axis and intersected the x axis at a, its equation would be $x = a$. In either case, we observe that the equations are of the first degree in x and y.

Theorem I. *Every straight line can be represented by an equation of the first degree.*

On the other hand, every equation of the first degree

$$Ax + By + C = 0 \tag{2}$$

represents a straight line. For if $B \neq 0$, we have

$$y = -\frac{A}{B}x - \frac{C}{B},$$

which by comparison with (1) indicates that it is a locus passing through the point $(0, -C/B)$ with a constant slope of $-A/B$. If $B = 0$, then $x = -C/A$, which is a line parallel to the y axis.

Theorem 2. *The locus of an equation of the first degree is always a straight line.*

Because of Theorem 2, equation (2) is called a *linear* equation in x and y. Observe also that the converse of Theorem 2 is not true, for $x + y = 0$, $(x + y)^2 = 0$, and $(x + y)(x^2 + y^2) = 0$ all represent the same line.

12. Standard Equations of Lines

We have seen that the equation of a line can be written in the form

$$\mathbf{A}x + \mathbf{B}y + \mathbf{C} = 0, \tag{1}$$

where A, B, and C are constants. This is called the **general equation** of a line.

Although the general equation could be used in all problems involving lines, it is usually more convenient to use other forms in which the constants have specific geometric meanings. We shall derive five such types of equations which are called **standard forms.**

1. The point-slope form. The equation of a line that passes through a fixed point $P_1(x_1,y_1)$ with a given slope m can be obtained as follows. Let $P(x,y)$, as shown in Figure 20, be any point of the line other than P_1. Then since the slope of PP_1 is m, we have

$$\frac{y - y_1}{x - x_1} = m,$$

or simplifying,

$$y - y_1 = m(x - x_1). \tag{2}$$

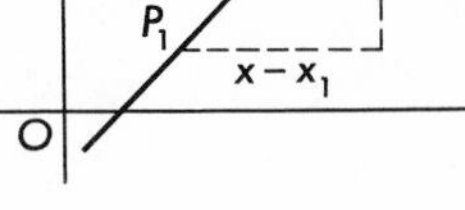

Figure 20

This is called the **point-slope form** of the equation of a line. It is satisfied by the coordinates of all points on the line including those of P_1.

Illustration 1. The equation of a line through the point $(3,-1)$ with a slope $-\frac{2}{3}$ is $y + 1 = -\frac{2}{3}(x - 3)$, or $2x + 3y - 3 = 0$.

2. The slope-intercept form. The intercepts of a line are the directed distances from the origin to the points where the line crosses the coordinate axes. Thus the equation of the line having a y intercept b and a slope m is

$$y = mx + b. \tag{3}$$

This is called the **slope-intercept form** of the equation of a line and it is obtained by substituting $(0,b)$ for (x_1,y_1) in (2).

Illustration 2. The equation of a line having a y intercept $-\frac{1}{2}$ and a slope $\frac{5}{4}$ is $y = \frac{5}{4}x - \frac{1}{2}$, or $5x - 4y - 2 = 0$.

3. The two-point form. The equation of a line that passes through two distinct points $P_1(x_1,y_1)$ and $P_2(x_2,y_2)$ is readily found by noting that its slope is

$$m = \frac{y_2 - y_1}{x_2 - x_1}, \qquad (x_2 \neq x_1).$$

Substituting this value of m in (2), we obtain

$$y - y_1 = \frac{y_2 - y_1}{x_2 - x_1}(x - x_1). \tag{4}$$

This is called the **two-point form** of the equation of a line. If $x_2 = x_1$, the line is parallel to the y axis and its equation is $x = x_1$.

Illustration 3. The equation of a line through the points $(-2,1)$ and $(3,5)$ is $y - 1 = \dfrac{5-1}{3+2}(x + 2)$, or $4x - 5y + 13 = 0$.

4. The intercept form. The equation of a line having an x intercept a and a y intercept b, neither of which is zero, can be found by substituting $(0,b)$ and $(a,0)$ for the two points in (4). Doing this and simplifying, we obtain

$$\frac{x}{a} + \frac{y}{b} = 1. \tag{5}$$

This is called the **intercept form** of the equation of a line. It is interesting as a check to observe in (5) that if $y = 0$ then $x = a$, and if $x = 0$ then $y = b$.

Illustration 4. The equation of a line having an x intercept -2 and a y intercept 3 is $\dfrac{x}{-2} + \dfrac{y}{3} = 1$, or $3x - 2y + 6 = 0$.

5. The normal form. A definite straight line L is determined if, as shown in Figure 21, we know the length p (normal intercept) of the perpendicular ON from the origin to the line, together with the counterclockwise angle α (normal angle) which this perpendicular makes with OX. To find the equation of this line, we note first that the coordinates of N are $x = p \cos \alpha$ and $y = p \sin \alpha$, and second that the slope of ON is $\tan \alpha$; hence the slope of L is $-1/\tan \alpha$. Since the slope and a point of L are known, its equation is given by substitution in (2)

$$y - p \sin \alpha = -\frac{1}{\tan \alpha}(x - p \cos \alpha).$$

Simplifying, we obtain

$$\boldsymbol{x \cos \alpha + y \sin \alpha = p.} \tag{6}$$

This is called the **normal form** of the equation of a line.

Even though the above derivation fails for $\alpha = 0°$ or $180°$, we observe that (6) gives the correct result in these cases, namely, $x = p$ and $x = -p$.

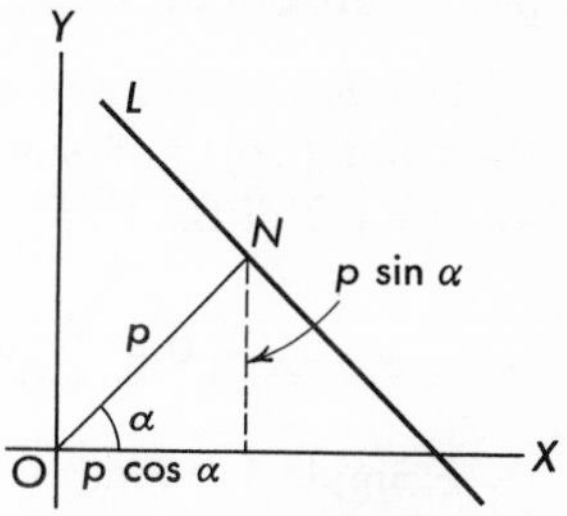

Illustration 5. The equation of a line having a normal intercept 2 and a normal angle 225° is $x \cos 225° + y \sin 225° = 2$, or $x + y + 2\sqrt{2} = 0$.

Figure 21

To reduce the general equation of a line to normal form, we observe that if (6) and (1) are to represent the same line their coefficients must be in proportion. Thus, if k is the constant of proportionality, we have

$$\frac{\cos \alpha}{A} = k, \qquad \frac{\sin \alpha}{B} = k, \qquad \frac{-p}{C} = k,$$

so that

$$\cos \alpha = kA, \qquad \sin \alpha = kB, \qquad p = -kC.$$

Squaring and adding the first two of these relations, we obtain

$$\cos^2 \alpha + \sin^2 \alpha = k^2(A^2 + B^2).$$

Thus we find

$$k^2(A^2 + B^2) = 1, \qquad \text{and} \qquad k = \frac{1}{\pm\sqrt{A^2 + B^2}}.$$

Therefore the normal form of $Ax + By + C = 0$ is

$$\frac{Ax}{\pm\sqrt{A^2 + B^2}} + \frac{By}{\pm\sqrt{A^2 + B^2}} = \frac{-C}{\pm\sqrt{A^2 + B^2}}, \tag{7}$$

where the sign of the radical is chosen so that the right side of (7) is positive.

Illustration 6. The normal form of the line $3x - 4y + 10 = 0$ is

$$\frac{3x}{-5} - \frac{4y}{-5} = \frac{-10}{-5}, \qquad \text{or} \qquad -\frac{3}{5}x + \frac{4}{5}y = 2.$$

Example 1. Find the equation of the line through the point $(2,-3)$ and perpendicular to the line $3x + 4y - 2 = 0$.

Solution: Writing the equation of the given line in the slope-intercept form, that is, $y = -\frac{3}{4}x + \frac{1}{2}$, we see that its slope is $-\frac{3}{4}$. Hence the slope of the required line is $\frac{4}{3}$, and so by (2) its equation is

$$y + 3 = \tfrac{4}{3}(x - 2) \qquad \text{or} \qquad 4x - 3y - 17 = 0.$$

Example 2. Find the equation of the line with an x intercept 2 that passes through the mid-point of the line segment joining (3,7) and (5,0).

Solution: To have an x intercept 2 means that the line passes through the point (2,0); and since the mid-point of the given segment is $(4,3\frac{1}{2})$, we find by use of the two-point form that

$$y - 0 = \frac{\frac{7}{2} - 0}{4 - 2}(x - 2) \qquad \text{or} \qquad 7x - 4y - 14 = 0.$$

Example 3. Find the distance from the origin to the line $2x - y - 5 = 0$.

Solution: Writing the given equation in normal form, we have

$$\frac{2x - y - 5}{\sqrt{(2)^2 + (-1)^2}} = 0 \qquad \text{or} \qquad \frac{2}{\sqrt{5}}x - \frac{1}{\sqrt{5}}y = \sqrt{5}.$$

Hence the distance from the origin to the line is $\sqrt{5}$.

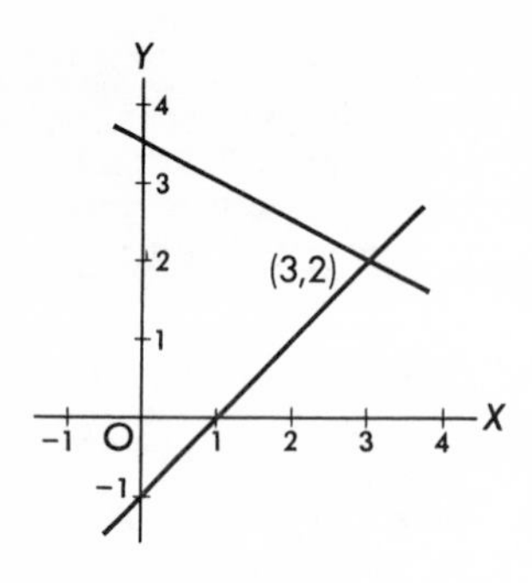

Figure 22

13. Intersection of Lines

If two lines are not parallel or coincident, they intersect in a single point. Since the coordinates of this point satisfy the equations of both lines, their values can be found by solving the two equations simultaneously for x and y.

Example. Find the point of intersection of the lines whose equations are $x + 2y - 7 = 0$ and $x - y - 1 = 0$.

Solution: Solving the equations simultaneously, we find that $x = 3$ and $y = 2$. Hence, as shown in Figure 22, (3,2) is the point of intersection of the lines.

EXERCISE 4

Find the equation of the line through the following point with the slope indicated.

1. $(3,-2)$, $\frac{3}{4}$. *Ans.* $3x - 4y - 17 = 0$.
2. $(0,5)$, $-\frac{7}{3}$.

Find the equation of the line through the following points.

3. $(-1,2)$, $(3,4)$. *Ans.* $x - 2y + 5 = 0$. 4. $(0,-3)$, $(4,0)$.

Find the equation of the line with the following slope and y intercept.

5. $m = \frac{2}{3}$, $b = -\frac{9}{5}$. *Ans.* $10x - 15y - 27 = 0$. 6. $m = 1.7$, $b = -2.3$.

Find the equation of the line with the following intercepts.

7. $a = 2$, $b = -5$. *Ans.* $5x - 2y - 10 = 0$. 8. $a = -\frac{3}{4}$, $b = \frac{7}{2}$.

Write the following equations in normal form, and determine the distance of the line from the origin.

9. $5x - 12y + 26 = 0$. *Ans.* 2. 10. $x + 3y - 5 = 0$.

Find the points of intersection of the following lines.

11. $\begin{cases} x + 2y - 3 = 0, \\ 2x - 3y + 8 = 0. \end{cases}$ *Ans.* $(-1,2)$. 12. $\begin{cases} 3x - y + 2 = 0, \\ -2x + 4y - 3 = 0. \end{cases}$

Find the equations of the following lines.

13. Passing through the point $(2,-1)$ and (*a*) with slope 2, (*b*) the point $(3,4)$, (*c*) parallel to the line $2x - 3y + 4 = 0$.
Ans. (*a*) $2x - y = 5$, (*b*) $5x - y = 11$, (*c*) $2x - 3y = 7$.
14. Having a slope $\frac{2}{3}$ and (*a*) passing through the point $(-1,3)$, (*b*) an x intercept 5, (*c*) containing the origin.
15. Passing through the point $(-3,2)$ and (*a*) with slope $\frac{1}{2}$, (b) having a y intercept 3, (*c*) the point $(5,-1)$.
Ans. (*a*) $2y - x = 7$, (*b*) $3y - x = 9$, (*c*) $3x + 8y = 7$.
16. Having an x intercept -2 and (*a*) a slope $-\frac{3}{4}$, (*b*) parallel to the y axis, (*c*) passing through the point $(1,1)$.

In the following, the vertices of triangle ABC are $A(-1,1)$, $B(6,2)$, and $C(2,5)$.

17. Find the equation of (*a*) the side AB, (*b*) the median from A to BC, (*c*) the altitude from A to BC.
Ans. (*a*) $7y - x = 8$, (*b*) $2y - x = 3$, (*c*) $3y - 4x = 7$.
18. Find the equation of (*a*) the side BC, (*b*) the median from B to AC, (*c*) the altitude from B to AC.
19. Find the equation of (*a*) the line through B parallel to AC, (*b*) the line through C parallel to AB. (*c*) Find the point of intersection of the lines (*a*) and (*b*). *Ans.* (*a*) $4x - 3y = 18$, (*b*) $7y - x = 33$, (*c*) $(9,6)$.
20. Find the point of intersection of the medians of triangle ABC.
21. Find (*a*) the inclination of AB, (*b*) the slope of AC, (*c*) the x intercept of BC. *Ans.* (*a*) $8.1°$, (*b*) $\frac{4}{3}$, (*c*) $\frac{26}{3}$.
22. Find the equation of the perpendicular bisector of (*a*) side AB, (*b*) side AC. (*c*) Find the point of intersection of the lines (*a*) and (*b*).

In the following, the equations of the sides AB, BC, and CA of the triangle ABC are $x + y - 3 = 0$, $3x + y - 15 = 0$, and $x - 2y + 9 = 0$, respectively.

23. Find (*a*) the coordinates of A, (*b*) the equation of the median from A to BC, (*c*) the equation of the altitude from A to BC.
Ans. (*a*) $(-1,4)$, (*b*) $5x + 11y = 39$, (*c*) $3y - x = 13$.

24. Find (*a*) the coordinates of C, (*b*) the equation of the median from C to AB, (*c*) the equation of the altitude from C to AB.

25. Find the equation of the line through A (*a*) parallel to BC, (*b*) and the origin, (*c*) with an x intercept 5.
Ans. (*a*) $3x + y = 1$, (*b*) $4x + y = 0$, (*c*) $2x + 3y = 10$.

26. Find the equation of the line through C (*a*) with an inclination $45°$, (*b*) parallel to the y axis, (*c*) perpendicular to CA.

27. Find the point of intersection of the medians of triangle ABC.
Ans. $(\frac{8}{3},\frac{7}{3})$.

28. Find the equation of the perpendicular bisector of (*a*) AB, (*b*) CA. (*c*) Find the point of intersection of the lines (*a*) and (*b*).

29. The equations of two sides of a parallelogram are $2x - 3y + 7 = 0$ and $4x + y = 21$, and one vertex is $(-1,-3)$. Find the other vertices.
Ans. $(5,1)$, $(4,5)$, $(-2,1)$.

30. A line segment has its ends on the coordinate axes and forms with them a triangle of area 36. If the segment passes through the point $(5,2)$, what is its slope?

31. Find the equations of the lines containing the point $(4,7)$ and passing at a distance 1 from the origin. *Ans.* $3y - 4x = 5$, $12x - 5y = 13$.

32. The vertices of the base of an isosceles triangle are $(-1,-2)$ and $(1,4)$. If the third vertex lies on the line $4x + 3y = 12$, find the area of the triangle.

14. Distance from a Line to a Point

The distance d from the line L to the point $P_1(x_1,y_1)$, as shown in Figure 23, can be determined in the following manner. If the equation of L in normal form is

$$x \cos \alpha + y \sin \alpha - p = 0,$$

the equation of a line L' through P_1 and parallel to L is

$$x \cos \alpha + y \sin \alpha - (p + d) = 0.$$

Since, however, $P_1(x_1,y_1)$ is a point on L', we have

$$x_1 \cos \alpha + y_1 \sin \alpha - p - d = 0,$$

whence

$$d = x_1 \cos \alpha + y_1 \sin \alpha - p.$$

Thus, in general terms, we have the following result.

Theorem. *The signed distance from the line*

$$\boldsymbol{Ax + By + C = 0}$$

to the point $\boldsymbol{P_1(x_1,y_1)}$ *is given by the formula*

$$\boldsymbol{d} = \frac{\boldsymbol{Ax_1 + By_1 + C}}{\pm\sqrt{\boldsymbol{A^2 + B^2}}}, \tag{1}$$

*where the sign of the radical is chosen to be opposite to the sign of C.**

In accordance with the definition of d in the above theorem, it should

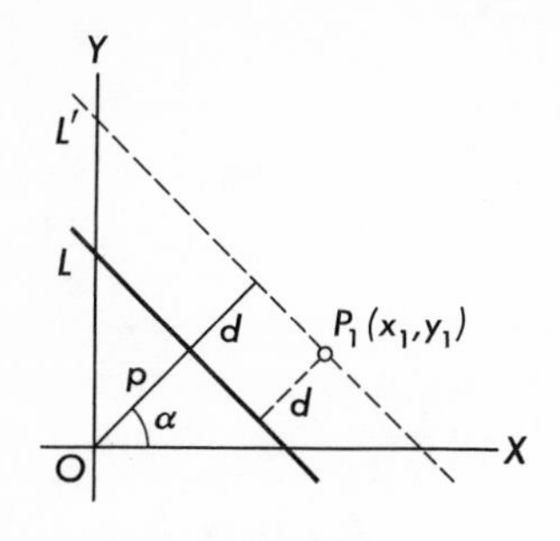

Figure 23

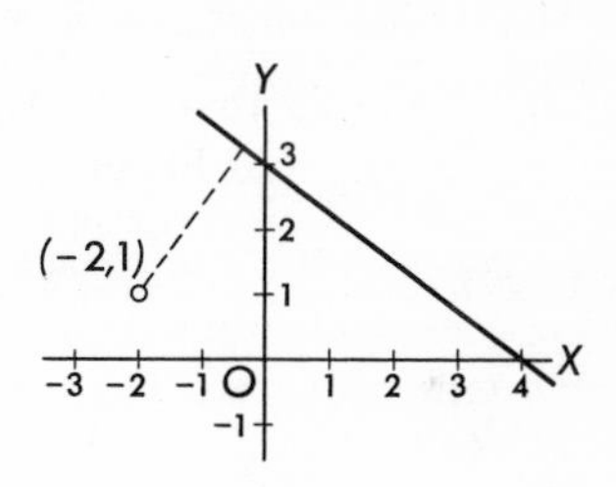

Figure 24

be noted that d is *positive* if the origin O and the point P_1 lie on opposite sides of the given line, and *negative* when O and P_1 lie on the same side.

Illustration. The distance from the point $(-2,1)$ to the line $3x + 4y - 12 = 0$ is

$$d = \frac{3(-2) + 4(1) - 12}{\sqrt{3^2 + 4^2}}$$

$$= -\frac{14}{5}.$$

The negative sign indicates that the given point and the origin are on the same side of the line as shown in Figure 24.

Example. Find the equation of the line that bisects the acute angle between the lines $x - y - 1 = 0$ and $7x + y - 7 = 0$.

Solution: We know from geometry that the bisector of the angle between two lines is the locus of points equidistant from the two lines.

* If $C = 0$, choose the sign of the radical to be the same as the sign of B. This will make d positive when P_1 lies above L. If $C = 0$ and $B = 0$, choose the sign of the radical to be the same as the sign of A. This will make d positive when P_1 is to the right of L.

Thus, if $P(x,y)$ is any point on the bisector, and d and d' are the signed distances to the given lines, it follows in this example that

$$d = -d'.$$

However, by (1), the distances from $P(x,y)$ to the given lines are

$$d = \frac{x - y - 1}{\sqrt{2}} \quad \text{and} \quad d' = \frac{7x + y - 7}{5\sqrt{2}}.$$

Hence the equation of the bisector is

$$\frac{x - y - 1}{\sqrt{2}} = -\frac{7x + y - 7}{5\sqrt{2}},$$

or

$$3x - y - 3 = 0.$$

Note in Figure 25 that by setting $d = d'$, we would have obtained the equation of the line that bisects the obtuse angle between the given lines.

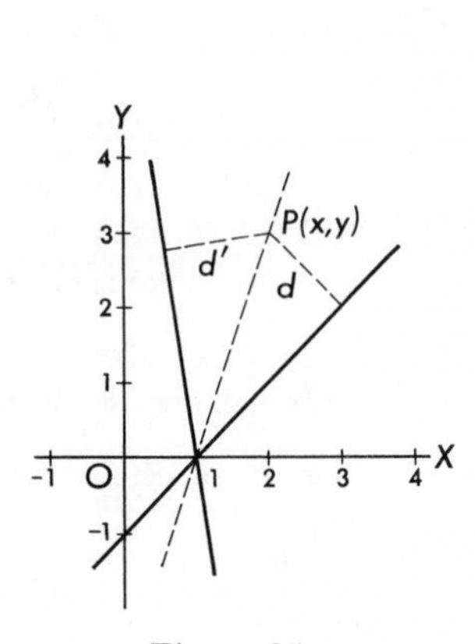

Figure 25

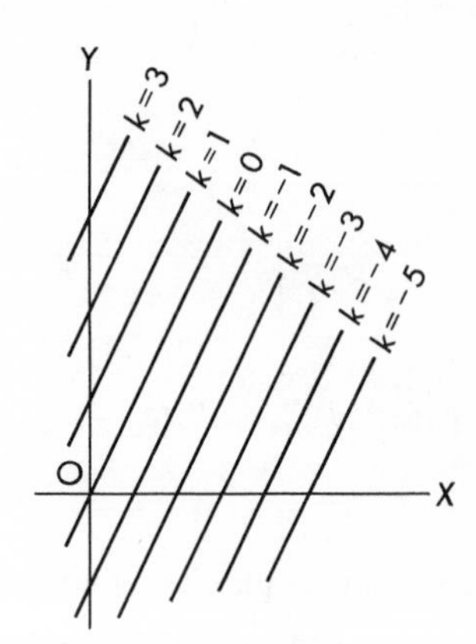

Figure 26

15. Family of Lines

In the equation of a line, the variables x and y are often called the *running coordinates* of the line. They represent the coordinates of a general point on the line, and are different for different points of the line. Any other arbitrary quantities occurring in the equation represent constant values for one line, but differ for another line. Thus for various values of k, the equation $2x - y + k = 0$ represents, as shown in Figure 26, what is called a **family** or **system** of lines having slope 2. The arbitrary constant k is called the **parameter** of the family; and when only one arbitrary constant occurs in the equation, it is often called a **one-parameter family.** A family such as this is also said to have **one degree of freedom.**

Illustration 1. The equation

$$y - 2 = m(x - 1)$$

represents, as shown in Figure 27, a family of lines passing through the point (1,2).

Illustration 2. If A, B, and C are fixed constants, the family of lines parallel to $Ax + By + C = 0$ has the equation $Ax + By + k = 0$, and the family of lines perpendicular to the given line has the equation $Bx - Ay + k = 0$.

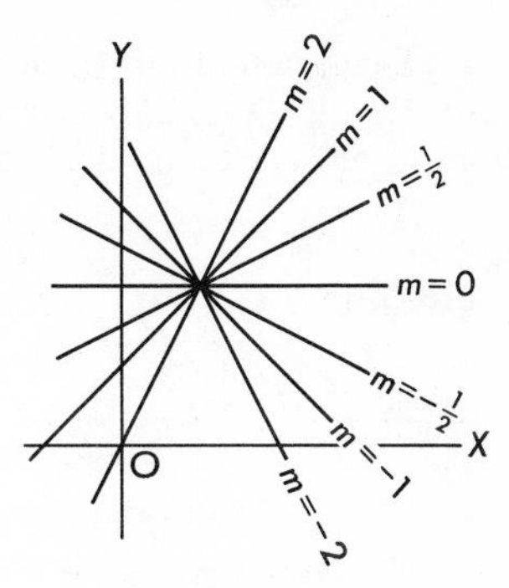

Figure 27

Example. Find the equation of the line that passes through $(2, -1)$ and is perpendicular to the line $3x + 4y - 5 = 0$.

Solution: The equation of the family of lines perpendicular to the given line can be written as

$$4x - 3y = k. \qquad (1)$$

To find the member of this family that passes through $(2, -1)$, we substitute $x = 2$ and $y = -1$; thus

$$4(2) - 3(-1) = k; \quad \text{hence } k = 11.$$

This value of k substituted in (1) gives the equation of the required line

$$4x - 3y = 11.$$

16. Line Through the Intersection of Two Lines

The concept and process of finding a family of curves which pass through the points of intersection of other curves is of considerable importance in analytic geometry. This idea as it applies to lines is expressed in the following theorem.

Theorem. *If* $\boldsymbol{A}$, $\boldsymbol{B}$, $\boldsymbol{C}$, $\boldsymbol{D}$, $\boldsymbol{E}$, *and* $\boldsymbol{F}$ *are fixed constants and*

$$\boldsymbol{Ax + By + C = 0, \qquad Dx + Ey + F = 0} \qquad (1)$$

are the equations of two intersecting lines, the equation

$$\boldsymbol{(Ax + By + C) + k(Dx + Ey + F) = 0,} \qquad (2)$$

where $\boldsymbol{k}$ *is a parameter, represents a family of lines passing through the point of intersection of the given lines.*

To prove this theorem, we note first that (2) is a line, since it is an equation of first degree in x and y. Second, we observe that the coordinates of the point of intersection of (1) satisfy (2), regardless of the value of k, since in this case the left side of (2) becomes $(0) + k(0)$ which is clearly zero.

Illustration. The equation of the family of lines passing through the point of intersection of the lines $x = 3$ and $x + y = 5$ is $(x - 3) + k(x + y - 5) = 0$. Observe that the line $x + y - 5 = 0$ is not a member of this family, since no value of k will give this equation.

Example. Find the equation of the line through the point of intersection of the lines $x + y = 7$ and $2x - y + 3 = 0$, and parallel to the line $3x - 2y + 5 = 0$.

Solution: The family of lines through the point of intersection of the given lines is

$$x + y - 7 + k(2x - y + 3) = 0,$$

which may be written in the form

$$(1 + 2k)x + (1 - k)y + (3k - 7) = 0. \tag{3}$$

Two lines are parallel when the coefficients of x and y are proportional. Thus to find the member of (3) that is parallel to the given line, we have

$$\frac{1 + 2k}{3} = \frac{1 - k}{-2}; \quad \text{hence } k = -5.$$

Putting $k = -5$ in (3), we obtain the required line

$$9x - 6y + 22 = 0.$$

EXERCISE 5

In each of the following, find the distance between the given line and point.

1. $3x + 4y = 10$, $(-2, -\frac{1}{2})$. *Ans.* 3.6.
2. $5x - 12y = 1$, $(4,1)$.
3. $3x - y = 0$, $(2, -4)$. $\sqrt{10}$.
4. $8x - 6y - 5 = 0$, $(-1,2)$.
5. $x + y = 2$, $(\frac{1}{2}, \frac{1}{3})$. $\frac{7}{12}\sqrt{2}$.
6. $5y + 7 = 0$, $(3,5)$.

Find the distance between the following parallel lines.

7. $3x - 4y - 10 = 0$, $3x - 4y - 20 = 0$. *Ans.* 2.
8. $12x + 5y = 8$, $12x + 5y = 0$.
9. $x + 2y = 6$, $2x + 4y = -9$. $2.1\sqrt{5}$.
10. $2y + 5 = 0$, $3y - 1 = 0$.
11. Give the equation of the family of lines (*a*) having slope $\frac{2}{3}$, (*b*) passing through the point $(2, -3)$, (*c*) parallel to the line $2x - 5y = 7$.
    Ans. (*a*) $y = \frac{2}{3}x + k$, (*b*) $y + 3 = k(x - 2)$, (*c*) $2x - 5y = k$.
12. Give the equation of the family of lines (*a*) having inclination 135°, (*b*) having x intercept 6, (*c*) perpendicular to the line $3x + 5y = 8$.

Find the equation of the line containing the point $(3,-2)$ and satisfying the following condition.

13. Parallel to the line $2x - y + 7 = 0$. *Ans.* $2x - y = 8$.
14. Parallel to the line $3x + 7y - 5 = 0$.
15. Perpendicular to the line $x - 5y - 2 = 0$. $5x + y = 13$.
16. Perpendicular to the line $4x - 3y + 5 = 0$.

Find the equation of the line that bisects the acute angle formed by the following lines.

17. $2x - y = 3$ and $x - 2y = 3$. *Ans.* $x - y = 2$.
18. $7x - y = 5$ and $y = x + 1$.
19. $x - y = 0$ and $x = 0$. $y = (1 + \sqrt{2})x$.
20. $5x - 12y + 18 = 0$ and $4x - 3y + 21 = 0$.

Find the equation of the line passing through the point of intersection of the given lines and satisfying the condition indicated.

21. $x - 2y = 3$, $3x + y = 5$, containing the point $(-1,3)$. *Ans.* $5x + 4y = 7$.
22. $2x + y = 0$, $4x - y = 2$, having an x intercept 4.
23. $3x - y = 5$, $x + 2y = 5$, having slope 2. $14x - 7y = 20$.
24. $2x + 5 = 0$, $4x - 3y = 5$, parallel to the line $x + y = 2$.
25. $x - y = 1$, $3x + y + 1 = 0$, perpendicular to the line $y = 2x + 1$. *Ans.* $x + 2y + 2 = 0$.
26. $x - y = 0$, $3x - 2y = 2$, cutting from the first quadrant a triangle whose area is 9.
27. Find the equations of the bisectors of the interior angles of the triangle whose vertices are $(0,4)$, $(-4,-4)$, and $(6,1)$. *Ans.* $y = 1$, $y = x$, $3x + y = 4$.
28. Find the equations of the bisectors of the interior angles of the triangle bounded by the lines $x = 3$, $y = 4$, and $x + y = 2$.
29. Find the radius of the circle inscribed in the triangle bounded by the lines $x - y + 4 = 0$, $7x - y - 2 = 0$, and $x + y + 4 = 0$. *Ans.* $\frac{5}{4}\sqrt{2}$.
30. Find the distance from the origin to a line that is perpendicular to the line $3x + 4y = 2$, and passes through the point of intersection of the lines $x + y = 8$ and $x + 7y = 14$.
31. Find the equation of the line that passes through the points of intersection of $y = x + 6$ with $2x + 3y = 24$, and $y = 2x$ with $x + 2y = 8$. *Ans.* $50x + 5y = 96$.
32. Draw perpendiculars from the point $(5,0)$ to the three sides of a triangle whose vertices are at the points $(4,3)$, $(-4,3)$, and $(0,-5)$. Show that the feet of the three perpendiculars lie on a straight line and find its equation.

33. If the vertices of triangle ABC are $A(7,3)$, $B(0,2)$, and $C(6,0)$, find the length from C to AB of (*a*) the median, (*b*) the altitude, (*c*) the bisector of angle C. *Ans.* (*a*) $\frac{5}{2}\sqrt{2}$, (*b*) $2\sqrt{2}$, (*c*) $\frac{4}{3}\sqrt{5}$.

34. A point moves so that its distance from the line $y = 5 + 2x$ is twice its distance from the line $y = 5 - 2x$. Find the equation of its locus. Do these lines trisect the angles between the given lines?

CHAPTER 2

Variables, Functions, and Limits

17. Introduction

In Article **1** we indicated that calculus is a mathematical theory which is based primarily on the concept of a limit. In its most elementary intuitive form, a limit can be described as a value approached by a variable quantity that changes in some prescribed manner. For example, as n increases through the positive integral values 1, 2, 3, 4, $\cdots$, the expression $1/n$ assumes the values 1, $\frac{1}{2}$, $\frac{1}{3}$, $\frac{1}{4}$, $\cdots$. It is evident that no number in this set will ever attain the value 0, no matter how large we select n. However, by choosing n sufficiently large, we can find a number in the succession that is as near to 0 as we wish to have it. Furthermore, all succeeding numbers in the set will be even closer to the value 0. In a case such as this, we say that the expression $1/n$ approaches the limit 0 as n increases indefinitely.

Actually, the calculus is concerned with two types of limiting processes. The first of these can be associated with the problem of determining the instantaneous rate of change of position of a moving body. Thus if an apple drops from a tree, how fast is it moving at any instant? An investigation of this problem leads us to the introduction of a new concept—that of a *derivative*. A study of these quantities forms the basis for the *differential calculus*.

The second type of limit concept can be associated with the problem of determining a definition for the area of a plane geometric figure when some of its boundaries are curved. Thus why is it that the area of a circle is given by πr^2? An investigation of this problem leads us to the introduction of still another concept—that of an *integral*. A study of these quantities gives rise to the theory called *integral calculus*.

In the development of the subject, we will find that these two apparently unrelated limit concepts are in fact very closely related, one being merely the inverse of the other. This fact allows us to unify these two theories into what is called the *differential and integral calculus*, or briefly the *calculus*.

18. Rate of Change

If a body falls from a position of rest and air resistance is neglected, we know from physics that an approximation formula for the distance s in feet fallen in time t in seconds is

$$s = 16t^2.$$

We observe that the velocity of the body is not constant since it falls 16 feet the first second, 48 feet the second second, 80 feet the third second, and so on. When an object such as this is moving at a varying velocity, its exact velocity at any particular instant can only be estimated by a process of calculating *average* velocities of the object over shorter and shorter intervals of time, each interval containing the instant in question. Thus to find the velocity of the falling body at the end of 2 seconds we could compile a table such as is illustrated below, and from this table we could conclude that the average velocity at time $t = 2$ is close to 64 feet per second.

Time Interval	*Distance Covered*	*Average Velocity*
1 to 2	48	48
1.9 to 2	6.24	62.4
1.99 to 2	0.6384	63.84
2 to 2.01	0.6416	64.16
2 to 2.1	6.56	65.6
2 to 3	80	80

This same conclusion can be reached more effectively by using algebraic methods of analysis. For example, if t and t_0 denote any two different times, the corresponding locations of the falling body are given by $s = 16t^2$ and $s_0 = 16t_0^2$, and the average velocity $\bar{v}$ for the time interval t_0 to t is

$$\bar{v} = \frac{s - s_0}{t - t_0} = \frac{16(t^2 - t_0^2)}{t - t_0} = 16(t + t_0).$$

As the time interval shortens and t gets closer to t_0, it is clear that $\bar{v}$ becomes more and more nearly equal to $16(t_0 + t_0)$. Thus if we denote by v_0 the exact velocity at time t_0, we conclude that

$$v_0 = 32t_0.$$

This formula gives $v_0 = 64$ feet per second when $t_0 = 2$ seconds, in agreement with the preceding arithmetical analysis.

The process by which we have defined the exact velocity v_0 is called *taking the limit as t approaches* t_0, and we write this operation symbolically as

$$v_0 = \lim_{t \to t_0} \frac{s - s_0}{t - t_0}.$$

The preceding limit process has a much wider application than that of merely finding the velocities of moving objects. Whenever any two measurable quantities are related in some manner, we may be interested in investigating their relative rates of change. Thus if x_0 and y_0 are specific values of two related quantities x and y, the rate of change of y with respect to x for the particular value x_0 is defined as the limit

$$\lim_{x \to x_0} \frac{y - y_0}{x - x_0}.$$

This limit is called the *derivative* of y with respect to x at $x = x_0$.

Illustration. For the function $y = \frac{4}{x}$, we have $y_0 = \frac{4}{x_0}$ and

$$y - y_0 = \frac{4}{x} - \frac{4}{x_0} = \frac{4(x_0 - x)}{xx_0}.$$

Thus the derivative of y with respect to x at x_0 is

$$\lim_{x \to x_0} \frac{y - y_0}{x - x_0} = \lim_{x \to x_0} \frac{-4}{xx_0} = -\frac{4}{x_0^2}.$$

19. The Concept of Area

In the preceding article we discussed the type of limit process that is associated with relative rates of change. We shall now consider another kind of limit process, one that consists of adding together many small divisions of a whole object. This process is most easily illustrated by attempting to determine the area of a plane figure that has curved boundaries.

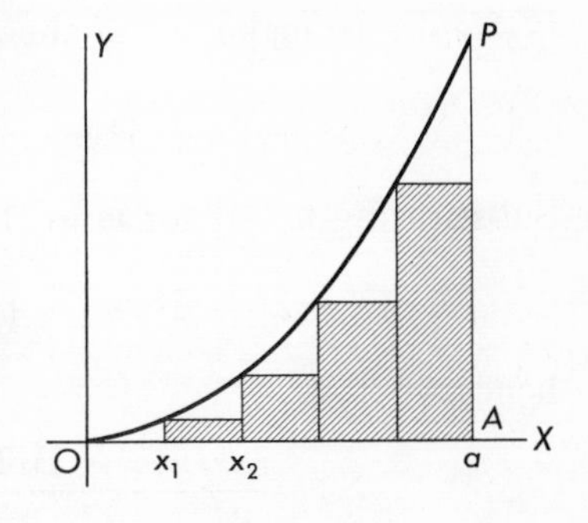

Figure 28

For this purpose let the bounding curve in Figure 28 have the equation $y = x^2$, and let us consider the area S of the three-sided figure OAP. Since a unit of area is defined as the area of a square with sides one unit long, the area of a rectangle is easily determined to be the product of its length and width. To determine the area of a figure with curved boundaries, we choose a set of non-overlapping rectangles that nearly cover the figure. The sum of the areas of these rectangles gives us an approximation to the area in question, and if the number of these rectangles is increased with corresponding decreases in all widths, the better, in general, will be the approximation.

To make such an investigation let the interval OA in Figure 28 be divided into n segments by the points $x_0, x_1, \cdots, x_n$, where $x_0 = 0$ and $x_n = a$. Although it is essential that all of these segments get smaller as n gets larger, it is not necessary that they all be of the same length. We shall, however, for the sake of simplicity assume that all of these segments do have the same length, namely a/n. In this case, then, we have

$$x_0 = 0, \quad x_1 = \frac{a}{n}, \quad x_2 = \frac{2a}{n}, \quad \cdots, \quad x_k = \frac{ka}{n}, \quad \cdots, \quad x_n = \frac{na}{n} = a.$$

Since the equation of OP is $y = x^2$, it follows that the heights of the n approximating rectangles are

$$0, \quad \left(\frac{a}{n}\right)^2, \quad \left(\frac{2a}{n}\right)^2, \quad \cdots, \quad \left(\frac{(n-1)a}{n}\right)^2,$$

and the sum S_n of their areas is

$$S_n = \left[\left(\frac{a}{n}\right)^2 + \left(\frac{2a}{n}\right)^2 + \cdots + \left(\frac{(n-1)a}{n}\right)^2\right]\frac{a}{n}$$

$$= \frac{a^3}{n^3}[1^2 + 2^2 + \cdots + (n-1)^2].$$

Our problem now is to see what happens to S_n as n gets larger and larger. This limit could be studied arithmetically for large values of n, but it is simpler to make use of the algebraic formula*

$$1^2 + 2^2 + 3^2 + \cdots + m^2 = \frac{m(m+1)(2m+1)}{6}. \tag{1}$$

Substituting $n - 1$ for m in (1) gives

$$1^2 + 2^2 + 3^2 + \cdots + (n-1)^2 = \frac{(n-1)n(2n-1)}{6};$$

hence we have

$$S_n = \frac{a^3}{n^3}\cdot\frac{n(n-1)(2n-1)}{6} = \left(\frac{1}{3} - \frac{1}{2n} + \frac{1}{6n^2}\right)a^3.$$

In this form it is easy to see that S_n tends toward the value $\frac{1}{3}a^3$ as n gets larger and larger. For this reason, we take $S = \frac{1}{3}a^3$. Geometrically, this result indicates that the area OAP is exactly one-third the area of the rectangle that has OA and AP as sides.

It is also interesting to observe that if a set of rectangles are

---

* See Thurman S. Peterson, *College Algebra*, 2nd ed., Harper & Brothers, 1958.

selected that extend above the curve, as shown in Figure 29, their combined area will exceed the area S but will tend toward S as the widths of the rectangles decrease. Thus if OA is divided into n equal parts and S'_n is the total area of the circumscribing rectangles, we find

$$\begin{aligned} S'_n &= \left[\left(\frac{a}{n}\right)^2 + \left(\frac{2a}{n}\right)^2 + \cdots + \left(\frac{na}{n}\right)^2\right]\frac{a}{n} \\ &= \frac{a^3}{n^3}[1^2 + 2^2 + \cdots + n^2] \\ &= \left(\frac{1}{3} + \frac{1}{2n} + \frac{1}{6n^2}\right)a^3. \end{aligned}$$

Hence in this case, as before, S'_n tends toward $\frac{1}{3}a^3$ as n gets larger and larger.

Instead of thinking in terms of an area, we may consider the operation of finding the limit of the sequence $S_1, S_2, \cdots, S_n, \cdots$ as a process being applied to the function $f(x) = x^2$ whose graph is the curved boundary in Figure 28. The limit S of the sequence is called the *definite integral* of x^2 from $x = 0$ to $x = a$, and is denoted by the symbol

$$\int_0^a x^2\,dx.$$

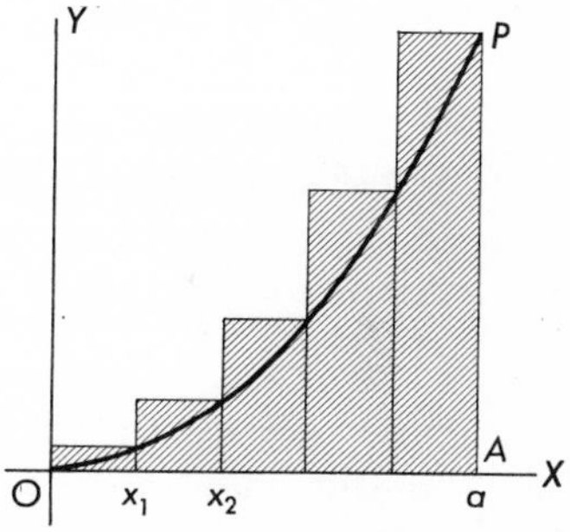

Figure 29

The two limit concepts, the derivative and the definite integral, form the basis of the calculus. The discussion that follows will indicate how these concepts are related.

EXERCISE 6

1. A ball rolling down an incline travels s feet in t seconds, where $s = 5t^2$. Derive a formula for the velocity of the ball at time $t = t_0$. How fast is it going (*a*) after 2 seconds, (*b*) after it has rolled 80 feet?

   Ans. (*a*) 20 ft./sec., (*b*) 40 ft./sec.

2. By definition, acceleration is the rate of change of velocity with respect of time. Find the acceleration of the falling body considered in Article **18**.

3. A ball thrown straight up is located s feet above the ground at t seconds after it is thrown in accordance with the formula $s = 112t - 16t^2$. Find a formula for the velocity of the ball and find (*a*) the time required to reach its highest point, (*b*) the distance of the highest point above the ground, and (*c*) the acceleration of the ball at this point.

   Ans. (*a*) 3.5 sec., (*b*) 196 ft., (*c*) -32 ft./sec^2.

4. Find the rate of change of the function $f(x) = x^3$ with respect to x at x_0.
5. Find the derivative of the function $f(x) = \sqrt{x}$ with respect to x at x_0. *Ans.* $1/2\sqrt{x_0}$.
6. By use of a procedure similar to that discussed in Article **19**, find the area of the triangle OAP (Figure 30) as the limit of a sum of inscribed rectangular areas. Do the same for circumscribed rectangular areas.

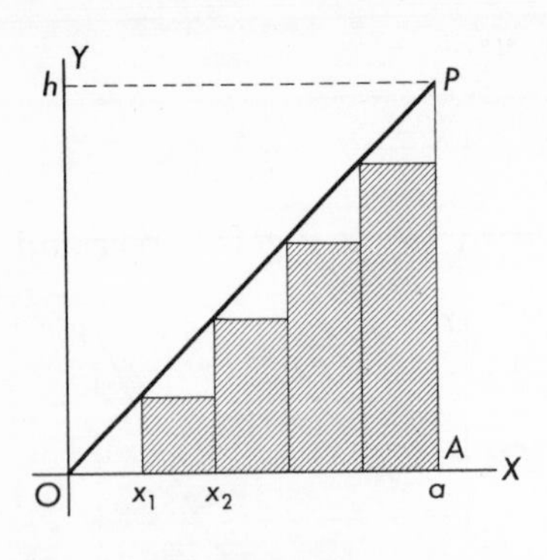

Figure 30

7. Using the methods suggested in the preceding problem, find the area of the trapezoid bounded by the line $y = x + 3$, the ordinates $x = 1$, $x = 3$, and the x axis. *Ans.* 10.
8. By use of a procedure similar to that discussed in connection with Figure 28, find the area OAP when the equation of OP is $y = x^3$ and P has the coordinates (a,a^3). *Hint:* Use the formula $1^3 + 2^3 + 3^3 + \cdots + m^3 = \frac{1}{4}m^2(m + 1)^2$.
9. By finding the limit of a sum of rectangles, find the area bounded by the curve $y = x^2$, the ordinates $x = 1$, $x = 2$, and the x axis. *Ans.* 7/3.
10. By summing both sides of the identity

$$h^3 - (h - 1)^3 = 3h^2 - 3h + 1$$

for $h = 1, 2, 3, \cdots, m$, show how to obtain the formula (1) given in Article **19**.

20. Constants and Variables

In mathematics a *constant* is a quantity that maintains a fixed value throughout a particular problem. *Numerical* or *absolute constants*, such as 2, $\sqrt{5}$, and π, retain the same values in all problems, whereas *arbitrary constants* remain constant in a particular problem but may assume different values in other problems. The **absolute** or **numerical value** of a constant a is denoted by $|a|$ and means the magnitude of a regardless of its algebraic sign. Thus $|3| = 3$ and $|-3| = -(-3) = 3$. If two numbers a and b have the same sign, then $|a + b| = |a| + |b|$, but if they have different signs, $|a + b| < |a| + |b|$. Since the cases when $a = 0$ or $b = 0$ are trivial, we see for all a and b that

$$|a + b| \leqq |a| + |b|. \tag{1}$$

Illustration 1. When $|a| > |b|$ it follows from the identity $a = b + (a - b)$ that

$$|a| \leqq |b| + |a - b| \qquad \text{or} \qquad |a - b| \geqq |a| - |b|.$$

A *variable* is a quantity that may assume various values in the course of a problem, and the set of values that it assumes is called the **domain** or **range** of the variable. Thus, for the ellipse $x^2/a^2+y^2/b^2=1$, a and b are constants for a particular ellipse, and x and y are variables. The variable x has the range from $-a$ to a inclusive and y ranges from $-b$ to b inclusive.

We know from analytic geometry that the totality of real numbers can be represented by the points on a straight line. A scale, such as shown in Figure 31, which indicates this ordered relationship is called a **real continuum** or **number scale.** In most applications, the

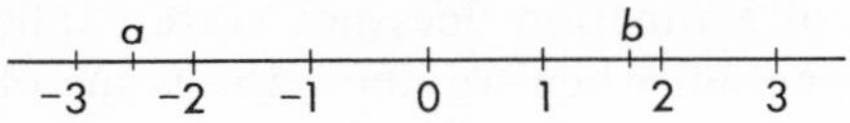

a b
-3 -2 -1 0 1 2 3

Figure 31

domain or range of a continuous variable x will be one or more of various kinds of **intervals** such as

$a < x < b$, open interval, all points between a and b;
$a \leqq x \leqq b$, closed interval, includes the end points;
$x < a$, open half interval to the left;
$x \geqq a$, closed half interval to the right.

Since an absolute value function such as $|x|$ means x when x is positive and $-x$ when x is negative, it is possible to represent a domain of a variable by an expression such as $|x| < 4$. Thus in this case we have

$$x < 4, \quad \text{when } x \text{ is positive,}$$
$$-x < 4 \text{ or } -4 < x, \quad \text{when } x \text{ is negative.}$$

Hence in all cases, zero included, the domain of x for $|x| < 4$ is the interval $-4 < x < 4$.

Illustration 2. The points of the interval $-1 < x < 5$ all lie within 3 units of the central point 2; therefore the domain of x can be represented as $|x-2| < 3$. In this sense we observe that the expression $|x-2|$ represents the distance between x and 2.

21. Functions

If two variables x and y are related so that, for each x in a domain R of real numbers, we obtain one or more real values for y, then y is said to be a **real function of the real variable** x defined in the domain R. Throughout this book the word "function" will refer to a *real* function of a *real* variable unless stated otherwise.

Since the implication of the above definition is that y depends on x, we call y the **dependent variable** or **function** and x the **independent variable.**

If only one value of y corresponds to each value of x in the domain R, y is called a **single-valued** function of x; otherwise it may be a **double-valued, triple-valued,** or **multiple-valued** function of x.

Illustration 1. If $y = 1/x^2$, y is a single-valued function of x for all real numbers except $x = 0$. If $y^2 = 4x$, y is a double-valued function $(\pm 2\sqrt{x})$ of x for all x in the domain $x \geqq 0$.

The definition of a function does not state explicitly how we find the value of the function when we know the value of the independent variable; it merely asserts that it can be found. In general, these functional values are determined in one of two ways; either from an equation or formula, or from a statistically determined table of values. In this book we shall be concerned primarily with functional relationships that are defined by equations.

Functions of a single variable are represented by symbols such as $f(x)$, $g(r)$, and $\phi(z)$. The letter in parentheses indicates the independent variable, and the prefixed letter denotes a given relationship. The symbol $f(x)$ is read "the f function of x" or briefly "f of x." The value of $f(x)$ when $x = a$ is denoted by $f(a)$.

Illustration 2. If $F(x) = x^2 + 4$, then $F(-2) = (-2)^2 + 4 = 8$, $F(n) = n^2 + 4$, and $F(x + y) = (x + y)^2 + 4$.

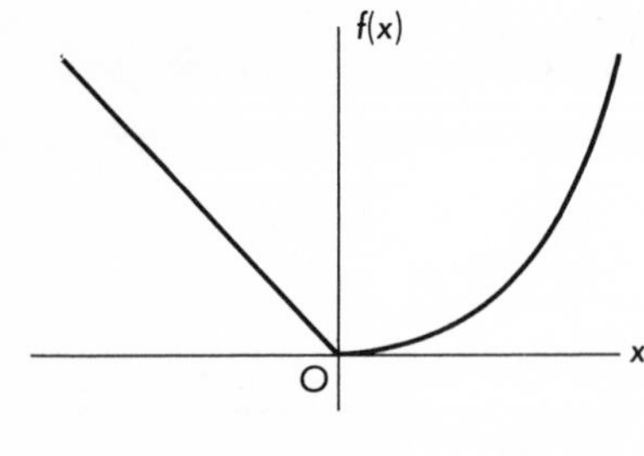

Figure 32

A functional definition cannot always be expressed by a single relationship; frequently, composite definitions are necessary. For example, the function

$$f(x) = \begin{cases} -x, & \text{when } x \leqq 0, \\ x^3, & \text{when } x > 0, \end{cases}$$

whose graph is shown in Figure 32, is defined differently in the positive and negative domains of x.

Example 1. Draw a sketch of the function $f(x) = |x| + |x - 1|$.

Solution: Since for absolute values

$$|x| = \begin{cases} x, & \text{when } x \geqq 0, \\ -x, & \text{when } x < 0, \end{cases} \qquad |x - 1| = \begin{cases} x - 1, & \text{when } x \geqq 1, \\ 1 - x, & \text{when } x < 1, \end{cases}$$

we see that $f(x)$ is defined differently in the three intervals $x \leqq 0$, $0 < x < 1$, and $x \geqq 1$. Thus an equivalent representation is

$$f(x) = \begin{cases} 1 - 2x, & \text{when } x \leqq 0, \\ 1, & \text{when } 0 < x < 1, \\ 2x - 1, & \text{when } x \geqq 1. \end{cases}$$

Plotting these line segments for the domains in question we obtain the graph shown in Figure 33.

A function that depends on two or more independent variables is represented symbolically in a similar manner. Thus a function of two variables x and y is written as $f(x,y)$ and is read "f of x and y." The value of $f(x,y)$ when $x = a$ and $y = b$ is denoted by $f(a,b)$.

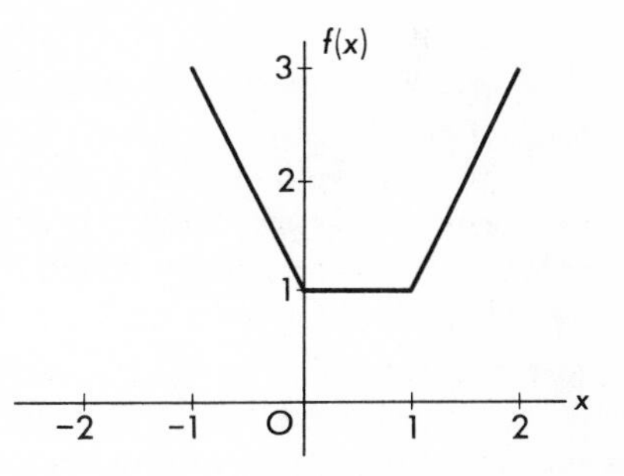

Figure 33

Example 2. If $f(x,y) = \dfrac{x}{x - y}$, show that $f(x,y) + f(x,-y) = 2f(x^2,y^2)$.

Solution: Substituting $-y$ for y in $f(x,y) = x/(x - y)$, we obtain $f(x,-y) = x/(x + y)$. Hence

$$f(x,y) + f(x,-y) = \frac{x}{x - y} + \frac{x}{x + y} = \frac{2x^2}{x^2 - y^2} = 2f(x^2,y^2).$$

EXERCISE 7

1. If $g(x) = \sqrt{25 - x^2}$, find $g(0)$, $g(-3)$, $g(\frac{7}{5})$. *Ans.* 5, 4, $\frac{24}{5}$.
2. If $\phi(z) = 4^z$, find $\phi(0)$, $\phi(-2)$, $\phi(\frac{1}{2})$.
3. If $h(\theta) = \cos^2 \theta$, find $h(0)$, $h(\frac{1}{4}\pi)$, $h(\frac{1}{2}\pi)$. 1, $\frac{1}{2}$, 0.
4. If $f(x) = \log_{10} x$, find $f(1)$, $f(10)$, $f(5)$.
5. If $G(x) = \sin 2x$, find $G(0)$, $G(-\frac{1}{4}\pi)$, $G(\frac{7}{8}\pi)$. 0, -1, $-\frac{1}{2}\sqrt{2}$.
6. If $\psi(t) = t^t$, find $\psi(1)$, $\psi(-2)$, $\psi(\frac{1}{4})$.
7. If $R(a,b) = \dfrac{a + 1}{b + 1}$, find $R(5,-3)$, $R(a - 1,4)$. -3, $a/5$.
8. If $F(m,n) = m^2 - n^2$, find $F(\frac{1}{3},\frac{1}{6})$, $F(x + y,x - y)$.

Find the domain of the variable x for which the following equations determine y as a real function of x.

9. $y - xy = 5$. *Ans.* $x \neq 1$.
10. $y = \sqrt{4 - x^2}$.
11. $y^2 = x - 3$. $x \geqq 3$.
12. $y^4 = 4 - x^2$.

13. $y = \tan x$. *Ans.* $x \neq (n + \frac{1}{2})\pi$.
14. $y = \log (1 - 2x)$.
15. $y^3 = 1 - x^2$. All real values.
16. $y = \sin^{-1} x$.
17. If $f(x) = x(x + 1)$, show that $f(x + h) - f(x) = h(2x + 1 + h)$.
18. If $g(y) = y/(1 - y)$, show that $\frac{1}{2}[g(y) + g(-y)] = g(y^2)$.
19. If $F(z) = \log z$, show that $F(xy) = F(x) + F(y)$.
20. If $\phi(r) = 2^r$, show that $\phi(r + 1) = 2\phi(r)$.
21. If $P(x) = \sqrt{x}$, show that $P(x + h) - P(x) = h/(\sqrt{x + h} + \sqrt{x})$.
22. If $f(x) = \sin x$, show that $f(2x) = 2f(x)f(\frac{1}{2}\pi - x)$.
23. If $f(x) = x^2 - 1$ and $g(x) = 2x + 1$, show that $f[g(x)] = 4x(x + 1)$.
24. If $f(x) = 10^x$ and $\phi(x) = \log_{10} x$, show that $f[\phi(x)] = \phi[f(x)] = x$.
25. If $f(x,y) = x^3 + 4xy^2 + y^3$, show that $f(ax,ay) = a^3f(x,y)$.
26. If $F(u,v) = \dfrac{u - v}{u + v}$, find $F(1/u,1/v) + F(u,v)$.
27. Prove that $|a + b| - |a - b| \leqq 2|b|$.

Find equivalent functional definitions for each of the following and draw a graph of the function.

28. $f(x) = 2x - |x| + |x - 1|$.
29. $f(x) = x + |x|$. *Ans.* $f(x) = \begin{cases} 0, & \text{when } x \leqq 0, \\ 2x, & \text{when } x > 0. \end{cases}$
30. $f(x) = |x|\cdot|x - 1|$.

22. Limit of a Function

In Article **18** we discussed briefly the limit process that is associated with the determination of relative rates of change. We concluded, for example, that as t gets closer and closer to t_0 the expression $16(t + t_0)$ becomes more and more nearly equal to $32t_0$. A limit such as this can be expressed formally as "$f(x)$ approaches the limit value A as x approaches the constant a." This we can write as $f(x) \to A$ as $x \to a$, or more commonly as

$$\lim_{x \to a} f(x) = A.$$

There are two important aspects in regard to this statement that have to do with the use of the word "approach." First, it is important to understand that the word is restricted to imply a certain degree of "closeness." What we actually mean is that the difference $|f(x) - A|$ can be made as small as we desire simply by requiring x to be near enough to a. Second, since it is possible that the function under consideration is undefined when $x = a$, we restrict the symbolism "$x \to a$" to mean "x nears but is never equal to a."

Illustration 1. $\lim_{x \to 3} \sqrt{x+6} = 3$, $\lim_{x \to 1/2} \sin \pi x = 1$, and $\lim_{x \to 0} 3^{-1/x^2} = 0$.

Note: Observe that the function $3^{-1/x^2}$ is undefined when $x = 0$, but the limit exists and is equal to 0. This is true since x small implies $1/x^2$ large, which in turn implies $3^{1/x^2}$ large, and so $3^{-1/x^2}$ is small.

In order that problems which involve limits may be analyzed with mathematical precision the preceding intuitive concept of a limit is incorporated into the following definition.

A function $f(x)$ is said to approach a value A as x approaches a, if corresponding to every positive number ϵ there is some positive number δ such that

$$|f(x) - A| < \epsilon$$

is true for every x that satisfies the inequality

$$0 < |x - a| < \delta.$$

Example. Prove that $\lim_{x \to 2} (5x - 2) = 8$.

Solution: To prove this we need to show that for any $\epsilon > 0$ there exists a number $\delta > 0$ such that

$$|(5x - 2) - 8| < \epsilon \tag{1}$$

is satisfied, whenever x is in the domain

$$0 < |x - 2| < \delta.$$

By dividing both sides of (1) by 5, we obtain

$$|x - 2| < \frac{\epsilon}{5}.$$

Hence $\delta = \epsilon/5$ is an adequate choice for δ and the proof is complete.

Letting $\epsilon = 0.005$, we see that the preceding result means that the function $5x - 2$ will lie in the range $7.995 < 5x - 2 < 8.005$ whenever the domain of x is $1.999 < x < 2.001$.

Although basic theorems must of necessity be proved in accordance with the preceding definition, subsequent results are usually derived from the theorems so established. One of the most important and useful of the theorems is the following.

Theorem 1. *If* $\lim_{x \to a} f(x) = A$ *and* $\lim_{x \to a} g(x) = B$, *then*

1. $\lim_{x \to a} [f(x) + g(x)] = A + B$,
2. $\lim_{x \to a} f(x)\, g(x) = AB$,
3. $\lim_{x \to a} \dfrac{f(x)}{g(x)} = \dfrac{A}{B}$, *provided* $B \neq 0$.

Intuitively the results of this theorem appear trivial since, for example, if $f(x)$ is near A and $g(x)$ is near B, it seems obvious that the sum, product, and quotient of the functions will be near $A + B$, AB, and A/B, respectively. The limit of the quotient must of course include the restriction $B \neq 0$ since the expression $A/0$ is meaningless.

We shall not give a complete proof of Theorem 1, but the method of proof will be illustrated by proving part 1. A similar procedure can be used to prove parts 2 and 3.

Proof of part 1: To prove this we need to show that for any $\epsilon > 0$ there exists a number $\delta > 0$ such that

$$|[f(x) + g(x)] - [A + B]| < \epsilon,$$

is satisfied, whenever x is in the domain

$$0 < |x - a| < \delta.$$

From $\lim_{x \to a} f(x) = A$ and $\lim_{x \leftarrow a} g(x) = B$ it follows that

$$|f(x) - A| < \epsilon_1, \quad \text{when } 0 < |x - a| < \delta_1,$$
$$|g(x) - B| < \epsilon_2, \quad \text{when } 0 < |x - a| < \delta_2.$$

If we let $\epsilon_1 = \epsilon_2 = \epsilon/2$ and take δ to be the smaller of δ_1 and δ_2, we find by use of equation (1) in Article **20** that

$$|[f(x) - A] + [g(x) - B]| \leqq |f(x) - A| + |g(x) - B| < \frac{\epsilon}{2} + \frac{\epsilon}{2} = \epsilon,$$

whenever x is in the domain defined by

$$0 < |x - a| < \delta.$$

As another illustration of the method of proof using the definition of a limit, we will establish the following theorem.

Theorem 2. *If $f(x) \to A$ and $h(x) \to A$ as $x \to a$, and if $f(x) \leqq g(x) \leqq h(x)$ for all values of x near a, then $g(x) \to A$ as $x \to a$.*

Proof: The existence of the limits for $f(x)$ and $h(x)$ means that

$$A - \epsilon < f(x) < A + \epsilon, \quad \text{when } 0 < |x - a| < \delta_1,$$
$$A - \epsilon < h(x) < A + \epsilon, \quad \text{when } 0 < |x - a| < \delta_2.$$

If we take δ to be the smaller of δ_1 and δ_2, we see by the hypothesis that for all x in the domain $0 < |x - a| < \delta$ we have

$$A - \epsilon < f(x) \leqq g(x) \leqq h(x) < A + \epsilon$$

or

$$A - \epsilon < g(x) < A + \epsilon.$$

This means, however, that $\lim_{x \to a} g(x)$ exists and equals A.

In some instances a function may approach two different limits according as x approaches a through values larger than a or through values smaller than a. We denote these limits by $\lim_{x \to a^+} f(x)$ and $\lim_{x \to a^-} f(x)$, respectively; and since they are not equal the limit of $f(x)$ as $x \to a$ is undefined.

Illustration 2. The function $2^{1/x}$ approaches zero as x approaches zero through negative values only. As x approaches zero through positive values only, the functional values become larger and larger.

23. Continuity

When $f(a)$ exists we find for most elementary functions that this is the limit that is usually approached by $f(x)$ as $x \to a$. This important property of functions is called *continuity* and is defined as follows.

A single-valued function $f(x)$ is said to be **continuous** *at a value a of its domain provided (1) $f(a)$ is defined, (2) $\lim_{x \to a} f(x)$ exists, and (3) $\lim_{x \to a} f(x) = f(a)$. If $f(x)$ is continuous at each point of an interval, it is said to be continuous on the interval.*

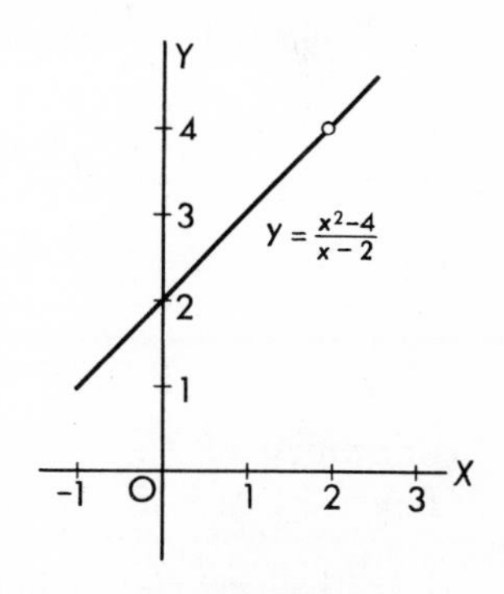

Figure 34

A function that is not continuous at a point is said to be **discontinuous** at that point. Thus the function $f(x) = |x|/x$ is discontinuous at $x = 0$ since $0/0$ is meaningless and moreover $\lim_{x \to 0} f(x)$ does not exist. Similarly, the function $g(x) = (x^2 - 4)/(x - 2)$ is discontinuous at $x = 2$ since $g(2)$ is undefined. In this case, however, $\lim_{x \to 2} g(x) = 4$, and we observe that the graph of $y = (x^2 - 4)/(x - 2)$ (Figure 34) is the entire line $y = x + 2$ with the single point (2,4) omitted.

Since $\lim_{x \to a} f(x) = f(a)$ means that for every $\epsilon > 0$ there exists a $\delta > 0$ such that

$$f(a) - \epsilon < f(x) < f(a) + \epsilon$$

for every x in the interval

$$a - \delta < x < a + \delta,$$

we see in Figure 35 that the continuity of $f(x)$ at $x = a$ means that the graph of $f(x)$ for the domain $a - \delta < x < a + \delta$ is entirely within a rectangle whose center is $(a, f(a))$ and whose height is 2ϵ.

Several important and useful theorems on continuity are as follows.

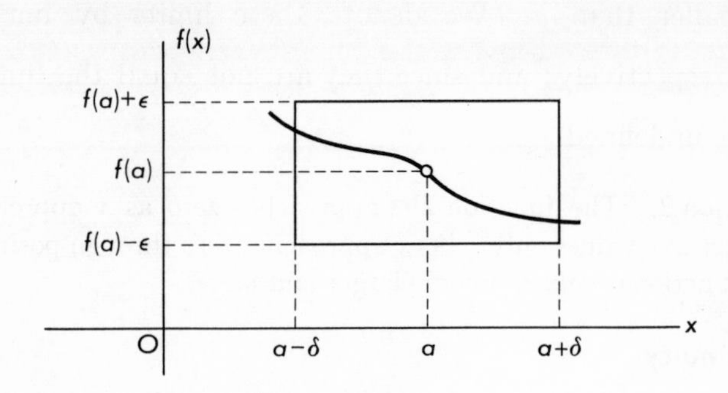

Figure 35

Theorem 1. *If $f(x)$ and $g(x)$ are two functions that are continuous at $x = a$, then the following functions are continuous at $x = a$.*

1. $f(x) + g(x)$,
2. $f(x)g(x)$,
3. $f(x)/g(x)$, *provided* $g(a) \neq 0$.

Proof: If all limits are taken as $x \to a$, we know from the continuity of $f(x)$ and $g(x)$ that $\lim f(x) = f(a)$ and $\lim g(x) = g(a)$. Hence, by use of Theorem 1, Article **22**, we find

1. $\lim [f(x) + g(x)] = \lim f(x) + \lim g(x) = f(a) + g(a)$,
2. $\lim f(x)g(x) = \lim f(x) \cdot \lim g(x) = f(a)g(a)$,
3. $\lim f(x)/g(x) = \lim f(x)/\lim g(x) = f(a)/g(a), \quad g(a) \neq 0$,

and the theorem is proved.

Since a polynomial, $P(x) = a_0x^n + a_1x^{n-1} + \cdots + a_n$, is a combination of sums and products of the variable x, we have the following conclusion.

Corollary 1. *A polynomial in x is a continuous function for all values of x.*

Similarly, since a rational function is the quotient of two polynomials, we have the following result.

Corollary 2. *A rational function in x is a continuous function for all values of x except those values for which the denominator is zero.*

Theorem 2. *When the function $f(x)$ is continuous for $a \leqq x \leqq b$ and $f(a) \neq f(b)$, then if k is any number between $f(a)$ and $f(b)$, there exists some number c between a and b such that $f(c) = k$.*

Theorem 3. *If the function $f(x)$ is continuous in the closed interval $a \leqq x \leqq b$, there exist numbers x_m and x_M in this domain such that $f(x_m)$ is the minimum and $f(x_M)$ is the maximum value of $f(x)$ in $a \leqq x \leqq b$.*

We shall not attempt to prove the preceding theorems, since rigorous proofs would require a more thorough study of the number system than we can possibly make at this time. It should be noted in Theorem 3, however, that the requirement of a closed interval is essential. The function $1/x$ which is continuous in the interval $0 < x \leqq 1$ has, for example, no maximum value in this domain.

Theorem 4. *If the function $f(y)$ is continuous at $y = A$ and if $\lim_{x \to a} g(x) = A$, then*

$$\lim_{x \to a} f[g(x)] = f\left[\lim_{x \to a} g(x)\right] = f(A).$$

Proof: The fact that $f(y)$ is continuous at $y = A$ means that for every $\epsilon > 0$ there exists a $\delta' > 0$ such that

$$|f(y) - f(A)| < \epsilon, \quad \text{when } |y - A| < \delta'.$$

If we substitute $g(x)$ for y, we obtain

$$|f[g(x)] - f(A)| < \epsilon, \quad \text{when } |g(x) - A| < \delta'. \tag{1}$$

Now the fact that $g(x) \to A$ as $x \to a$ means that for any number, say δ' in this case, there is some $\delta > 0$ such that

$$|g(x) - A| < \delta', \quad \text{when } 0 < |x - a| < \delta. \tag{2}$$

Thus it follows from (1) and (2) that for every $\epsilon > 0$ there exists a $\delta > 0$ such that

$$|f[g(x)] - f(A)| < \epsilon, \quad \text{for every } x \text{ in } 0 < |x - a| < \delta.$$

This, however, means that $f[g(x)] \to f(A)$ as $x \to a$, and the theorem is proved.

Since functions $f(y)$, such as y^n, $\sqrt[n]{y}$, $\log y$, and $\sin y$, are continuous functions in their domains of definition, it follows by the preceding theorem that $\lim g^n(x) = [\lim g(x)]^n$, $\lim \sqrt[n]{g(x)} = \sqrt[n]{\lim g(x)}$, $\lim [\log g(x)] = \log [\lim g(x)]$, and $\lim [\sin g(x)] = \sin [\lim g(x)]$. This interchange of the operations of limit and function facilitates the evaluation of many problems concerning limits.

Illustration. $\lim_{x\to\pi} \sqrt{1 - \cos x} = \sqrt{\lim_{x\to\pi} (1 - \cos x)} = \sqrt{1 - \cos \lim_{x\to\pi} x}$

$$= \sqrt{1 - \cos \pi} = \sqrt{2}.$$

Example. If $f(x) \to A$ and $g(x) \to B$ as $x \to a$, prove that $f(x) \cdot g(x) \to AB$ as $x \to a$.

Proof: This is an alternate proof for the second part of Theorem 1, Article **22**. It follows from Theorem 4 that if $\phi(x) \to L$ as $x \to a$, then

$$\lim_{x\to a} \phi^2(x) = \left[\lim_{x\to a} \phi(x)\right]^2.$$

We use this relation in the following way. Consider the identity

$$f(x)\, g(x) = \tfrac{1}{4}[f(x) + g(x)]^2 - \tfrac{1}{4}[f(x) - g(x)]^2.$$

If we take the limit of both sides as $x \to a$, the proof is completed by use of the above relation and the fact that the limit of a sum is equal to the sum of the limits.

$$\begin{aligned} \lim fg &= \lim \tfrac{1}{4}[f + g]^2 - \lim \tfrac{1}{4}[f - g]^2 \\ &= \tfrac{1}{4}[\lim (f + g)]^2 - \tfrac{1}{4}[\lim (f - g)]^2 \\ &= \tfrac{1}{4}[A + B]^2 - \tfrac{1}{4}[A - B]^2 = AB. \end{aligned}$$

24. Infinity

In considering the function $f(x) = 1/x$, we observe that, as x approaches zero through positive values, the corresponding values of the function become larger and larger. To indicate the behavior of the function in a case like this, we say that $f(x)$ **increases without limit** or **approaches infinity** as $x \to 0$ through positive values. In symbols, we write $\lim_{x\to 0^+} f(x) = +\infty$. Similarly, as x approaches zero through negative values, the value of the function **decreases without limit,** and we write $\lim_{x\to 0^-} f(x) = -\infty$. The word "infinite" signifies only a state of being non-finite, and the introduction of the symbol ∞ does not in any way justify its use as a number. Division by zero in mathematics is a meaningless operation and it is not intended that the symbol ∞ represent $1/0$.

A state of approaching infinity is determined in accordance with the following definition.

A function $f(x)$ is said to approach $+\infty$ as $x \to a^+$, if for any number N, however large it may be, there exists a $\delta > 0$ such that $f(x) > N$ for every x in the domain $a < x < a + \delta$. Similarly, $f(x) \to -\infty$ as $x \to a^-$ means that $f(x) < -N$ for every x in the domain $a - \delta < x < a$.

The definition is stated in terms of "left-hand" and "right-hand" limits since only one of them may be infinite; for example,

$$\lim_{x \to 0^-} 2^{1/x} = 0 \qquad \text{and} \qquad \lim_{x \to 0^+} 2^{1/x} = +\infty.$$

Illustration 1. If $1/\sqrt{x - a} > N$, we have $\sqrt{x - a} < 1/N$ and $x - a < 1/N^2$. Hence $\lim_{x \to a^+} 1/\sqrt{x - a} = +\infty$, because $1/\sqrt{x - a} > N$ for every x in the domain $a < x < a + 1/N^2$.

As the value of a variable x becomes larger and larger without bound it is possible that a function $f(x)$ may approach a finite limit. This situation is defined as follows.

A function $f(x)$ is said to approach the limit A as $x \to +\infty$, if for any number ϵ, however small it may be, there exists an $N > 0$ such that $|f(x) - A| < \epsilon$ for every x in the domain $x > N$.

A similar definition holds when $x \to -\infty$.

Illustration 2. As $x \to +\infty$ the limit of $\dfrac{3x + 2}{x}$ is 3, because $\dfrac{3x + 2}{x} = 3 + \dfrac{2}{x}$ and $3 < 3 + \dfrac{2}{x} < 3 + \epsilon$ is true provided $x > \dfrac{2}{\epsilon}$.

The evaluation of limits as $x \to \pm\infty$ is most easily accomplished, when possible, by expressing the function in terms of $1/x$ and using the fact that $1/x \to 0$.

Example. Evaluate $\displaystyle\lim_{x \to +\infty} \frac{3x^3 - 2x + 4}{2 - 3x^2 - 2x^3}$.

Solution: Dividing the numerator and denominator by x^3, the highest power of x in the denominator, we obtain

$$\lim_{x \to +\infty} \frac{3x^3 - 2x + 4}{2 - 3x^2 - 2x^3} = \lim_{x \to +\infty} \frac{3 - \dfrac{2}{x^2} + \dfrac{4}{x^3}}{\dfrac{2}{x^3} - \dfrac{3}{x} - 2} = -\frac{3}{2}.$$

25. Limit of a Sequence

In determining the area of a plane figure, we discussed a type of limit process that is common in the integral calculus. This limit process is concerned with sequences and their limits.

An ordered succession of numbers $s_1, s_2, \cdots, s_n, \cdots$ is called a **sequence** of numbers, if for each positive integer n there corresponds a real number s_n. The expression $\{s_n\}$ is used to denote a sequence, and s_n refers to the nth term. Sequences may be defined in various ways but some fixed rule for determining s_n must be given. Thus, for the sequences indicated below, we have listed the first five terms.

(*a*) $\left\{\frac{n}{n+3}\right\}$; $\frac{1}{4}, \frac{2}{5}, \frac{3}{6}, \frac{4}{7}, \frac{5}{8}, \cdots$.

(*b*) $\{(-1)^n 2\}$; $-2, 2, -2, 2, -2, \cdots$.

(*c*) $\{5\}$; $5, 5, 5, 5, 5, \cdots$.

(*d*) $\{1 - (-1)^n\}$; $2, 0, 2, 0, 2, \cdots$.

(*e*) $\left\{\begin{matrix}\text{Number of} \\ \text{integral} \\ \text{divisors of } n\end{matrix}\right\}$; $1, 2, 2, 3, 2, \cdots$.

As n gets larger and larger the general term s_n of a sequence may get closer and closer to some value A. If it does, we say that the limit of the sequence exists and we write $s_n \to A$ as $n \to \infty$, or $\lim_{n\to\infty} s_n = A$. For example, the sequences (*a*) and (*c*) have the limits 1 and 5, respectively, and (*b*), (*d*), and (*e*) have no limits. A formal definition for the limit of a sequence can be stated as follows.

A sequence is said to approach a value A as n increases, if corresponding to every positive number ϵ there is some positive integer N such that

$$|s_n - A| < \epsilon$$

is true for every integer n that satisfies the inequality $n > N$.

Illustration. The sequence $\{1/n^2\} \to 0$ as $n \to \infty$, because $|(1/n^2) - 0| < \epsilon$ is true for all integers $n > 1/\sqrt{\epsilon}$.

The limit concept for sequences is very similar to the limit concept for functions and most methods of proof that can be used for one can also be applied to the other. The limit theorem for sequences would have the following form.

Theorem. *If $\{s_n\} \to A$ and $\{s'_n\} \to B$ as $n \to \infty$, then as $n \to \infty$*

$$\{s_n + s'_n\} \to A + B, \qquad \{s_n s'_n\} \to AB, \qquad \left\{\frac{s_n}{s'_n}\right\} \to \frac{A}{B},$$

the quotient sequence having the restriction $B \neq 0$.

Example. Find the limit of the sequence $\left\{\frac{\sqrt{n^2+1}}{n+1}\right\}$.

Solution: Dividing the numerator and denominator of s_n by n, we find

$$\lim_{n\to\infty} \frac{\sqrt{1 + \frac{1}{n^2}}}{1 + \frac{1}{n}} = \frac{\sqrt{1+0}}{1+0} = 1.$$

EXERCISE 8

Evaluate the following limits, when possible.

1. $\lim_{x\to 1} \dfrac{x^2 - 1}{x - 1}$. *Ans.* 2.

2. $\lim_{x\to 2} \dfrac{x^2 - x - 2}{x^2 - 3x + 2}$.

3. $\lim_{x\to \infty} \dfrac{x^3 - 2x + 5}{2x^3 - 7}$. $\frac{1}{2}$.

4. $\lim_{x\to 2} \dfrac{8 - x^3}{x^2 - 2x}$.

5. $\lim_{x\to 0^+} \dfrac{\cos x}{\log x}$. 0.

6. $\lim_{x\to 0} \dfrac{\tan 2x}{\tan x}$.

7. $\lim_{x\to 0} \sin \dfrac{1}{x}$. No limit.

8. $\lim_{x\to 0} x \sin \dfrac{1}{x}$.

Find the limits of the following as $n \to \infty$.

9. $(-1)^n 2^{-n}$. *Ans.* 0.

10. $\dfrac{n^2 + a^2}{n^3 + a^3}$.

11. $\dfrac{2^{-n} - 2^n}{2^{-n} + 2^n}$. -1.

12. $\dfrac{(n + 1)^3 - (n - 1)^3}{n^2}$.

13. $\dfrac{\sin n}{n}$. 0.

14. $\dfrac{\sin (2/n)}{\sin (1/n)}$.

15. $\dfrac{1}{n^2} [n + (n + 1) + \cdots + 2n]$. *Ans.* $\frac{3}{2}$.

16. $\dfrac{a^n - 1}{a^n + 1}$, when $a > 1$, $a = 1$, and $0 < a < 1$.

Find the values of x for which the following functions are discontinuous.

17. $\dfrac{x - 2}{x + 1}$. *Ans.* -1.

18. $\dfrac{x + 1}{x^3 + x}$.

19. $\dfrac{x^2 - 4}{x^2 - x - 2}$. 2, -1.

20. $\sqrt{\dfrac{x + 1}{x - 1}}$.

21. $\csc 2x$. $\frac{1}{2}n\pi$.

22. $\tan (x + \frac{1}{2}\pi)$.

23. $\log (2x - 5)$. $2\frac{1}{2}$.

24. $\log \dfrac{x - 2}{x}$.

25. $\dfrac{1}{2^x - 1}$. 0.

26. $\log \sin x$.

27. If $f(x) = x^2$, show that $\lim_{h\to 0} \dfrac{f(x + h) - f(x)}{h} = 2x$.

28. If $f(x) = \dfrac{1}{x}$, show that $\lim_{h\to 0} \dfrac{f(x + h) - f(x)}{h} = -\dfrac{1}{x^2}$.

29. If $f(x) = \sqrt{x}$, show that $\lim_{h\to 0} \dfrac{f(x + h) - f(x)}{h} = \dfrac{1}{2\sqrt{x}}$.

Hint: Multiply the numerator and denominator by $\sqrt{x + h} + \sqrt{x}$.

30. If n is a positive integer, prove that $\lim_{h\to 0} \dfrac{(x + h)^n - x^n}{h} = nx^{n-1}$.

31. If $f(x) = x^2$, find a δ such that $0 < |x - 2| < \delta$ implies $|x^2 - 4| < \epsilon$ (*a*) when $\epsilon = 1$, (*b*) when $\epsilon = 0.1$, and (*c*) when $0 < \epsilon < 5$.
Ans. (*a*) 0.2, (*b*) 0.02, (*c*) $\epsilon/5$ will do.

32. If $f(n) = 2^{-n}$, find an N such that $n > N$ implies $|2^{-n} - 0| < \epsilon$ (*a*) when $\epsilon = 0.1$, (*b*) when $\epsilon = 0.001$, and (*c*) when $\epsilon > 0$.

33. If $|x - 2| < 0.1$ and $|y - 3| < 0.2$, then $|(x + y) - 5| < \alpha$, $|xy - 6| < \beta$, and $\left|\frac{x}{y} - \frac{2}{3}\right| < \gamma$. Find α, β, and γ. *Hint:* Write $|x - 2| < 0.1$ as $1.9 < x < 2.1$.
Ans. $\alpha = 0.3$, $\beta = 0.72$, $\gamma = 1/12$.

34. Find $\lim_{x\to 0+} |x|/x$, $\lim_{x\to 0-} |x|/x$, and draw a graph of $y = |x|/x$.

35. If $g(x)$ is continuous at $x = a$ and $f(y)$ is continuous at $y = g(a)$, prove that $F(x) \equiv f[g(x)]$ is continuous at $x = a$.

36. Write the first ten terms of the sequence $s_n = \frac{2}{n}\left[\frac{n}{2}\right]$, where the notation $[a]$ denotes the greatest integer less than or equal to a; for example, $[5] = 5$, $[9/2] = 4$, and $[1.99] = 1$. Find an alternate definition for the odd and even terms of s_n that does not use this notation. Does the sequence have a limit?

CHAPTER 3

Differentiation and Applications

26. Increments

If a variable x changes from one fixed value x_1 to another x_2, the difference $x_2 - x_1$ is called an **increment** *of x.* In general an increment of x may be positive or negative, and it is denoted by the symbol Δx, read "delta x." Similarly, Δy denotes an increment of y, $\Delta f(x)$ an increment of $f(x)$, and so on.

Let y be a continuous, single-valued function of x denoted by

$$y = f(x). \tag{1}$$

If the independent variable changes from the value x to another value $x + \Delta x$, the function (1) will change from y to $y + \Delta y$; thus

$$y + \Delta y = f(x + \Delta x). \tag{2}$$

Subtracting (1) from (2), we obtain the increment of the function

$$\Delta y \equiv \Delta f(x) = f(x + \Delta x) - f(x)$$

corresponding to the increment Δx of the variable x.

Illustration. If $y = x^2$, then $\Delta y = (x + \Delta x)^2 - x^2 = 2x\,\Delta x + (\Delta x)^2$. Hence, if x changes from 3 to 3.1, we have $x = 3$, $\Delta x = 0.1$, and $\Delta y = 2(3)(0.1) + (0.1)^2 = 0.61$.

27. Derivative

If an increment Δy of a function $y = f(x)$ is divided by Δx, the quotient gives the *average rate of change* of y with respect to x in the interval from x to $x + \Delta x$. Symbolically,

$$\frac{\Delta y}{\Delta x} = \frac{f(x + \Delta x) - f(x)}{\Delta x}. \tag{1}$$

Illustration. When $y = x^2$, we obtain

$$\frac{\Delta y}{\Delta x} = \frac{2x\,\Delta x + (\Delta x)^2}{\Delta x} = 2x + \Delta x.$$

Thus the average rates of change for the intervals (3,4), (3,3.1), and (3,3.01) are respectively 7, 6.1, and 6.01. Observe that the average rate of change approaches the limit 6 as the length of the interval Δx approaches zero.

If, for a fixed value of x, the quotient (1) approaches a limit as the increment Δx approaches zero, this limit is called the **derivative of y with respect to x** for the given value of x, and it is denoted by the symbol $\frac{dy}{dx}$, or dy/dx. Thus, by definition,

$$\frac{dy}{dx} = \lim_{\Delta x \to 0} \frac{\Delta y}{\Delta x} = \lim_{\Delta x \to 0} \frac{f(x + \Delta x) - f(x)}{\Delta x}.$$

Other symbols used to denote the derivative are

$$D_x y, \quad D_x f(x), \quad y', \quad f'(x), \quad \frac{d}{dx} f(x).$$

The process of finding dy/dx, when $y = f(x)$ is known, is called **differentiation;** and if the derivative exists, $f(x)$ is said to be a **differentiable function.** The procedure for finding the derivative of a given function may be summarized in the following **four-step rule.**

1. *Substitute $x + \Delta x$ for x and $y + \Delta y$ for y in $y = f(x)$.*
2. *Subtract $y = f(x)$ from the result of 1 to obtain Δy in terms of x and Δx.*
3. *Divide both sides of 2 by Δx.*
4. *Find the limit of 3 as Δx approaches zero.*

Example 1. If $y = \frac{1}{x + 1}$, find $\frac{dy}{dx}$ (*a*) for any value of x, (*b*) for $x = 2$.

Solution: (*a*) In accordance with the four-step rule, we have

1. $$y + \Delta y = \frac{1}{x + \Delta x + 1},$$

2. $$\Delta y = \frac{1}{x + \Delta x + 1} - \frac{1}{x + 1} = \frac{-\Delta x}{(x + \Delta x + 1)(x + 1)},$$

3. $$\frac{\Delta y}{\Delta x} = -\frac{1}{(x + \Delta x + 1)(x + 1)},$$

4. $$\frac{dy}{dx} = \lim_{\Delta x \to 0} \frac{\Delta y}{\Delta x} = -\frac{1}{(x + 1)^2}.$$

(*b*) When $x = 2$, by substitution we find $\frac{dy}{dx} = -\frac{1}{(2 + 1)^2} = -\frac{1}{9}$.

Example 2. Find dy/dx, if $y = \sqrt{x}$.

Solution:

$$1.\quad y + \Delta y = \sqrt{x + \Delta x},$$

$$2.\quad \Delta y = \sqrt{x + \Delta x} - \sqrt{x}$$

$$= \frac{\sqrt{x + \Delta x} - \sqrt{x}}{1} \cdot \frac{\sqrt{x + \Delta x} + \sqrt{x}}{\sqrt{x + \Delta x} + \sqrt{x}}$$

$$= \frac{\Delta x}{\sqrt{x + \Delta x} + \sqrt{x}},$$

$$3.\quad \frac{\Delta y}{\Delta x} = \frac{1}{\sqrt{x + \Delta x} + \sqrt{x}},$$

$$4.\quad \frac{dy}{dx} = \frac{1}{2\sqrt{x}}, \quad x \neq 0.$$

Example 3. Find the rate of change of the volume of a sphere with respect to its radius when the radius is 6 inches.

Solution: Using **12**, page 1, and applying the four-step rule, we have

$$V = \frac{4}{3}\pi r^3,$$

$$V + \Delta V = \frac{4}{3}\pi(r + \Delta r)^3,$$

$$\Delta V = \frac{4}{3}\pi[(r + \Delta r)^3 - r^3]$$

$$= \frac{4}{3}\pi[3r^2\,\Delta r + 3r(\Delta r)^2 + (\Delta r)^3],$$

$$\frac{\Delta V}{\Delta r} = \frac{4}{3}\pi[3r^2 + 3r\,\Delta r + (\Delta r)^2],$$

$$\frac{dV}{dr} = \lim_{\Delta r \to 0} \frac{\Delta V}{\Delta r} = 4\pi r^2.$$

Hence, when $r = 6$, the volume of the sphere is increasing at the rate $4\pi(6)^2 = 144\pi$ cubic inches per inch of increase in the radius.

The existence of a derivative implies the continuity of the function as is shown in the following theorem.

Theorem. *If $f'(x)$ exists at $x = a$, then $f(x)$ is continuous at $x = a$.*

Proof: For $x \neq a$ consider the identity

$$f(x) = \frac{f(x) - f(a)}{x - a}(x - a) + f(a).$$

Taking the limit of both sides as $x \to a$, we have

$$\lim_{x \to a} f(x) = f'(a) \cdot 0 + f(a) = f(a).$$

This, by definition, means that the function is continuous at $x = a$.

EXERCISE 9

Find dy/dx in each of the following.

1. $y = x^2 - 5x.$ *Ans.* $y' = 2x - 5.$
2. $y = 1 + 3x - x^2.$
3. $y = 2x^3 + x.$ $y' = 6x^2 + 1.$
4. $y = x^3 - 2x^2 - 3.$
5. $y = \dfrac{3}{x}.$ $y' = -\dfrac{3}{x^2}.$
6. $y = \dfrac{3}{2 - x}.$
7. $y = \dfrac{x}{x + 1}.$ $y' = \dfrac{1}{(x + 1)^2}.$
8. $y = \dfrac{1}{3x^3}.$
9. $y = \sqrt{x + 1}.$ $y' = \dfrac{1}{2\sqrt{x + 1}}.$
10. $y = \sqrt{2x}.$
11. $y = (ax + b)^2.$ $y' = 2a(ax + b).$
12. $y = \dfrac{c}{ax + b}.$

In each of the following evaluate dy/dx, when $x = 2$.

13. $y = 8x - x^3.$ *Ans.* $y' = -4.$
14. $y = x^4.$
15. $y = ax^2 + bx + c.$ $y' = 4a + b.$
16. $y = (x + a)^3.$
17. $y = \dfrac{1}{x^2 - 1}.$ $y' = -\dfrac{4}{9}.$
18. $y = \dfrac{2 - x}{3 - x}.$
19. $y = \dfrac{a + 2}{a + x}.$ $y' = -\dfrac{1}{a + 2}.$
20. $y = \dfrac{a + bx^2}{x^2}.$
21. $y = \sqrt{x^2 - 3}.$ $y' = 2.$

22. $y = \dfrac{1}{\sqrt{2x}}$.

23. If $y = 3x^2 - 2x + 1$, find the value of x for which $y' = 0$. *Ans.* $\frac{1}{3}$.

24. If $f(x) = x^3 - 3x^2$, find the values of x for which $f'(x) = 0$.

25. For what values of x is the derivative of $(2x - x^{-1})$ equal to 3? *Ans.* ± 1.

26. For the function $y = x\sqrt{x}$ find the value of x for which the rate of change of y with respect to x is 6.

27. Find the rate of change of the area of a circle with respect to its radius when the radius is 3 feet. *Ans.* 6π sq. ft./ft.

28. Find the rate of change of the area of a sphere with respect to its radius when the radius is 6 inches.

29. Find the rate at which the volume of a right circular cylinder of constant altitude 10 feet changes with respect to its diameter when the radius is 5 feet. *Ans.* 50π cu. ft./ft.

30. If $f(x)$ is continuous at $x = a$, can we conclude that $f'(x)$ exists at $x = a$? Sketch two continuous curves that have no derivative at $x = a$, and give their equations.

28. Derivatives of Powers of x

The four-step rule indicates the basic procedure to be followed in determining the derivative of any given function. Continued use of this process, however, is exceedingly laborious and consequently, in actual practice, special rules are derived for differentiating certain standard types of functions. Three of such rules are as follows, where c is a constant, n a positive integer, and $f(x)$ and $g(x)$ denote two differentiable functions of x.

$$\text{I} \qquad \frac{dc}{dx} = 0.$$

$$\text{II} \qquad \frac{d}{dx}(cx^n) = cnx^{n-1}.$$

$$\text{III} \qquad \frac{d}{dx}[f(x) + g(x)] = \frac{d}{dx}f(x) + \frac{d}{dx}g(x).$$

Proof of I: If $y = c$, by the four-step rule we have $y + \Delta y = c$, $\Delta y = 0$, $\Delta y/\Delta x = 0$; hence $dy/dx = dc/dx = 0$.

Illustration 1. If $y = 7$, by I we have $dy/dx = 0$.

The converse of this rule is also true, that is, if $f'(x) = 0$, then $f(x) =$ constant. This fact will be proved in Article **114**.

Proof of II: Applying the four-step rule to $y = cx^n$ and using the binomial formula, we have

1. $y + \Delta y = c(x + \Delta x)^n$

$$= c\left[x^n + nx^{n-1}\Delta x + \frac{n(n-1)}{2!}x^{n-2}(\Delta x)^2 + \cdots + (\Delta x)^n\right],$$

2. $$\Delta y = cnx^{n-1}\Delta x + \frac{cn(n-1)}{2!}x^{n-2}(\Delta x)^2 + \cdots + c(\Delta x)^n,$$

3. $$\frac{\Delta y}{\Delta x} = cnx^{n-1} + \frac{cn(n-1)}{2!}x^{n-2}\Delta x + \cdots + c(\Delta x)^{n-1},$$

4. $$\frac{dy}{dx} = \lim_{\Delta x \to 0} \frac{\Delta y}{\Delta x} = cnx^{n-1}.$$

Illustration 2. If $y = 3x^5$, by II we have $dy/dx = 3(5)x^{5-1} = 15x^4$.

Note: Although II has been established only for the case when n is a positive integer, it will be proved later that the formula is valid when n is any real number. In the meantime we shall assume its validity for all real n's.

Illustration 3. If $y = 8x^{-3/4}$, by II we have $dy/dx = 8(-\frac{3}{4})x^{-3/4-1} = -6x^{-7/4}$.

Proof of III: Applying the four-step rule and using Theorem 1, Article **22**, we have

$$y = f(x) + g(x),$$

$$y + \Delta y = f(x + \Delta x) + g(x + \Delta x),$$

$$\Delta y = [f(x + \Delta x) - f(x)] + [g(x + \Delta x) - g(x)],$$

$$\lim_{\Delta x \to 0} \frac{\Delta y}{\Delta x} = \lim_{\Delta x \to 0} \frac{f(x + \Delta x) - f(x)}{\Delta x} + \lim_{\Delta x \to 0} \frac{g(x + \Delta x) - g(x)}{\Delta x},$$

$$\frac{dy}{dx} = \frac{d}{dx}f(x) + \frac{d}{dx}g(x).$$

A similar proof holds for any finite number of functions. Hence *the derivative of the sum of a finite number of functions is equal to the sum of their derivatives.*

Illustration 4. If $y = 2x^4 - x^3 - 2x + 7$, then

$$\frac{dy}{dx} = \frac{d}{dx}(2x^4) - \frac{d}{dx}(x^3) - \frac{d}{dx}(2x) + \frac{d}{dx}(7) \qquad \text{by III}$$

$$= 8x^3 - 3x^2 - 2 \qquad \text{by I and II.}$$

Example 1. If $f(x) = \dfrac{3x^3 - 4}{x^2}$, find $f'(x)$.

Solution: Writing $f(x)$ in the form $f(x) = 3x - 4x^{-2}$, by III and II we have

$$f'(x) = \frac{d}{dx}(3x) - \frac{d}{dx}(4x^{-2}) = 3 + 8x^{-3}.$$

Example 2. For what values of x is the derivative of the function $x^{3/2} - x^{1/2}$ equal to zero?

Solution: If $y = x^{3/2} - x^{1/2}$, then

$$\frac{dy}{dx} = \frac{3}{2}x^{1/2} - \frac{1}{2}x^{-1/2}. \tag{1}$$

Setting (1) equal to zero and solving for x, we find $x = \frac{1}{3}$.

Example 3. If $f(x) = x^{1/4}$, prove that $f'(x) = \frac{1}{4}x^{-3/4}$.

Proof: The first two steps in the derivative rule yield

$$f(x + \Delta x) - f(x) = (x + \Delta x)^{1/4} - x^{1/4}. \tag{2}$$

In accordance with the algebraic identity

$$u^4 - v^4 = (u - v)(u^3 + u^2v + uv^2 + v^3),$$

it is clear that if we multiply the numerator and denominator of the right side of (2) by

$$(x + \Delta x)^{3/4} + (x + \Delta x)^{2/4}x^{1/4} + (x + \Delta x)^{1/4}x^{2/4} + x^{3/4},$$

the relation (2) can be written as

$$f(x + \Delta x) - f(x) = \frac{(x + \Delta x) - x}{(x + \Delta x)^{3/4} + (x + \Delta x)^{1/2}x^{1/4} + (x + \Delta x)^{1/4}x^{1/2} + x^{3/4}}.$$

Hence we conclude that

$$f'(x) = \lim_{\Delta x \to 0} \frac{f(x + \Delta x) - f(x)}{\Delta x} = \frac{1}{4x^{3/4}} = \frac{1}{4}x^{-3/4}.$$

EXERCISE 10

Find y' in each of the following.

1. $y = x^3(2x^2 - 1)$. *Ans.* $y' = 10x^4 - 3x^2$.
2. $y = (x - 1)(2x^2 + 3)$.
3. $y = ax^2 + bx + c$. $y' = 2ax + b$.
4. $y = 2x^{1/2} + 3x^{2/3}$.
5. $y = 4x^{-2} + 3x^{-1} + 7$. $y' = -8x^{-3} - 3x^{-2}$.
6. $y = \frac{1}{2}(x^2 - x^{-2})$.

7. $y = \sqrt[3]{x^2} - 3\sqrt[3]{x} - 5.$ *Ans.* $y' = \frac{2}{3}x^{-1/3} - x^{-2/3}.$
8. $y = 2(x + 1)^3.$
9. $y = \dfrac{x^5 - 2x^3 - 3}{x^2}.$ $y' = \dfrac{3x^5 - 2x^3 + 6}{x^3}.$
10. $y = \dfrac{(2 - x)(2x + 1)}{x}.$

In each of the following, find y' for the given value of x.

11. $y = 2x^3 - 3x^2 - x + 5, \quad x = 2.$ *Ans.* 11.
12. $y = (x - 1)(x + 3)^2, \quad x = -3.$
13. $y = 2\sqrt{x}(3x - 2), \quad x = 4.$ 17.
14. $y = 3(\sqrt[3]{x} - 2)^2, \quad x = -8.$
15. $y = \dfrac{x + 1}{\sqrt{x}}, \quad x = \dfrac{1}{4}.$ $-3.$
16. $y = \dfrac{(1 + \sqrt{x})(2 + \sqrt{x})}{x}, \quad x = 1.$
17. $y = x\sqrt{a} - a\sqrt{x}, \quad x = a.$ $\frac{1}{2}\sqrt{a}.$
18. $y = (x - a)(x^2 - a^2), \quad x = a.$
19. $y = \sqrt[3]{ax^2} + \sqrt[3]{a^2x}, \quad x = a.$ 1.
20. $y = \dfrac{x^2}{a^2} + \dfrac{a^2}{x^2}, \quad x = a.$
21. If $y = 2x^4 - x^2$, find the values of x for which $y' = 0$. *Ans.* $0, \pm\frac{1}{2}.$
22. If $f(x) = x^3 + 4x^2 - 3x - 5$, find the values of x for which $f'(x) = 0$.
23. For what values of x is the derivative of the function $2x - 3x^{-1}$ equal to 14? *Ans.* $\pm\frac{1}{2}.$
24. For what values of x is the derivative of the function $\sqrt[3]{x^2} + \sqrt[3]{x}$ equal to 1?
25. For what values of x is the derivative of x^3 equal to the derivative of $x^2 + x$? *Ans.* $1, -\frac{1}{3}.$
26. Find the area of a circle when the rate of change of the area with respect to a diameter is 4π square feet per foot.
27. Find the rate of change of the circumference of a circle with respect to the area, when the area equals 4π square feet. *Ans.* $\frac{1}{2}$ ft./sq. ft.
28. If m is a positive integer, by applying the four-step rule, prove that
$$\frac{d}{dx}(x^{-m}) = -mx^{-m-1}.$$
29. If $y = cf(x)$, where c is a constant and $f(x)$ is a differentiable function, prove that $dy/dx = cf'(x)$.
30. Let $f(x)$ and $g(x)$ be two continuous differentiable functions such that $f'(x) = g(x)$ and $g'(x) = -f(x)$. If $h(x) = f^2(x) + g^2(x)$, and $h(0) = 1$, find $h(1)$.

29. Slope of a Curve

In Figure 36, if P and Q are any two distinct points of a curve C, the line PQ is called a **secant** of C. If the point P is fixed and Q is made to approach P along C, the secant PQ will usually approach a definite line PT as a limit. This line is called the **tangent** to C at P.

These definitions lead to the following interpretation of the derivative which is of basic importance in all applications of the calculus to geometry. Let $y = f(x)$ be the equation of C, and let (x,y) and $(x + \Delta x, y + \Delta y)$ be the coordinates of P and Q respectively. We see in Figure 36 that the slope of the secant PQ is $RQ/PR = \Delta y/\Delta x$. Since the slope of the tangent PT is the limit of RQ/PR as Q approaches P, that is, as Δx approaches zero, we have by definition*

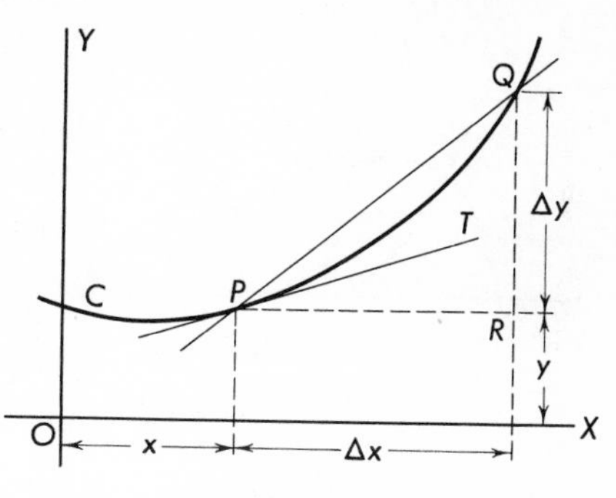

Figure 36

$$\textbf{Slope of tangent at } P(x,y) = \frac{dy}{dx}.$$

The slope of the tangent line defines the **slope of a curve** at the point of tangency; hence

The slope of the curve $y = f(x)$ at the point (h,k) is $f'(h)$.

Illustration 1. If $y = 3x - 2x^2$, we have $y' = 3 - 4x$. Hence the slope of the curve at the point $(2,-2)$ is $3 - 4(2) = -5$.

Since the tangent to the curve $y = f(x)$ at the point (h,k) has the slope $f'(h)$, the equation of the **tangent line** is

$$y - k = f'(h)(x - h).$$

The **normal line** to the curve $y = f(x)$ at (h,k) is defined as the line through (h,k) perpendicular to the tangent at that point. Hence the slope of the normal is $-1/f'(h)$ and its equation is

$$y - k = -\frac{1}{f'(h)}(x - h).$$

---

* If $\Delta y/\Delta x$ is unbounded as $\Delta x \to 0$, the tangent line PT is parallel to the y axis and has no slope.

Illustration 2. The slope of the tangent to the curve $y = 4x - x^3$ at the point (2,0) is $f'(2) = 4 - 3(2)^2 = -8$. Hence the equation of the tangent is $y - 0 = -8(x - 2)$ or $8x + y - 16 = 0$, and the equation of the normal is $y - 0 = \frac{1}{8}(x - 2)$ or $x - 8y - 2 = 0$.

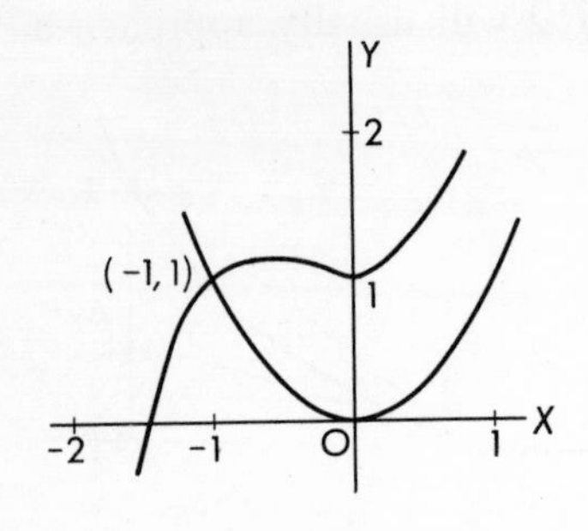

Figure 37

Note: When $f'(h) = 0$, the equations of the tangent and normal are respectively $y = k$ and $x = h$; and when $-1/f'(h) = 0$, they are respectively $x = h$ and $y = k$. For example, the tangent and normal to the curve $y = x^{1/3}$ (Figure 44, page 78) at (0,0) are $x = 0$ and $y = 0$, respectively.

Example. Find the angle between the two curves $y = x^2$ and $y = x^3 + x^2 + 1$ at their point of intersection.

Solution: The angle between two curves at a point of intersection is defined as the angle between their tangent lines at that point, and the angle between two lines having the slopes m_1 and m_2 is defined by the relation

$$\tan \phi = \frac{m_1 - m_2}{1 + m_1 m_2}. \tag{1}$$

Solving the given equations simultaneously, we find the point of intersection $(-1,1)$ shown in Figure 37. The slopes of the curves at this point are respectively $m_1 = 2(-1) = -2$ and $m_2 = 3(-1)^2 + 2(-1) = 1$. Hence, by substitution in (1), we obtain $\tan \phi = 3$ or $\phi = \tan^{-1} 3 = 71.6°$.

EXERCISE 11

Find the slope of the given curve at the point indicated.

1. $y = 8x - 3x^2$, (2,4). *Ans.* -4.
2. $y = x^4 - x^2 + 2$, $(-1,2)$.
3. $y = x^3 - 1$, $(0,-1)$. 0.
4. $y = 8/x^2$, (2,2).
5. $y = x + 2x^{-1}$, (2,3). $\frac{1}{2}$.
6. $y = 2\sqrt[3]{x}$, $(-8,-4)$.
7. At what point is 2 the slope of the curve $y = 4x + x^2$? $(-1,-3)$.
8. At what points is 9 the slope of the curve $y = x^3 - 3x^2$?
9. Find where the slope of $y = \sqrt{x}$ is 1. $(\frac{1}{4},\frac{1}{2})$.
10. Find where the slope of $y = 2x^{-2}$ is $\frac{1}{2}$.

Find the equations of the tangent and normal to the following curves at the point indicated.

11. $y = 2x - x^2$, (2,0). *Ans.* $2x + y = 4$, $x - 2y = 2$.
12. $y = 2 + x - \frac{1}{3}x^3$, $(3,-4)$.

13. $y = x(2 - x)^2$, $(1,1)$. *Ans.* $x + y = 2$, $x - y = 0$.
14. $y = (x + 1)^3$, $(-2,-1)$.
15. $y = x^3 + 3x^{-1}$, $(1,4)$. $y = 4$, $x = 1$.
16. $y = x + x^{2/3}$, $(0,0)$.
17. $y = a^2 - x^2$, $(a,0)$. $2ax + y = 2a^2$, $x - 2ay = a$.
18. $y = (ax - b)^2$, $(b/2a, b^2/4)$.
19. $y = \dfrac{x}{a} + \dfrac{a}{x}$, $\left(\dfrac{1}{2}a, \dfrac{5}{2}\right)$. $3x + ay = 4a$, $2ax - 6y = a^2 - 15$.
20. $y = \sqrt[3]{ax^2} + \sqrt[3]{a^2x}$, $(a,2a)$.

Find the angle of intersection between the following pairs of curves.

21. $\begin{cases} y = x^3 + x - 8, \\ y = x. \end{cases}$ *Ans.* 40.6°.

22. $\begin{cases} x + 2y - 3 = 0, \\ y = \sqrt{x}. \end{cases}$

23. $\begin{cases} y = x^2 + 1, \\ y = x + x^{-1}. \end{cases}$ 63.4°.

24. $\begin{cases} y = x^3 + x, \\ y = x^2. \end{cases}$

25. At what point of the parabola $y = x^2 - 3x - 5$ is the tangent line parallel to $3x - y = 2$? Find its equation. *Ans.* $3x - y = 14$.
26. At what point of the curve $y = x^4$ is the normal line parallel to $2x + y = 3$? Find its equation.
27. Find the point where the normal to $y = x + \sqrt{x}$ at $(4,6)$ crosses the y axis. *Ans.* $y = 9.2$.
28. For the curve $y = x^2 + x$, at what point does the normal line at $(0,0)$ intersect the tangent line at $(1,2)$?
29. The tangent to $y = x^3 - 6x^2 + 8x$ at $(3,-3)$ intersects the curve at another point. Find this point. *Ans.* $(0,0)$.
30. Prove that the line tangent to the curve $y = x + 2x^2 - x^4$ at the point $(-1,0)$ is also tangent to the curve at the point $(1,2)$.

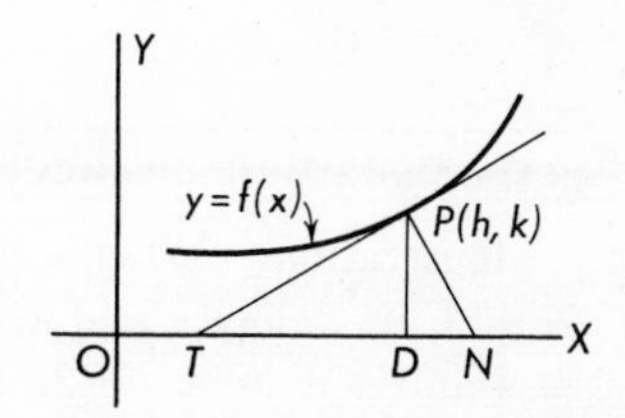

Figure 38

31. The lengths of the line segments PT and PN in Figure 38 are called, respectively, the **tangent length** and **normal length** of the curve $y = f(x)$ at the point $P(h,k)$. Show that these lengths are given by

$$PT = \left|\frac{f(h)\sqrt{1 + [f'(h)]^2}}{f'(h)}\right|, \qquad PN = |f(h)\sqrt{1 + [f'(h)]^2}|.$$

32. Find the tangent and normal lengths for the curve $y = \frac{1}{3}x^3 - x^2 + \frac{7}{3}x + \frac{1}{3}$ at the point $(1,2)$. (See Problem 31.)
33. The lengths of the line segments TD and DN in Figure 38 are called respectively the **subtangent** and **subnormal** of the curve $y = f(x)$ at the point $P(h,k)$. Show that these lengths are given by

$$TD = \left|\frac{f(h)}{f'(h)}\right|, \qquad DN = |f(h)f'(h)|.$$

34. Find the subtangent and subnormal for the curve $y = x^3 + 5x^2 - 8$ at the point $(-2,4)$. (See Problem 33.)
35. If on the interval $a \leqq x \leqq b$ two differentiable functions satisfy the relation $f(x) < g(x)$, does it necessarily follow that $f'(x) < g'(x)$? Give an illustration.

30. Velocity and Acceleration

Let us suppose that a particle is moving on the straight line OA, and passes the points P and Q (Figure 39) at the times t and $t + \Delta t$, respectively. If s and $s + \Delta s$ are the respective distances of P and Q from some fixed point O, then $\Delta s/\Delta t$ is the average velocity of the particle during the time interval Δt, and

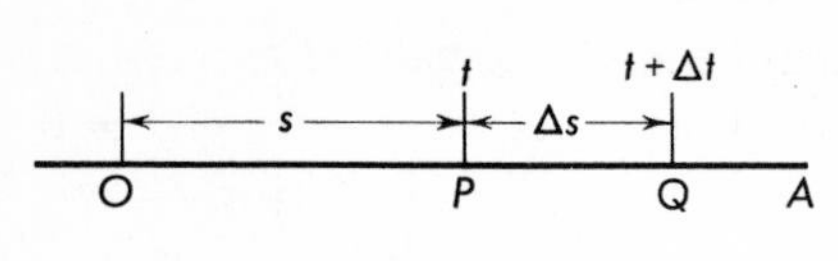

Figure 39

$$v = \lim_{\Delta t \to 0} \frac{\Delta s}{\Delta t} = \frac{ds}{dt}$$

is the instantaneous **velocity** of the particle at the time t.

Similarly, if Δv is the change in the velocity of the particle as it moves from P to Q during the time interval Δt, then

$$a = \lim_{\Delta t \to 0} \frac{\Delta v}{\Delta t} = \frac{dv}{dt}$$

is the instantaneous **acceleration** of the particle at the time t.

Illustration. When a particle moves in accordance with the law $s = t^2 - 2t + 3$, its velocity and acceleration when $t = 3$ are $v = ds/dt = [2t - 2]_{t=3} = 4$ and $a = dv/dt = [2]_{t=3} = 2$.

If a body is thrown vertically upward with a certain initial velocity v_0 (feet per second), its distance s (feet) from the starting point is given approximately in terms of the time t (seconds) by the formula

$$s = v_0 t - 16t^2, \tag{1}$$

where s is positive or negative according as the body is above or below the starting point.

Example. From the top of a building 96 feet high, a ball is thrown directly upward with a velocity of 80 feet per second. Find (a) the time required to reach the highest point, (b) the maximum height attained, and (c) the velocity of the ball when it reaches the ground.

Solution: Substituting $v_0 = 80$ in (1), we obtain

$$s = 80t - 16t^2; \quad \text{hence} \quad v = \frac{ds}{dt} = 80 - 32t. \tag{2}$$

(*a*) At the highest point $v = 0$; hence from (2) we have $0 = 80 - 32t$, or $t = 2\frac{1}{2}$ seconds.

(*b*) When $t = 2\frac{1}{2}$, the distance above the top of the building is given by $s = 80(\frac{5}{2}) - 16(\frac{5}{2})^2 = 100$ feet. Hence the height of the ball above the ground is 196 feet.

(*c*) Since the ball will reach the ground when $s = -96$, it follows that $-96 = 80t - 16t^2$ or $16(t - 6)(t + 1) = 0$. Hence $t = 6$ and, by (2), the velocity is $v = 80 - 32(6) = -112$ feet per second when the ball strikes the ground. The negative sign merely indicates that the velocity of the ball is directed downward.

EXERCISE 12

In each of the following, find the velocity and acceleration when $t = 2$.

1. $s = 8t^2 - 3t$. *Ans.* 29, 16.
2. $s = 40 - 10t - 5t^2$.
3. $s = t^3 - 3t - 5$. 9, 12.
4. $s = 160t - 32t^3$.
5. $s = 20 - 4t^2 - t^4$. -48, -56.
6. $s = \sqrt{2t} + \sqrt{2t^3}$.
7. $s = 5t - 4t^{-1}$. 6, -1.
8. $s = t^2 + 8t^{-2}$.
9. $s = \frac{10}{t}(t^3 + 8)$. 20, 40.
10. $s = (t + 2t^{-1})^3$.
11. If $s = t^3 - 5t^2 + 5t - 3$, when will the velocity be 2? *Ans.* $t = \frac{1}{3}$, 3.
12. If $s = t^5 - 10t^2$, when will the acceleration be zero?
13. If $s = t^2 - t^3$, find the velocity when the acceleration is zero. *Ans.* $\frac{1}{3}$.
14. Two particles have positions at time t given by the equations $s_1 = 4t - t^2$ and $s_2 = t^2 - 2$. Find their positions when they have the same velocity.
15. Two particles have positions at time t given by the equations $s_1 = t^3 - t$ and $s_2 = 6t^2 - t^3$. Find their velocities when they have the same acceleration. *Ans.* 2 and 9.
16. A baseball is thrown directly upward with an initial velocity of 64 feet per second. How high will it rise?
17. A cliff 128 feet high overhangs a lake. A man on the edge of the cliff throws a stone vertically upward with a velocity of 32 feet per second. at what velocity does the stone strike the water? *Ans.* 96 ft./sec.
18. A bomb is dropped ($v_0 = 0$) from an airplane 6400 feet high. Find when and at what velocity the bomb will strike the ground.
19. Find the initial velocity needed in order to shoot a projectile vertically upward a distance of 10,000 feet. *Ans.* 800 ft./sec.
20. From a height of 64 feet a ball is thrown vertically upward with a velocity of 24 feet per second. One second later another ball is dropped from the same height. At what height above the ground do the two balls pass each other?

31. Maxima and Minima; Critical Points

A function $y = f(x)$ is said to be an *increasing function* of x if its value increases as x increases. Similarly, it is a *decreasing function* of x if y decreases as x increases. Thus, in Figure 40, the function is increasing from A to B, decreasing from B to D, and increasing from D to F. At points, such as B, D, and E, where the slope of the curve is zero, the function $f(x)$ is said to be *stationary*.

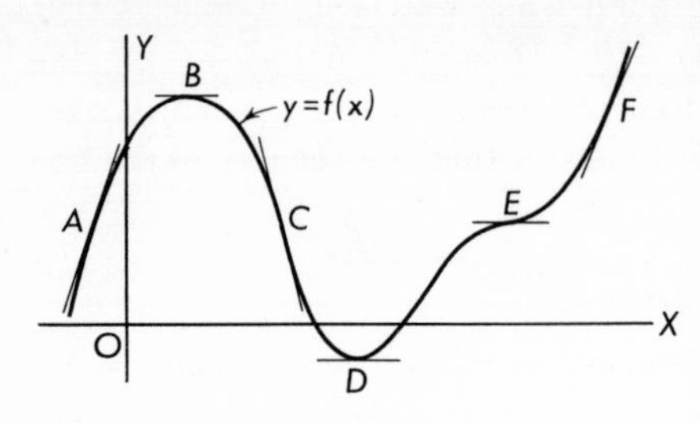

Figure 40

The point B of the curve, where the function changes from increasing to decreasing is called a **maximum point,** and the function is said to have a relative maximum value at B. Likewise, the point D, where the function changes from decreasing to increasing, is called a **minimum point,** and the function is said to have a relative minimum value at D.

Relative maximum and minimum values should not be confused with absolute maximum and minimum values. Thus if a function, say $f(x) = 4x - x^2$, is defined only in the domain $0 \leqq x \leqq 3$, it is apparent from Figure 41 that $f(2) = 4$ is the absolute maximum and $f(0) = 0$ is the absolute minimum for $f(x)$ in the given domain. Observe especially that the derivative $f'(x) = 4 - 2x$ exists at $x = 0$ and is equal to 4, not zero! When the representation of a function is different for different intervals the end points should always be checked for either absolute or relative maximum and minimum points. Note that the function $f(x) = |x| + |x - 1|$, whose graph is shown in Figure 33, has a minimum value of 1 at all points of the interval $0 \leqq x \leqq 1$.

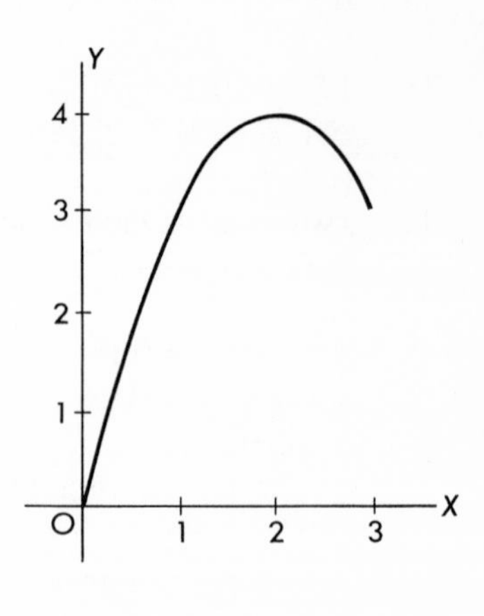

Figure 41

For relative maxima and minima, we have the following result.

Theorem. *If a function $f(x)$ has a relative maximum or minimum at $x = a$, and if the derivative $f'(a)$ exists, then $f'(a) = 0$.*

Proof: For $f(x)$ to be a maximum when $x = a$ means that

$$f(a + \Delta x) - f(a) < 0$$

for all numerically small positive or negative values of Δx. Hence it follows that

$$\frac{f(a + \Delta x) - f(a)}{\Delta x} < 0 \quad \text{when} \quad \Delta x > 0,$$

$$\frac{f(a + \Delta x) - f(a)}{\Delta x} > 0 \quad \text{when} \quad \Delta x < 0.$$

In taking the limit of these expressions as $|\Delta x| \to 0$, we find that $f'(a) \leqq 0$ and $f'(a) \geqq 0$, respectively, and since these two limits must be the same, we conclude that $f'(a) = 0$. A similar proof holds when $f(x)$ has a relative minimum value for $x = a$.

If the function $f(x)$ has a derivative for every value of x, we see geometrically that

1. *$f(x)$ is increasing at $x = a$, when $f'(a)$ is positive.*
2. *$f(x)$ is decreasing at $x = a$, when $f'(a)$ is negative.*
3. *$f(x)$ is a maximum at $x = a$, when $f'(a) = 0$, and $f'(x)$ changes sign from $+$ to $-$ as x increases through a.*
4. *$f(x)$ is a minimum at $x = a$, when $f'(a) = 0$, and $f'(x)$ changes sign from $-$ to $+$ as x increases through a.*

Note: The above results can be established rigorously. For example, consider part 1, where $f'(a) > 0$. Since the limit of $[f(x) - f(a)]/(x - a)$ exists as $x \to a$, it follows that for any $\epsilon > 0$ there is a $\delta > 0$ such that

$$\left|\frac{f(x) - f(a)}{x - a} - f'(a)\right| < \epsilon, \quad \text{when} \quad |x - a| < \delta.$$

Taking $\epsilon = \frac{1}{2}f'(a)$, we see for all x in $a - \delta < x < a + \delta$ that

$$\frac{f(x) - f(a)}{x - a} > \tfrac{1}{2}f'(a); \quad \text{hence} \quad \frac{f(x) - f(a)}{x - a} > 0.$$

Thus $f(x) - f(a)$ and $x - a$ must have the same sign, and so if x_1 and x_2 are two values in the domain that satisfy $a - \delta < x_1 < a < x_2 < a + \delta$, we find

$$f(x_1) < f(a) \qquad \text{and} \qquad f(a) < f(x_2).$$

Hence $f(x)$ is an increasing function at $x = a$. The other statements can be proved by similar considerations.

Illustration. For the function $y = x^3 - 3x - 5$, we have $y' = 3x^2 - 3 = 3(x + 1)(x - 1)$. Testing with the values $x = -2, -1, 0$, we find respectively $y' = +, 0, -$; hence $(-1,-3)$ is a maximum point of the curve. Testing with the values $x = 0, 1, 2$, we find respectively $y' = -, 0, +$; hence $(1,-7)$ is a minimum point of the curve.

If a value x_0 in the domain of $f(x)$ is such that $f'(x_0)$ is zero or undefined, x_0 is called a **critical value** of $f(x)$, and the corresponding point on the curve $y = f(x)$ is called a **critical point.** Thus the points B, D, and E in Figure 40 are critical points. A point such as E where the slope changes from $+$ to 0 to $+$, or $-$ to 0 to $-$, is called a **point of inflection with horizontal tangent.**

Example. Find the maximum and minimum points of the curve $y = x^2 + \frac{16}{x}$.

Solution: Differentiating $y = x^2 + 16x^{-1}$, we have

$$y' = 2x - 16x^{-2} = 2x - \frac{16}{x^2} = \frac{2(x^3 - 8)}{x^2} = \frac{2(x - 2)(x^2 + 2x + 4)}{x^2}.$$

Setting $y' = 0$, we obtain the critical value $x = 2$. Testing $x = 2-, 2, 2+$, we find $y' = -, 0, +$. Hence this gives a minimum point (2,12) of the curve. Observe also that y' does not exist at $x = 0$; hence $x = 0$ is a critical value. The curve, however, is not defined at $x = 0$, so there is no corresponding critical point.

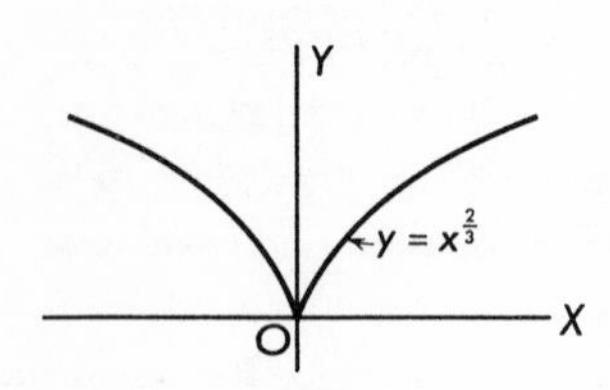

Figure 42

Note: A critical point may sometimes exist at a point where the slope function $f'(x)$ is undefined. For example, the slope of the curve $y = x^{2/3}$ (Figure 42) is undefined at $x = 0$, but since $f(0) < f(x)$ for all other values of x, it follows that (0,0) is a minimum point. Note also that a function defined as $f(x) = x^{2/3}$ for $x \neq 0$ and $f(0) = 1$ does not have a minimum value.

EXERCISE 13

In each of the following, find the range of x for which y (*a*) increases, (*b*) decreases, as x increases.

1. $y = x^2 - 6x - 7$. *Ans.* (*a*) $x > 3$, (*b*) $x < 3$.
2. $y = 9 - 5x - 2x^2$.
3. $y = x^3 + 3x^2 + 3x$. (*a*) All x, (*b*) None.
4. $y = 3x^4 - 8x^3 + 5$.
5. $y = x^4 - 2x^2$. (*a*) $-1 < x < 0, x > 1$, (*b*) $x < -1, 0 < x < 1$.
6. $y = x^2 - x^{-2}$.

Find the maximum and minimum points for each of the following curves.

7. $y = x^2 - 4x - 1$. *Ans.* $(2, -5)$, min.
8. $y = 7 + 3x - 2x^2$.
9. $y = x^3 - 9x^2 + 15x - 5$. (1,2), max.; $(5, -30)$, min.

10. $y = x^3 - 3x^2 + 4$.
11. $y = 2x^3 - x^2 + 3x - 1$. *Ans.* None.
12. $y = (x + 1)(x - 1)^2$.
13. $y = x^4 + 4x$. $(-1, -3)$, min.
14. $y = 3x^4 - 16x^3 + 24x^2$.
15. $y = x^5 - 5x^3 - 20x - 2$. $(2, -50)$, min.; $(-2, 46)$, max.
16. $y = x^3(2 - x)^2$.
17. $y = x + x^{-1}$. $(-1, -2)$, max.; $(1, 2)$, min.
18. $y = 2x^{-2} + 3x^{-1} - 2$.
19. $y = \sqrt{x} - \dfrac{1}{\sqrt{x}}$. None.
20. $y = x - 2x^{1/2} + 2$.
21. Find a and b so that the curve $y = x^3 + ax^2 + b$ will have a critical point at $(2,5)$. *Ans.* $a = -3$, $b = 9$.
22. Find a and b so that $y = ax + bx^{-1}$ will have a critical point at $(2,4)$.
23. Show that the function $y = ax^3 + bx^2 + cx + d$ increases for all x, when $b^2 < 3ac$ and $a > 0$.
24. Show that the function $y = x^3(x + a)$ attains a minimum of $-27a^4/256$.

32. Higher Derivatives

The derivative of a function $y = f(x)$ gives a new function which may in turn be differentiated. If the derivative of the first derivative exists, it is called the **second derivative** of the original function and is represented by the symbols

$$\frac{d^2y}{dx^2}, \quad \frac{d^2}{dx^2}f(x), \quad y'', \quad f''(x), \quad D_x^2y, \quad D_x^2f(x).$$

Similarly, the derivative of the second derivative is called the **third derivative,** and so on. In general, the nth derivative is represented by the symbols

$$\frac{d^ny}{dx^n}, \quad \frac{d^n}{dx^n}f(x), \quad y^{(n)}, \quad f^{(n)}(x), \quad D_x^ny, \quad D_x^nf(x).$$

Illustration. If $y = x^3 - 2x^2 - 3x + 5$, then $y' = 3x^2 - 4x - 3$, $y'' = 6x - 4$, $y''' = 6$, $y^{(4)} = y^{(5)} = \cdots = 0$.

33. Points of Inflection; Concavity

Let us suppose that the curve of Figure 43 is the graph of a function $y = f(x)$ which has a first and second derivative for every value of x for which $f(x)$ is defined. As a point P traces the curve from A to B, the slope function is increasing and the arc AB is said to be **concave**

upward (holds water). From B to C, the slope function is decreasing and the arc is said to be **concave downward.** The point B where the curve changes its sense of concavity is called a **point of inflection** of the curve.

Since the rate of change of any function is represented by its derivative, the rate of change of the slope function $f'(x)$ is given by the second derivative $f''(x)$. Hence we have

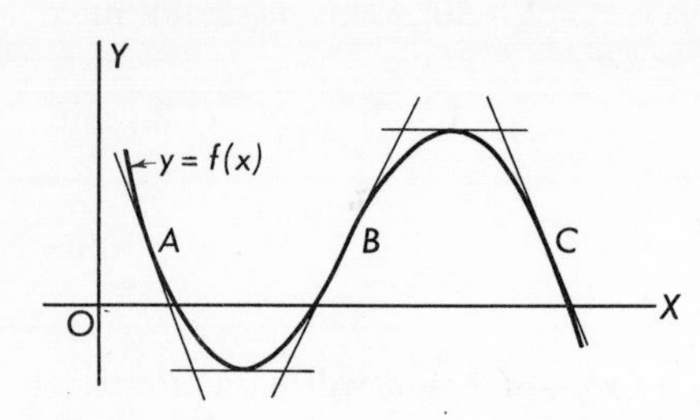

Figure 43

1. *$y = f(x)$ is concave upward at $x = a$, when $f''(a)$ is positive.*
2. *$y = f(x)$ is concave downward at $x = a$, when $f''(a)$ is negative.*
3. *$y = f(x)$ has a point of inflection at $x = a$, when $f''(a) = 0$, and $f''(x)$ changes sign as x increases through a.*

Illustration. When $y = x^3 - 6x^2 + 12$, we have $y' = 3x^2 - 12x$ and $y'' = 6x - 12$. Setting $y'' = 0$ gives $x = 2$. Since the curve changes from concave downward (y'' negative) to concave upward (y'' positive) as x increases through 2, the point $(2, -4)$ is a point of inflection.

Note: A point of inflection may sometimes exist at a point where $f''(x)$ is undefined. For example, consider the curve $y = x^{1/3}$ (Figure 44). Differentiating, we have $y' = \frac{1}{3}x^{-2/3}$ and $y'' = -\frac{2}{9}x^{-5/3}$. When $x < 0$ we have $y'' > 0$, and when $x > 0$ we have $y'' < 0$. This means that (0,0) is a point of inflection, since the curve changes from concave upward to concave downward as x increases through O.

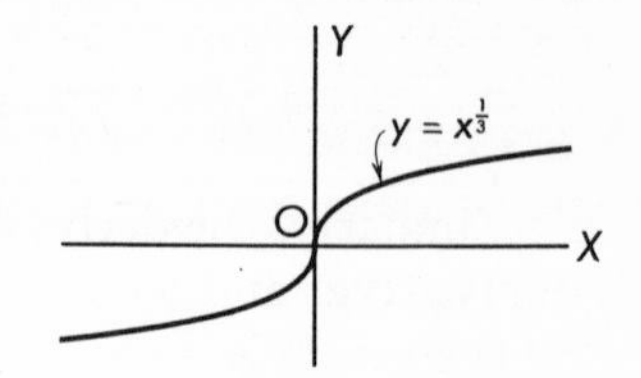

Figure 44

Since a curve is usually concave upward at a minimum point and concave downward at a maximum point, we have the following alternate test for maximum and minimum values.

$f(x)$ is a maximum at $x = a$, if $f'(a) = 0$ and $f''(a)$ is negative.

$f(x)$ is a minimum at $x = a$, if $f'(a) = 0$ and $f''(a)$ is positive.

When $f''(a)$ is zero or does not exist, the test given in Article **31** should be used.

Example 1. For the curve $y = 3x^5 + 5x^4$, find the critical points, the points of inflection, and trace the curve.

Solution: Computing the first and second derivatives, we have

$$y' = 15x^4 + 20x^3 = 5x^3(3x + 4),$$
$$y'' = 60x^3 + 60x^2 = 60x^2(x + 1).$$

Setting $y' = 0$, we obtain the critical points $(-\frac{4}{3}, \frac{256}{81})$ and $(0,0)$. At the first point y'' is negative; hence this point is a maximum. At the second point y'' is zero, but since the slope changes from $-$ to $+$ as x increases through zero, this point is a minimum.

Setting $y'' = 0$, we obtain $x = -1$ and $x = 0$. As x increases through -1, y'' changes sign; hence $(-1,2)$ is a point of inflection. As x increases through zero, y'' does not change sign; hence $(0,0)$ is not a point of inflection.

Plotting these points and the additional points $(-\frac{5}{3},0)$ and $(0.5,0.4)$, we obtain the curve shown in Figure 45.

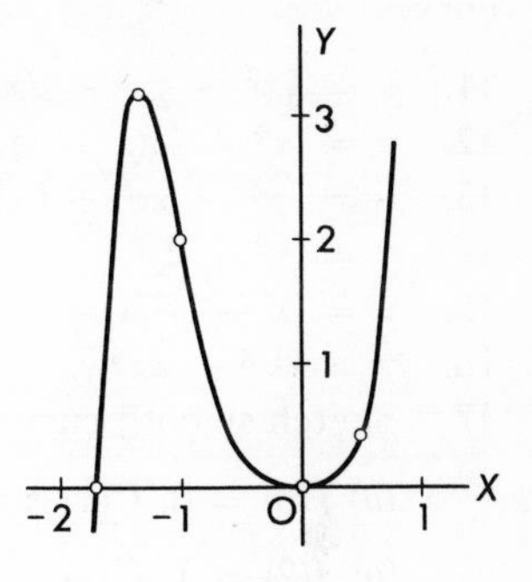

Figure 45

Example 2. If a, b, and c are positive constants, prove that $ax + b/x \geqq c$, for all positive values of x, when $4ab \geqq c^2$.

Proof: Consider the function $f(x) = ax + bx^{-1} - c$, and its derivatives $f'(x) = a - bx^{-2}$ and $f''(x) = 2bx^{-3}$.

By setting $f'(x)$ equal to zero, we find $x = \sqrt{b/a}$. Since $f''(x) > 0$ for all positive values of x, it follows that $f(x)$ has its minimum value when $x = \sqrt{b/a}$. Computing this minimum value, we obtain

$$f(\sqrt{b/a}) = \sqrt{ab} + \sqrt{ab} - c,$$

which by hypothesis is greater than or equal to zero. Hence $f(x) \geqq 0$, or $ax + b/x \geqq c$, for all positive values of x.

EXERCISE 14

In each of the following, find y', y'', and y'''.

1. $y = x^4 - 2x^2 + 5$. *Ans.* $y' = 4x^3 - 4x$, $y'' = 12x^2 - 4$, $y''' = 24x$.
2. $y = (x + 1)^3$.
3. $y = \dfrac{1}{x}(x^2 - 3x)^2$. $y' = 3x^2 - 12x + 9$, $y'' = 6x - 12$, $y''' = 6$.
4. $y = \sqrt{2x}$.
5. $y = x^2 - 2x^{-1}$. $y' = 2x + 2x^{-2}$, $y'' = 2 - 4x^{-3}$, $y''' = 12x^{-4}$.

Find the points of inflection for the following curves.

6. $y = 5 - 2x - 3x^2 - x^3$.
7. $y = x^4 - 24x^2 + 75$. *Ans.* $(\pm 2, -5)$.
8. $y = x(x^2 - 5)^2$.
9. $y = x^2 - x^{-1}$. $(1,0)$.
10. $y = x^{1/2} + x^{-1/2}$.

Find the critical points, the points of inflection, and trace the following curves.

11. $y = \frac{1}{3}x^3 - \frac{1}{2}x^2 - 2x$. *Ans.* $(2, -\frac{10}{3})$ min., $(-1, \frac{7}{6})$ max., $(\frac{1}{2}, -\frac{13}{12})$ infl.
12. $y = (x^2 + 1)(x - 1)$.
13. $y = 3x^4 - 8x^3 + 6x^2$. $(0,0)$ min., $(1,1)$ infl., $(\frac{1}{3}, \frac{11}{27})$ infl.
14. $y = (x^2 + 2)^2$.
15. $y = (x + 1)^2/x$. $(1,4)$ min., $(-1,0)$ max.
16. $y = x^{1/3} + 2x^{4/3}$.
17. Sketch smooth curves $y = f(x)$ that have the following properties:

    (*a*) $f(0) = 0, f'(x) > 0$ for $x < 0, f'(x) < 0$ for $x > 0$,

    (*b*) $f(2) = 1, f''(x) > 0$ for $x < 2, f''(x) < 0$ for $x > 2$.

18. Sketch a smooth curve $y = f(x)$ that has the following properties: $f(0) = 1, f'(0) = 0, f''(0) = 0, f'(x) > 0$ for $x \neq 0, f''(x) < 0$ for $x < 0$, $f''(x) > 0$ for $x > 0$.

19. Find the equation of the line tangent to the curve $y = x^3 - 6x^2 + 5x + 2$ at its point of inflection. *Ans.* $7x + y = 10$.
20. Find the equation of the line tangent to the curve $y = (x + 3)/\sqrt{x}$ at its point of inflection.
21. Find the equation of the line normal to the curve $y = 3x^5 + 10x^3 + 15x + 1$ at its point of inflection. *Ans.* $x + 15y = 15$.
22. Find the equation of the line normal to the curve $y = x(x + a)(x + 2a)$ at its point of inflection.
23. Determine a and b so that the curve $y = ax^3 + bx^2$ will have a point of inflection at $(1,2)$. *Ans.* $a = -1, b = 3$.
24. Determine a and b so that the curve $y = ax^2 + bx^{-2}$ will have a point of inflection at $(1,3)$.
25. Determine a, b, and c so that the curve $y = ax^3 + bx^2 + cx$ will have a slope of 4 at its point of inflection $(-1,-5)$. *Ans.* $a = 1, b = 3, c = 7$.
26. Determine a, b, and c so that the line $16x - y + 20 = 0$ will be tangent to curve $y = ax^4 + bx^2 + c$ at its point of inflection $(-1,4)$.
27. Determine a, b, c, and d so that the curve $y = ax^3 + bx^2 + cx + d$ will have a critical point at the origin and a point of inflection at $(2,4)$. *Ans.* $a = -\frac{1}{4}, b = \frac{3}{2}, c = d = 0$.

28. Determine a, b, c, and d so that the curve $y = ax^3 + bx^2 + cx + d$ will have horizontal tangents at the points (1,2) and (2,3).
29. Indicate by a sketch the nature of the curve $y = f(x)$ at the point (h,k), when

$$\begin{aligned} (a)\ & f'(x) > 0, f''(x) > 0, \quad \text{for } x < h, \\ & f'(x) < 0, f''(x) > 0, \quad \text{for } x > h, \\ (b)\ & f'(x) > 0, f''(x) > 0, \quad \text{for } x < h, \\ & f'(x) > 0, f''(x) < 0, \quad \text{for } x > h. \end{aligned}$$

30. Indicate by a sketch the nature of the curve $y = f(x)$ at the point (h,k), when

$$\begin{aligned} (a)\ & \lim_{x \to h^-} f'(x) = +\infty, f''(x) > 0, \quad \text{for } x < h, \\ & \lim_{x \to h^+} f'(x) = 0, \quad f''(x) < 0, \quad \text{for } x > h, \\ (b)\ & \lim_{x \to h^-} f'(x) = +\infty, f''(x) > 0, \quad \text{for } x < h, \\ & \lim_{x \to h^+} f'(x) = -\infty, f''(x) > 0, \quad \text{for } x > h. \end{aligned}$$

31. If a, b, and c are positive constants, show that $ax^2 + b/x \geqq c$ for all positive values of x, when $27ab^2 \geqq 4c^3$.
32. If n is greater than one, prove that $x^n - 1 \geqq n(x - 1)$ for all positive values of x. *Hint:* Show that $f(x) \geqq 0$, where $f(x) = x^n - nx + n - 1$.
33. If the positive functions $f(x)$ and $g(x)$ are such that $f'(a) = 0$, $g'(a) = 0$, $f''(a) < 0$, and $g''(a) < 0$, prove that their product also has a relative maximum value at $x = a$.
34. The functions $f(x)$ and $g(x)$ are such that $f''(a) = 0$ and $g''(a) = 0$. Is the condition $f'(a) = 0$ or $g'(a) = 0$ sufficient to assure for their product the existence of an inflection point at $x = a$? Consider the functions $f(x) = x^3$ and $g(x) = x^5$ at $x = 0$.
35. If a function $f(x)$ satisfies $|f(x + h) - f(x)| \leqq h^2$ for all real h and x, show that $f(x)$ is a constant.

34. Applications of Maxima and Minima

In geometry and applied fields we often encounter problems in which the maximum or minimum value of some quantity is required. In general these values may be found by proceeding as follows.

1. *Express the quantity to be maximized or minimized in terms of a single variable.*
2. *Differentiate the function determined in 1 and set the derivative equal to zero.*
3. *Solve 2 for values of the variable and determine by inspection or otherwise whether they maximize or minimize the given quantity.*

Example 1. Find two numbers whose sum is 10, and the sum of whose squares is a minimum.

Solution: Let x and $10 - x$ represent the numbers, and y the sum of their squares. Following the procedure outlined above, we have

1. $y = x^2 + (10 - x)^2 = 2x^2 - 20x + 100.$
2. $y' = 4x - 20 = 0,$
3. $x = 5$ gives a minimum, since $y'' = 4 > 0.$

Therefore the numbers are 5 and 5.

Occasionally the analysis of a problem is clearer when two or more variables are used. In all cases, however, the quantity to be maximized or minimized should be expressed in terms of a single variable before it is differentiated.

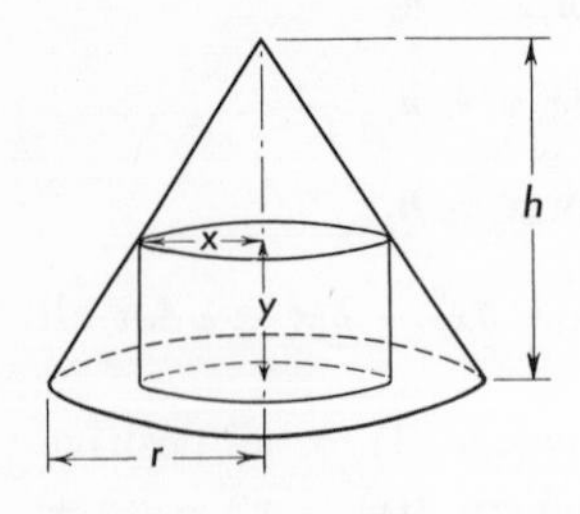

Figure 46

Example 2. Find the altitude of the cylinder of maximum volume which can be inscribed in a right circular cone of radius r and height h.

Solution: If x and y represent the radius and height, respectively, the volume of the cylinder is $V = \pi x^2 y$. To express V in terms of a single variable, we observe in Figure 46 that, by similar triangles,

$$\frac{x}{r} = \frac{h - y}{h}; \quad \text{hence} \quad y = \frac{h}{r}(r - x). \tag{1}$$

Thus

$$V = \frac{\pi h}{r}(rx^2 - x^3),$$

and by differentiating we obtain

$$\frac{dV}{dx} = \frac{\pi h}{r}(2rx - 3x^2) = \frac{\pi h}{r}x(2r - 3x) = 0. \tag{2}$$

Therefore $x = \frac{2}{3}r$, and by (1) the altitude is $h(r - \frac{2}{3}r)/r$ or $\frac{1}{3}h$.

It is clear that this solution yields a maximum volume, since, as x increases from 0 to r, the volume increases from zero to a maximum and then decreases to zero again. Equation (2) also has the root $x = 0$, but this value is rejected since it obviously gives a cylinder of minimum volume zero.

In solving certain maxima and minima problems in which radicals occur, it is sometimes advantageous to use the fact that if $f(x)$ has a maximum (or minimum) value when $x = a$, then $[f(x)]^2$, $[f(x)]^3$, and so on, have maximum or minimum values when $x = a$.

Example 3. Find the area of the largest rectangle that can be inscribed in the ellipse $\frac{x^2}{a^2} + \frac{y^2}{b^2} = 1$.

Solution: Inscribe a rectangle in the ellipse as shown in Figure 47. If the vertex in the first quadrant is denoted by $P(x,y)$, the area of the rectangle is $A = 4xy$.

Since the coordinates of the point P satisfy the equation of the ellipse, we have

$$y = \frac{b}{a}\sqrt{a^2 - x^2};$$

hence

$$A = \frac{4bx}{a}\sqrt{a^2 - x^2}.$$

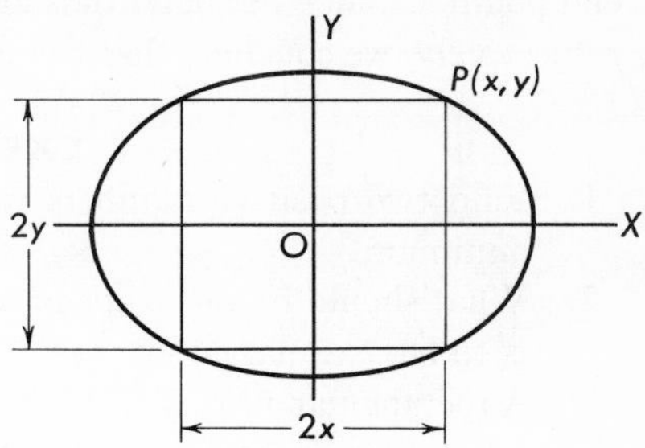

Figure 47

Using the fact that A is a maximum when A^2 is a maximum, we proceed as follows.

$$A^2 = \frac{16b^2x^2}{a^2}(a^2 - x^2) = \frac{16b^2}{a^2}(a^2x^2 - x^4).$$

Hence

$$\frac{d}{dx}(A^2) = \frac{16b^2}{a^2}(2a^2x - 4x^3) = \frac{32b^2x}{a^2}(a^2 - 2x^2) = 0.$$

Since x was chosen to be positive, we obtain $x = \frac{a}{\sqrt{2}}$. Hence $y = \frac{b}{a}\sqrt{a^2 - \left(\frac{a}{\sqrt{2}}\right)^2} = \frac{b}{\sqrt{2}}$, and the maximum area is $A = 4\left(\frac{a}{\sqrt{2}}\right)\left(\frac{b}{\sqrt{2}}\right) = 2ab$.

Example 4. The electric potential at a point (x,y) on the line segment extending from $(0,3)$ to $(2,0)$ is given by $P = 3x^2 + 2y^2$. At what point on this segment is the potential a maximum?

Solution: The equation of the line segment is readily found to be $3x + 2y = 6$ with $0 \leqq x \leqq 2$. If we solve for y and substitute into the expression for P, we obtain

$$P = 3x^2 + 2\left\{\frac{6 - 3x}{2}\right\}^2 = \frac{3}{2}(5x^2 - 12x + 12), \quad 0 \leqq x \leqq 2.$$

By differentiation, we find

$$\frac{dP}{dx} = 3(5x - 6).$$

Hence it would appear that $x = 6/5$ and $y = 6/5$ is the point that we are seeking. However, by noting that $d^2P/dx^2 = 15$, we see that the point (6/5,6/5) gives a minimum potential and furthermore that the graph depicting the potential in the domain $0 \leqq x \leqq 2$ is concave upward at all points. This means that the potential reaches its absolute maximum value at one of the end points. Since the potentials at the points (0,3) and (2,0) are 18 and 12, respectively, we conclude that the potential is a maximum at the point (0,3).

EXERCISE 15

1. Find two positive numbers whose product is 64, and whose sum is a minimum. *Ans.* 8, 8.
2. What should be the shape of a rectangular field of given perimeter, if it is to have a maximum area?
3. A rectangular field is to be enclosed by a fence and divided into three lots by fences parallel to one of the sides. Find the dimensions of the largest field that can be enclosed with 800 feet of fencing. *Ans.* 100×200 ft.
4. A rectangular lot adjacent to a highway is to be enclosed by a fence. If the fencing costs $2.50 per foot along the highway and $1.50 per foot on the other sides, find the dimensions of the largest lot that can be fenced off for $720.
5. A closed box, whose length is twice its width, is to have a surface of 192 square inches. Find the dimensions of the box when the volume is maximum. *Ans.* $4 \times 8 \times 5\frac{1}{3}$ in.
6. An open box is formed from a piece of cardboard 12 inches square by cutting equal squares out of the corners and turning up the sides. Find the volume of the largest box that can be made in this way.
7. If the length of the hypotenuse of a right triangle is 10, find the lengths of the other sides when the area is a maximum. *Ans.* $5\sqrt{2} \times 5\sqrt{2}$.
8. Find the maximum area of an isosceles triangle whose perimeter is 18 inches.
9. Find the most economical dimensions for a closed cylindrical can containing a quart. *Ans.* Diameter = height.
10. Find the dimensions of the largest right circular cylinder that can be inscribed in a sphere of radius 6 inches.
11. If three sides of a trapezoid are each 6 inches long, how long must the fourth side be if the area is a maximum? *Ans.* 12 in.
12. Find the dimensions of the largest right circular cone that can be inscribed in a sphere of radius 12 inches.
13. A triangle has a base 12 feet long and an altitude 8 feet high. Find the area of the largest rectangle that can be inscribed in the triangle so that the base of the rectangle falls on the base of the triangle. *Ans.* 24 sq. ft.

14. Find the dimensions of the right circular cone of greatest lateral area that can be inscribed in a sphere of radius a.

15. Find the dimensions of the right circular cone of least volume that can be circumscribed about a sphere of radius a. *Hint:* Let $x + 2a =$ altitude of cone. *Ans.* Alt. $= 4a$.

16. A triangular corner lot has perpendicular sides of lengths 120 feet and 160 feet. Find the dimensions of the largest rectangular building that can be constructed on the lot with sides parallel to the streets.

17. Find the point on the line $y = x$ nearest to the point $(4,1)$. *Ans.* $(\frac{5}{2}, \frac{5}{2})$.

18. Find the point on the parabola $4y = x^2$ nearest to the point $(1,2)$.

19. Find the area of the largest rectangle with sides parallel to the coordinate axes which can be inscribed in the area bounded by the two parabolas $y = 26 - x^2$ and $y = x^2 + 2$. *Ans.* 64.

20. Find the area of the largest rectangle having one side on the x axis and inscribed in the triangle formed by the lines $y = x$, $y = 0$, and $3x + y = 20$.

21. Find the area of the largest isosceles triangle that can be inscribed in a circle of radius 6 inches. *Ans.* $27\sqrt{3}$ sq. in.

22. The strength of a rectangular beam varies as the product of the width and the square of the depth. Find the dimensions of the strongest beam that can be cut from a circular log of diameter 15 inches.

23. A window consists of a rectangle surmounted by a semicircle. What shape gives the most area for a given perimeter? *Ans.* Width = height.

24. A manufacturer contracts to make 50,000 articles or less at a rate of $60 per hundred. If the number of articles exceeds 50,000, the price per hundred on the whole order is made 5 cents less for each hundred in excess of 50,000. On how large an order will the manufacturer's gross receipts be greatest?

25. The cost of fuel per hour for running a ship is proportional to the cube of the speed and is $27 per hour when the speed is 12 miles per hour. Other costs amount to $128 per hour regardless of the speed. Express the cost per mile as a function of the speed, and find the speed that makes this cost a minimum. *Ans.* $C = \frac{v^2}{64} + \frac{128}{v}$; 16 mi./hr.

26. At noon a ship S_1 is 20 miles north of a ship S_2. If S_1 is sailing south at a rate of 6 miles per hour and S_2 is sailing east at a rate of 8 miles per hour, find the time when they are nearest together.

27. A military courier is located on a desert 6 miles from a point P which is the point on a long straight road nearest to him. He is ordered to get to a point Q on the road. Assuming that he can travel 14 miles per

hour on the desert and 50 miles per hour on the road, find the point where he should reach the road in order to get to Q in the least possible time when (*a*) Q is 3 miles from P, (*b*) Q is 6 miles from P, (*c*) Q is 1 mile from P.

Ans. (*a*) 1.75 mi. from P, (*b*) 1.75 mi. from P, (*c*) at Q.

28. What is the greatest value of $f(x) = 2x^3 - 9x^2 + 12x$ in the interval $0 \leqq x \leqq 3$?

29. Find the point on the parabola $y = x^2$ nearest to the point $(0,k)$, if (*a*) $k \leqq \frac{1}{2}$, (*b*) $k > \frac{1}{2}$. *Ans.* (*a*) $(0,0)$, (*b*) $(\pm\sqrt{k - \frac{1}{2}}, k - \frac{1}{2})$.

30. Prove that no one of the family of parabolas $y = 4kx - \frac{1}{2}(k^4 + 16)x^2$ extends more than one unit above the x axis.

35. Differentials

If $y = f(x)$, it follows from the definition of a derivative and the meaning of a limit that

$$\lim_{\Delta x \to 0} \frac{\Delta y}{\Delta x} = f'(x);$$

hence

$$\frac{\Delta y}{\Delta x} = f'(x) + \epsilon,$$

where ϵ is as small as we please, when Δx is sufficiently small. Thus the increment Δy may be written

$$\Delta y = f'(x)\,\Delta x + \epsilon\,\Delta x.$$

Since ϵ is numerically small when Δx is small, we see that Δy is given approximately by $f'(x)\,\Delta x$. This product is called the **differential** of $f(x)$ and is denoted by the symbol dy or $df(x)$. Thus

$$dy \equiv df(x) = f'(x)\,\Delta x. \quad (1)$$

If $f(x) = x$, we have $f'(x) = 1$, and (1) reduces to $dx = \Delta x$. For this reason, the *differential of the independent variable* is defined to be the increment Δx, and we write the differential of a function as

$$\boldsymbol{dy = f'(x)\,dx.}$$

Illustration. When $y = 2x^4$, we have $dy = 8x^3\,dx$.

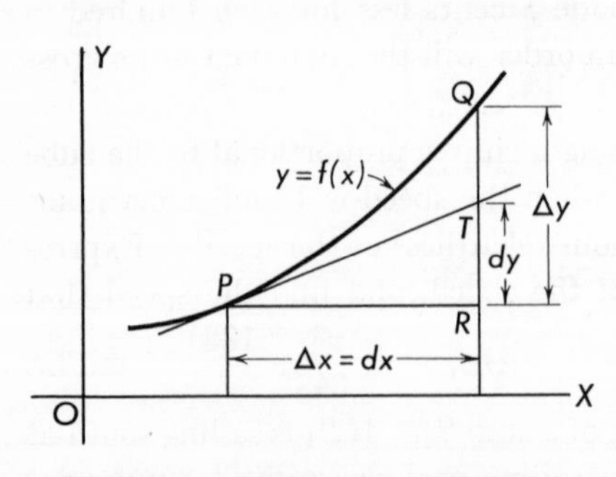

Figure 48

Geometrically the differential of a function may be interpreted in the following manner. In Figure 48 let $P(x,y)$ and $Q(x + \Delta x, y + \Delta y)$

be two points on the curve $y = f(x)$. Since the value of the derivative at P is equal to the slope of the tangent line PT, we have

$$dy = f'(x)\,dx = \frac{RT}{PR}\cdot PR = RT.$$

Thus dy $(=RT)$ is the increment of the ordinate of the tangent line corresponding to dx, whereas Δy $(=RQ)$ is the corresponding increment of the ordinate of the curve.

36. Approximations and Errors

From the considerations in the preceding article it follows that the differential dy is a good approximation for Δy in that dy differs but little from Δy when compared to a small change Δx in the variable x; in fact,

$$\lim_{\Delta x\to 0} \frac{\Delta y - dy}{\Delta x} = 0.$$

The preceding limit is correct since $dy = f'(x)\,\Delta x$ and

$$\frac{\Delta y - f'(x)\,\Delta x}{\Delta x} = \frac{\Delta y}{\Delta x} - f'(x).$$

By the definition of a derivative the limit of this latter expression is zero as $\Delta x \to 0$.

Written in functional form the increment $\Delta f(x) = f(x + \Delta x) - f(x)$ is approximately given by $df(x)$; hence we can write

$$f(x + \Delta x) \approx f(x) + df(x).$$

This means that the value of a function at a point of its domain can be obtained approximately, provided we know the value of the function and its differential at a nearby point.

Example 1. If $y = x^4 - 2x^3 + 9x + 7$, using differentials find an approximate value of y when $x = 1.997$.

Solution: The value 1.997 may be considered as the result of applying an increment $\Delta x = dx = -0.003$ to an original value of $x = 2$. Hence, by differentials, we obtain

$$\begin{aligned} dy &= (4x^3 - 6x^2 + 9)\,dx \\ &= (32 - 24 + 9)(-0.003) = -0.051. \end{aligned}$$

Since $y = 25$ when $x = 2$, and -0.051 is the approximate change in y as x changes from 2 to 1.997, we have

$$y + dy = 25 - 0.051 = 24.949$$

as an approximation to y when $x = 1.997$.

In order to obtain an estimation of the accuracy of this approximation, let us compute the error of the approximation $\Delta y - dy$. Thus in this case we have

$$\begin{aligned}\Delta y - dy &= 6x^2(\Delta x)^2 + 4x(\Delta x)^3 + (\Delta x)^4 - 6x(\Delta x)^2 - 2(\Delta x)^3 \\ &= [24 - 12](-0.003)^2 + [8 - 2](-0.003)^3 + (-0.003)^4 \\ &= 0.000107838081.\end{aligned}$$

Hence $y + \Delta y = y + dy + (\Delta y - dy) = 24.949107838081$, and we see that the above approximation is valid to the three decimal places computed.

Example 2. Using differentials, find an approximate value of $\sqrt{98}$.

Solution: We first observe that the number 98 differs but little from the *square* number 100. As a result, if we find the change in $y = \sqrt{x}$ corresponding to a change in x from 100 to 98, we may add this change to $y = \sqrt{100} = 10$, and thus find $\sqrt{98}$. Since $dy = dx/2\sqrt{x}$, an approximate change in y for $x = 100$ and $dx = -2$ is

$$dy = \frac{-2}{2\sqrt{100}} = -0.1;$$

hence $\sqrt{98} = \sqrt{100} - 0.1 = 9.9$ approximately.

Relative and percentage errors. If dy is the error in y, the ratio dy/y is called the **relative error** in y, and $100(dy/y)$ the **percentage error.**

Example 3. If the radius of a sphere is measured as 5 inches with a possible error of 0.02 inch, find approximately the greatest possible error and percentage error in the computed value of the volume.

Solution: The exact maximum error in $V = \frac{4}{3}\pi r^3$ will be the change ΔV in its value as x changes from 5 to 5 ± 0.02. An approximate error is given by the value dV; thus

$$dV = 4\pi r^2\,dr = 4\pi(5)^2(\pm 0.02) = \pm 2\pi \text{ cu. in.}$$

Since the computed value of the volume is $V = 4\pi(5)^3/3 = 500\pi/3$, we have a relative error of

$$\frac{dV}{V} = \frac{\pm 2\pi}{\frac{1}{3}(500\pi)} = \pm 0.012,$$

and a percentage error of $\pm 1.2\%$.

EXERCISE 16

Find the differential dy in each of the following.

1. $y = x^3 - 2x^2 + 5$. *Ans.* $dy = (3x^2 - 4x)\,dx$.
2. $y = 2x^4 - 3x^3 - 5x$.

3. $y = \sqrt[3]{6x}$. *Ans.* $dy = \dfrac{2\,dx}{\sqrt[3]{36x^2}}$.

4. $y = 5x^2 + \dfrac{3}{x^3}$.

5. $y = (x + a)^2$. $dy = 2(x + a)\,dx$.

6. $y = ax\sqrt{x}$.

In each of the following, find Δy and dy for the values indicated.

7. $y = x^4 - \frac{1}{2}x^2$, for $x = 2$ and $\Delta x = 0.1$. *Ans.* 3.2431, 3.

8. $y = x^3 - 3x^2 - 2x - 5$, for $x = 4$ and $\Delta x = -0.1$.

9. $y = 12.8/x$, for $x = 10$ and $\Delta x = 0.24$. -0.03, -0.03072.

10. $y = \sqrt{x}$, for $x = 4$ and $\Delta x = 0.41$.

11. $y = (x + 1)^3$, for $x = -3$ and $\Delta x = -0.003$. -0.036^+, -0.036.

12. $y = \dfrac{x}{2} + \dfrac{2}{x}$, for $x = 2$ and $\Delta x = 0.1$.

Use differentials to find approximate values for the following radicals.

13. $\sqrt{27}$. *Ans.* 5.2.
14. $\sqrt{97}$.
15. $\sqrt[3]{61}$. $3\frac{15}{16}$.
16. $\sqrt[3]{122}$.
17. $\sqrt[4]{83.7}$. 3.025.
18. $\sqrt[5]{34}$.

19. If A is the area of a square of side s, find dA. Draw a figure showing A, dA, and ΔA. *Ans.* $dA = 2s\,ds$.

20. Considering the area of a circular ring as an increment of area of a circle, find approximately the area of a ring whose inner and outer radii are 3 inches and 3.02 inches, respectively.

21. Find approximately the difference between the areas of two spheres whose radii are 4 feet and 4.05 feet. *Ans.* 1.6π sq. ft.

22. If a particle moves in accordance with the law $s = t^{3/2}$, where s is expressed in feet and t in seconds, find the approximate change in speed as t changes from 4 to 4.04.

23. The altitude of a certain right circular cone is the same as the radius of the base, and is measured as 5 inches with a possible error of 0.02 inch. Find approximately the percentage error in the calculated value of the volume. *Ans.* 1.2%.

24. What is the approximate error in the volume and surface of a cube of edge 2 feet if an error of $\frac{1}{8}$ inch is made in measuring an edge?

25. Considering the volume of a spherical shell as an increment of volume of a sphere, find approximately the volume of a spherical shell whose outer diameter is 8 inches and whose thickness is $\frac{1}{16}$ inch. *Ans.* 4π cu. in.

26. Find an approximate formula for the volume of a thin right circular cylindrical shell if r, h, and t denote respectively the radius, length, and thickness.

27. A container is to be made in the form of a cube to hold one liter (1000 cc.). How accurately must the inner edge be made so that the volume will be correct to within 3 cc.? *Ans.* Error $\leqq 0.01$ cm.
28. Using differentials, find the allowable percentage error in the diameter of a circle if the area is to be correct to within 4%.
29. Show that the relative error in the nth power of a measurement is approximately n times the relative error in the measurement.
30. Show that the relative error in the nth root of a measurement is approximately $1/n$ times the relative error in the measurement.

CHAPTER 4

Integration of Powers

37. Antidifferentiation

In the preceding chapter we were concerned with the problem of determining the derivative of a known function. The inverse process of determining a function whose derivative is known is called **anti-differentiation,** and the required function is called an **antiderivative** of the given function. Thus x^4 is an antiderivative of $4x^3$, because $4x^3$ is the derivative of x^4 with respect to x. In this connection we observe that if any constant C is added to x^4, the sum $x^4 + C$ is also an antiderivative of $4x^3$. This raises a question as to whether anything other than a constant could be added to x^4, so that we still would obtain $4x^3$ as the derivative. The following theorem whose proof will be given in Article **114** indicates that there is no such quantity.

Theorem. *Two functions $F_1(x)$ and $F_2(x)$ that have the same derivative differ at most by a constant.*

For reasons that will soon be evident, instead of saying that $F(x)$ is an antiderivative of $f(x)$, we will say that $F(x)$ is an **integral** of $f(x)$, and their relationship will be expressed in the form

$$\int f(x)\,dx = F(x) + C.$$

We call the symbol $\int$ an **integral sign,** $f(x)$ the **integrand,** $F(x)$ a **particular integral,** C the **constant of integration,** and $F(x) + C$ the **indefinite integral** of $f(x)$.

38. Integration of Powers

The following properties of indefinite integrals may be proved by differentiation and comparison with the corresponding properties of derivatives.

1. $\displaystyle\int dx = x + C.$

2. $\displaystyle\int a\,dx = a\int dx$, **where a is a constant.**

3. $\displaystyle\int [f(x) + g(x)]\,dx = \int f(x)\,dx + \int g(x)\,dx.$

4. $\displaystyle\int x^n\,dx = \frac{x^{n+1}}{n+1} + C, \qquad n \neq -1.$

Illustration 1. $\displaystyle\int 2x^{-2}\,dx = 2\frac{x^{(-2)+1}}{(-2)+1} + C = -2x^{-1} + C.$

Illustration 2. $\displaystyle\int (x^3 - 6x + 4)\,dx = \tfrac{1}{4}x^4 - 3x^2 + 4x + C.$

Illustration 3. $\displaystyle\int (x^2 + 1)^2\,dx = \int (x^4 + 2x^2 + 1)\,dx$

$$= \tfrac{1}{5}x^5 + \tfrac{2}{3}x^3 + x + C.$$

Note 1: Observe in 2 that a must be a constant. Thus $\int 2x^2\,dx$ equals $2\int x^2\,dx$, and is not equal to $2x\int x\,dx$ or $2x^2\int dx$.

Note 2: It is advisable at first to check *mentally* each problem of integration by differentiating the result and comparing with the given integrand.

Example. Evaluate $\displaystyle\int \frac{(1 + \sqrt{3x})^2}{\sqrt{x}}\,dx.$

Solution: Substituting $x^{1/2}$ for $\sqrt{x}$ and writing the integrand as a sum, we find

$$\int \frac{(1 + \sqrt{3x})^2}{\sqrt{x}}\,dx = \int (x^{-1/2} + 2\sqrt{3} + 3x^{1/2})\,dx$$

$$= \frac{x^{1/2}}{\frac{1}{2}} + 2\sqrt{3}x + 3\frac{x^{3/2}}{\frac{3}{2}} + C$$

$$= 2x^{1/2} + 2\sqrt{3}x + 2x^{3/2} + C.$$

EXERCISE 17

Find the indefinite integral in each of the following problems.

1. $\displaystyle\int 5\,dx.$ *Ans.* $5x + C.$

2. $\displaystyle\int (3x^2 - 5)\,dx.$

3. $\displaystyle\int (x - 7)\,dx.$ $\tfrac{1}{2}x^2 - 7x + C.$

4. $\int (x + 1)(2 - x)\,dx.$

5. $\int (3x - 2)^2\,dx.$ *Ans.* $3x^3 - 6x^2 + 4x + C.$

6. $\int (3x - 2)^2 x\,dx.$

7. $\int (x^8 - 4x^3 - x)\,dx.$ $\frac{1}{9}x^9 - x^4 - \frac{1}{2}x^2 + C.$

8. $\int (3x^5 - 2x^3 - 1)\,dx.$

9. $\int \frac{dx}{x^3}.$ $-\frac{1}{2x^2} + C.$

10. $\int (1 - x^{-1/3})\,dx.$

11. $\int \frac{3 + 2x^2}{x^2}\,dx.$ $\frac{2x^2 - 3}{x} + C.$

12. $\int \left(x^2 - \frac{1}{x^2}\right)^2 dx.$

13. $\int x\sqrt{x}\,dx.$ $\frac{2}{5}x^2\sqrt{x} + C.$

14. $\int \left(\sqrt{x} + \frac{1}{\sqrt{x}}\right) dx.$

15. $\int \sqrt[3]{3x}\,dx.$ $\frac{3}{4}x\sqrt[3]{3x} + C.$

16. $\int (4 - 7x)\sqrt[3]{x}\,dx.$

17. $\int (\sqrt{x} + \sqrt{a})^2\,dx.$ $\frac{1}{2}x^2 + \frac{4}{3}x\sqrt{ax} + ax + C.$

18. $\int (\sqrt{x} + \sqrt{a})^2 x\,dx.$

19. $\int \frac{dx}{x\sqrt{2x}}.$ $-\sqrt{\frac{2}{x}} + C.$

20. $\int \frac{\sqrt{x} - 1}{x^2}\,dx.$

21. $\int (x\sqrt{x} - 5)^2\,dx.$ $\frac{1}{4}x^4 - 4x^{5/2} + 25x + C.$

22. $\int x^{-4}(x - 2)^2\,dx.$

23. $\int \frac{x^3 - 1}{x - 1}\,dx.$ $\frac{1}{3}x^3 + \frac{1}{2}x^2 + x + C.$

24. $\int \sqrt{x^3 + 2x^2 + x}\,dx.$

39. Constant of Integration

We have seen that the integration of a function gives a function that involves an arbitrary additive constant. If supplementary conditions are given, this constant can be determined as is illustrated in the following examples.

Example 1. Find the curve (*a*) whose slope at any point is $2x$, and (*b*) that passes through the point (1,2).

Solution: From the first condition, slope $= dy/dx = 2x$, we obtain by integration

$$y = x^2 + C. \tag{1}$$

This equation represents a **family of curves,** as shown in Figure 49. To determine the curve that passes through the point (1,2) we substitute these coordinates in (1) and find $2 = (1)^2 + C$; hence $C = 1$.

Thus the required curve is $y = x^2 + 1$.

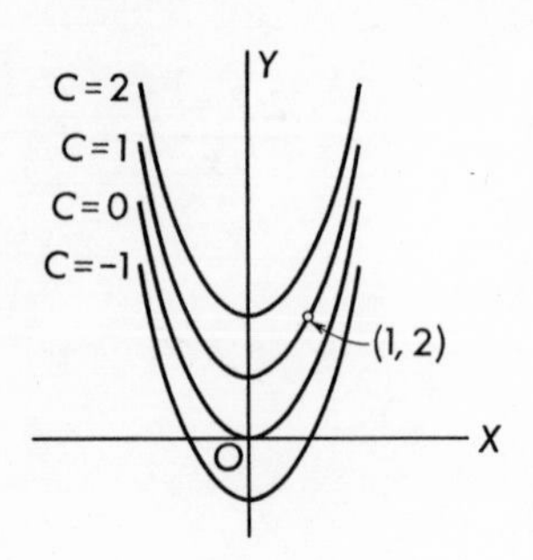

Figure 49

Example 2. A particle moves on a line with a constant acceleration of 4 feet per second per second. Find its equation of motion if $s = 2$ feet and $v = -3$ feet per second, when $t = 2$ seconds.

Solution: From acceleration $= dv/dt = 4$, we obtain by integration $v = 4t + C_1$. Since $v = -3$ when $t = 2$, we find by substitution that $C_1 = -11$. Hence the equation giving the velocity at any time t is

$$v = 4t - 11.$$

From velocity $= ds/dt = 4t - 11$, we obtain by integration $s = 2t^2 - 11t + C_2$. Since $s = 2$ when $t = 2$, by substitution we obtain $2 = 2(2)^2 - 11(2) + C_2$; hence $C_2 = 16$. Thus the required equation of motion is

$$s = 2t^2 - 11t + 16.$$

EXERCISE 18

Find the curve having the given slope that passes through the indicated point.

1. $y' = 2x - 5$, $(5,4)$. *Ans.* $y = x^2 - 5x + 4$.
2. $y' = x^2 - 2x - 4$, $(3,-6)$.
3. $y' = 3x^4 - x^2$, $(1,1)$. $y = \frac{3}{5}x^5 - \frac{1}{3}x^3 + \frac{11}{15}$.
4. $y' = x^3 - 3x^2 + 2x - 5$, $(2,-5)$.
5. $y' = (x + 1)(x + 2)$, $(-3,-\frac{3}{2})$. $y = \frac{1}{3}x^3 + \frac{3}{2}x^2 + 2x$.
6. $y' = (2 - x)^3$, $(-2,10)$.

7. $y' = x^2\sqrt{x}$, (1,0). *Ans.* $y = \frac{2}{7}(x^3\sqrt{x} - 1)$.
8. $y' = 2/x^2$, $(-2,4)$.
9. $y' = (x^2 - 4)/x^2$, (4,1). $y = (x - 2)^2/x$.
10. $y' = x^{1/2} - x^{-1/2}$, (9,9).
11. If $dy = (2x - 3)\,dx$ and $y = 2$ when $x = 3$, find the value of y when $x = 5$. *Ans.* 12.
12. If $dP = dx/\sqrt{2ax}$ and $P = 2a$ when $x = \frac{1}{2}a^3$, find the value of P when $x = 2a^3$.
13. Find the equation of the curve for which $y'' = x$, and which passes through the point (1,2) with a slope of $\frac{5}{2}$. *Ans.* $6y = x^3 + 12x - 1$.
14. Find the equation of the curve for which $y'' = 4/x^3$, and which is tangent to the line $2x + y = 5$ at the point (1,3).
15. Find the equation of the curve for which $y'' = 6x^2$, and which passes through the points (0,2) and $(-1,3)$. *Ans.* $2y = x^4 - x + 4$.
16. Find the equation of the curve for which $y''' = 2$, and which has a slope of -2 at its point of inflection (1,3).

Find the equation of motion in each of the following.

17. $v = 2t$, and $s = 1$ when $t = 0$. *Ans.* $s = t^2 + 1$.
18. $v = \sqrt{kt}$, and $s = -\frac{1}{3}k^2$ when $t = k$.
19. $a = 12/t^4$, and $s = 3$, $v = 1$, when $t = 2$. *Ans.* $2s = 4t^{-2} + 3t - 1$.
20. $a = 1/t\sqrt{t}$, and $s = 9$ when $t = 1$, and $s = 16$ when $t = 4$.
21. A stone is thrown vertically upward with a velocity of 40 feet per second from the top of a tower 200 feet high. When will it strike the ground? *Hint:* Take $a = -32$, and $s = 0$, $v = 40$, when $t = 0$. *Ans.* In 5 sec.
22. A ball is dropped from the top of the Washington Monument (555 feet high). Neglecting the resistance of the air, how long will the ball take to reach the ground and with what speed will it strike?
23. Find how far an airplane will move in landing, if in t seconds after touching the ground its speed in feet per second is given by the equation $v = 180 - 18t$. *Ans.* 900 ft.
24. What constant acceleration will bring an automobile traveling 60 miles per hour to rest in 160 feet?

40. Differential of Area

Let $PQQ'R$ in Figure 50 be the graph of a function $y = f(x)$ that is continuous in the interval from $x = a$ to $x = b$. Let us denote by A the variable area $PCDQ$ extending from the fixed ordinate CP to the moving ordinate DQ.

When x increases by a small amount Δx, A increases by a corresponding amount ΔA = area $QDD'Q'$. If, as shown in the figure, the ordinate y increases* as x increases, then on completing the rectangles $QDD'N$ and $MDD'Q'$ we see that

$$\text{Area } QDD'N < \Delta A < \text{Area } MDD'Q'$$

or

$$y\,\Delta x < \Delta A < (y + \Delta y)\,\Delta x.$$

Dividing each member of this inequality by Δx, we have

$$y < \frac{\Delta A}{\Delta x} < y + \Delta y;$$

and letting Δx approach zero, we obtain

$$\frac{dA}{dx} = y \qquad \text{or} \qquad dA = y\,dx.$$

Thus *the* **differential of area** *between a curve and the x axis is equal to the product of the ordinate and the differential of the abscissa.*

Note 1: Observe that we have derived the above relationship only on the basis of a "right-hand" limit, that is, $\Delta x > 0$. By taking $\Delta x < 0$, we see that $\Delta y < 0$, $\Delta A < 0$, and $y > \Delta A/\Delta x > y + \Delta y$, whence in the limit as $\Delta x \to 0$ we obtain $dA/dx = y$. Since the limit from the left is the same as that from the right, we are assured that the limit exists.

Note 2: The above result is also valid even if the function is not properly increasing or decreasing. From the continuity of $f(x)$ we know (Theorem 3, Article **23**) that $f(x)$ has a maximum value M and a minimum value m, each for some x' in the interval $x \leqq x' \leqq x + \Delta x$. In this case it is clear that $m\Delta x \leqq \Delta A \leqq M\Delta x$ or $m \leqq \Delta A/\Delta x \leqq M$, where for a fixed value of x the numbers m and M will depend on Δx. However, the fact that $f(x)$ is a continuous function means that m and M both approach the value $f(x)$ as $\Delta x \to 0$; hence $dA/dx = f(x)$. Again we observe that $\Delta A < 0$ when $\Delta x < 0$, so we still have $m \leqq \Delta A/\Delta x \leqq M$, and the result is valid when Δx is either positive or negative.

41. Area as an Integral

From $dA = y\,dx$, it follows by inspection that

$$A = \int y\,dx = \int f(x)\,dx = F(x) + C, \tag{1}$$

where $F(x)$ is a function whose derivative is $f(x)$. The variable area

* The result is valid without this restriction. For example, when Δy is negative we simply reverse the inequality signs.

$PCDQ$ in Figure 50 may be found from (1) by using the condition that $A = 0$ when $x = a$. Thus by substituting $x = a$ in (1) we have $0 = F(a) + C$; hence, in denoting the area from a to x by $A(a,x)$, we have

$$A(a,x) = F(x) - F(a).$$

As a result, we also have

$$\text{Area } PCER = A(a,b) = F(b) - F(a). \quad (2)$$

The difference $F(b) - F(a)$ is often denoted by $\Big[F(x)\Big]_a^b$, where a is called the **lower limit** and b the **upper limit.**

In evaluating (2) observe that the constant of integration may be omitted, since if we use $F(x) + C$ in place of $F(x)$ we find

$$\begin{aligned} A(a,b) &= [F(b) + C] - [F(a) + C] \\ &= F(b) - F(a). \end{aligned}$$

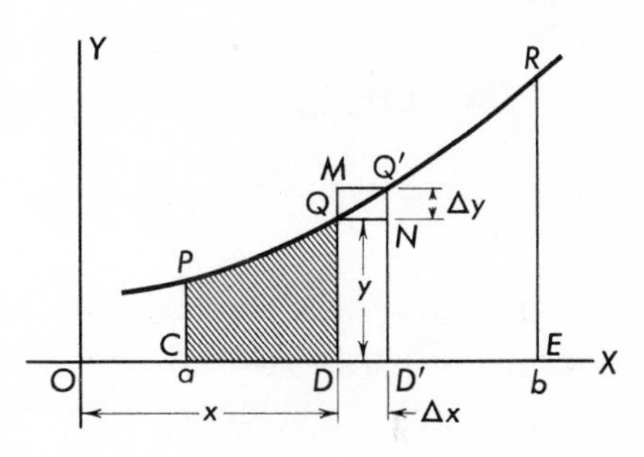

Figure 50

Illustration. The area between the parabola $y = x^2$ and the x axis from $x = -1$ to $x = 2$ is obtained by first finding $F(x) = \int x^2\,dx = x^3/3$, and then computing $\Big[F(x)\Big]_{-1}^{2} = F(2) - F(-1)$. Thus the required area is

$$A(-1,2) = \left[\frac{x^3}{3}\right]_{-1}^{2} = \frac{(2)^3}{3} - \frac{(-1)^3}{3} = \frac{8}{3} + \frac{1}{3} = 3.$$

42. Calculation of Areas

If in the interval $a \leqq x \leqq b$, a curve $y = f(x)$ lies on or above the x axis, we have shown in the preceding article that the area bounded by the curve, the x axis, and the ordinates at $x = a$ and $x = b$ is given by

$$A(a,b) = \left[\int f(x)\,dx\right]_a^b = \Big[F(x)\Big]_a^b = F(b) - F(a). \quad (1)$$

If the curve lies on or below the x axis the value given by (1) will be negative since $f(x)$ is negative. The actual area in this case will be given by the absolute value of (1). Hence if the curve $y = f(x)$ crosses the x axis between $x = a$ and $x = b$, the total area bounded by the curve, the x axis, and the ordinates at $x = a$ and $x = b$ is obtained by considering separately the areas above and below the x axis.

Example. Find the area bounded by $y = 2x + x^2 - x^3$, the x axis, and the lines $x = -1$ and $x = 1$.

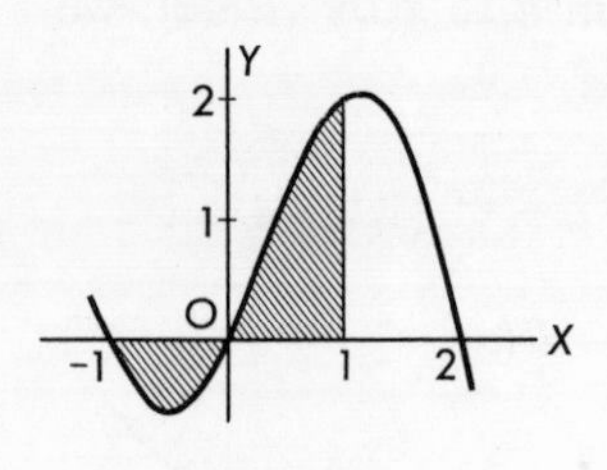

Figure 51

Solution: The graph of $y = 2x + x^2 - x^3$ (Figure 51) indicates that the required area is in two parts.

The area from $x = -1$ to $x = 0$ is obtained from

$$\left[\int (2x + x^2 - x^3)\,dx\right]_{-1}^{0} = \left[x^2 + \frac{x^3}{3} - \frac{x^4}{4}\right]_{-1}^{0}$$

$$= \left[0\right] - \left[1 - \frac{1}{3} - \frac{1}{4}\right] = -\frac{5}{12},$$

while the area from $x = 0$ to $x = 1$ is

$$\left[\int (2x + x^2 - x^3)\,dx\right]_{0}^{1} = \left[x^2 + \frac{x^3}{3} - \frac{x^4}{4}\right]_{0}^{1} = 1 + \frac{1}{3} - \frac{1}{4} = \frac{13}{12}.$$

Thus the required area is $\frac{5}{12} + \frac{13}{12} = \frac{3}{2}$. Note that the integral from $x = -1$ to $x = 1$ would give the algebraic sum of the above values, or $\frac{2}{3}$.

EXERCISE 19

Evaluate each of the following.

1. $\left[\int (2 - x)\,dx\right]_{0}^{1}$. *Ans.* $\frac{3}{2}$.
2. $\left[\int (2x + 1)(3 - x)\,dx\right]_{1}^{3}$.
3. $\left[\int (2x + x^2)\,dx\right]_{-2}^{2}$. $\frac{16}{3}$.
4. $\left[\int (x^2 + 1)^2\,dx\right]_{-1}^{1}$.
5. $\left[\int x(x + 1)^2\,dx\right]_{-3}^{-2}$. $-\frac{73}{12}$.
6. $\left[\int (a + x)\,dx\right]_{a}^{2a}$.
7. $\left[\int \left(x^2 + \frac{1}{x^2}\right)dx\right]_{2}^{5}$. 39.3.
8. $\left[\int \frac{x^2 - 1}{x^4}\,dx\right]_{1}^{2}$.
9. $\left[\int (\sqrt{a} - \sqrt{x})^2\,dx\right]_{0}^{a}$. $\frac{1}{6}a^2$.
10. $\left[\int (x^{1/3} - x^{-1/3})\,dx\right]_{1}^{8}$.

Find the area bounded by the curve, the x axis, and the given ordinates. Draw the figure.

11. $y = 2x + 1$; from $x = 0$ to $x = 4$. *Ans.* 20.
12. $y = 10x - x^2$; from $x = 2$ to $x = 5$.
13. $y = x^3 + 3x^2$; from $x = 0$ to $x = 2$. 12.
14. $y = (x + 2)^2$; from $x = -2$ to $x = 0$.
15. $y = x^{99}$; from $x = 0$ to $x = 1$. 0.01.
16. $y = a^2 - x^2$; from $x = -a$ to $x = a$.
17. $y = \sqrt{x}$; from $x = 1$ to $x = 16$. 42.
18. $y^3 = x^2$; from $x = 0$ to $x = 8$.

19. $x^2y = x^2 - 4$; from $x = 2$ to $x = 4$. *Ans.* 1.
20. $x^3y = x - 1$; from $x = 1$ to $x = 5$.
21. Find the area in the first quadrant bounded by the x axis and the curve $y = 6x + x^2 - x^3$. *Ans.* $15\frac{3}{4}$.
22. Find the area bounded by the x axis and the curve $y = 4 - x^{2/3}$.
23. Find the total area between the parabola $y = x^2 - 4x$, the x axis, and the ordinates $x = -2$ and $x = 3$. *Ans.* $19\frac{2}{3}$.
24. Find the total area between the cubic $y = 2x^3 - 3x^2 - 12x$, the x axis, and its maximum and minimum ordinates.
25. Find the area between the curve $y = 2x^4 - x^2$, the x axis, and its two minimum ordinates. *Ans.* $\frac{7}{120}$.
26. Find the area enclosed by the loop of the curve whose equation is $y^2 = x(3 - x)^2$.
27. Find the area bounded by the coordinate axes and the parabolic arc $\sqrt{x} + \sqrt{y} = \sqrt{a}$. *Ans.* $\frac{1}{6}a^2$.
28. Find the area in the first quadrant bounded by the coordinate axes and the curve $\sqrt[3]{x} + \sqrt[3]{y} = \sqrt[3]{a}$.
29. Show that $\Big[F(x)\Big]_a^b = -\Big[F(x)\Big]_b^a$.
30. Show that $\Big[F(x)\Big]_a^b = \Big[F(x)\Big]_a^c + \Big[F(x)\Big]_c^b$.

43. Area as a Limit

In Article **19** we discussed briefly the concept of a definite integral in order to point out its fundamental importance as a basic limiting process in the calculus. It would be of value to reread this earlier discussion after first reading the present article.

In contrast to the definition of area as given in Article **41**, our problem here is to find a value for the area, $A(a,b)$, by determining the limit that is approached by a sum of approximating rectangles as the size of these rectangles decrease and their number increase.

In Figure 52, we indicate the graph of a function, $y = f(x)$, that is single-valued, positive, and continuous for $a \leqq x \leqq b$. We divide the interval from a to b into n subintervals by inserting points x_0, x_1, x_2, $\cdots$, x_n along the x axis in such a manner that $a = x_0 < x_1 < x_2 < \cdots < x_{n-1} < x_n = b$. These points need not be equally spaced, and the width of the kth interval from x_{k-1} to x_k will be denoted by Δx_k. The total area is thus divided into n **increments of area** such, for example, as that area above Δx_k and under the curve. Let the maximum and minimum values of $f(x)$ in the kth subinterval be M_k and m_k, respectively. Then each increment of area may be approximated by an inscribed or a circumscribed rectangular element, such as the kth element with Δx_k as base and m_k or M_k as height. These rectangles, whether inscribed or circumscribed, are called **elements of area.**

If $\underline{S}_n$ denotes the sum of the inscribed elements and $\overline{S}_n$ the sum of the circumscribed elements, we observe from the figure that

$$\underline{S}_n = m_1\Delta x_1 + m_2\Delta x_2 + \cdots + m_n\Delta x_n \leqq A(a,b),$$
$$\overline{S}_n = M_1\Delta x_1 + M_2\Delta x_2 + \cdots + M_n\Delta x_n \geqq A(a,b).$$

Since $\underline{S}_n$ underestimates the area, we call it a *lower sum*, and similarly, since $\overline{S}_n$ overestimates the area, we call it an *upper sum*.

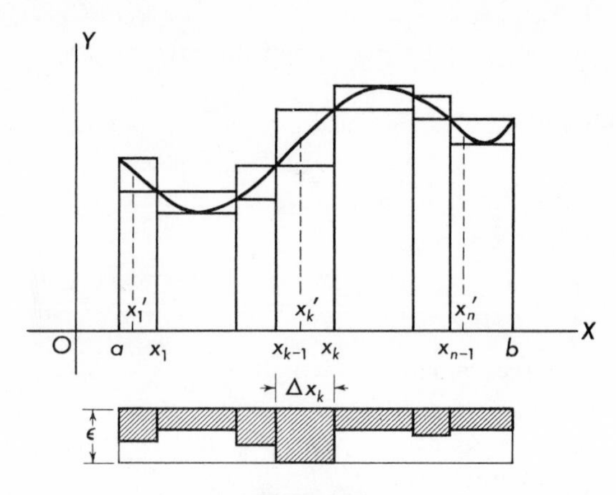

Figure 52

Now in considering the difference (shaded area in Figure 52)

$$\overline{S}_n - \underline{S}_n = (M_1 - m_1)\Delta x_1 + (M_2 - m_2)\Delta x_2 + \cdots + (M_n - m_n)\Delta x_n,$$

and letting ϵ represent the magnitude of the largest of the n differences $M_k - m_k$, it follows that every $M_k - m_k \leqq \epsilon$ and so, as shown in Figure 52, we have

$$\overline{S}_n - \underline{S}_n \leqq \epsilon(\Delta x_1 + \Delta x_2 + \cdots + \Delta x_n) = \epsilon(b - a).$$

However, in the limit as $n \to \infty$ and every $\Delta x_k \to 0$, it follows from the continuity of $f(x)$ that each $M_k - m_k \to 0$; hence $\epsilon \to 0$. Thus we have proved that

$$\lim_{n\to\infty} (\overline{S}_n - \underline{S}_n) = 0.$$

If we subtract $\underline{S}_n$ from each term of the inequality

$$\underline{S}_n \leqq A(a,b) \leqq \overline{S}_n, \qquad (1)$$

we obtain

$$0 \leqq A(a,b) - \underline{S}_n \leqq \overline{S}_n - \underline{S}_n.$$

Hence in the limit as $n \to \infty$ and every $\Delta x_k \to 0$, we find that

$$\lim_{n\to\infty} [A(a,b) - \underline{S}_n] = 0 \qquad \text{or} \qquad \lim_{n\to\infty} \underline{S}_n = A(a,b).$$

In a similar manner, by subtracting $\overline{S}_n$ from each member of (1), we can show that

$$\lim_{n\to\infty} \overline{S}_n = A(a,b).$$

Furthermore, if x_1' denotes *any* value in the closed interval from a to x_1, x_2' *any* value in the closed interval from x_1 to x_2, and so on, it follows from the inequality $m_k \leqq f(x_k') \leqq M_k$ that the sum

$$S_n = f(x_1')\,\Delta x_1 + f(x_2')\,\Delta x_2 + \cdots + f(x_n')\,\Delta x_n$$

satisfies the inequality

$$\underline{S}_n \leqq S_n \leqq \overline{S}_n.$$

Hence in the limit as $n \to \infty$ and every $\Delta x_k \to 0$, it follows from $\lim \underline{S}_n = \lim \overline{S}_n$ that

$$\lim_{n\to\infty} S_n = A(a,b).$$

Theorem. *Let the function $y = f(x)$ be single-valued, positive, and continuous for $a \leqq x \leqq b$. Let $a = x_0 < x_1 < x_2 < \cdots < x_n = b$, and define $\Delta x_k = x_k - x_{k-1}$ and $x_{k-1} \leqq x_k' \leqq x_k$, for $k = 1, 2, \cdots, n$. If the number n of subintervals of the interval $a \leqq x \leqq b$ increases indefinitely in such a way that the length of the largest subinterval tends toward zero, the limit approached by the sum*

$$S_n = f(x_1')\,\Delta x_1 + f(x_2')\,\Delta x_2 + \cdots + f(x_n')\,\Delta x_n \tag{2}$$

gives the area $A(a,b)$ under the curve, above the x axis, and between the ordinates at $x = a$ and $x = b$.

Note: It facilitates our work in mathematics to have a more compact notation for representing sums such as that given in (2); the Greek letter capital sigma, $\sum$, is used for this purpose. The symbol $\sum_{k=1}^{n}$, read as the sum on k from 1 to n, is used to denote the sum of n terms, each term being obtained from the expression that follows the symbol by substituting $1, 2, 3, \cdots, n$ successively for k. $\sum$ is called the **sign of summation** and k the **index of summation**; for example,

$$\sum_{k=1}^{4} u_k^2 = u_1^2 + u_2^2 + u_3^2 + u_4^2,$$

$$\sum_{r=1}^{n} r^3 = 1^3 + 2^3 + 3^3 + \cdots + n^3.$$

Making use of this notation, the sum given in (2) can be written as

$$S_n = \sum_{k=1}^{n} f(x'_k)\,\Delta x_k. \tag{3}$$

44. Definite Integrals

The common value approached by any of the sums indicated in equation (3) of the preceding article is called the **definite integral** of $f(x)$ from $x = a$ to $x = b$, and is denoted by $\int_a^b f(x)\,dx$. Thus, by definition,

$$\int_a^b f(x)\,dx = \lim_{n\to\infty} \sum_{k=1}^{n} f(x'_k)\,\Delta x_k, \tag{1}$$

where x'_k may be any point in the subinterval $x_{k-1} \leqq x'_k \leqq x_k$. The function $f(x)$ is called the *integrand*; and the numbers a and b are called the *limits of integration*, a being the *lower limit* and b the *upper limit*.

Note: Because of the above relationship with sums, it is understandable why the Old English elongated letter S was chosen to denote integration. Thus, whereas $\sum$ denotes an ordinary sum, the symbol $\int$ denotes a limit-sum; symbolically, we could write $\int = \lim \sum$.

Since the limit of the right side of (1) depends in no way on the variable that is used, it is evident that

$$\int_a^b f(x)\,dx = \int_a^b f(z)\,dz = \int_a^b f(t)\,dt.$$

For this reason, the variable that is used in a definite integral is often referred to as a "dummy" variable.

The definition (1) was made under the assumption that $a < b$. If a similar limit-sum were to be established for a subdivision $b = x_n < x_{n-1} < \cdots < x_1 < x_0 = a$, it is apparent that each Δx_k would be negative. For this reason, if $b < a$, we define the integral from a to b as

$$\int_a^b f(x)\,dx = -\int_b^a f(x)\,dx. \tag{2}$$

To be consistent, we also make the definition

$$\int_a^a f(x)\,dx = 0.$$

Interpreting the integral in (1) as the area considered in the preceding article, it is evident that if $a < h < b$, then

$$\int_a^h f(x)\,dx + \int_h^b f(x)\,dx = \int_a^b f(x)\,dx.$$

By making use of (2), we see that the preceding relation is also valid when $h < a < b$ or $a < b < h$.

Other properties of definite integrals that are easily proved are

$$\int_a^b c\,f(x)\,dx = c\int_a^b f(x)\,dx, \quad c \text{ constant},$$

$$\int_a^b [f(x) + g(x)]\,dx = \int_a^b f(x)\,dx + \int_a^b g(x)\,dx.$$

Mean-Value Theorem for Integrals. *If $f(x)$ is continuous on the interval of integration, then there exists a number x' such that*

$$\int_a^b f(x)\,dx = (b - a)f(x'), \quad a \leqq x' \leqq b.$$

45. Fundamental Theorem

There does not appear to be much connection between the definite integral defined as a limit-sum and the indefinite integral defined as an antiderivative, but the fact that both are related to the area $A(a,b)$ in the following way:

$$A(a,b) = \lim_{n\to\infty} \sum_{k=1}^{n} f(x_k')\,\Delta x_k = \int_a^b f(x)\,dx,$$

$$A(a,b) = \left[\int f(x)\,dx\right]_a^b = \left[F(x)\right]_a^b = F(b) - F(a),$$

indicates the validity of the conclusion

$$\lim_{n\to\infty} \sum_{k=1}^{n} f(x_k')\,\Delta x_k = \int_a^b f(x)\,dx = F(b) - F(a), \quad \text{where } F'(x) = f(x).$$

This relation shows that to evaluate a definite integral over the interval $a \leqq x \leqq b$, one needs only to find the antiderivative of the integrand and to substitute limits as indicated.

Illustration.

$$\int_2^4 x^{-3}\,dx = \left[\frac{x^{-2}}{-2}\right]_2^4 = \frac{(4)^{-2}}{-2} - \frac{(2)^{-2}}{-2} = -\frac{1}{32} + \frac{1}{8} = \frac{3}{32}.$$

Since the concept of area is not involved in the final result, we can state this important conclusion in the following way.

Fundamental Theorem of the Integral Calculus. *If $f(x)$ is a continuous function in the interval $a \leqq x \leqq b$ and I is a quantity that can be expressed as*

$$I = \lim_{n\to\infty} \sum_{k=1}^{n} f(x'_k)\, \Delta x_k = \int_a^b f(x)\, dx, \tag{1}$$

then $I = F(b) - F(a)$, where

$$\frac{d}{dx} F(x) = f(x).$$

Occasionally rather involved limits can be evaluated by use of this theorem.

Example. Evaluate $\lim_{n\to\infty} [1 + \sqrt{2} + \sqrt{3} + \cdots + \sqrt{n}]/n^{3/2}$.

Solution: Consider the function $y = \sqrt{x}$ for $0 \leqq x \leqq 1$, as shown in Figure 53. Divide the interval from 0 to 1 into n equal subintervals each of length $1/n$. Let x'_k be x_k; then by the Fundamental Theorem, we have

$$\lim_{n\to\infty} \left\{\frac{1}{n}\sqrt{\frac{1}{n}} + \frac{1}{n}\sqrt{\frac{2}{n}} + \cdots + \frac{1}{n}\sqrt{\frac{n}{n}}\right\} = \int_0^1 \sqrt{x}\, dx = \left[\frac{x^{3/2}}{3/2}\right]_0^1 = \frac{2}{3}.$$

Note: If the magnitude of a quantity I depends on a variable, such as x, we will often represent a typical element in the differential form $dI = f(x)\, dx$, where the subinterval considered extends from x to $x + dx$. In all cases, however, it should be realized that a sum such as that given in (1) is actually involved in the analysis.

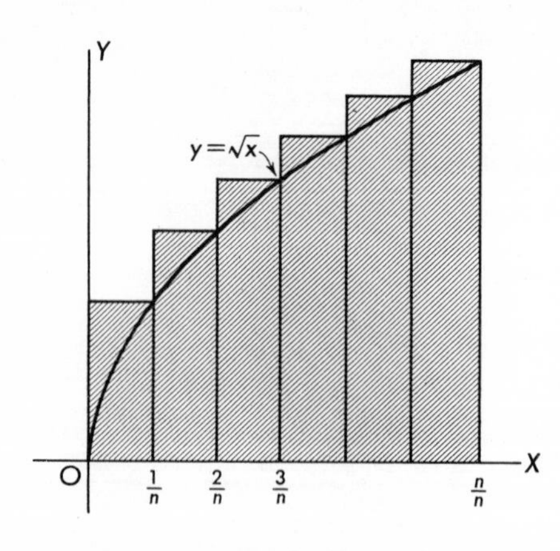

Figure 53

The general operating procedure for using the Fundamental Theorem to compute some quantity I, which is defined on the interval $a \leqq x \leqq b$, is to divide the interval into subintervals, and for the subinterval Δx_k to express the increment of I in the form

$$\Delta I_k = f(x'_k)\, \Delta x_k,$$

where $x_{k-1} \leqq x'_k \leqq x_k$. In many applied problems it is difficult to express ΔI_k in this precise form, but it is often simple to express the increment as

$$\Delta I_k = f(x_k')g(x_k'')\,\Delta x_k \tag{2}$$

where $x_{k-1} \leqq x_k' \leqq x_k$ and $x_{k-1} \leqq x_k'' \leqq x_k$. The following theorem, attributed to the American mathematician G. A. Bliss (1876–1950), indicates that the limit of the sum of the increments in (2) gives a definite integral.

Theorem. *Let the functions $f(x)$ and $g(x)$ be continuous for $a \leqq x \leqq b$. Let $a = x_0 < x_1 < \cdots < x_n = b$, and define $\Delta x_k = x_k - x_{k-1}$ and $x_{k-1} \leqq x_k', x_k'' \leqq x_k$, for $k = 1, 2, \cdots, n$. If the number n of subintervals of the interval $a \leqq x \leqq b$ increases indefinitely in such a way that the length of the largest subinterval tends toward zero, then*

$$\lim_{n\to\infty} \sum_{k=1}^{n} f(x_k')g(x_k'')\,\Delta x_k = \int_a^b f(x)g(x)\,dx. \tag{3}$$

Proof: Let F be a number such that $|f(x)| \leqq F$ for $a \leqq x \leqq b$, and let m_k and M_k be the minimum and maximum values respectively of $g(x)$ in the subinterval Δx_k. Since $f(x)$ and $g(x)$ are continuous functions, the product $f(x)g(x)$ is continuous and by the Fundamental Theorem we know that

$$\lim_{n\to\infty} \sum_{k=1}^{n} f(x_k')g(x_k')\,\Delta x_k = \int_a^b f(x)g(x)\,dx.$$

Now consider the difference

$$\begin{aligned} D_n &= \left| \sum_{k=1}^{n} f(x_k')g(x_k'')\,\Delta x_k - \sum_{k=1}^{n} f(x_k')g(x_k')\,\Delta x_k \right| \\ &= \left| \sum_{k=1}^{n} f(x_k')[g(x_k'') - g(x_k')]\,\Delta x_k \right|. \end{aligned}$$

By use of theorems on absolute values, we find

$$\begin{aligned} 0 \leqq D_n &\leqq \sum_{k=1}^{n} |f(x_k')|\,|g(x_k'') - g(x_k')|\,\Delta x_k \\ &\leqq F \sum_{k=1}^{n} |g(x_k'') - g(x_k')|\,\Delta x_k. \end{aligned}$$

Since x_k' and x_k'' are points in Δx_k, the greatest value that $|g(x_k'') - g(x_k')|$ can attain is $M_k - m_k$, and if ϵ denotes the greatest of the n differences $M_k - m_k$, we have

$$0 \leqq D_n \leqq F \sum_{k=1}^{n} (M_k - m_k)\,\Delta x_k \leqq F\epsilon \sum_{k=1}^{n} \Delta x_k = F\epsilon(b - a).$$

As $n \to \infty$, every $M_k - m_k \to 0$, and so $\epsilon \to 0$. Hence $\lim_{n\to\infty} D_n = 0$, and thus

$$\lim_{n\to\infty} \sum_{k=1}^{n} f(x_k')g(x_k'') \, \Delta x_k = \lim_{n\to\infty} \sum_{k=1}^{n} f(x_k')g(x_k') \, \Delta x_k$$

$$= \int_a^b f(x)g(x) \, dx.$$

EXERCISE 20

1. If the functions $f(x)$ and $g(x)$ are continuous, and $f(x) \leqq g(x)$ for $a \leqq x \leqq b$, prove that $\int_a^b f(x)\,dx \leqq \int_a^b g(x)\,dx$.
2. If $f(x)$ is an increasing function and the interval $a \leqq x \leqq b$ is divided into n subintervals each of length $\Delta x = (b - a)/n$, show that $\overline{S}_n - \underline{S}_n = [f(b) - f(a)]\,\Delta x$.
3. If the subintervals in the preceding problem are not of equal length, show that $\overline{S}_n - \underline{S}_n \leqq [f(b) - f(a)](\max \Delta x)$.
4. If $a < b < h$, prove that $\int_a^h f(x)\,dx + \int_h^b f(x)\,dx = \int_a^b f(x)\,dx$.
5. Evaluate $\lim_{n\to\infty} (1 + \sqrt[3]{2} + \sqrt[3]{3} + \cdots + \sqrt[3]{n})/n^{4/3}$. *Ans.* $\frac{3}{4}$.
6. Evaluate $\lim_{n\to\infty} \left\{\frac{n}{(n+1)^2} + \frac{n}{(n+2)^2} + \cdots + \frac{n}{(n+n)^2}\right\}$. *Hint:* Consider the function $f(x) = 1/x^2$ from $x = 1$ to $x = 2$.
7. In the expression for S_n, consider $f(x) = x$, $a = 0$, and $b > 0$. When x_k' is taken to be $\frac{1}{2}(x_{k-1} + x_k)$, show that S_n has a constant value that is independent of n.
8. As for the preceding problem, when $f(x) = x^2$, $a = 0$, and $b > 0$, what value x_k' in the interval Δx_k will give a sum S_n that is independent of n?
9. Using the four-step rule, show that the derivative of $\int_a^x f(t)\,dt$ with respect to x is $f(x)$.
10. If M and m are the maximum and minimum values of the continuous function $f(x)$ in the interval $a \leqq x \leqq b$, and if x' and x'' are any two values of x in this interval, show that $|f(x') - f(x'')| \leqq M - m$.
11. If $f(x)$ and $g(x)$ are continuous functions, prove that $\int_a^b [f(x) + g(x)]\,dx = \int_a^b f(x)\,dx + \int_a^b g(x)\,dx$.
12. Prove the Mean-Value Theorem for integrals.

46. Plane Areas in Rectangular Coordinates

In the determination of areas by use of the Fundamental Theorem, it is convenient to think of $dA = y\,dx$ as a typical rectangular element of area that has height y or $f(x)$ and a small width dx; the latter extending from x to $x + dx$. We know that a finite sum of such elements from $x = a$ to $x = b$ gives an approximation to the area, and that the limit-sum as denoted by the definite integral gives the area exactly.

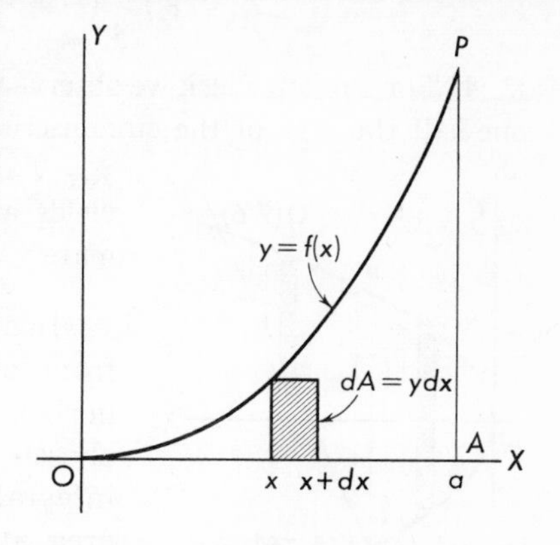

Figure 54

Thus, for the area OAP shown in Figure 54, we have a typical element of area $dA = y\,dx$, and so

$$\text{Area } OAP = \int_0^a f(x)\,dx.$$

The Fundamental Theorem may also be used to determine in the same manner any plane area that is bounded by curves whose equations are given in rectangular coordinates. The following examples illustrate the procedure suggested below.

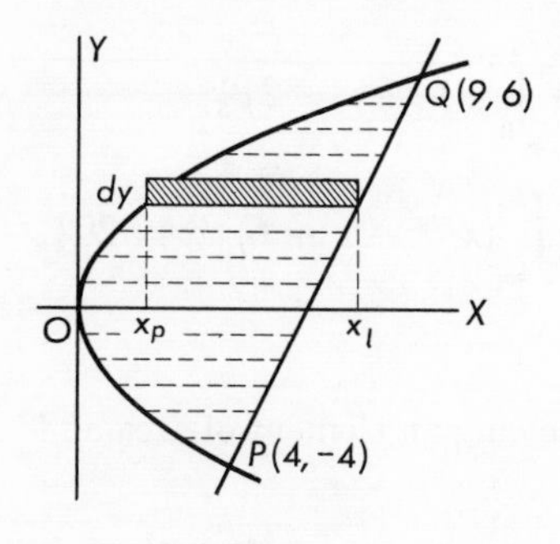

Figure 55

1. *Make a sketch of the area to be determined.*
2. *Draw a general vertical (or horizontal) rectangular element of area and express its area as a function of x and dx (or y and dy).*
3. *Determine the limits of integration from the figure and integrate to obtain the area.*
4. *Make a rough check of the result by estimating the area graphically.*

Example. Find the area bounded by the parabola $y^2 = 4x$ and the line $2x - y = 12$.

Solution: 1. Solving the two equations simultaneously, we find their points of intersection as given in Figure 55.

2. Drawing a horizontal element of area, we have

$$\begin{aligned} dA &= [(x \text{ of line}) - (x \text{ of parabola})]\,dy \\ &= [\tfrac{1}{2}(y + 12) - \tfrac{1}{4}y^2]\,dy \\ &= \tfrac{1}{4}(-y^2 + 2y + 24)\,dy. \end{aligned}$$

3. In order to evaluate the total area OPQ the horizontal elements of area must be summed from one extreme P to the other extreme Q; hence by the Fundamental Theorem

$$A = \frac{1}{4}\int_{-4}^{6} (-y^2 + 2y + 24)\, dy = 41\tfrac{2}{3}.$$

4. For a rough check we observe that the area OPQ equals approximately one-half the area of the circumscribing rectangle extending from $x = 0$ to $x = 9$ and $y = -4$ to $y = 6$. This observation yields an estimate of 45 which agrees approximately with the above result.

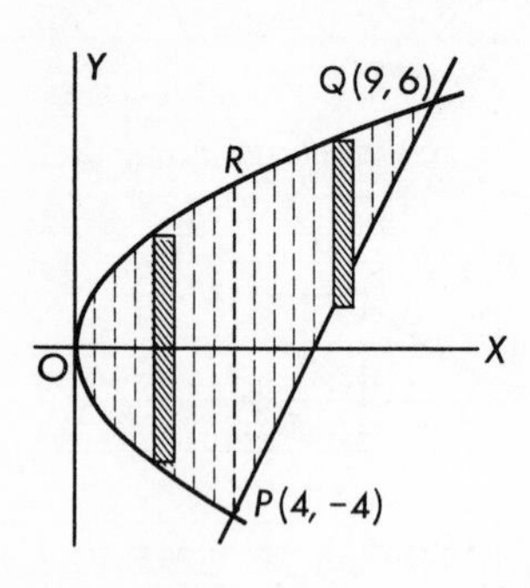

Figure 56

In evaluating a plane area it is immaterial from a theoretical point of view whether horizontal or vertical elements of area are chosen. The choice depends on how many integrals are needed to determine the given area and how difficult the integrals are to evaluate. For instance, the area in the preceding example may be determined by using vertical elements of area. In this case, however, it is necessary to consider the area OPQ in two parts OPR and RPQ. (Figure 56.)

$$\text{Area } OPR = \int_0^4 [(\sqrt{4x}) - (-\sqrt{4x})]\, dx = 4\int_0^4 x^{1/2}\, dx = 21\tfrac{1}{3},$$

$$\text{Area } RPQ = \int_4^9 [(\sqrt{4x}) - (2x - 12)]\, dx = 2\int_4^9 (x^{1/2} - x + 6)\, dx = 20\tfrac{1}{3}.$$

EXERCISE 21

In each of the following, draw the figures showing an element of area and find the area bounded by the given curves.

1. $y = x^2, \quad y = x.$ *Ans.* $\frac{1}{6}$.
2. $y = x^2 + 2x, \quad y = x + 2.$
3. $y^2 = 2x, \quad y = x - 4.$ 18.
4. $y = x^2, \quad y = 2x^2 - 3x.$
5. $x^2 = 2ay, \quad y = 2a.$ $\frac{16}{3}a^2$.
6. $x^2 + 3y = 4, \quad x - 2y = 4.$
7. $y = x - x^2, \quad y = -x.$ $\frac{4}{3}$.
8. $4ay = x^2, \quad y = x + 3a.$
9. $y^2 = 4ax, \quad x^2 = 4ay.$ $\frac{16}{3}a^2$.
10. $y = x^4, \quad y = 3x^2 + 4.$

11. $y = x^3, \quad y = 4x^2.$ *Ans.* $21\frac{1}{3}$.
12. $y = x(x - 1), \quad y = 2(x - 1).$
13. $y^2 = x, \quad y = x^3.$ $\frac{5}{12}$.
14. $y = x^3 - 4x, \quad y = 8(x - 2).$
15. $y = (x - 1)^3, \quad y = x^2 - x - 1.$ $\frac{4}{3}$.
16. $y = x^4 - 2x^2 - 6, \quad y = 2.$
17. $y^2 = 5a^2 - ax, \quad y^2 = 4ax.$ $\frac{40}{3}a^2$.
18. $y = x(x - 1)(x - 2), \quad x + y = 2, \quad x = 0.$
19. $x^2y = 4, \quad y = 7 - 3x.$ $\frac{1}{2}$.
20. $x^2 - 2x + 2y + 5 = 0, \quad x^2 - 2x + y + 1 = 0.$
21. Find the area bounded by the parabola $y = 5 + 2x - x^2$ and the chord joining $(-2,-3)$ and $(3,2)$. *Ans.* $20\frac{5}{6}$.
22. Find the area bounded by the parabolic arc $\sqrt{x} + \sqrt{y} = 7$ and the chord joining (9,16) and (16,9).
23. Show that the area bounded by a parabola $y^2 = 4ax$ and any right chord $x = b$ is equal to two-thirds the area of the circumscribing rectangle.
24. Show that the curve $y = x^n$ $(n > 0)$ divides the unit square $x = 0$, $x = 1$, $y = 0$, $y = 1$ in the ratio $n:1$.

In each of the following, find the area bounded by the three given curves.

25. $x + 2y = 2, \quad y - x = 1, \quad 2x + y = 7.$ *Ans.* 6.
26. $y = 9 - x^2, \quad y = 4x + 12, \quad 7x + 2y = 24.$
27. $y = x^2, \quad y = 8 - x^2, \quad y = 4x + 12.$ 64.
28. $y = x^3, \quad x - y = 6, \quad 2x + y = 0.$
29. $y^3 = x^2, \quad 2x + y + 1 = 0, \quad x - y = 4.$ 18.3.
30. $y^2 = x, \quad y = x^3, \quad x + y = 2.$

47. Volumes of Solids of Revolution

Consider the area $ABCD$ bounded by the x axis, two ordinates $x = a, x = b$, and a continuous curve $y = f(x)$. Let $ABCD$ be revolved about the x axis, thus forming a solid of revolution, one quarter of which is shown in Figure 57.

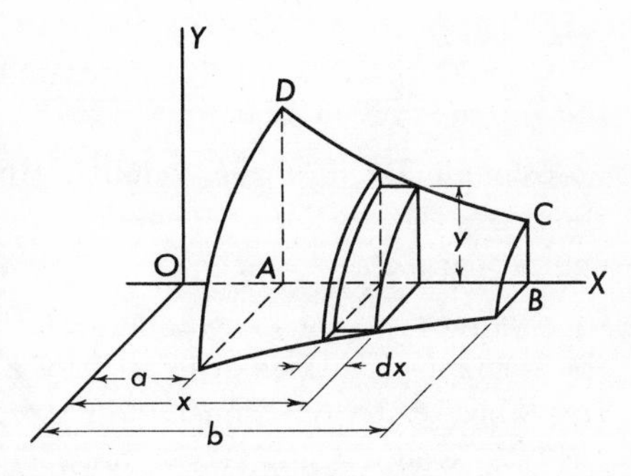

Figure 57

Let this solid be divided into n slices of equal thickness dx by planes perpendicular to the axis of revolution. Now, suppose that for each slice, a *circular disk* is constructed having a radius equal to that of the right-hand face of the slice as indicated in the figure. The volume of this disk is $\pi y^2\,dx$, and as the value of dx decreases, the volume of each disk more nearly approximates the volume of the corresponding slice.

Since the required volume is the limit, as $n \to \infty$, of the sum of the n disks which lie between $x = a$ and $x = b$, it follows by the Fundamental Theorem that

$$V = \pi \int_a^b y^2\,dx, \tag{1}$$

where the value of y in terms of x must be substituted from the equation of the given curve.

Similarly, when an area bounded by the curve $x = g(y)$ and the y axis from $y = c$ to $y = d$ is revolved about the y axis, we obtain the formula

$$V = \pi \int_c^d x^2\,dy, \tag{2}$$

where the value of x in terms of y must be substituted from the equation of the given curve.

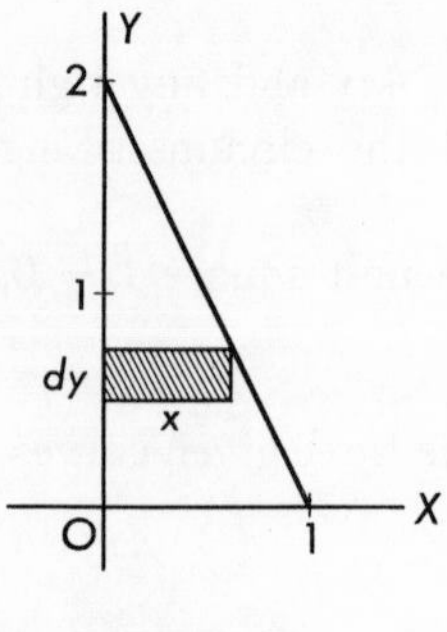

Figure 58

Example 1. Find the volume of the cone generated by revolving about the y axis the area (Figure 58) bounded by the line $2x + y = 2$ and the coordinate axes.

Solution: Drawing a horizontal element of area and using (2), we obtain

$$V = \pi \int_0^2 \left(\frac{2 - y}{2}\right)^2 dy = \frac{\pi}{4}\left[4y - 2y^2 + \frac{y^3}{3}\right]_0^2 = \frac{2\pi}{3}.$$

Observe that this result is in agreement with $V = \frac{1}{3}\pi r^2 h$, the formula for the volume of a circular cone.

Example 2. Find the volume of the solid generated by revolving about the x axis the smaller area bounded by the circle $x^2 + y^2 = 2$ and the semicubical parabola $y^3 = x^2$.

Solution: If the area as shown in Figure 59 is revolved about the x axis, the element of volume generated by a vertical element of area is a *circular ring* whose outer and inner radii are the respective ordinates of the given curves. Hence, using (1), we have

$$V = \pi \int_{-1}^1 (y_2^2 - y_1^2)\,dx = \pi \int_{-1}^1 [(2 - x^2) - (x^{4/3})]\,dx$$
$$= \pi \left[2x - \frac{1}{3}x^3 - \frac{3}{7}x^{7/3}\right]_{-1}^1 = \frac{52}{21}\pi.$$

The volume of a solid of revolution may sometimes be determined more conveniently by using a volume element in the form of a *cylindrical shell*. For example, consider the volume V of the solid formed by revolving about the y axis the area bounded by the curve $y = f(x)$ and the x axis from $x = a$ to $x = b$.

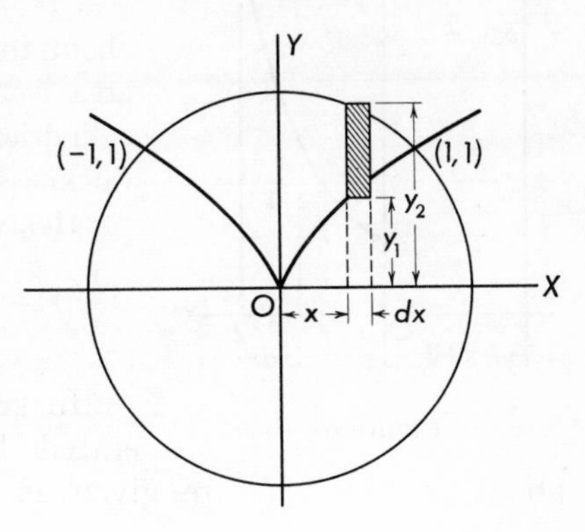

Figure 59

Let us suppose that the given area is divided into n vertical strips each of width dx. As the area is revolved, a typical strip, as shown in Figure 60, generates a thin cylindrical shell whose inner and outer radii may be taken as x and $x + dx$, respectively. Since the base of this shell is a ring bounded by two concentric circles, it has an area given by

$$\pi[(x + dx)^2 - x^2] = \pi[2x\, dx + (dx)^2] = 2\pi(x + \tfrac{1}{2}\, dx)\, dx.$$

When the function $f(x)$ is continuous, we know by the Mean-Value Theorem that the shell will have a mean height given by $y = f(x'')$ for some value x'' in the interval from x to $x + dx$. Hence the exact increment of volume is

$$\Delta V = 2\pi x' f(x'')\, dx,$$

where $x' = x + \frac{1}{2}\, dx$ and $x \leqq x'' \leqq x + dx$.

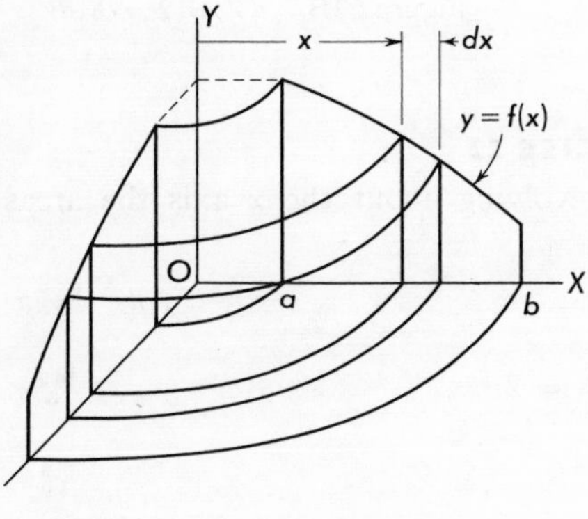

Since the required volume is the limit, as $n \to \infty$, of the sum of the n shells that lie between a and b, it follows by the theorem of Bliss that

$$V = 2\pi \int_a^b xy\, dx,$$

where $y = f(x)$.

Figure 60

Note: Observe that the volume element for a cylindrical shell is given by *circumference* $\times$ *height* $\times$ *thickness*.

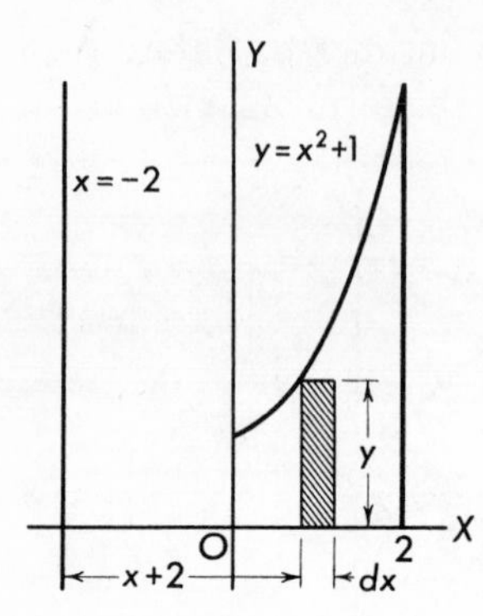

Figure 61

Illustration. Consider the solid which is formed by revolving the area between the curve $y = x^2 + 1$ and the x axis from $x = 0$ to $x = 2$ about the line $x = -2$. A vertical element of area as shown in Figure 61 will generate a cylindrical shell whose circumference, height, and thickness are respectively $2\pi(x + 2)$, y and dx. Hence

$$V = 2\pi \int_0^2 (x + 2)(x^2 + 1)\, dx = \frac{92}{3}\pi.$$

In summary, the volume elements generated by revolving a rectangular strip about an axis AB are given as shown in Figures 62A and 62B.

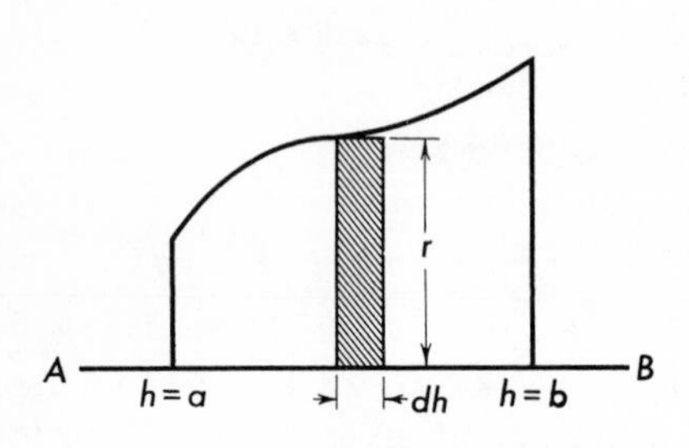

Figure 62A. $dV = \pi r^2 \cdot dh$

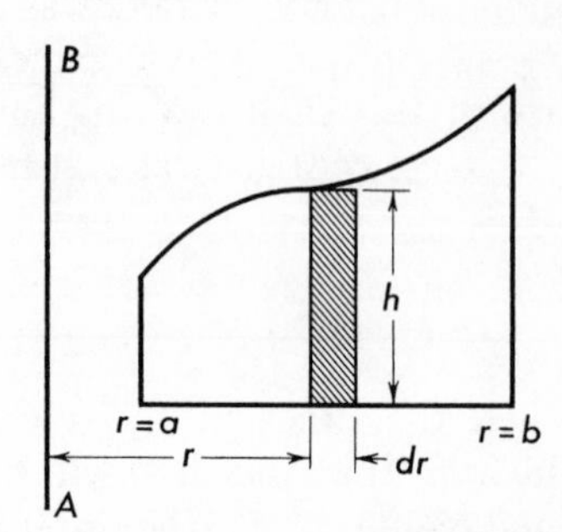

Figure 62B. $dV = 2\pi r \cdot h \cdot dr$

EXERCISE 22

Find the volume generated by revolving about the x axis the areas bounded by the following curves.

1. $y = x^3, \quad y = 0, \quad x = 2.$ *Ans.* $\frac{128}{7}\pi$.
2. $y = 6x - x^2, \quad y = 0.$
3. $y = 2x + 1, \quad y = 0, \quad x = 1, \quad x = 2.$ $\frac{49}{3}\pi$.
4. $y = x^2 - x^3, \quad y = 0.$
5. $y = x^2, \quad y = 2x.$ $\frac{64}{15}\pi$.
6. $y = x^3, \quad y^2 = x.$

Find the volume generated by revolving about the y axis the areas bounded by the following curves.

7. $y = x^3, \quad x = 0, \quad y = 8.$ *Ans.* $\frac{96}{5}\pi$.
8. $y^2 = 4x, \quad y = 4, \quad x = 0.$

9. $y = x^2, \quad y = x.$ *Ans.* $\frac{1}{6}\pi.$
10. $x = y(y + 2)^2, \quad x = 0.$
11. $y = x^2 + 4, \quad y = 2x^2.$ $8\pi.$
12. $y = 12 - x^2, \quad y = x, \quad x = 0.$ (First quadrant.)
13. Find the volume of the sphere generated by revolving the area of a circle of radius a about a diameter. *Ans.* $\frac{4}{3}\pi a^3.$
14. Find the volume generated by revolving the area bounded by the parabolic arc $\sqrt{x} + \sqrt{y} = \sqrt{a}$ and the coordinate axes about the x axis.
15. Find the volume generated by revolving the area bounded by the hypocycloid $x^{2/3} + y^{2/3} = a^{2/3}$ about the y axis. *Ans.* $\frac{32}{105}\pi a^3.$
16. Find the volume generated by revolving the area of the circle $x^2 + y^2 = 2ay$ about the y axis.
17. The equation of the curve OP in Figure 63 is $y = x^2$. Find the volume generated when the area OAP is revolved about (*a*) OX, (*b*) OY, (*c*) AP, (*d*) BP. *Ans.* (*a*) $243\pi/5$, (*b*) $81\pi/2$, (*c*) $27\pi/2$, (*d*) $567\pi/5$.
18. Solve Problem 17 when the equation of OP is $y^2 = x^3$ and the coordinates of the points are $P(4,8)$, $A(4,0)$, and $B(0,8)$.

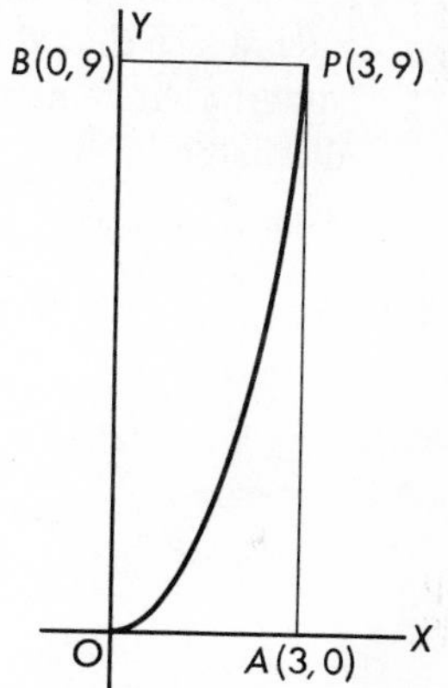

Figure 63

Find the volume of the solid generated by revolving about the indicated axis the area bounded by the given curves.

19. $y^2 = 4x, \quad x = 4;$ about $x = 4$. *Ans.* $1024\pi/15.$
20. $y = x^3, \quad x = 0, \quad y = 8;$ about $y = 8$.
21. $y = x^2, \quad y^2 = x;$ about $x = -1$. $29\pi/30.$
22. $y^2 - x = 2, \quad y = x;$ about $x = 2$.
23. $y^2 = 5 - x, \quad x = 0;$ about $x = 5$. $40\pi\sqrt{5}.$
24. $y = x^2 + 1, \quad y = 5;$ about $y = -1$.
25. $y = 1 - x^2, \quad y = 0;$ about $x = 1$. $8\pi/3.$
26. $x^3y = 1, \quad y = 0, \quad x = 1, \quad x = 2;$ about $x = 1$.
27. $y = 4x - x^2, \quad y = x;$ about $x = 3$. $27\pi/2.$
28. $y = x^2 - x, \quad y = 3 - x^2;$ about $y = 4$.

Revolve the area bounded by the given curves about the indicated axis and find the volume generated by dividing the solid into two or more parts.

29. $y = 2x, \quad y = x, \quad x + y = 6;$ about x axis. *Ans.* $14\pi.$
30. $y = 3x, \quad y = x, \quad x + y = 8;$ about y axis.
31. Outside $y = x^2$, and between $y = 2x - 1$ and $y = x + 2$; about y axis. *Ans.* $\frac{7}{2}\pi.$

32. Outside $x^2 + y^2 = 25$, and between the tangents $4x + 3y = 25$ and $4y - 3x = 25$; about x axis.
33. $2y = x + 3$, and outside $y^2 + x = 0$ and $y^2 - 4x = 0$; about $y = -1$.
Ans. $\frac{25}{6}\pi$.
34. $y + x^3 = 0, \quad y - 3x^3 = 0, \quad y = x + 2$; about $y = 3$.
35. Pentagon with vertices (1,0), (2,2), (0,4), (−2,2), (−1,0); about x axis.
Ans. $104\pi/3$.
36. If a cylindrical hole which is bored through the center of a sphere is of such a size that the length of the hole is L, show that the volume of the sphere that remains is constant and equal to the volume of a sphere of diameter L.

CHAPTER 5

Applications of Integration

48. Moment of Mass; Centroids

If a particle of mass m is located at a distance r from a fixed point, line, or plane, the product $m \times r$ is called the **moment of mass** of m with respect to the point, line, or plane.

If n particles of masses $m_1, m_2, \cdots, m_n$ are located at the points $P_1(x_1,y_1,z_1)$, $P_2(x_2,y_2,z_2)$, $\cdots$, $P_n(x_n,y_n,z_n)$, respectively, the moments of mass of this system of particles with respect to the three rectangular coordinate planes are

$$M_{yz} = \sum_{i=1}^{n} m_i x_i, \qquad M_{zx} = \sum_{i=1}^{n} m_i y_i, \qquad M_{xy} = \sum_{i=1}^{n} m_i z_i.$$

The **centroid** or **center of gravity** of this system of particles is defined as the point $C(\bar{x},\bar{y},\bar{z})$ whose coordinates are given by

$$M\bar{x} = M_{yz}, \qquad M\bar{y} = M_{zx}, \qquad M\bar{z} = M_{xy}, \tag{1}$$

where M denotes the total mass $m_1 + m_2 + \cdots + m_n$.

Note 1: It is important to observe that the position of the centroid depends only on the system of masses and not on the coordinate system which is used. For example, the centroid of two equal masses is the midpoint of the line segment joining the two masses, no matter what reference frame is used.

By direct computation the definitions (1) lead to the following conclusions.

1. *The moment of a system of masses with respect to any plane is the same as that obtained in considering the total mass to be concentrated at the centroid.*
2. *The moment of a mass with respect to any plane passing through the centroid is zero.*

Illustration. Masses of 1, 4, and 5 units, located at the points $(-1,2)$, $(1,-1)$, and $(3,1)$, respectively, have the following mass-moments with respect to the x and y axes,

$$M_y = 1(-1) + 4(1) + 5(3) = 18, \qquad M_x = 1(2) + 4(-1) + 5(1) = 3.$$

Since the total mass M is 10 units, the coordinates of the centroid are

$$\bar{x} = \frac{18}{10} = 1.8, \qquad \bar{y} = \frac{3}{10} = 0.3.$$

In accordance with the preceding discussion, the concept of a centroid for a continuous mass system can be derived as follows. Let the total mass M be subdivided into n small elements of mass which we denote as $\Delta m_1, \Delta m_2, \cdots, \Delta m_n$. When the number of such elements is large and all dimensions of each element are small, we have a discrete mass system that approximates the given mass. The limit approached by such a system as $n \to \infty$ gives the results desired. Thus the centroid $C(\bar{x},\bar{y},\bar{z})$ of a continuous mass M is *defined* by the equations

$$M\bar{x} = \int x_c\,dm, \qquad M\bar{y} = \int y_c\,dm, \qquad M\bar{z} = \int z_c\,dm,$$

where x_c, y_c, z_c are the coordinates of the centroid for the element of mass dm, and the integration extends over the whole mass.

Note 2: When a mass is *homogeneous* (has constant density throughout), the density factor in the element of mass dm may be disregarded and the centroid is determined by the geometrical nature of the mass.

49. Centroid of a Plane Area

For a plane area the general formulas of the preceding article become

$$A\bar{x} = \int x_c\,dA, \qquad A\bar{y} = \int y_c\,dA. \tag{1}$$

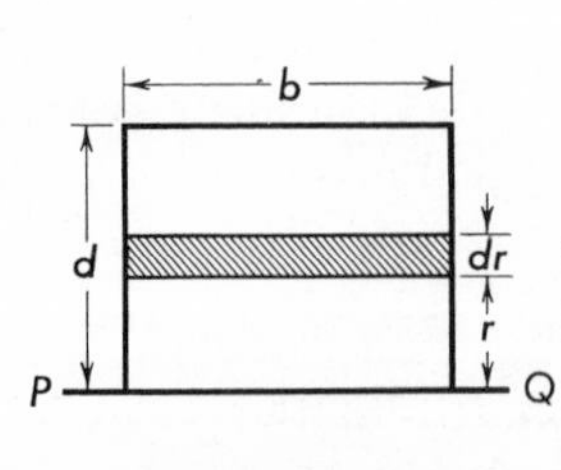

Figure 64

Illustration 1. For the axis PQ, in Figure 64, the moment of area for the rectangle, of dimensions b and d, is*

$$M_{PQ} = \int r\,dA = \int_0^d r(b\,dr) = \tfrac{1}{2}bd^2.$$

Dividing by the total area bd, we see that the centroid is located at a distance $\frac{1}{2}d$ from the axis PQ.

---

* Actually the centroid of dA is located at a distance $\bar{r}$ from PQ where $r < \bar{r} < r + dr$. In accordance with the Fundamental Theorem, however, $\int \bar{r}\,dA$ and $\int r\,dA$ give the same result.

Example 1. Find the centroid of the area bounded by the curves $y^2 = 4x$, $x = 0$, and $y = 4$.

Solution: For the rectangular element as shown in Figure 65, we have

$$dA = x\,dy, \qquad x_c = \tfrac{1}{2}x, \qquad y_c = y;$$

hence

$$A = \int_0^4 x\,dy = \int_0^4 \tfrac{1}{4}y^2\,dy = \tfrac{16}{3},$$

$$A\bar{x} = \int_0^4 \tfrac{1}{2}x(x\,dy) = \int_0^4 \tfrac{1}{32}y^4\,dy = \tfrac{32}{5},$$

$$A\bar{y} = \int_0^4 y(x\,dy) = \int_0^4 \tfrac{1}{4}y^3\,dy = 16.$$

Thus the coordinates of the centroid are

$$\bar{x} = \frac{\frac{32}{5}}{\frac{16}{3}} = \frac{6}{5}, \qquad \bar{y} = \frac{16}{\frac{16}{3}} = 3.$$

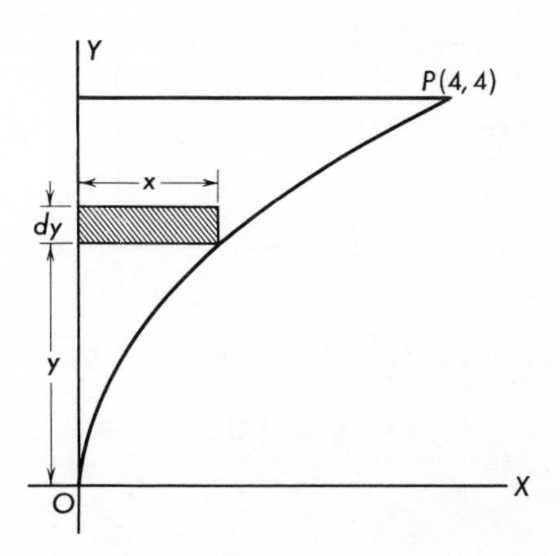

Figure 65

The following properties, whose proofs are left to the student, are often useful in the determination of centroids.

1. *The centroid must lie on any line of symmetry of a homogeneous figure.*
2. *If a homogeneous figure has a geometrical center, that point is the centroid.*
3. *If a figure A consists of several parts $A_1, A_2, \cdots,$ and the distances of their centroids from an axis s are respectively $r_1, r_2, \cdots,$ the centroid of A lies at a distance r from s given by*

$$Ar = A_1r_1 + A_2r_2 + \cdots.$$

Illustration 2. The area shown in Figure 66 consists of two squares and its centroid may be found in accordance with properties 2 and 3. Thus

$$20\bar{x} = 16(2) + 4(3); \quad \text{hence} \quad \bar{x} = 2.2,$$

$$20\bar{y} = 16(2) + 4(5); \quad \text{hence} \quad \bar{y} = 2.6.$$

Example 2. Find the centroid of the area bounded by the parabola $y = x^2$ and the line $y = 2x + 3$.

Solution: For the vertical element of area shown in Figure 67, we have

$$dA = [(2x + 3) - x^2]\,dx, \qquad x_c = x, \qquad y_c = \tfrac{1}{2}[(2x + 3) + x^2].$$

Hence

$$A = \int_{-1}^{3} (2x + 3 - x^2)\,dx = \tfrac{32}{3},$$

$$A\bar{x} = \int_{-1}^{3} x(2x + 3 - x^2)\,dx = \tfrac{32}{3},$$

$$A\bar{y} = \int_{-1}^{3} \tfrac{1}{2}(2x + 3 + x^2)(2x + 3 - x^2)\,dx = \tfrac{544}{15}.$$

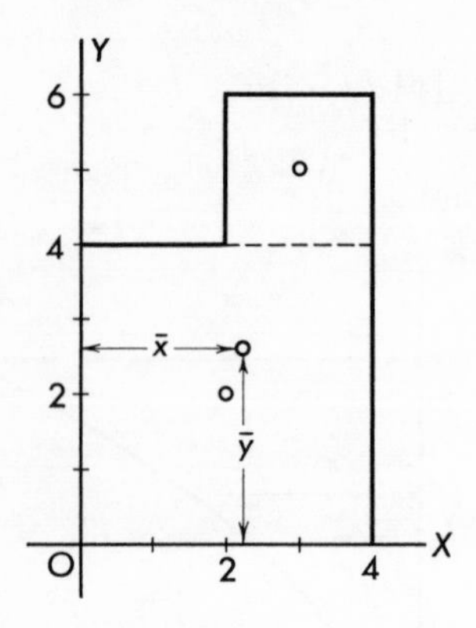

Figure 66

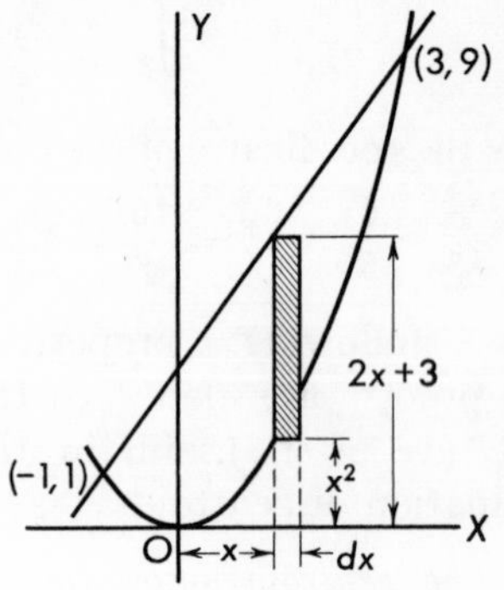

Figure 67

Thus we obtain the centroid

$$\bar{x} = \frac{\frac{32}{3}}{\frac{32}{3}} = 1, \qquad \bar{y} = \frac{\frac{544}{15}}{\frac{32}{3}} = \frac{17}{5}.$$

Note: For a rough check on the accuracy of the work, we observe by estimation that the point (1,3.4) is approximately the center of the area.

The following theorem is useful in the determination of volumes of revolution.

Second Theorem of Pappus.* *If a plane area is revolved about a coplanar axis not crossing the area, the volume generated is equal to the product of the area by the circumference of the circle described by the centroid of the area.*

Proof: For a volume as shown in Figure 57, we have

$$V = \int_a^b \pi y^2 \cdot dx \qquad \text{and} \qquad A\bar{y} = \int_a^b \tfrac{1}{2} y \cdot y\,dx;$$

---

* For the first theorem of Pappus, see page 334.

hence

$$V = 2\pi \int_a^b \tfrac{1}{2}y^2\,dx = 2\pi \cdot A\bar{y} = A \cdot 2\pi\bar{y}.$$

Illustration 3. Revolving a circle of radius a about a tangent line, we generate a solid whose volume is $V = (\pi a^2)\cdot 2\pi a = 2\pi^2 a^3$.

EXERCISE 23

Find the centroid of each of the following systems of masses.

1. Equal masses at (3,0), (2,2), (2,4), (−1,2). *Ans.* $(\frac{3}{2}, 2)$.
2. Equal masses at (1,4,3), (−1,3,5), (3,−1,1).
3. Masses of 1, 2, 3 units at (−1,3), (2,1), (3,−1), respectively. $(2, \frac{1}{3})$.
4. Masses of 2, 3, 3, 4 units at (−1,−2), (1,3), (0,5), (2,1), respectively.
5. Masses of 3, 5, 7 units at (3,−2,3), (0,1,2), (3,−2,3), respectively. *Ans.* $(2, -1, \frac{8}{3})$.
6. Masses of 2, 5, 9 units at (3,0,1), (−2,3,2), (4,1,4), respectively.
7. Show that the centroid of three equal masses lies at the intersection of the medians of the triangle formed by the masses.
8. Find in two ways the centroid of the area in Figure 68.
9. Find in two ways the centroid of the area in Figure 69. *Ans.* $(\frac{13}{11}, \frac{65}{22})$.
10. Find in two ways the centroid of the area in Figure 70.

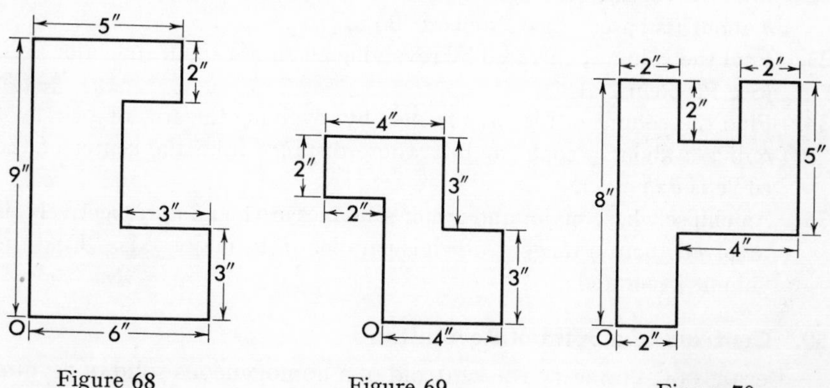

Figure 68 Figure 69 Figure 70

Find the centroid of each of the areas bounded by the following curves.

11. $2x + y = 6, \quad x = 0, \quad y = 0.$ *Ans.* (1, 2).
12. $y = x + 5, \quad y = 0, \quad x = 1, \quad x = 4.$
13. $y = 2x + 1, \quad x + y = 7, \quad x = 8.$ (6, 7).
14. $y = x^2, \quad y = 4.$
15. $y^2 = x, \quad y = x - 2.$ $(\frac{8}{5}, \frac{1}{2})$.
16. $y = x^3, \quad x = 0, \quad y = 8.$
17. $y = x^3, \quad y = 4x.$ (First quadrant.) $(\frac{16}{15}, \frac{64}{21})$.

18. $y^2 = x^3, \quad x = 4.$
19. $y^2 = x^3, \quad y = 2x.$ *Ans.* $(\frac{40}{21}, \frac{10}{3})$.
20. $y = 4 - x^2, \quad 2y = 4 - x^2.$
21. $y = x^2, \quad y = x^3.$ $(\frac{3}{5}, \frac{12}{35})$.
22. $y = 1 - x^2, \quad y = 2 + 2x, \quad y = 2 - 2x.$
23. $y = x^2 - 4, \quad y = 2x - x^2.$ $(\frac{1}{2}, -\frac{3}{2})$.
24. $y^3 = x^2, \quad x - y = 2, \quad x + y = 2, \quad x = 0.$
25. $y + x^2 = 0, \quad y + 2 = x, \quad y + 2 = -x, \quad y = 2.$ $(0, \frac{192}{205})$.
26. $y^2 = 4ax, \quad x^2 = 4by.$
27. $\sqrt{x} + \sqrt{y} = \sqrt{a}, \quad x = 0, \quad y = 0.$ $(\frac{1}{5}a, \frac{1}{5}a)$.
28. The first-quadrant area of the circle $x^2 + y^2 = a^2$. *Hint:* Assume the known fact that $A = \frac{1}{4}\pi a^2$.
29. The first-quadrant area of the ellipse $b^2x^2 + a^2y^2 = a^2b^2$. *Hint:* Assume the known fact that $A = \frac{1}{4}\pi ab$. *Ans.* $\left(\frac{4a}{3\pi}, \frac{4b}{3\pi}\right)$.
30. Prove that the centroid for the area of any triangle is at the point of intersection of the medians.

Solve the following problems using the theorem of Pappus.

31. Find the volume generated by revolving a rectangle of sides a and b about the side a. *Ans.* πab^2.
32. Find the volume generated by revolving a triangle of base b and altitude h about its base. (See Problem 30.)
33. Find the volume generated by revolving an ellipse about its major axis. (See Problem 29.) *Ans.* $\frac{4}{3}\pi ab^2$.
34. Find the volume of the *torus* formed by revolving the area of a circle of radius a about a coplanar line whose distance from the center of the circle is b $(b > a)$.
35. An ellipse whose major and minor semiaxes are a and b, respectively, is revolved about a tangent which is parallel to the major axis. Find the volume generated. *Ans.* $2\pi^2ab^2$.

50. Centroid of a Solid of Revolution

Because of symmetry the centroid of a homogeneous solid of revolution lies on its axis. Hence only one coordinate is needed to determine its exact position. If the x axis is taken as the axis of revolution, the general formulas of Article **48** reduce to

$$V\bar{x} = \int x_c \, dv, \tag{1}$$

where dv is any element of volume, usually a disk, ring, or shell, and x_c is the x coordinate of the centroid for the element selected.

Example 1. Find the centroid of the solid formed by revolving about the y axis the first-quadrant area bounded by the parabola $y^2 = 4ax$ and the lines $y = 0$ and $x = a$.

First Solution: Selecting a vertical strip as indicated in Figure 71, we obtain as the element of volume a circular shell whose volume dv is $2\pi x \cdot y \cdot dx$ and whose centroidal coordinate y_c is $\frac{1}{2}y$. Hence

$$V = \int dv = \int_0^a (2\pi xy\, dx) = 2\pi \int_0^a 2a^{1/2}x^{3/2}\, dx = \tfrac{8}{5}\pi a^3,$$

$$V\bar{y} = \int y_c\, dv = \int_0^a \tfrac{1}{2}y(2\pi xy\, dx) = \pi \int_0^a 4ax^2\, dx = \tfrac{4}{3}\pi a^4.$$

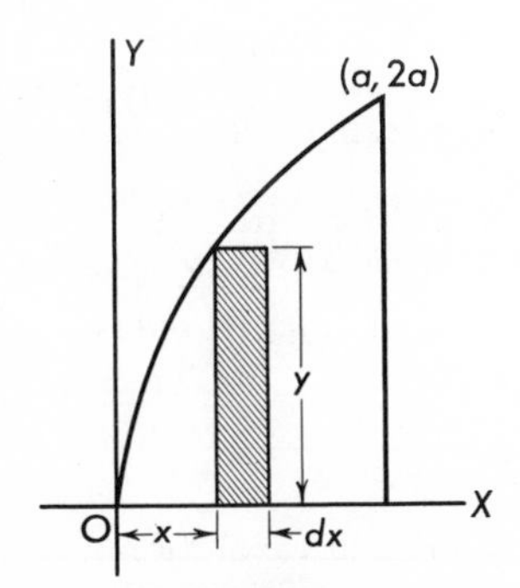

Figure 71

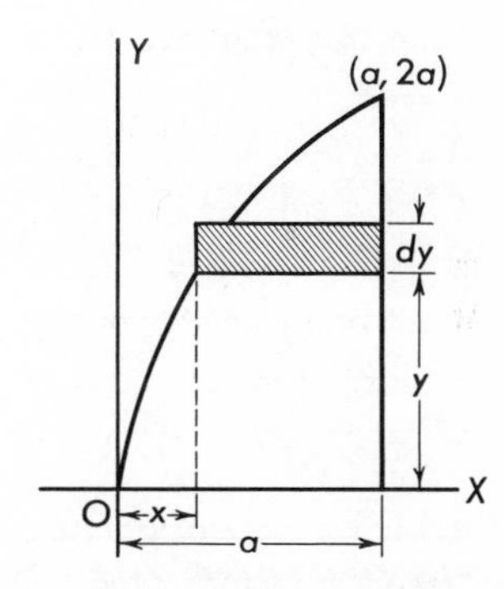

Figure 72

Thus the centroid is on the y axis and such that

$$\bar{y} = \frac{\frac{4}{3}\pi a^4}{\frac{8}{5}\pi a^3} = \frac{5}{6}\, a.$$

Second Solution: Selecting a horizontal strip as indicated in Figure 72, we get as the element of volume a circular ring whose volume dv is $\pi(a^2 - x^2)\, dy$ and whose centroidal coordinate y_c is y. Hence, in computing V and $V\bar{y}$,

$$V = \pi \int_0^{2a} (a^2 - x^2)\, dy = \pi \int_0^{2a} \left(a^2 - \frac{y^4}{16a^2}\right) dy = \frac{8}{5}\,\pi a^3,$$

$$V\bar{y} = \int_0^{2a} y[\pi(a^2 - x^2)\, dy] = \pi \int_0^{2a} \left(a^2 y - \frac{y^5}{16a^2}\right) dy = \frac{4}{3}\,\pi a^4,$$

we obtain the same result as before.

EXERCISE 24

Find the centroid of the solid generated by revolving about the indicated axis the area bounded by the given curves.

1. $2x + y = 2, \quad x = 0, \quad y = 0$; about $x = 0$. *Ans.* $\bar{y} = \frac{1}{2}$.
2. $y^2 = 4x, \quad x = 1, \quad y = 0$; about $y = 0$.
3. $y = 4x - x^2, \quad y = 0$; about $x = 0$. $\bar{y} = \frac{8}{5}$.
4. $y = x^2, \quad y = 2x + 3$; about $y = 0$.
5. $y^3 = x^2, \quad y = 4$; about $x = 0$. $\bar{y} = \frac{16}{5}$.
6. $y = x^3, \quad x + y = 2, \quad y = 0$; about $y = 0$.
7. $x^4y = 1, \quad y = 1, \quad y = 4$; about $x = 0$. $\bar{y} = \frac{7}{3}$.
8. First-quadrant arc of $x^2 + y^2 = a^2, \quad x = 0, \quad y = 0$; about $y = 0$.
9. $y^2 = 4ax, \quad y = mx$; about $x = 0$. *Ans.* $\bar{y} = 5a/2m$.
10. First-quadrant arc of $y = 4 - x^2, \quad x = 0, \quad y = 0$; about $x = -2$.
11. $y = x^3, \quad x = 2, \quad y = 0$; about $x = 2$. *Ans.* $(2, \frac{10}{7})$.
12. $y = x^2, \quad y = x + 2$; about $y = 4$.
13. First-quadrant arc of $x^2 + y^2 = a^2$, fourth-quadrant arc of $2x - y = 2a$, $x = 0$; about $x = 0$. *Ans.* $\bar{y} = -a/16$.
14. First-quadrant arc of $y = 3 + 2x - x^2, \quad x = 0, \quad y = 0$; about $x = 0$.
15. $y = x, \quad y = 2x, \quad x + y = 6$; about $x = 0$. *Ans.* $\bar{y} = \frac{13}{5}$.
16. $y^2 = x, \quad 2y = x, \quad y = x$; about $y = 0$.

Find the center of gravity of the following solids of revolution when the densities vary as indicated. For an element of mass use $\rho\, dv$ where ρ represents the density factor.

17. Cone of Problem 1 when $\rho = ky$. *Ans.* $\bar{y} = \frac{4}{5}$.
18. Solid of Problem 2 when $\rho = k(1 - x)$.
19. Solid of Problem 5 when $\rho = kx$. $\bar{y} = \frac{44}{13}$.
20. Hemisphere of Problem 8 when $\rho = k(a - x)$.

51. Moment of Inertia; Radius of Gyration

If a particle of mass m is located at a distance r from a fixed line, or *axis*, the product $m \times r^2$ is called the second moment, or **moment of inertia,** of m with respect to the axis.

If n particles of masses $m_1, m_2, \cdots, m_n$ are located respectively at distances $r_1, r_2, \cdots, r_n$ from a fixed axis, the moment of inertia of this system of particles with respect to the axis is

$$I = \sum_{i=1}^{n} m_i r_i^2. \tag{1}$$

If M denotes the total mass of the system, the positive number k defined by

$$I = Mk^2 \qquad \text{or} \qquad k = \sqrt{\frac{I}{M}}$$

is called the **radius of gyration** of M with respect to the axis.

Illustration. If masses of 2 and 3 units are located at the points $(1,2,-1)$ and $(0,3,5)$, respectively, their moments of inertia with respect to the z axis are computed from the relation $I_z = mr^2 = m(x^2 + y^2)$; thus

$$I_z = 2(1 + 4) + 3(0 + 9) = 37.$$

Since the total mass is 5 units, the radius of gyration with respect to the z axis is

$$k_z = \sqrt{\frac{I}{M}} = \sqrt{\frac{37}{5}} = 2.72.$$

When a continuous mass M is divided into n small elements $\Delta m_1, \Delta m_2, \cdots, \Delta m_n$, its moment of inertia is given approximately by $\sum_{k=1}^{n} r_k^2 \, \Delta m_k$, where r_k is the radius of gyration of Δm_k. The limit approached by this sum as $n \to \infty$ and every dimension of $\Delta m_k \to 0$ gives the desired result. Hence we *define* the moment of inertia of a continuous mass M by the relation

$$I = \int r^2 \, dm,$$

where r is the radius of gyration for the element of mass dm, and the integration extends over the whole mass.

Note: If the density factor in a mass is uniform and equal to 1, we refer to I as the moment of inertia of a volume, an area, etc., depending on the geometrical nature of the element.

As an immediate consequence of the definition, we have the following result.

Theorem. *If a mass is divided in any way into two or more parts, the moment of inertia of the whole mass with respect to an axis is equal to the sum of the moments of inertia of its parts.*

52. Moment of Inertia of an Area

For a plane area the general formula of the preceding article becomes

$$I = \int r^2 \, dA,$$

where r is the radius of gyration for the element of area dA.

Illustration 1. For the axis PQ the moment of inertia of the rectangle shown in Figure 64 (page 116) is

$$I_{PQ} = \int r^2 \, dA = \int_0^d r^2(b \, dr) = \tfrac{1}{3}bd^3.$$

The preceding illustration leads to the following conclusions which we summarize for future reference.

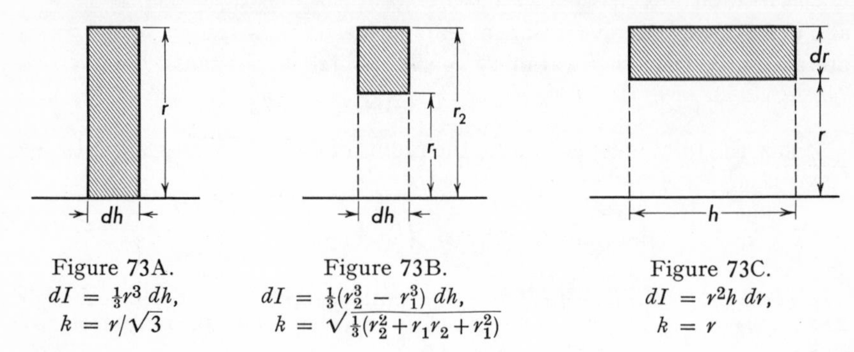

Figure 73A. $dI = \frac{1}{3}r^3 \, dh$, $k = r/\sqrt{3}$

Figure 73B. $dI = \frac{1}{3}(r_2^3 - r_1^3) \, dh$, $k = \sqrt{\frac{1}{3}(r_2^2 + r_1 r_2 + r_1^2)}$

Figure 73C. $dI = r^2 h \, dr$, $k = r$

Example. Find the moment of inertia of the first-quadrant area bounded by the curves $y^2 = 4ax$ and $x = a$ with respect to the y axis.

First Solution: Selecting a vertical strip as shown in Figure 74 and comparing with the preceding summary, we have $r = x$, $h = y$, and $dr = dx$; hence

$$I_y = \int_0^a x^2 y \, dx = 2a^{1/2} \int_0^a x^{5/2} \, dx = \frac{4}{7} a^4.$$

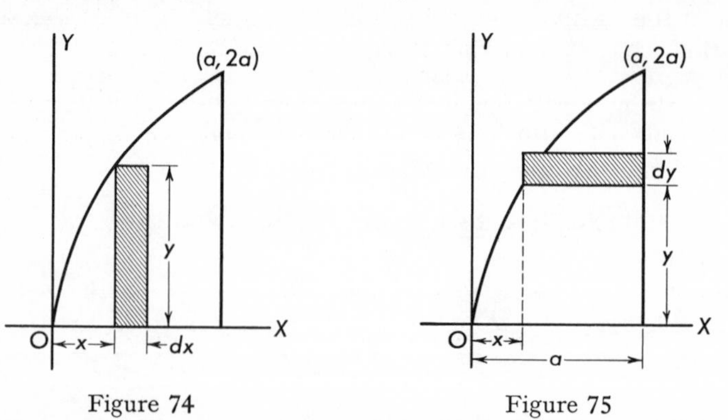

Figure 74

Figure 75

Second Solution: Selecting a horizontal strip as shown in Figure 75 and comparing with the preceding summary, we have $r_2 = a$, $r_1 = x$, and $dh = dy$; hence

$$I_y = \int_0^{2a} \frac{1}{3}(a^3 - x^3) \, dy = \frac{1}{3} \int_0^{2a} \left(a^3 - \frac{y^6}{64a^3}\right) dy = \frac{4}{7} a^4.$$

If the moment of inertia of an area with respect to a coplanar axis is known, the moment of inertia of the area with respect to a parallel coplanar axis can be found without integration by use of the following theorem.

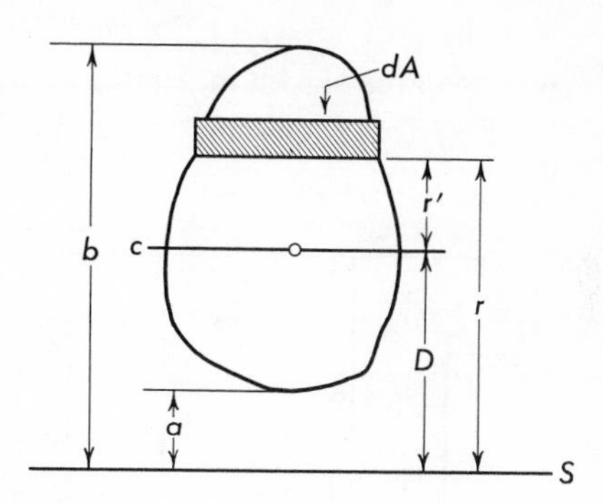

Figure 76

Theorem. *The moment of inertia of an area with respect to any coplanar line equals the moment of inertia of the area with respect to the parallel centroidal line plus the area times the square of the distance between the lines; symbolically,*

$$\boldsymbol{I_s = I_c + AD^2}.$$

Proof: For the element of area shown in Figure 76, we have $dI_s = r^2\,dA$. Since $r = r' + D$, it follows that

$$I_s = \int_{r=a}^{r=b} (r' + D)^2\,dA$$

$$= \int r'^2\,dA + 2D\int r'\,dA + D^2\int dA$$

$$= I_c + 0 + D^2A.$$

The second integral in the right-hand member of the equation above is zero, since $\int r'dA = \bar{r}'A$ and for the centroidal axis $\bar{r}' = 0$.

Illustration 2. Since by Illustration 1 the moment of inertia of a rectangle about its base is $\frac{1}{3}bd^3$, it follows by the theorem above that the moment of inertia of a rectangle about a line through its center and parallel to the base is

$$I_c = I_s - AD^2 = \tfrac{1}{3}bd^3 - (bd)(\tfrac{1}{2}d)^2 = \tfrac{1}{12}bd^3.$$

EXERCISE 25

In each of the following, find the moment of inertia and the radius of gyration with respect to each coordinate axis.

1. Unit masses at (2,0), (−1,3), (4,2), (3,1).
   Ans. $I_x = 14$, $k_x = 1.9$; $I_y = 30$, $k_y = 2.7$.
2. Masses of 1, 2, 4 units at (−1,2), (3,−2), (4,3), respectively.
3. Masses of 2, 4, 5 units at (1,0,0), (2,1,−1), (3,2,4), respectively.
   Ans. $I_x = 108$, $k_x = 3.1$; $I_y = 147$, $k_y = 3.7$; $I_z = 87$, $k_z = 2.8$.
4. Masses of 3, 5, 6 units at (2,1,−1), (0,2,0), (−1,3,2), respectively.

For each of the following areas, find the moment of inertia and the radius of gyration with respect to the axis s.

5. The area shown in Figure 77. *Ans.* $I = 245\frac{1}{3}$, $k = 3.92$.
6. The area shown in Figure 78.
7. The area shown in Figure 79. $I = 306\frac{2}{3}$, $k = 3.43$.

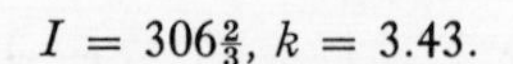

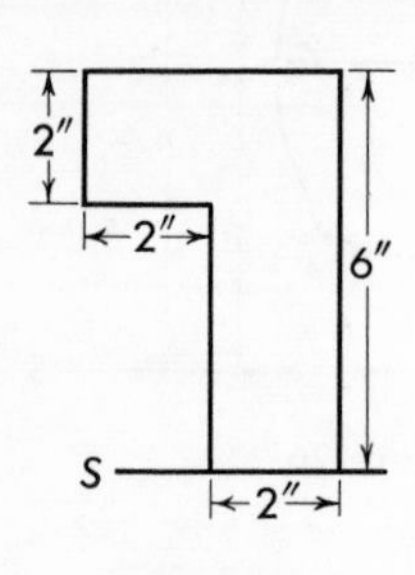

Figure 77

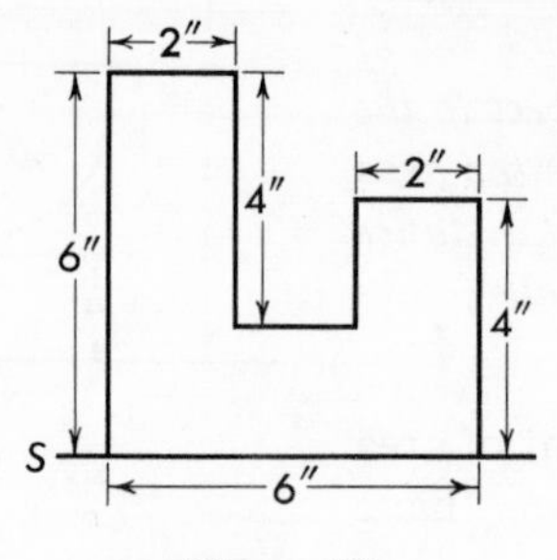

Figure 78

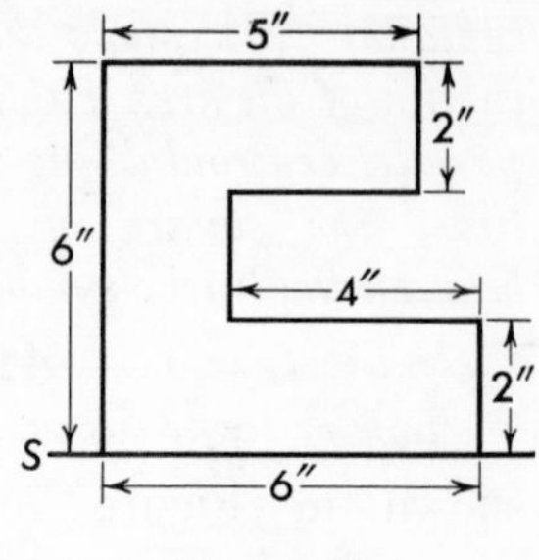

Figure 79

In each of the following, find the moment of inertia of the area bounded by the given curves with respect to the axis indicated.

8. $3x + 2y = 6, \quad x = 0, \quad y = 0;$ axis OY.
9. $y = x, \quad x = 0, \quad y = 1;$ axis OX. *Ans.* $\frac{1}{4}$.
10. $y = 2x, \quad x = 0, \quad y = 2, \quad y = 6;$ axis OX.
11. $x + y = 3, \quad x = 0, \quad y = 0;$ axis $x = 3$. $\frac{81}{4}$.
12. $y = x^2, \quad y = 1;$ axis OX.
13. $y^2 = x + 4, \quad x = 0;$ axis OY. $\frac{4096}{105}$.
14. $y = ax^2, \quad y = ax;$ axis OX.
15. $y = 3x - x^2, \quad y = x;$ axis OX. $\frac{104}{35}$.
16. $y = x^3, \quad x = 0, \quad y = 8;$ axis OX.
17. $y = x^3, \quad x = 2, \quad y = 0;$ axis $x = 2$. $\frac{16}{15}$.
18. $y^3 = x^2, \quad y = 1;$ axis $y = 1$.
19. $y = x^2, \quad y = x^3;$ axis OY. $\frac{1}{30}$.
20. $2y = x^2 + 4, \quad y = x^2;$ axis OX.
21. $y^2 = ax, \quad x^2 = ay;$ axis OX. $\frac{3}{35}a^4$.
22. $y^3 = x^2, \quad y = 2 - x^2;$ axis OY.
23. Show that the moment of inertia of a triangle of base b and altitude h with respect to its base is $\frac{1}{12}bh^3$.
24. Show that the moment of inertia of a rectangle of dimensions b and d with respect to a diagonal is $b^3d^3/6(b^2 + d^2)$.
25. Show that the moment of inertia of a straight rod or wire of length l with respect to a perpendicular axis through one end is $\frac{1}{3}Ml^2$.

26. If the moment of inertia of a triangle with respect to its base is $\frac{1}{12}bh^3$, find its moment of inertia with respect to a line through the centroid parallel to the base.
27. If the moment of inertia of a circle with respect to a diameter is $\frac{1}{4}\pi r^4$, find its moment of inertia with respect to a tangent. *Ans.* $\frac{5}{4}\pi r^4$.
28. Using the answer to Problem 9, find the moment of inertia of the given area with respect to the axis $y = 1$.
29. Using the answer to Problem 11, find the moment of inertia of the given area with respect to the y axis. *Ans.* $\frac{27}{4}$.
30. Using the answer to Problem 21, find the moment of inertia of the given area with respect to the centroidal axis $y = \frac{9}{20}a$.

In each of the following, find the moment of inertia of the area bounded by the given curves with respect to the axis indicated.

31. $y = x,\quad y = 2x,\quad x + y = 12;\quad$ axis OY. *Ans.* 152.
32. $y = x,\quad x + y = 8,\quad 5x + y = 12;\quad$ axis OX.
33. $y = 2x^3,\quad y + x^3 = 0,\quad 2y = x + 3;\quad$ axis OX. $\frac{11}{5}$.
34. $y^3 = x^2,\quad y = 2x + 3,\quad x + y = 12;\quad$ axis OX.
35. $y = x^2,\quad y = 2x - 1,\quad 4x + y = -4;\quad$ axis $x = 1$. $\frac{891}{160}$.

53. Moment of Inertia of a Solid of Revolution

For a homogeneous solid of constant unit density, the general formula of Article **51** becomes

$$\boldsymbol{I} = \int \boldsymbol{r}^2\, \boldsymbol{dv}, \tag{1}$$

where r is the radius of gyration for the element of volume dv.

Illustration. Consider the right circular cylinder, one-fourth of which is shown in Figure 80. If the cylinder is divided into elements of volume in the form of cylindrical shells, by (1) the moment of inertia of the cylinder with respect to its axis is

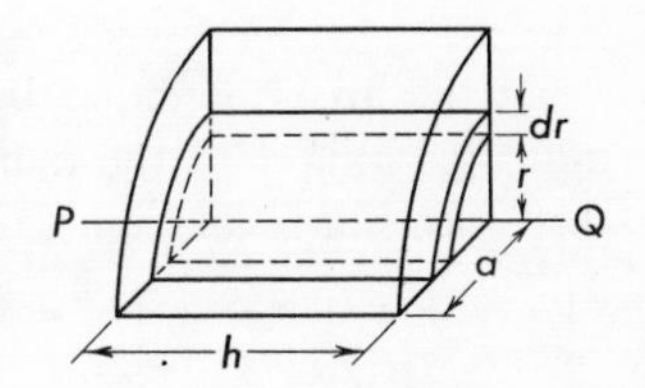

$$I_{PQ} = \int r^2\, dv = \int_0^a r^2 \cdot 2\pi rh\, dr = \tfrac{1}{2}\pi a^4 h = \tfrac{1}{2}Va^2.$$

Figure 80

Thus *the moment of inertia of a right circular cylinder with respect to its axis is one-half the volume times the square of the radius.*

The preceding illustration leads to the following conclusions which we summarize for future reference.

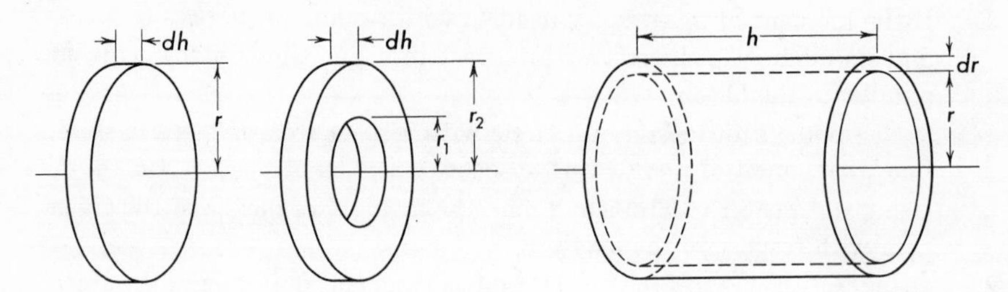

Figure 81A. Disk
$dI = \frac{1}{2}\pi r^4 dh,$
$k = r/\sqrt{2}$

Figure 81B. Ring
$dI = \frac{1}{2}\pi(r_2^4 - r_1^4)\,dh,$
$k = \sqrt{\frac{1}{2}(r_2^2 + r_1^2)}$

Figure 81C. Shell
$dI = 2\pi r^3 h\,dr,$
$k = r$

Example. If the first-quadrant area bounded by the parabola $y^2 = 4ax$ and the line $x = a$ is revolved about the x axis, find the moment of inertia of the solid formed with respect to the axis of revolution.

First Solution: Selecting a vertical strip (Figure 74) which generates an element of volume in the form of a disk, we see on comparison with the preceding summary that $r = y$ and $dh = dx$; hence

$$I_x = \tfrac{1}{2}\pi \int_0^a y^4\,dx = \tfrac{1}{2}\pi \int_0^a 16a^2x^2\,dx = \tfrac{8}{3}\pi a^5.$$

Second Solution: Selecting a horizontal strip (Figure 75) which generates an element of volume in the form of a shell, we see on comparison with the preceding summary that $r = y$, $h = a - x$, and $dr = dy$; hence

$$I_x = 2\pi \int_0^{2a} y^3(a - x)\,dy = 2\pi \int_0^{2a} y^3\left(a - \frac{y^2}{4a}\right) dy = \tfrac{8}{3}\pi a^5.$$

EXERCISE 26

If the areas bounded by the following curves are revolved about the indicated axis, find the moment of inertia of the solid formed with respect to the axis of revolution.

1. $y = x, \quad x = 2, \quad y = 0;$ about $y = 0$. *Ans.* $\frac{16}{5}\pi$.
2. $2x + y = 4, \quad x = 0, \quad y = 0;$ about $x = 0$.
3. $y = x + 1, \quad x = 1, \quad x = 2, \quad y = 0;$ about $y = 0$. $\frac{211}{10}\pi$.
4. $x + 2y = 8, \quad x = 2, \quad y = 2;$ about $y = 0$.
5. $y = x^2, \quad x = 2, \quad y = 0;$ about $y = 0$. $\frac{256}{9}\pi$.
6. $y = x^2, \quad x = 2, \quad y = 0;$ about $x = 0$.
7. $y = x - x^2, \quad y = 0;$ about $y = 0$. $\pi/1260$.
8. $y^2 = 4ax, \quad x = a;$ about $x = 0$.
9. $y = x^3, \quad x = 1, \quad x = 2, \quad y = 0;$ about $x = 0$. $\frac{254}{7}\pi$.

10. $xy = 1, \quad x = 1, \quad x = 4, \quad y = 0;$ about $x = 0$.
11. $y = x^3, \quad x = 1, \quad y = 0;$ about $x = -1$. *Ans.* $\frac{209}{70}\pi$.
12. $y^3 = x^2, \quad y = 1;$ about $x = 0$.
13. $x^{1/2} + y^{1/2} = a^{1/2}, \quad x = 0, \quad y = 0;$ about $y = 0$. $\pi a^5/90$.
14. $x^{2/3} + y^{2/3} = a^{2/3};$ about $x = 0$.

Find the moment of inertia of each of the following homogeneous solids of revolution with respect to its axis. Express the result as a multiple of its mass.

15. A right circular cone. *Ans.* $\frac{3}{10}Ma^2$.
16. A frustum of a right circular cone.
17. A sphere. $\frac{2}{5}Ma^2$.
18. A prolate spheroid. (Ellipse revolved about its major axis.)
19. An oblate spheroid. (Ellipse revolved about its minor axis.) $\frac{2}{5}Ma^2$.
20. A paraboloid of revolution.

54. Fluid Pressure

In hydrostatics it is shown that the pressure p (force per unit area) at a point h units below the surface of a fluid is given by

$$p = wh, \tag{1}$$

where w, the specific weight, is the weight of a unit volume of the fluid.

Illustration 1. Water weighs 62.4 pounds per cubic foot; hence the water pressure at a depth of 10 feet is 62.4×10 or 624 pounds per square foot.

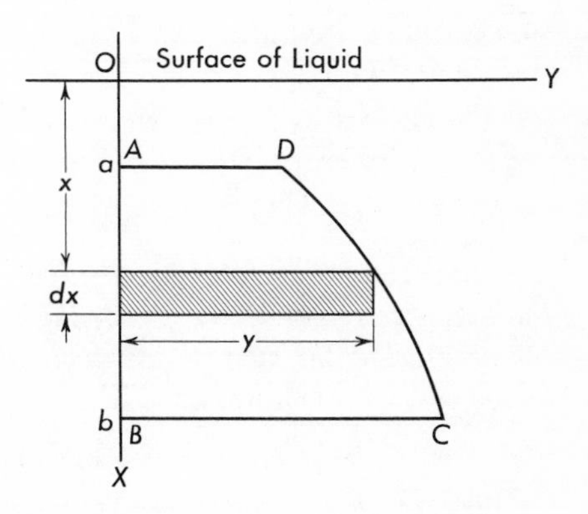

Figure 82

In accordance with (1), if a horizontal area A is located at a uniform depth of h, the force exerted by the fluid on one side of the area is

$$F = whA.$$

To determine the force exerted by a fluid on a vertical plane area, such as $ABCD$ in Figure 82, we proceed as follows. Draw the axes as shown in the figure with the y axis lying in the surface of the fluid and the positive x axis downward. Divide AB into n intervals, each of width dx, and construct horizontal rectangular elements within the area.

Since the pressure at the top of an element of area is wx, the force exerted by the fluid on the rectangle is approximately $wx\,dA$. Thus, in accordance with the Fundamental Theorem, an **element of force** may be taken as

$$dF = wx\,dA = wxy\,dx.$$

Since the total force F is the limit of the sum of the force-elements as $n \to \infty$, it follows by the Fundamental Theorem that

$$\mathbf{F = w \int_a^b xy\,dx.} \tag{2}$$

Example 1. The vertical end of a water trough is an isosceles triangle with a width of 6 feet and depth of 3 feet. Find the force on one end when the trough is filled with water.

Solution: The equation of the line AB in Figure 83 is $x + y = 3$. Hence, substituting $w = 62.4$, $y = 3 - x$, $a = 0$, and $b = 3$ in (2), we obtain

$$\tfrac{1}{2}F = 62.4 \int_0^3 x(3 - x)\,dx = 281.$$

Thus the required force is 2×281 or 562 pounds.

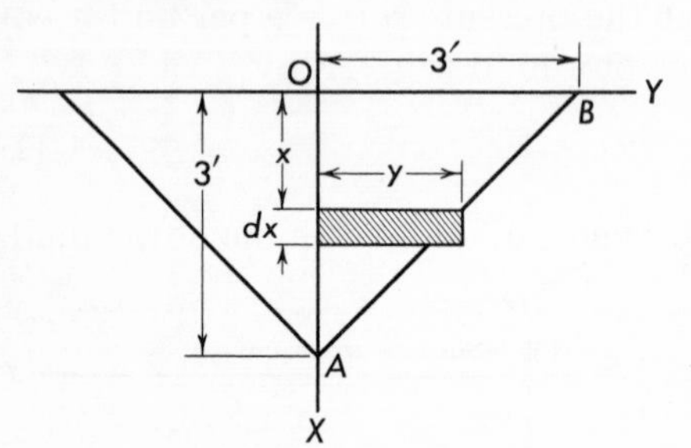

Figure 83

Since the depth x in the integral (2) may be considered as a moment arm for the area $y\,dx$, we have the following result.

Theorem. *The force on a submerged plane area equals the product of the specific weight of the fluid, the area, and the depth of the centroid of the area below the surface; symbolically,*

$$\mathbf{F = wA\bar{x}.} \tag{3}$$

Illustration 2. For the example above, we have $w = 62.4$, $A = 9$, and $\bar{x} = 1$. Hence the total force is $(62.4)(9)(1)$ or 562 pounds.

Occasionally the work is simpler if the system of axes is chosen in some other way than that suggested above. In all cases, however, the force is to be computed from the relation

$$\textit{Force} = \textit{Specific weight} \times \textit{Depth} \times \textit{Area}. \tag{4}$$

Example 2. The cross section of a trough is a parabolic segment 8 feet wide and 4 feet deep. If the trough is filled with a liquid weighing 45 pounds per cubic foot, find the total force on one end.

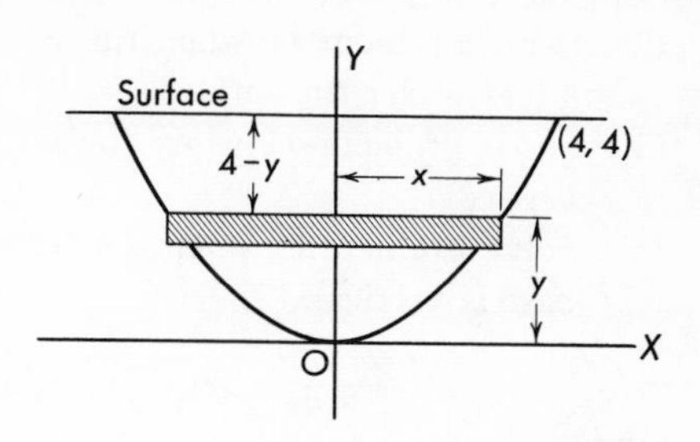

Figure 84

Solution: Choosing axes as shown in Figure 84, the equation of the parabola is $x^2 = 4y$. Then, in accordance with (4), we have the element of force.

$$dF = 45 \times (4 - y) \times 2x\, dy.$$

Hence the total force on one end is

$$F = 90 \int_0^4 x(4 - y)\, dy = 180 \int_0^4 (4y^{1/2} - y^{3/2})\, dy = 1536 \text{ pounds.}$$

EXERCISE 27

In each of Problems 1–10, the given surfaces are submerged vertically in a fluid of specific weight w. Find the force on one side of the surface by integration and check the result using equation (3). Express answers in terms of w.

1. A rectangle 10 feet wide and 8 feet deep with the upper edge lying in the surface. *Ans.* 320 w.
2. Solve Problem 1, if the upper edge is 6 feet below the surface.
3. An equilateral triangle of sides 4 feet with one edge lying in the surface. *Ans.* 8 w.
4. Solve Problem 3, if one vertex lies in the surface and the opposite side is horizontal.
5. An isosceles right triangle with legs 6 feet long and one leg lying in the surface. *Ans.* 36 w.
6. Solve Problem 5, if one vertex lies in the surface and the opposite leg is horizontal.
7. An isosceles trapezoid of height 4 feet and bases 6 feet and 12 feet with the smaller base lying in the surface. *Ans.* 80 w.
8. Solve Problem 7, if the larger base lies in the surface.
9. A triangle of base 6 feet and altitude 3 feet with the vertex and base lying respectively 2 feet and 5 feet below the surface. *Ans.* 36 w.
10. A square of sides 2 feet with one diagonal horizontal and lying 2 feet below the surface.
11. Find the force on one side of a plane parabolic segment of base 8 feet and altitude 4 feet when the segment is submerged vertically in water

with its base horizontal, and the base and vertex are respectively 4 feet and 8 feet under the surface. *Ans.* 7450 lb.

12. Solve Problem 11 when the vertex lies in the surface and the base is 4 feet under the surface.
13. Solve Problem 11 when the vertex lies in the surface and the base is vertical. *Ans.* 998 lb.
14. Solve Problem 11 when the vertex lies 2 feet under the surface and the base is vertical.

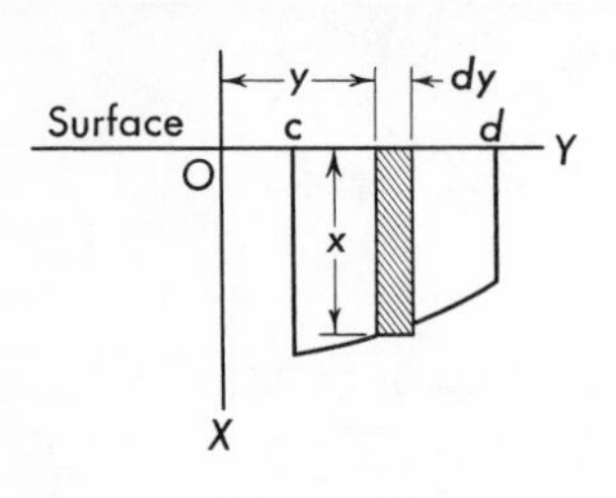

Figure 85

15. Solve Problem 11 when the vertex lies 4 feet under the surface and the base is vertical. *Ans.* 5320 lb.
16. Solve Problem 7 using centroids when one of the equal sides lies in the surface.
17. A vertical cylindrical tank of diameter 20 feet and height 30 feet, is full of water. Find the total force normal to the curved surface. *Ans.* 882 tons.
18. Show that for an area submerged as in Figure 85 the force is

$$F = \tfrac{1}{2}w \int_c^d x^2\,dy.$$

19. Using the result of Problem 18, find the force on a face of a vertical semicircle of radius a whose base diameter lies in the surface. *Ans.* $\frac{2}{3}wa^3$.
20. Using the result of Problem 18, find the force on a face of a vertical semielliptical segment of base 10 feet and depth 3 feet when the base is in the surface of oil weighing 60 pounds per cubic foot.

55. Work

If the application of a constant force F to a body results in a displacement s in the line of action of the force F, the force is said to do **work** on the body amounting in magnitude to the product Fs.

Illustration 1. The work required to raise a 50-pound weight to a height of 4 feet is 50×4 or 200 foot-pounds.

Let us now consider the work done by a variable force acting in the direction of and along a straight line segment. We assume that the magnitude of the force is a continuous function $F(x)$ of its position x on the line.

In order to determine the work done by the force as the point of application moves from $x = a$ to $x = b$, we divide the interval into n

increments each of length dx. Since the force changes but little in the interval from x to $x + dx$, we conclude from the definition that the work done is approximately $F(x)\,dx$. Thus, in accordance with the Fundamental Theorem, an **element of work** dW may be taken as

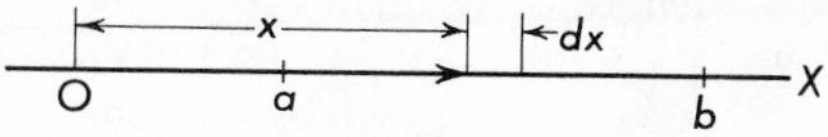

$$dW = F(x)\,dx.$$

Figure 86

The total work done by the variable force from $x = a$ to $x = b$ is the limit, as $n \to \infty$, of the sum of the elements of work. Hence it follows by the Fundamental Theorem that

$$\boldsymbol{W = \int_a^b F(x)\,dx.}$$

Illustration 2. Hooke's law states that within the limits of elasticity the displacement produced in a body is proportional to the force applied, that is, $F = kx$, where the constant k is called the *modulus*. Thus if the modulus of a spring is 20 pounds per inch, the work required to stretch or compress the spring a distance of 6 inches is

$$W = \int_0^6 20x \cdot dx = 360 \text{ in-lb.} = 30 \text{ ft-lb.}$$

Example. A hemispherical tank of radius 10 feet is full of water. Find the work done in pumping the water to the top of the tank.

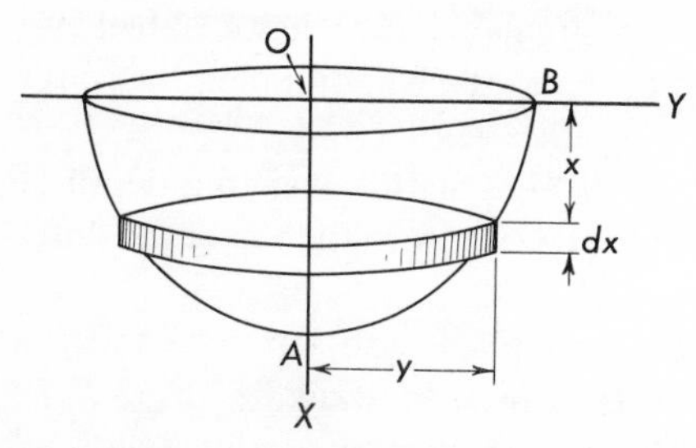

Figure 87

Solution: If the water in the tank is divided into elementary disks as indicated in Figure 87, it follows from the relation $W = Fs$ that the element of work needed to raise a disk of water to the top of the tank is

$$dW = 62.4 \times \pi y^2\,dx \times x.$$

Hence the total work done in pumping all the water to the top of the tank is

$$W = 62.4\pi \int_0^{10} xy^2\,dx.$$

Since the equation of the curve AB is $x^2 + y^2 = 100$, we obtain

$$W = 62.4\pi \int_0^{10} x(100 - x^2)\,dx = 245 \text{ ft-tons.}$$

EXERCISE 28

1. A spring whose normal length is 10 inches has a modulus of 12 pounds per inch. How much work is done in stretching this spring from a length of 12 inches to a length of 15 inches? *Ans.* 126 in-lb.
2. Find the work required to compress a spring of modulus 72,000 pounds per foot a distance of $\frac{1}{2}$ inch.
3. Find the work required to compress the spring of Problem 2 an additional $\frac{1}{2}$ inch. *Ans.* $187\frac{1}{2}$ ft-lb.
4. What is the modulus of a spring if 120 inch-pounds of work are required to stretch it a distance of 4 inches?
5. A cable 100 feet long and weighing 3 pounds per foot hangs from a windlass. Find the work done in winding it up. *Ans.* $7\frac{1}{2}$ ft-tons.
6. A cage of weight M pounds is to be lifted from the bottom of a mine shaft h feet deep. If the weight of the cable used to hoist it is w pounds per foot, find the work done.
7. The force of attraction between two masses is k/x^2 pounds, where k is a constant and x feet is the distance between them. How much work must be done to increase the distance between the masses from 50 to 100 feet? *Ans.* $k/100$ ft-lb.
8. A right circular tank of depth 15 feet and radius 5 feet is full of water. Find the work done in pumping the water to the top of the tank.
9. A right circular tank of depth 12 feet and radius 4 feet is half full of oil weighing 60 pounds per cubic foot. Find the work done in pumping the oil to a height 6 feet above the tank. *Ans.* 136 ft-tons.
10. A tank in the form of an inverted right circular cone of depth 10 feet and radius 4 feet is full of water. Find the work done in pumping the water to a point 1 foot above the tank.
11. A hemispherical tank of radius 6 feet is filled with water to a depth of 4 feet. Find the work done in pumping the water to the top of the tank. *Ans.* 25.1 ft-tons.
12. A hemispherical tank of radius 20 feet is filled with water. Find the work done in pumping the water to the top of the tank.
13. A tank in the form of a frustum of a right circular cone is filled with oil weighing 50 pounds per cubic foot. If the height of the tank is 10 feet, the base radius 6 feet, and the top radius 4 feet, find the work required to pump the oil to a height 10 feet above the tank. *Ans.* 312 ft-tons.
14. Find the work done in pumping out a semielliptical tank of water, if the top is a circle of radius 4 feet and the depth is 5 feet.
15. A tank filled with water has the form of a paraboloid of revolution whose axis is vertical. If the depth of the tank is 12 feet and the diameter of the top is 8 feet, find the work done in pumping the water to the top of the tank. *Ans.* 37.6 ft-tons.

CHAPTER 6

Differentiation of Algebraic Functions

56. Introduction

The definition of a derivative, as it is summarized by the four-step rule, gives the basic method for differentiating functions of a single variable. To save labor, however, we develop in this and subsequent chapters a set of *standard formulas* by means of which the derivatives of most elementary functions can be determined with less difficulty.

Although these formulas are valid for any differentiable functions, in this chapter we shall limit their use to explicit algebraic functions* of the form obtained by applying to a variable a finite number of additions, subtractions, multiplications, divisions, and extractions of roots. For example, $x(x + 1)^{-1}$ and $\sqrt[3]{x^2 - 1}$ are algebraic functions, whereas 2^x and $\log x$ are not.

57. Formulas for Differentiation

In the following formulas u and v will be used to denote any functions of x that are differentiable.

Formula D_1. *The derivative of a constant is zero.*

$$D_1 \qquad \frac{dc}{dx} = 0.$$

This was proved in Article **28**.

Formula D_2. *The derivative of the product of a constant and a function is equal to the product of the constant and the derivative of the function.*

$$D_2 \qquad \frac{d}{dx}(cu) = c\frac{du}{dx}.$$

Proof: If $y = cu$, and Δu and Δy are the increments of u and y corresponding to the increment Δx of x, by the four-step rule we have

$$y + \Delta y = c(u + \Delta u), \qquad \Delta y = c\Delta u, \qquad \text{and} \qquad \frac{\Delta y}{\Delta x} = c\frac{\Delta u}{\Delta x}.$$

* For a general definition of an algebraic function, see Article **123**.

By Theorem 1, Article **22**, we obtain $\boldsymbol{D}_2$ when Δx approaches zero.

Formula D_3. *The derivative of an algebraic sum of two functions is equal to the sum of their derivatives.*

$$\boldsymbol{D}_3 \qquad \frac{d}{dx}(u+v) = \frac{du}{dx} + \frac{dv}{dx}.$$

This was proved in Article **28**.

Formula D_4. *The derivative of the product of two functions is equal to the sum of the products obtained in multiplying each function by the derivative of the other.*

$$\boldsymbol{D}_4 \qquad \frac{d}{dx}(uv) = u\frac{dv}{dx} + v\frac{du}{dx}.$$

Proof: If $y = uv$, and Δy, Δu, and Δv are the increments of y, u, and v corresponding to the increment Δx of x, we have

$$y + \Delta y = (u + \Delta u)(v + \Delta v) = uv + u\,\Delta v + v\,\Delta u + \Delta u\,\Delta v,$$

$$\Delta y = u\,\Delta v + v\,\Delta u + \Delta u\,\Delta v,$$

$$\frac{\Delta y}{\Delta x} = u\frac{\Delta v}{\Delta x} + v\frac{\Delta u}{\Delta x} + \Delta u\frac{\Delta v}{\Delta x}.$$

Taking the limit as Δx approaches zero, we obtain $\boldsymbol{D}_4$, since

$$\lim \Delta u \cdot \frac{\Delta v}{\Delta x} = \lim \Delta u \cdot \lim \frac{\Delta v}{\Delta x} = 0 \cdot \frac{dv}{dx} = 0.$$

Illustration 1. If $y = (x^2 + 1)(x^3 - x^2)$, then by $\boldsymbol{D}_4$

$$\begin{aligned}\frac{dy}{dx} &= (x^2+1)\frac{d}{dx}(x^3 - x^2) + (x^3 - x^2)\frac{d}{dx}(x^2+1)\\ &= (x^2+1)(3x^2 - 2x) + (x^3 - x^2)\,2x\\ &= 5x^4 - 4x^3 + 3x^2 - 2x.\end{aligned}$$

Note 1: If we write $\boldsymbol{D}_4$ in the form

$$\frac{\dfrac{d}{dx}(uv)}{uv} = \frac{\dfrac{du}{dx}}{u} + \frac{\dfrac{dv}{dx}}{v},$$

we see for a product of three functions that

$$\frac{\dfrac{d}{dx}(uvw)}{uvw} = \frac{\dfrac{du}{dx}}{u} + \frac{\dfrac{d}{dx}(vw)}{vw} = \frac{\dfrac{du}{dx}}{u} + \frac{\dfrac{dv}{dx}}{v} + \frac{\dfrac{dw}{dx}}{w},$$

or

$$\frac{d}{dx}(uvw) = \frac{du}{dx}vw + u\frac{dv}{dx}w + uv\frac{dw}{dx}.$$

In like manner, if $y = u_1u_2 \cdots u_n$, it can be shown that

$$y' = u_1'u_2 \cdots u_n + u_1u_2' \cdots u_n + \cdots + u_1u_2 \cdots u_n', \tag{1}$$

where the primes indicate differentiation with respect to the independent variable.

Formula D_5. *The derivative of the nth power of a function is equal to n times the product of the $(n-1)$th power of the function and the derivative of the function.*

$$D_5 \qquad \frac{d}{dx}(u^n) = nu^{n-1}\frac{du}{dx}.$$

Proof: If the n factors $u_1, u_2, \cdots, u_n$ in (1) are each set equal to u, we have the result as stated above.

Although this proof establishes D_5 only for the case in which n is a positive integer, it will be proved later that D_5 is valid when n is any real number. In the meantime we shall assume its validity for all real values of n.

Illustration 2. If $y = (x^2+1)^4$, then by D_5

$$\frac{dy}{dx} = 4\cdot(x^2+1)^3\cdot\frac{d}{dx}(x^2+1) = 8x(x^2+1)^3.$$

Note 2: The two cases in which $n = -1$ and $n = \frac{1}{2}$ occur frequently and it is advisable to learn them in the following forms

$$\frac{d}{dx}\left(\frac{1}{u}\right) = -\frac{1}{u^2}\frac{du}{dx}, \qquad \frac{d}{dx}(\sqrt{u}) = \frac{1}{2\sqrt{u}}\frac{du}{dx}. \tag{2}$$

Illustration 3. If $y = \sqrt{x^4-3}$, then by (2)

$$\frac{dy}{dx} = \frac{1}{2\sqrt{x^4-3}}\frac{d}{dx}(x^4-3) = \frac{2x^3}{\sqrt{x^4-3}}.$$

Formula D_6. *The derivative of the quotient of two functions is equal to the denominator times the derivative of the numerator minus the numerator times the derivative of the denominator, all divided by the square of the denominator.*

$$D_6 \qquad \frac{d}{dx}\left(\frac{u}{v}\right) = \frac{v\dfrac{du}{dx} - u\dfrac{dv}{dx}}{v^2}.$$

Proof: Letting $y = u/v$ and giving x an increment Δx, we have by the four-step rule

1. $y + \Delta y = \dfrac{u + \Delta u}{v + \Delta v}$,

2. $\Delta y = \dfrac{u + \Delta u}{v + \Delta v} - \dfrac{u}{v} = \dfrac{v\,\Delta u - u\,\Delta v}{v(v + \Delta v)}$,

3. $\dfrac{\Delta y}{\Delta x} = \dfrac{v\dfrac{\Delta u}{\Delta x} - u\dfrac{\Delta v}{\Delta x}}{v(v + \Delta v)}$,

4. $\dfrac{dy}{dx} = \dfrac{v\dfrac{du}{dx} - u\dfrac{dv}{dx}}{v^2}$.

Illustration 4. If $y = (x^2 - 4)/(x^2 + x)$, then by $\boldsymbol{D_6}$

$$\frac{dy}{dx} = \frac{(x^2 + x)\dfrac{d}{dx}(x^2 - 4) - (x^2 - 4)\dfrac{d}{dx}(x^2 + x)}{(x^2 + x)^2}$$

$$= \frac{(x^2 + x)2x - (x^2 - 4)(2x + 1)}{(x^2 + x)^2} = \frac{x^2 + 8x + 4}{x^2(x + 1)^2}.$$

Example 1. Find dy/dx, when $y = x^2 - \sqrt{2x + 1}$.

Solution:

$$\frac{dy}{dx} = \frac{d}{dx}(x^2) - \frac{d}{dx}\sqrt{2x + 1} \qquad \text{by } \boldsymbol{D_3}$$

$$= 2x - \frac{1}{2\sqrt{2x + 1}}\frac{d}{dx}(2x + 1) \qquad \text{by } \boldsymbol{D_5}$$

$$= 2x - \frac{1}{\sqrt{2x + 1}}. \qquad \text{by } \boldsymbol{D_2} \text{ and } \boldsymbol{D_1}$$

Example 2. Find dy/dx, when $y = \sqrt[3]{\dfrac{1 - x}{1 + x}}$.

Solution: Writing $y = \left(\dfrac{1 - x}{1 + x}\right)^{1/3}$, we have

$$\frac{dy}{dx} = \frac{1}{3}\left(\frac{1 - x}{1 + x}\right)^{-2/3}\frac{d}{dx}\left(\frac{1 - x}{1 + x}\right) \qquad \text{by } \boldsymbol{D_5}$$

$$= \frac{1}{3}\left(\frac{1 + x}{1 - x}\right)^{2/3}\frac{(1 + x)(-1) - (1 - x)(1)}{(1 + x)^2} \qquad \text{by } \boldsymbol{D_6}$$

$$= \frac{-2}{3(1 - x)^{2/3}(1 + x)^{4/3}}.$$

Note 3: A given expression should be reduced to its simplest form before differentiating. Thus, to obtain the derivative of $y = (x^4 - 9)/(x^2 + 3)$, we differentiate the equivalent relation $y = x^2 - 3$ and find $y' = 2x$.

EXERCISE 29

Find the derivatives of the following functions with respect to x and simplify the results.

1. $(1 + 3x)^5$. *Ans.* $15(1 + 3x)^4$.
2. $(5 - 2x)^4$.
3. $(x^2 - 4)^3$. $6x(x^2 - 4)^2$.
4. $(3 - 2x)^2(x^2 - 2)$.
5. $\sqrt{9 - x^2}$. $-x/\sqrt{9 - x^2}$.
6. $\sqrt{2x} + \sqrt[3]{3x}$.
7. $\dfrac{x + 1}{x + 2}$. $\dfrac{1}{(x + 2)^2}$.
8. $\dfrac{(x - 1)^2}{x}$.
9. $(x^2 - 1)(2x^2 - 3)$. $8x^3 - 10x$.
10. $x^5(1 + x)^5$.
11. $\sqrt[3]{(3x + 1)^4}$. $4\sqrt[3]{3x + 1}$.
12. $(2x - 3)^{-3}$.
13. $\dfrac{x}{2 - 3x^2}$. $\dfrac{2 + 3x^2}{(2 - 3x^2)^2}$.
14. $\dfrac{4x^2 - 9}{2x + 3}$.
15. $x\sqrt{1 - x}$. $\dfrac{2 - 3x}{2\sqrt{1 - x}}$.
16. $x^2\sqrt{1 - x^2}$.
17. $(2x + 1)^{48}$. $96(2x + 1)^{47}$.
18. $x^3(x + 1)^2(x + 2)$.
19. $\dfrac{2}{x^2 - 1}$. $-\dfrac{4x}{(x^2 - 1)^2}$.
20. $\dfrac{1}{\sqrt{4x - 3}}$.
21. $\sqrt{\dfrac{1 - x}{1 + x}}$. $\dfrac{-1}{(1 + x)\sqrt{1 - x^2}}$.
22. $\sqrt[3]{\dfrac{1 - x^2}{1 + x^2}}$.
23. $\dfrac{a^2 + x^2}{a^2 - x^2}$. $\dfrac{4a^2x}{(a^2 - x^2)^2}$.
24. $\dfrac{\sqrt{a} + \sqrt{x}}{\sqrt{a} - \sqrt{x}}$.
25. $\dfrac{x^3 + a^3}{x + a}$. $2x - a$.
26. $\dfrac{a - x}{\sqrt{a} - \sqrt{x}}$.
27. $(a^{2/3} - x^{2/3})^{3/2}$. $-x^{-1/3}(a^{2/3} - x^{2/3})^{1/2}$.
28. $\sqrt{\dfrac{ax + b}{cx + d}}$.

In each of the following, find the value of dy/dx for the given value of x.

29. $y = \dfrac{4 - x^2}{2x + 3}$, $x = -1$. *Ans.* -4.
30. $y = (3x)^{1/3} + (3x)^{2/3}$, $x = 9$.
31. $y = x\sqrt{1 + x^3}$, $x = 2$. 7.
32. $y = \sqrt{5 - \sqrt{x}}$, $x = 1$.

Find the equations of the tangent and normal to each of the following curves at the point indicated.

33. $y = \sqrt{25 - x^2}$, $(3,4)$. *Ans.* $3x + 4y = 25$, $4x - 3y = 0$.
34. $y = (x^3 - 7)^5$, $(2,1)$.
35. $y = 1/\sqrt{x + 3}$, $(1,\frac{1}{2})$. $x + 16y = 9$, $32x - 2y = 31$.
36. $y(x + 2)^2 = x$, $(-1,-1)$.

Find the angle of intersection between the two given curves at the point indicated.

37. $y = \dfrac{x}{1 - x^2}$, $y = \dfrac{x^2}{1 - x}$; $(0,0)$. *Ans.* 45°.
38. $y = x$, $xy = (x + 2)^2$; $(-1,-1)$.
39. $y = \sqrt{x + 2}$, $y\sqrt{x + 2} = 1$; $(-1,1)$. 53.1°.
40. $y = x - 1$, $x^2 + y^2 = 25$; $(4,3)$.

Find the maximum and minimum points for each of the following curves.

41. $x^2y = x^3 - 4$. *Ans.* $(-2,-3)$, max.
42. $y\sqrt{2x + 1} = x$.
43. $y = x\sqrt{x + 1}$. $(-\frac{2}{3}, -\frac{2}{9}\sqrt{3})$, min.
44. In the isosceles triangle ABC, $AB = AC = 5$ units, and $BC = 6$ units. Find the location of the point D on the altitude from A to BC for which the sum $DA + DB + DC$ is a minimum.
45. A farmer estimates that if he digs his potatoes now he will have 120 bushels, which he can sell at \$1.75 per bushel. If he expects his crop to increase 8 bushels per week, but the price to drop 5 cents per bushel per week, in how many weeks should he sell to realize the maximum amount for his crop? *Ans.* 10 weeks.
46. Find the point of the parabola $9y = x^2$ that is closest to the point $(5,-2)$.
47. Find the area of the largest rectangle that can be constructed with its base on the x axis and two vertices on the witch $y = 8a^3/(x^2 + 4a^2)$. *Ans.* $4a^2$.
48. If p is the price per unit at which x units of a certain commodity can be sold, then p is usually a decreasing function of x called the *demand function*, $R = px$ is the *total revenue*, and dR/dx is called the *marginal revenue*. Determine reasonable domains for the following demand functions and find the production number that gives a maximum revenue.

$$(a)\ p = \left(5 - \frac{x}{60}\right)^2, \qquad (b)\ p = \frac{1000}{x + 8} - 10.$$

49. If C is the total cost at which x units of a certain commodity can be produced, then C is usually an increasing function of x called the *cost function*, $c = C/x$ is the *average cost* per unit, and $M = dC/dx$ is called the *marginal cost*. Determine a reasonable domain for the cost function $C = 6000 + 24x - 0.004x^2$, and find (*a*) the average cost and (*b*) the marginal cost when 300 units are being produced.

Ans. (*a*) \$42.80, (*b*) \$21.60.

50. If n is a positive integer prove that the derivative of x^{-n} is $-nx^{-n-1}$. *Hint:* Write x^{-n} in the form $1/x^n$ and use $\boldsymbol{D}_6$.

58. Formulas for Differentiation (*Continued*)

If y is a function of u, and u is a function of x, then y is dependent on x and its derivative with respect to x is determined as follows in what is called the **chain rule** of differentiation.

Formula D_7. *If $y = f(u)$ and $u = \phi(x)$, the derivative of y with respect to x is equal to the product of the derivative of y with respect to u by the derivative of u with respect to x.*

$$\boldsymbol{D}_7 \qquad \frac{dy}{dx} = \frac{dy}{du}\frac{du}{dx}, \qquad \text{or} \qquad \frac{dy}{dx} = f'(u)\,\phi'(x).$$

Proof: An increment Δx in x produces an increment Δu in u, which in turn gives an increment Δy in y. These increments satisfy the algebraic identity

$$\frac{\Delta y}{\Delta x} = \frac{\Delta y}{\Delta u}\cdot\frac{\Delta u}{\Delta x}.$$

Taking the limit as Δx approaches zero, by Theorem 1, Article **22,** we obtain

$$\frac{dy}{dx} = \frac{dy}{du}\cdot\frac{du}{dx} = f'(u)\,\phi'(x),$$

provided $f(u)$ and $\phi(x)$ are differentiable functions.

Illustration 1. If $y = u/(u + 1)$ and $u = x/(x + 1)$, we have

$$\frac{dy}{du} = \frac{1}{(u+1)^2} \qquad \text{and} \qquad \frac{du}{dx} = \frac{1}{(x+1)^2}.$$

Hence by $\boldsymbol{D}_7$

$$\frac{dy}{dx} = \frac{1}{(u+1)^2}\cdot\frac{1}{(x+1)^2} = \frac{1}{(2x+1)^2}.$$

The following two formulas may be proved in a similar manner.

Formula D_8. *The derivative of y with respect to x is equal to the reciprocal of the derivative of x with respect to y.*

$$\mathbf{D_8} \qquad \frac{dy}{dx} = \frac{1}{\dfrac{dx}{dy}}, \qquad \left(\frac{dx}{dy} \neq 0\right).$$

Illustration 2. If $x = \sqrt{y^2 + 1}$, we have

$$\frac{dx}{dy} = \frac{y}{\sqrt{y^2 + 1}}.$$

Hence by $\boldsymbol{D_8}$

$$\frac{dy}{dx} = \frac{\sqrt{y^2 + 1}}{y}.$$

Formula D_9. *If $y = f(u)$ and $x = g(u)$, the derivative of y with respect to x is equal to the ratio of the derivative of y with respect to u divided by the derivative of x with respect to u.*

$$\mathbf{D_9} \qquad \frac{dy}{dx} = \frac{\dfrac{dy}{du}}{\dfrac{dx}{du}} \qquad \text{or} \qquad \frac{dy}{dx} = \frac{f'(u)}{g'(u)}, \quad g'(u) \neq 0.$$

Illustration 3. If $y = u/(1 - u)$ and $x = u/(1 - u^2)$, we have

$$\frac{dy}{du} = \frac{1}{(1 - u)^2} \qquad \text{and} \qquad \frac{dx}{du} = \frac{1 + u^2}{(1 - u^2)^2}.$$

Hence by $\boldsymbol{D_9}$

$$\frac{dy}{dx} = \frac{\dfrac{1}{(1 - u)^2}}{\dfrac{1 + u^2}{(1 - u^2)^2}} = \frac{(1 + u)^2}{1 + u^2}.$$

59. Differentiation of Implicit Functions

An equation, such as $y = f(x)$, is said to define y as an **explicit function** of x for some domain R. Not all functions are defined in such an explicit way. For example, an equation in x and y, such as

$$x^3 - 2x^2 = y^4 - y + 5,$$

is not easily solved for y in terms of x. However, if a function $f(x)$ exists such that

$$x^3 - 2x^2 = f^4(x) - f(x) + 5$$

holds for every x in the domain of $f(x)$, then the function $y = f(x)$ is said to be defined **implicitly** by the given equation.

Illustration 1. The equation $4x^2 + 9y^2 = 36$ defines either variable implicitly in terms of the other. If the equation is solved for x or y, we obtain the equivalent explicit equations

$$x = \pm \tfrac{3}{2}\sqrt{4 - y^2} \qquad \text{or} \qquad y = \pm \tfrac{2}{3}\sqrt{9 - x^2}.$$

It is often inconvenient or impossible to solve a given equation for one of the variables. Hence, in order to find the derivative of an implied function, we proceed in accordance with the following rule.

Rule. *Differentiate each term of the equation $F(x,y) = 0$ with respect to x, considering y to be a function of x.*

Illustration 2. Applying the above rule to $x^3 + y^3 - 3xy = 0$ and solving for dy/dx, we obtain

$$\frac{d}{dx}(x^3) + \frac{d}{dx}(y^3) - 3\frac{d}{dx}(xy) = 0,$$

$$3x^2 + 3y^2\frac{dy}{dx} - 3\left(y + x\frac{dy}{dx}\right) = 0,$$

$$3(y^2 - x)\frac{dy}{dx} = 3(y - x^2),$$

$$\frac{dy}{dx} = \frac{y - x^2}{y^2 - x}, \quad y^2 - x \neq 0.$$

Example 1. If $x^2 + y^2 = a^2$, find y' and y''.

Solution: Differentiating implicitly, we obtain

$$2x + 2yy' = 0;$$

hence

$$y' = -\frac{x}{y}, \quad y \neq 0.$$

Differentiating again, we obtain by $\boldsymbol{D_6}$

$$y'' = -\frac{y - xy'}{y^2}.$$

Since $y' = -x/y$ and $x^2 + y^2 = a^2$, the second derivative can be expressed in the following simplified form

$$y'' = -\frac{y - x(-x/y)}{y^2} = -\frac{y^2 + x^2}{y^3} = -\frac{a^2}{y^3}.$$

Note: The equation $x + yy' = 0$ may itself be differentiated implicitly giving $1 + (y')^2 + yy'' = 0$. Thus, as above, we obtain

$$yy'' = -\left(1 + \frac{x^2}{y^2}\right) = -\frac{a^2}{y^2};$$

hence

$$y'' = -\frac{a^2}{y^3}.$$

When one is solving a problem concerning a maximum or minimum, it is advisable in general to express the quantity which is to be maximized (or minimized) in terms of a single variable. Such problems can, however, be solved implicitly by using more than one variable. This method is illustrated in the following example.

Example 2. An isosceles triangle with vertex at $(0, -1)$ is to be inscribed in the ellipse $x^2 + 4y^2 = 4$. Find the largest area that the triangle can have.

Solution: If the base of the triangle intersects the ellipse at the point $P(x,y)$, it follows from Figure 88 that the area to be maximized is

$$A = x(y + 1), \quad \text{where} \quad x^2 + 4y^2 = 4. \tag{1}$$

Differentiating each of these equations with respect to x, we have

$$\frac{dA}{dx} = y + 1 + x\frac{dy}{dx},$$

$$x + 4y\frac{dy}{dx} = 0. \tag{2}$$

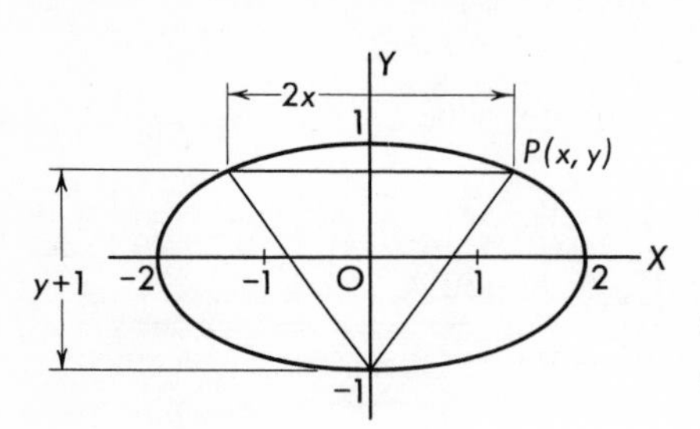

Figure 88

Since A is to be a maximum, we set $dA/dx = 0$. Then eliminating dy/dx between the two equations in (2), we obtain

$$4y^2 + 4y = x^2. \tag{3}$$

This equation we solve simultaneously with the second equation of (1). Thus, on eliminating x, we find

$$4y^2 + 4y = 4 - 4y^2; \quad \text{hence} \quad y = \tfrac{1}{2} \text{ or } -1.$$

The value $y = -1$ is rejected since it obviously gives a minimum area of zero. Hence substituting $y = \frac{1}{2}$ in (3), we obtain $x = \sqrt{3}$, and from (1) the maximum area is found to be $\sqrt{3}(\frac{1}{2} + 1)$ or $\frac{3}{2}\sqrt{3}$.

Rule. *To find the values of x and y which satisfy $\phi(x,y) = 0$ and make the function $M = f(x,y)$ a maximum or minimum, we proceed as follows.*

(*a*) *Differentiate each of the given equations with respect to one of the variables, say x.*

(*b*) *Set* $dM/dx = 0$, *and eliminate* dy/dx *between the two equations obtained in* (*a*).

(*c*) *Solve the equation obtained in* (*b*) *simultaneously with* $\phi(x,y) = 0$.

60. Summary of Formulas

The differentiation formulas which have been derived in this chapter are of fundamental importance and should be memorized. For convenience, we repeat the list here, and write the first six formulas in their equivalent differential forms.

D_1 $\quad dc = 0.$

D_2 $\quad d(cu) = c\,du.$

D_3 $\quad d(u + v) = du + dv.$

D_4 $\quad d(uv) = u\,dv + v\,du.$

D_5 $\quad d(u^n) = nu^{n-1}\,du.$

D_6 $\quad d\left(\dfrac{u}{v}\right) = \dfrac{v\,du - u\,dv}{v^2}.$

D_7 $\quad \dfrac{dy}{dx} = \dfrac{dy}{du}\cdot\dfrac{du}{dx}.$

D_8 $\quad \dfrac{dy}{dx} = 1\Big/\dfrac{dx}{dy}.$

D_9 $\quad \dfrac{dy}{dx} = \dfrac{dy}{du}\Big/\dfrac{dx}{du}.$

EXERCISE 30

In each of the following find dy/dx.

1. $\begin{cases} y = u^2 + 6u - 2, \\ u = 4x^2 + 8x + 1. \end{cases}$ *Ans.* $64(x + 1)^3$.

2. $\begin{cases} y = u\sqrt{u + 1}, \\ u = 2x^2 - \frac{2}{3}. \end{cases}$

3. $\begin{cases} y = 1/(1 - u), \\ u = 1/(1 + x). \end{cases}$ $-1/x^2$.

4. $\begin{cases} y = u^2 + 2u, \\ u = v^2 + 2v, \\ v = x^2 + 2x. \end{cases}$

5. $x = \frac{1}{3}y^3 + y.$ $1/(y^2 + 1)$.

6. $x = \sqrt[3]{y^3 + 3y}.$

7. $x = \dfrac{y - 1}{\sqrt{y}}.$ $\dfrac{2y\sqrt{y}}{y + 1}$.

8. $x = \dfrac{3y + 2y^2}{2 - y^2}.$

9. $\begin{cases} x = 2u^3 - 3u^2, \\ y = u^3 - 3u. \end{cases}$ $\dfrac{u + 1}{2u}$, $u \neq 1$.

10. $\begin{cases} x = u/(1 + u^3), \\ y = u^2/(1 + u^3). \end{cases}$

11. $\begin{cases} x = t + t^{-1}, \\ y = t^2 + t^{-2}. \end{cases}$ $2(t + t^{-1})$.

12. $\begin{cases} x = 1/(t - 1), \\ y = 1/(t^2 - 1). \end{cases}$

Find dy/dx in each of the following by implicit differentiation. Also find d^2y/dx^2 in the first four problems.

13. $x^2 - 4y^2 = 4.$ *Ans.* $x/4y$, $-1/4y^3$.
14. $5x^2 + 2y^2 = 10.$
15. $x^{1/2} + y^{1/2} = a^{1/2}.$ $-y^{1/2}/x^{1/2}$, $a^{1/2}/2x^{3/2}$.
16. $x^{2/3} + y^{2/3} = a^{2/3}.$
17. $y^3 + y = x^4.$ $4x^3/(3y^2 + 1)$.

18. $x^3 + 3y = 3xy$.
19. $xy = (x - y)^2$. *Ans.* $(3y - 2x)/(2y - 3x)$.
20. $x^4 + y^3 = 2x^2y^2$.
21. $x^2 + y^2 = 2xy$. 1.
22. $(x + y)^{1/2} + (x - y)^{1/2} = a$.
23. $(x + y)^2 = 2ay$. $(x + y)/(a - x - y)$.
24. When $x = \int_0^y \frac{dt}{\sqrt{1 + t^2}}$, show that $\frac{d^2y}{dx^2} = y$.

Find the equations of the tangent and the normal to the following curves at the point indicated.

25. $x^3 + y^3 = 9$; $(1,2)$. *Ans.* $x + 4y = 9$, $4x - y = 2$.
26. $x^2 + y^2 - 2x - 6y + 8 = 0$; $(0,4)$.
27. $y + \sqrt{x + y} = x$; $(3,1)$. $3x - 5y = 4$, $5x + 3y = 18$.
28. $x^2 - 2xy - 2y^2 = 1$; $(-3,-1)$.

Find the angle of intersection of the following pairs of curves.

29. $\begin{cases} y = 2x, \\ x^5 + y^5 = 33. \end{cases}$ *Ans.* 67.0°.

30. $\begin{cases} y = x + 1, \\ x^2 - 2xy + y^2 = x. \end{cases}$

31. $\begin{cases} xy + y = 1, \\ y^3 = (x + 1)^2. \end{cases}$ 78.7°.

32. $\begin{cases} y + x^2y = 1, \\ y + x^2y = x. \end{cases}$

33. Find the points on the ellipse $x^2 - 2xy + 4y^2 = 12$ where the abscissa x has its greatest and least values. *Ans.* $(4,1)$ and $(-4,-1)$.
34. Find the points of inflection of the curve $x^2 + y^{2/3} = 2$.
35. Find by differentials an approximate value of $\sqrt{3.98}$. *Ans.* 1.995.
36. An isosceles trapezoid has constant bases of 6 and 12 inches, respectively. Find the approximate change in its area when the equal sides change from 5 to 5.2 inches.
37. A point moves along the parabola $y^2 = 3x$. Find the approximate change in its distance from the origin as its x coordinate changes from 1 to 1.1. *Ans.* 0.125.
38. Find the area of the largest isosceles triangle which can be cut from a semicircular board, the vertex of the triangle being at the mid-point of the diameter.
39. The strength of a rectangular beam is proportional to the product of its breadth and the square of its depth. Find the dimensions of the strongest rectangular beam that can be cut from a circular log of diameter 18 inches. *Ans.* $6\sqrt{3} \times 6\sqrt{6}$ in.
40. Find the dimensions of the largest rectangle that can be inscribed in the curve $x^{2/3} + y^{2/5} = 8$.

41. If $\frac{a^2}{x} + \frac{b^2}{y} = 1$, where a and b are positive constants, show that the sum $(x + y)$ has a relative maximum of $(a - b)^2$ and a relative minimum of $(a + b)^2$.

42. A right circular cone is generated by revolving an isosceles triangle of constant perimeter about its altitude. Show that the cone of greatest volume is obtained when the length of a side of the triangle is three-fourths the length of the base.

43. $ABCD$ is a rectangle, and a straight line APQ cuts BC in P and DC extended in Q. Find BP so that the sum of the areas of the two triangles ABP and PCQ will be a minimum. *Ans.* $BP = \frac{1}{2}\sqrt{2}\,BC$.

44. Writing the expression $y = x^{1/q}$ in the form $y^q = x$, where q is a positive integer, show by use of $\boldsymbol{D}_8$ that

$$\frac{dy}{dx} = \frac{1}{q}\,x^{(1/q)-1}.$$

45. Find a formula for $\frac{d^2}{dx^2}(uv)$. *Ans.* $u''v + 2u'v' + uv''$.

46. Find a formula for $\frac{d^2}{dx^2}\left(\frac{u}{v}\right)$.

47. Using the fact that $\frac{dy}{dx} = 1\Big/\frac{dx}{dy}$, show that $\frac{d^2y}{dx^2} = -\frac{d^2x}{dy^2}\Big/\left(\frac{dx}{dy}\right)^3$.

48. If $y = f(u)$ and $u = \phi(x)$, show that $\frac{d^2y}{dx^2} = f''(u)\phi'^2(x) + f'(u)\phi''(x)$.

49. If x and y are functions of time t, show that $\frac{d^2y}{dx^2} = (\dot{x}\ddot{y} - \ddot{x}\dot{y})/\dot{x}^3$. See *Note 1*, page 227.

50. If $y = x\,f(x)$, show that $\frac{d^ny}{dx^n} = x\,f^{(n)}(x) + n\,f^{(n-1)}(x)$.

CHAPTER 7

Equations of the Second Degree

61. The Graph of an Equation

If a locus is described on a coordinate system, we saw in the first chapter that the coordinates x and y of every point on the locus satisfy an equation in x and y. On the other hand, for every equation in x and y, there is usually a locus in the xy plane. This locus, if it exists, is called a **graph** of the equation.

The graph of an equation is a curve containing those points, and only those points, whose coordinates satisfy the equation.

The process of plotting a graph is often called the graphing of an equation; and, in accordance with the above definition, it consists of plotting points whose coordinates satisfy the equation, and connecting these points with a curve. This procedure may be systemized as follows.

1. *Solve for y in terms of x (or x in terms of y, if simpler).*
2. *Choose arbitrary values for x, compute the corresponding values for y, and arrange these in tabular form.*
3. *Plot the points and draw a smooth curve through them.*

Example 1. Plot the graph of the equation $y = x^3 - x$.

Solution: By substitution, we find the following pairs of corresponding values of x and y.

x	-2	$-\frac{3}{2}$	-1	$-\frac{1}{2}$	0	$\frac{1}{2}$	1	$\frac{3}{2}$	2
y	-6	$-\frac{15}{8}$	0	$\frac{3}{8}$	0	$-\frac{3}{8}$	0	$\frac{15}{8}$	6

Plotting these points, we have the graph shown in Figure 89. There is no set rule to indicate what arbitrary values of x to choose in setting up the table of points. Observe in this instance that it was essential to choose fractional values for x. If the four points having fractional abscissas are suppressed, the remaining five points by no means give a clear picture of the nature of the curve. In general, *when in doubt as to the character of the curve in any neighborhood, plot points in that neighborhood to locate the curve definitely.*

Quite often the process of drawing a graph is considerably simplified by determining certain general properties of the curve before plotting any points. Some of these properties and their tests are discussed below.

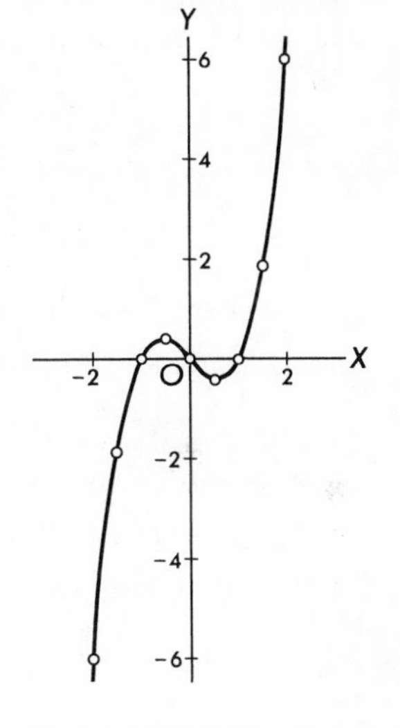

Figure 89

Extent. In plotting a curve we are concerned only with points having real coordinates. Hence, in determining x and y from an equation, we are interested only in real solutions. The totality of real values of x which give real values for y is called the **range** of x, or the **extent** of the curve in the x direction. Likewise, the permissible values of y give the extent of the curve in the y direction.

Illustration 1. For $y = \sqrt{x}$, we see that $x \geqq 0$, since otherwise y is imaginary, and that $y \geqq 0$, since by definition the radical denotes the non-negative square root of x. Hence the curve lies in the first quadrant.

Intercepts. The values of x where a curve intersects the x axis are called the x intercepts of the curve, and the values of y where the curve intersects the y axis are called the y intercepts. These intercepts are determined from the equation of the curve in the same manner that points of the curve are found.

1. *To find the x intercepts, set $y = 0$ and solve for x.*
2. *To find the y intercepts, set $x = 0$ and solve for y.*

Illustration 2. Setting $y = 0$ in the equation $x^2 + xy + y^2 - 5x + 3y + 4 = 0$, we obtain from $x^2 - 5x + 4 = 0$ or $(x - 1)(x - 4) = 0$ the x intercepts $x = 1$ and $x = 4$. Setting $x = 0$, we observe that $y^2 + 3y + 4 = 0$ has imaginary roots; hence there are no y intercepts.

Symmetry. Two points P and Q are said to be symmetric with respect to a line if the line is the perpendicular bisector of the segment PQ. Similarly, they are said to be symmetric with respect to a point if the point is the mid-point of the segment PQ. In either case a curve is said to be symmetric with respect to a line or a point if for every point P on the curve there is a symmetric point Q which is also on the curve. Thus $y = x^2$ is symmetric with respect to the y axis, since for every point (x_1,y_1) on the curve the symmetric point $(-x_1,y_1)$ is also on the curve. It is important to note here that a curve will always be symmetric to the y axis when its equation contains only even powers of x. A few tests for symmetry may be summarized as follows.

If the equation of a curve is unchanged when any of the following substitutions of variables are made in it, the curve is symmetric with respect to the line or point indicated.

1. *$-x$ for x,* — *y axis,*
2. *$-y$ for y,* — *x axis,*
3. *$-x$ for x and $-y$ for y,* — *origin,*
4. *x for y and y for x,* — *line $y = x$.*

Illustration 3. Substituting $-x$ for x and $-y$ for y in the equation $y = \dfrac{x}{1 + x^2}$, we obtain $(-y) = \dfrac{(-x)}{1 + (-x)^2}$, which when simplified gives the original equation. Hence its graph is symmetric with respect to the origin, as shown in Figure 90.

Asymptotes. When a straight line has a position with respect to a curve such that as the two are indefinitely prolonged the distance between them becomes and remains less than any preassigned amount, however small, the straight line is called an **asymptote** of the curve.

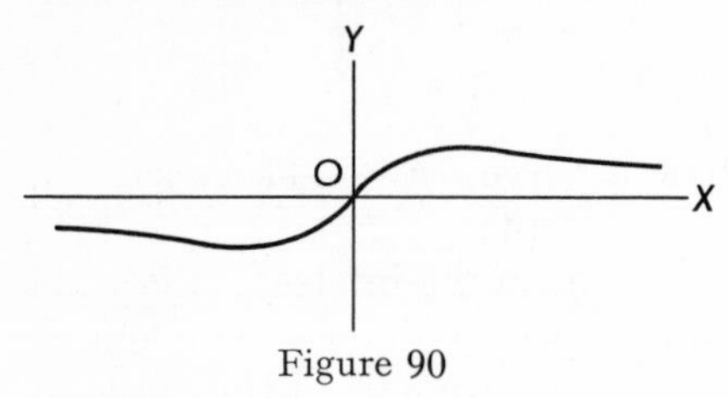

Figure 90

In particular if, as shown in Figure 91, the ordinate y of a point on a curve increases numerically without limit as x approaches a value a, the line $x = a$ is called a *vertical asymptote* of the curve. Also, as shown in Figure 92, if y approaches the value b as x increases numerically without limit, the line $y = b$ is called a *horizontal asymptote* of the curve.

Thus, for algebraic curves, a value a of x which causes the denominator in the expression for y to vanish gives a vertical asymptote $x = a$; similarly, a value b of y which causes the denominator in the expression for x to vanish gives a horizontal asymptote, $y = b$.

Illustration 4. The equation $xy - 2x + 3y = 0$ expressed in the form $y = \dfrac{2x}{x + 3}$ shows that $x = -3$ is a vertical asymptote; and written as $x = \dfrac{3y}{2 - y}$, that $y = 2$ is a horizontal asymptote.

When an equation can be expressed as the product of several factors equated to zero, the graph of the equation consists of all the lines and

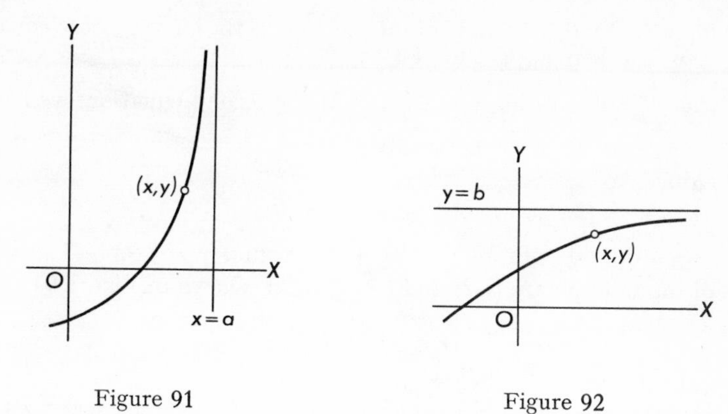

Figure 91 Figure 92

curves whose equations are obtained by setting each of the factors equal to zero separately.

Example 2. Plot the graph of the equation $x^2 - xy - xy^2 + y^3 = 0$.

Solution: Factoring by grouping terms, we can write the given equation as $(x - y)(x - y^2) = 0$. Hence the graph consists of the line $x - y = 0$ and the curve $x - y^2 = 0$, as shown in Figure 93.

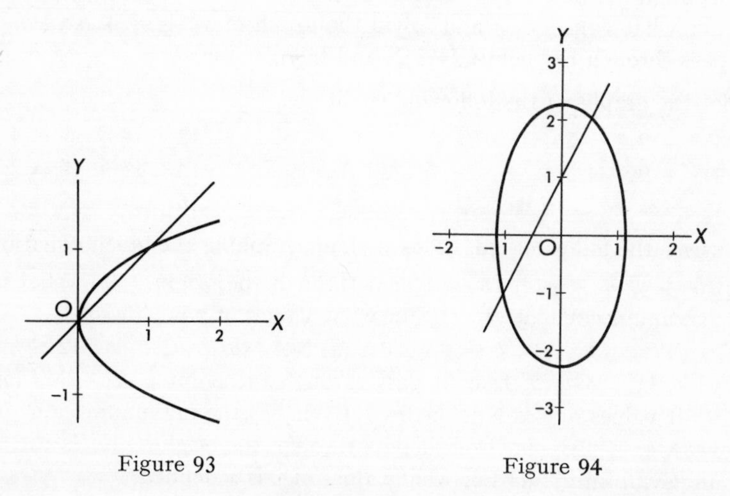

Figure 93 Figure 94

If two curves are drawn on the same coordinate system, the points of intersection are the points whose coordinates satisfy both equations. Hence *the points of intersection of two curves are found by solving their equations simultaneously.* If the values thus found are imaginary or if the equations have no solutions whatever, the curves do not intersect.

Example 3. Find the points of intersection of the curves whose equations are $2x - y + 1 = 0$ and $4x^2 + y^2 = 5$.

Solution: Substituting $y = 2x + 1$ in the second equation, we have

$$4x^2 + (2x + 1)^2 = 5,$$

which reduces to

$$2x^2 + x - 1 = 0;$$

hence $x = \frac{1}{2}$ or -1. From $y = 2x + 1$, we find $y = 2$ or -1; thus the points of intersection are $(\frac{1}{2},2)$ and $(-1,-1)$, as shown in Figure 94.

EXERCISE 31

Plot the graphs of the following equations.

1. $y = x^2 - 2x - 3$.
2. $x = y^2 - 4$.
3. $y = x^3$.
4. $y^2 = x^3$.
5. $x = y(y - 2)(y - 4)$.
6. $y = x^4 - 2x^2 + 1$.
7. For what value of a will the graph of $y^2 = 4ax$ pass through the point (*a*) $(4,16)$, (*b*) $(-8,2)$, (*c*) $(0,0)$? *Ans.* (*a*) 16, (*b*) $-\frac{1}{8}$, (*c*) all values.
8. For what value of m will the graph of $y = x^2 + mx$ pass through the point (*a*) $(3,-2)$, (*b*) $(2,4)$, (*c*) $(0,0)$?
9. For what values of A and B will the graph of $Ax^2 + By^2 = 4$ pass through the points $(1,4)$ and $(-2,3)$? *Ans.* $A = \frac{28}{55}$, $B = \frac{12}{55}$.
10. For what values of h and k will the graph of $x^2 + y^2 + hx + ky = 0$ pass through the points $(-1,2)$ and $(8,4)$?

Plot the graphs of the following equations.

11. $4x^2 + 9y^2 = 36$.
12. $x^2 - y^2 = 4$.
13. $4x^2 + 9y^2 = 36x$.
14. $x^2 + y^2 = 2x$.
15. $xy - 3x + 2y = 0$.
16. $xy + x^2 - y = 0$.

Answer the following questions without graphing the given equation.

17. $2x^2 + y^2 = 8$. (*a*) Does it pass through the origin? (*b*) What is the maximum value of y? (*c*) For what values of x is y defined? *Ans.* (*a*) No, (*b*) $2\sqrt{2}$, (*c*) $-2 \leqq x \leqq 2$.
18. $y^2 + 4x = 4$. (*a*) Does it pass through the point $(-2,-2)$? (*b*) For what values of x is y defined? (*c*) What is the maximum value of x?
19. $xy = 4x + 8y$. (*a*) Does it pass through the origin? (*b*) Is the x axis an asymptote? (*c*) For what values of y is x defined? *Ans.* (*a*) Yes, (*b*) no, (*c*) all but $y = 4$.
20. $y = x^2 - 3x - 10$. (*a*) Does it pass through the point $(10,60)$? (*b*) For what values of x is y negative? (*c*) What is the minimum value of y?

After factoring, plot the graphs of the following equations.

21. $xy = 0$.
22. $x^2 - 6x + 5 = 0$.
23. $9x^2 - 4y^2 = 0$.
24. $2x^2 - 3xy - 4x + 6y = 0$.
25. $x^3 - y^3 = xy(x - y)$.
26. $(x + y)^2 + (x + y) = 2$.

Find the points of intersection of the following curves.

27. $2x + y = 5$ and $x^2 - y^2 = 7$. *Ans.* $(4, -3)$, $(\frac{8}{3}, -\frac{1}{3})$.
28. $x + 4y = 9$ and $x^2 + 4y = 9$.
29. $y = 2x - 3$ and $2x^2 - xy = 15$. $(5,7)$.
30. $x + 2y = 4$ and $2x^2 + 2y^2 = 5xy$.
31. $xy = 3$ and $4x^2 + y^2 = 13$. $(1,3)$, $(-1,-3)$, $(\frac{3}{2},2)$, $(-\frac{3}{2},-2)$.
32. $x^2 + 4y^2 = 20$ and $4x^2 + y^2 = 20$.
33. $5x^2 + 2y^2 = 13$ and $y^2 = 2x + 2$. $(1, \pm 2)$.
34. $x^2 + xy = 1 + k$ and $x - xy = 1 - k$.

Plot the graphs of the following equations.

35. $x^{1/2} + y^{1/2} = 2$.
36. $x^{2/3} + y^{2/3} = 4$.
37. $x^{-2} + y^{-2} = 1$.
38. $y = x + |x|$.
39. $y = 1 - |x|$.
40. $y = |1 - x|$.

62. Equations of the Second Degree

A general equation of the second degree in two variables, also called a **quadratic equation** in x and y, has the form

$$Ax^2 + Bxy + Cy^2 + Dx + Ey + F = 0,$$

where A, B, and C are not all zero. It is shown in more extensive books on analytic geometry that the graph of this equation is generally a circle, an ellipse, a parabola, or a hyperbola, although exceptional cases exist in which the equation has no graph at all, or a graph consisting of a single point, one line, or two lines. Since all of the above curves can be obtained as the intersection of a plane with a right circular cone, they are often called **conic sections** or simply **conics.** The exceptions are usually referred to as *degenerate* conics.

In the remainder of this chapter we shall discuss some standard forms of the above equation which are useful in studying the properties of the corresponding curves.

63. The Circle

A circle is the locus of a point moving in a plane in such a way that its distance from a fixed point remains constant. The fixed point is called the **center** of the circle, and the constant distance the **radius.**

Let $P(x,y)$ be any point on a circle of radius r and center $C(h,k)$, as shown in Figure 95. By the definition of a circle we have $CP = r$, or

$$\sqrt{(x-h)^2 + (y-k)^2} = r.$$

Hence, on squaring both sides, we have

$$(x-h)^2 + (y-k)^2 = r^2, \qquad (1)$$

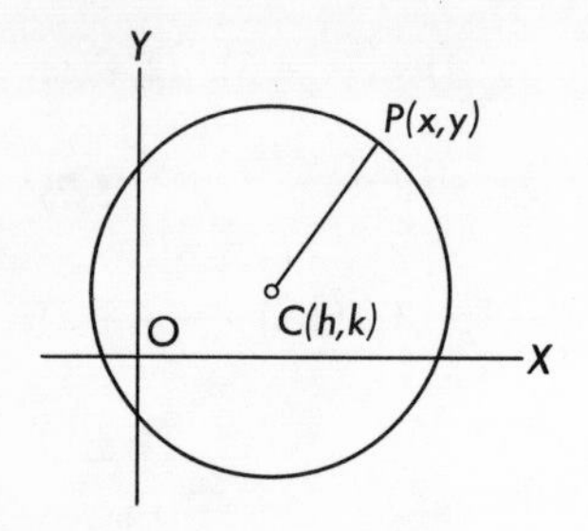

Figure 95

which is called the **standard form** of the equation of a circle.

If we expand the parentheses in (1) and collect terms, we obtain

$$x^2 + y^2 - 2hx - 2ky + (h^2 + k^2 - r^2) = 0.$$

This is an equation of the form

$$x^2 + y^2 + Dx + Ey + F = 0,$$

which is called the **general form** of the equation of a circle. The equation of a circle that is given in the general form can be written in form (1) by completing the squares in x and y.

Example. Find the center and radius of the circle whose equation is

$$4x^2 + 4y^2 - 8x + 4y + 1 = 0.$$

Solution: Divide by 4, transpose the constant, and write the equation as

$$x^2 - 2x + y^2 + y = -\tfrac{1}{4}.$$

Completing the squares in x and y, we have

$$x^2 - 2x + 1 + y^2 + y + \tfrac{1}{4} = -\tfrac{1}{4} + 1 + \tfrac{1}{4},$$

or

$$(x-1)^2 + (y+\tfrac{1}{2})^2 = 1.$$

Hence the center of the circle is $(1, -\frac{1}{2})$ and the radius is 1. A graph of the equation is shown in Figure 96.

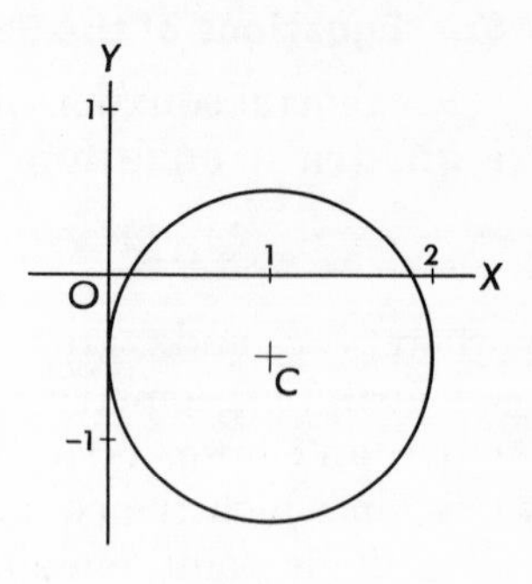

Figure 96

Note: When completing the squares in x and y, if we obtain an equation of the form (1) with $r^2 = 0$, the graph consists of the single point (h,k). If r^2 is negative, there is no graph at all.

64. Circle Determined by Three Conditions

In the preceding article we found that the equation of a circle, when written in either the standard or the general form, contains three arbitrary constants. This means analytically that three *independent* conditions are necessary in order to describe a specific circle.

Since the constants h, k, and r have geometric significance, they are usually the constants most easily found from given conditions. Occasionally, however, the general equation is simpler to use.

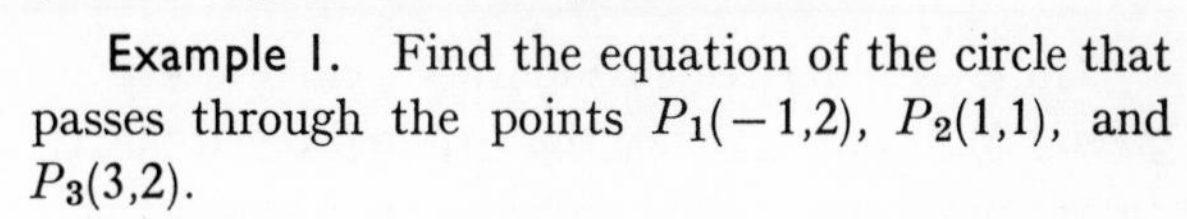

Figure 97

Example 1. Find the equation of the circle that passes through the points $P_1(-1,2)$, $P_2(1,1)$, and $P_3(3,2)$.

First solution: Substituting the coordinates of the given points in the general equation of a circle, we obtain

$$5 - D + 2E + F = 0,$$
$$2 + D + E + F = 0,$$
$$13 + 3D + 2E + F = 0.$$

Solving these equations, we find $D = -2$, $E = -7$, and $F = 7$. Hence the required equation is

$$x^2 + y^2 - 2x - 7y + 7 = 0.$$

Second solution: By the methods used in the first chapter, we find that the equations of the perpendicular bisectors of P_1P_2 and P_2P_3 are, respectively,

$$4x - 2y + 3 = 0,$$

and

$$4x + 2y - 11 = 0,$$

as shown in Figure 97. Since (h,k) is the point of intersection of these lines, we find on solving the equations that $h = 1$ and $k = \frac{7}{2}$. Hence, since the radius is $CP_1 = \sqrt{(1+1)^2 + (\frac{7}{2} - 2)^2} = \frac{5}{2}$, the required equation is

$$(x - 1)^2 + (y - \tfrac{7}{2})^2 = \tfrac{25}{4}.$$

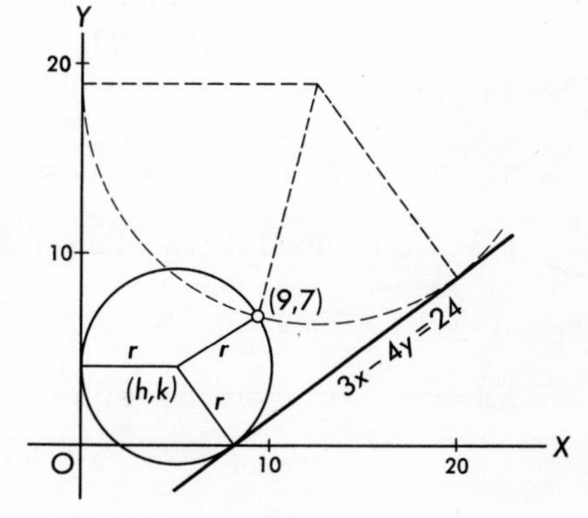

Figure 98

Example 2. Find the equation of the circle that passes through the point (9,7) and is tangent to both the y axis and the line $3x - 4y = 24$.

Solution: The three constants h, k, and r as shown in Figure 98 must satisfy the conditions

$$h = r,$$
$$(h - 9)^2 + (k - 7)^2 = r^2,$$
$$-\left(\frac{3h - 4k - 24}{5}\right) = r.$$

On solving this system of equations, we obtain two solutions

$$h = 5, \qquad k = 4, \qquad r = 5,$$
$$h = \tfrac{25}{2}, \qquad k = 19, \qquad r = \tfrac{25}{2}.$$

Thus, as indicated in Figure 98, there are two circles which satisfy the given conditions. Hence the required equation is

$$(x - 5)^2 + (y - 4)^2 = 25 \qquad \text{or} \qquad (x - \tfrac{25}{2})^2 + (y - 19)^2 = \tfrac{625}{4}.$$

65. Radical Axis

If

$$x^2 + y^2 + Dx + Ey + F = 0$$

and

$$x^2 + y^2 + D'x + E'y + F' = 0$$

are the equations of two non-concentric circles, the equation

$$x^2 + y^2 + Dx + Ey + F + k(x^2 + y^2 + D'x + E'y + F') = 0 \qquad (1)$$

represents a circle for all values of k except $k = -1$. If the given circles intersect in two distinct points, all members of the family (1) will pass through these points. This is evident since any point (x_1,y_1) that satisfies the given equations will make the left side of (1) read $0 + k0$, which is zero for any value of k. If the given circles are tangent at a point, the family (1) will be tangent to them at the point of tangency.

Example 1. Find the equation of the circle that passes through the points of intersection of the circles $x^2 + y^2 = 2x$, $x^2 + y^2 = 2y$, and contains the point (2,1).

Solution: In accordance with (1), the required equation has the form

$$x^2 + y^2 - 2x + k(x^2 + y^2 - 2y) = 0. \qquad (2)$$

To find the member of this family that passes through the point (2,1), we substitute $x = 2$ and $y = 1$; thus

$$4 + 1 - 4 + k(4 + 1 - 2) = 0; \quad \text{hence } k = -\tfrac{1}{3}.$$

Substituting this value of k in (2) and simplifying, we obtain

$$x^2 + y^2 - 3x + y = 0.$$

If we set $k = -1$ in (1), we obtain

$$\mathbf{(D - D')x + (E - E')y + (F - F') = 0.}$$

This line, called the **radical axis** of the two circles, has the following properties which are stated without proof.

1. *If two circles intersect in two distinct points, their radical axis contains the common chord of the circles.*
2. *If two circles are tangent, their radical axis is the common tangent to the circles at their point of tangency.*
3. *The radical axis of two circles is perpendicular to their line of centers.*
4. *All tangents drawn to two circles from a point on their radical axis have the same length.*

Example 2. Find the point where the common chord of the circles $x^2 + y^2 = 25$ and $x^2 + y^2 - 12x - 6y + 35 = 0$ crosses their line of centers.

Solution: Subtracting the given equations, we obtain the equation of the radical axis

$$2x + y = 10. \tag{3}$$

Writing the equation of the second circle in standard form,

$$(x - 6)^2 + (y - 3)^2 = 10,$$

we obtain its center (6,3). Since the center of the first circle is at the origin, the equation of the line of centers is

$$x - 2y = 0. \tag{4}$$

Solving (3) and (4) simultaneously, we obtain the required point (4,2).

EXERCISE 32

In each of the following, find the equation of the circle determined by the given conditions, and draw the figure.

1. Radius 4, center at $(-2,5)$. *Ans.* $x^2 + y^2 + 4x - 10y + 13 = 0$.
2. Containing the origin, center at $(0,-3)$.
3. Containing $(-4,-3)$, center at $(4,2)$. $x^2 + y^2 - 8x - 4y - 69 = 0$.
4. Tangent to y axis, center at $(4,-1)$.
5. Tangent to both axes, center in second quadrant, radius 2.
   Ans. $x^2 + y^2 + 4x - 4y + 4 = 0$.
6. Having as diameter the line segment from $(-1,1)$ to $(3,4)$.
7. Tangent to the line $4x - 3y + 10 = 0$, center at $(5,5)$.
   Ans. $x^2 + y^2 - 10x - 10y + 41 = 0$.
8. Tangent to the y axis at $(0,5)$, radius 3. (Two answers.)

Find the center and radius of the following circles.

9. $x^2 + y^2 + 4x - 6y - 12 = 0$. *Ans.* $(-2,3)$, 5.
10. $4x^2 + 4y^2 - 4x + 12y - 15 = 0$.

11. $2x^2 + 2y^2 - 17x = 0$. *Ans.* $(\frac{17}{4},0)$, $\frac{17}{4}$.

12. $5x^2 + 5y^2 - 19x + 30y + 15 = 0$.

In each of the following, find the equation of the circle determined by the given conditions.

13. Passes through the points (2,3), (6,1), and (4,−3).
Ans. $x^2 + y^2 - 6x - 1 = 0$.

14. Passes through the points (−3,1), (5,−3), and (−2,4).

15. Center on the y axis, and passes through the origin and the point (4,2).
Ans. $x^2 + y^2 - 10y = 0$.

16. Center on the line $y = x$, tangent to the line $y = 5$, and has radius 2.

17. Passes through the point (2,2), and tangent to the lines $x = 1$ and $x = 6$.
Ans. $x^2 + y^2 - 7x + 6 = 0$, or $x^2 + y^2 - 7x - 8y + 22 = 0$.

18. Tangent to the y axis, and passes through the points (1,5) and (8,−2).

19. Has radius 5 and tangent to the line $3x + 4y = 24$ at the point $(2,4\frac{1}{2})$.
Ans. $4x^2 + 4y^2 + 8x - 4y - 95 = 0$,
$4x^2 + 4y^2 - 40x - 68y + 289 = 0$.

20. Center on the line $8x + 5y = 8$ and passes through the points (2,1) and (3,5).

21. Circumscribes the triangle determined by the lines $y = 0$, $y = x$, and $2x + 3y = 10$. *Ans.* $x^2 + y^2 - 5x + y = 0$.

22. Is inscribed in the triangle determined by the lines $y = 0$, $3x - 4y + 30 = 0$, and $4x + 3y = 60$.

23. Passes through the points of intersection of the circles $x^2 + y^2 = 5$, $x^2 + y^2 - x + y = 4$, and through the point (2,−3).
Ans. $x^2 + y^2 - 2x + 2y - 3 = 0$.

24. Passes through the points of intersection of the circles $x^2 + y^2 = 5y - 4$, $2x^2 + 2y^2 = x + 5$, and through the point (−2,0).

25. Passes through the points of intersection of the circles $x^2 + y^2 = 2x$, $x^2 + y^2 = 2y$, and has its center on the line $y = 2$.
Ans. $x^2 + y^2 + 2x - 4y = 0$.

26. Passes through the points of intersection of the circles $x^2 + y^2 - 4x + 6y = 12$, $x^2 + y^2 + 4x - 8y = 28$, and has its center on the y axis.

27. Find the equation of the diameter of the circle $x^2 + y^2 + 2x - 4y = 4$ that is parallel to the line $3x + 5y = 4$. *Ans.* $3x + 5y = 7$.

28. Find the equation of the line tangent to the circle $x^2 + y^2 - 8x - 8y + 7 = 0$ at the point (1,0).

29. Find the equation of the smaller circle that is tangent to the axes and the circle $x^2 + y^2 = 2x + 2y - 1$.
Ans. $x^2 + y^2 = (3 - 2\sqrt{2})(2x + 2y - 3 + 2\sqrt{2})$.

30. Determine whether or not the radical axis of the circles $x^2 + y^2 = 4x$ and $2x^2 + 2y^2 - 3x - y = 5$ passes through the point $(\frac{1}{2},-2)$.

31. Find the radius and center of the circle that passes through the points (2,0), (18,0), and is tangent to the curve $x = \sqrt{y}$.
Ans. $C(10,2), r = 2\sqrt{17}$.

32. Find the equations of the two lines parallel to the line $4x - 3y = 0$ and tangent to the circle $x^2 + y^2 + 6x - 6y = 7$.

33. Prove that the equation of the line tangent to the circle $x^2 + y^2 = r^2$ at any point (x_1, y_1) on the circle is $x_1x + y_1y = r^2$.

34. The point $P_1(x_1, y_1)$ lies outside the circle whose center is (h,k) and whose radius is r. If T is the length of a tangent from P_1 to the circle, prove that $T^2 = (x_1 - h)^2 + (y_1 - k)^2 - r^2$.

35. Given three circles whose centers are not collinear, prove analytically that the radical axes of the circles taken in pairs meet in a point (called the *radical center*).

36. Prove analytically that the radical axis of two circles is perpendicular to their line of centers.

66. The Parabola

The locus of a point which moves so that its distances from a fixed point and a fixed line are equal is called a parabola. The fixed point and line are called the **focus** and **directrix** of the parabola, respectively.

In accordance with this definition, a parabola can be constructed with a ruler and compass by locating points on it as follows. In Figure 99 let DD' be the directrix and F the focus. The line FA, drawn through F perpendicular to DD', is called the **axis** of the parabola, and the mid-point V of the segment AF is a point on the parabola called the **vertex.**

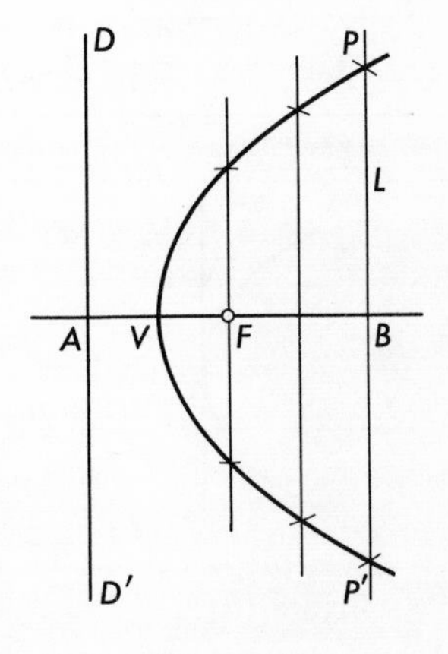

Figure 99

To obtain other points on the parabola draw any line, such as L, parallel to DD' and intersecting the axis at a point, say B. Now with F as a center and AB as a radius, describe arcs intersecting L at P and P'. Since these points are each equidistant from F and DD', they are points on the parabola. When a sufficient number of points are determined in this manner, the parabola can be drawn.

Although a parabola can be located on a coordinate system in any position whatsoever, it is advisable when possible to select a position that will avoid unnecessary complications. Thus let us consider, as shown in Figure 100, a parabola that has its axis coinciding with the x axis, its vertex at the origin, its focus at the point $(a,0)$, and its directrix coinciding with the line $x = -a$, where a, called the **focal distance,** is positive.

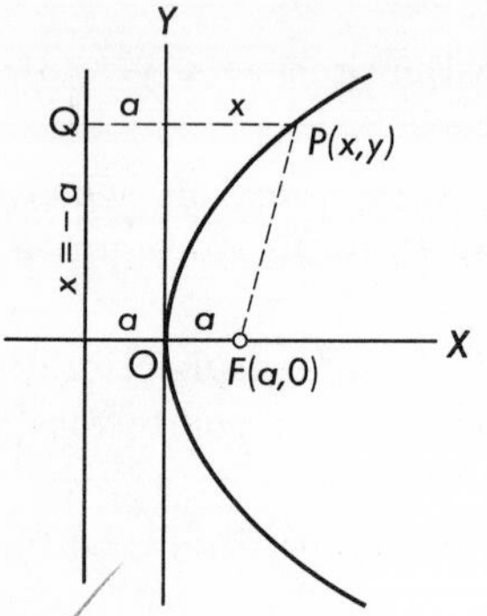

Figure 100

To find the equation of this parabola, we choose any point $P(x,y)$ on the locus and draw PQ perpendicular to the directrix. Then by the definition of a parabola, we have $FP = PQ$, or, in terms of the co-ordinates,

$$\sqrt{(x-a)^2 + y^2} = a + x.$$

Squaring and simplifying, we obtain the equation

$$\mathbf{y^2 = 4ax.} \tag{1}$$

The chord through the focus and perpendicular to the axis is called the **latus rectum** of a parabola. Substituting $x = a$ in (1), we find $y = \pm 2a$; hence the length of the latus rectum is $4a$, or four times the focal distance. This is an intrinsic property common to all parabolas.

By a derivation similar to that above, it can be proven that the

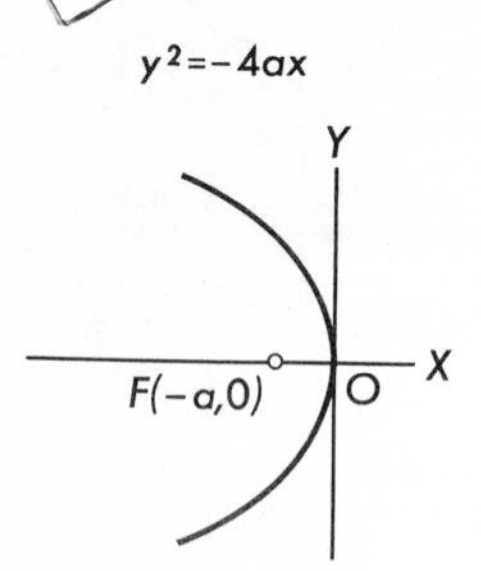

Figure 101A

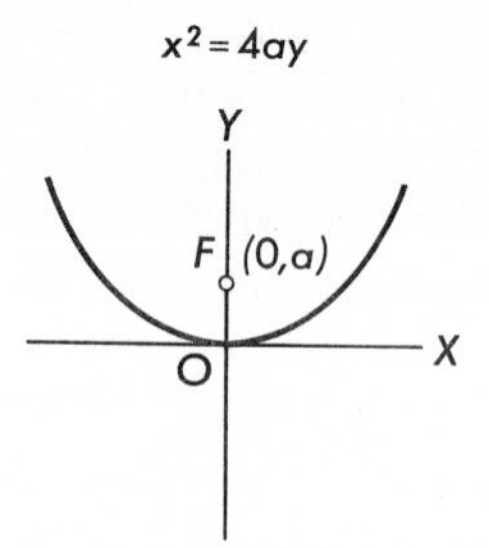

Figure 101B

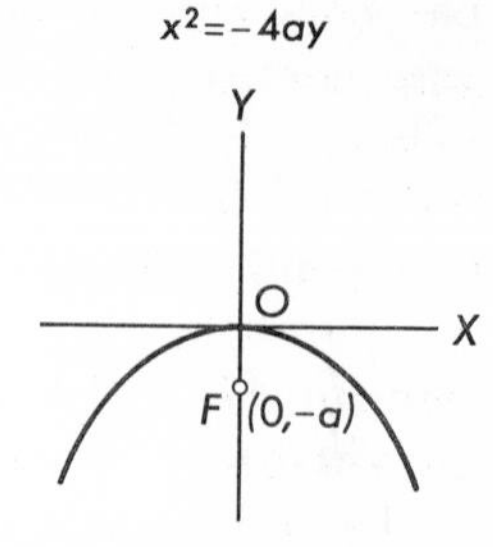

Figure 101C

parabolas shown in Figures 101A, 101B, and 101C, have the equations as indicated.

Illustration. By writing the equation of the parabola $3x^2 + 8y = 0$ in the form $x^2 = -\frac{8}{3}y$, we note that its focal distance is $\frac{2}{3}$. Hence the focus of the parabola is at the point $(0, -\frac{2}{3})$, its directrix is the line $x = \frac{2}{3}$, and the length of its latus rectum is $\frac{8}{3}$.

67. Another Construction of a Parabola

Inasmuch as the parabola has many technical applications in engineering, it is of some importance to be able to construct a parabolic arc when only its height and span are known.

Thus, for the parabolic arch shown in Figure 102, let $2c$ denote the span $B'B$ and h the height OA. The arc is constructed by dividing OC into any desired number of equal parts, and CB into the same number of equal parts. Then through the points of division on OC draw lines parallel to OA, and join the points of division of CB to O. The intersection of corresponding lines in these two sets of lines is a point on the arc.

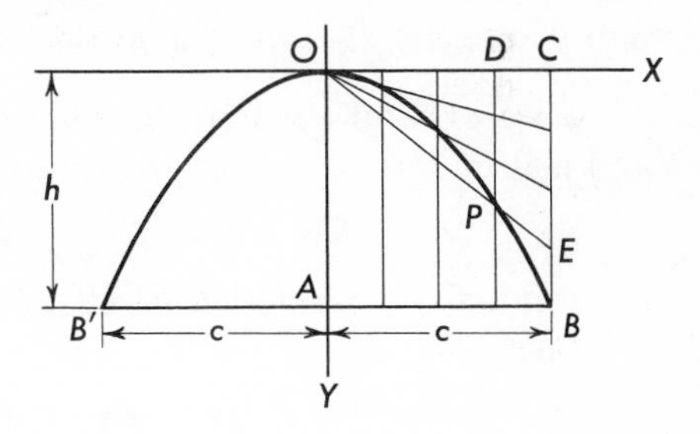

Figure 102

To verify this fact let us take O as the origin and the positive direction of the y axis downward. Then, if $P(x,y)$ is the point of intersection of two corresponding lines, we see that $x = OD$, $y = DP$, and by similar triangles

$$\frac{x}{c} = \frac{y}{CE}.$$

Since OC and CB were divided into the same number of equal parts, it follows that

$$\frac{x}{c} = \frac{CE}{h}.$$

Hence, on eliminating CE from these equations, we obtain

$$x^2 = \frac{c^2}{h}y,$$

which is the equation of a parabola.

68. General Equations of a Parabola

By methods similar to those discussed in Article **66**, we can readily establish the following results, which are now summarized for convenience.

A parabola whose axis is horizontal or vertical and whose vertex is the point (h,k) has the equation

$$(y - k)^2 = 4a(x - h), \quad \textit{when it opens to the right;}$$
$$(y - k)^2 = -4a(x - h), \quad \textit{when it opens to the left;}$$

$$(x - h)^2 = 4a(y - k), \qquad \textit{when it opens upward;}$$
$$(x - h)^2 = -4a(y - k), \qquad \textit{when it opens downward;}$$

where a denotes the distance from the vertex to the focus.

These are called the **standard forms** of the equation of a parabola.

Illustration. Let (3,2) and (3,1) be the vertex and focus of a parabola, respectively. Since the focal distance from the vertex to the focus is one unit downward, the equation of the parabola is $(x - 3)^2 = -4(y - 2)$.

If we expand the parentheses in each of the above standard forms and collect terms, we obtain equations of the form

$$y^2 + Dx + Ey + F = 0, \quad \text{or} \quad x^2 + Dx + Ey + F = 0.$$

Since the above reduction is reversible, we have the following result.

Theorem. *The equations of the second degree in* x *and* y

$$y^2 + Dx + Ey + F = 0, \qquad (D \neq 0)$$
$$x^2 + Dx + Ey + F = 0, \qquad (E \neq 0)$$

which contain no xy term and only one squared term represent parabolas whose axes are parallel to the x and y axes, respectively.

These equations are called **general forms** of the equation of a parabola.

Example. Find the vertex, focus, end points of the latus rectum, and sketch the parabola whose equation is $4y^2 + 8x - 12y - 7 = 0$.

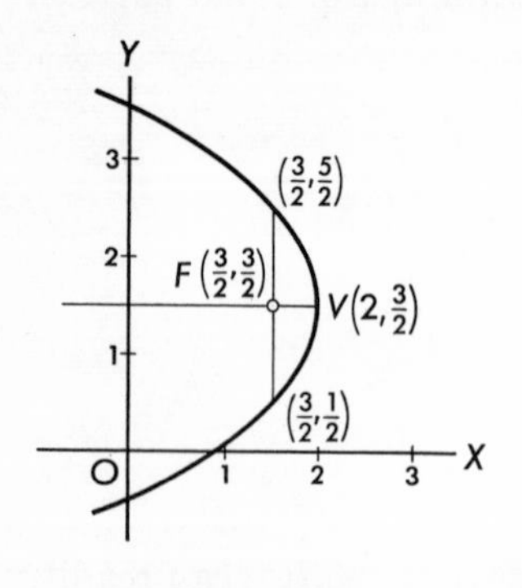

Figure 103

Solution: Divide by 4 and write the equation as

$$y^2 - 3y = -2x + \tfrac{7}{4}.$$

Adding $\frac{9}{4}$ to both sides and factoring, we obtain

$$(y - \tfrac{3}{2})^2 = -2(x - 2).$$

Hence, as shown in Figure 103, the parabola has its vertex at $(2,\frac{3}{2})$ and its focus $\frac{1}{2}$ unit to the left at the point $(\frac{3}{2},\frac{3}{2})$. Since the latus rectum extends $2a$ units above and below the focus, its end points are $(\frac{3}{2},\frac{5}{2})$ and $(\frac{3}{2},\frac{1}{2})$.

69. Parabolas Determined by Three Conditions

Since the equations of the parabolas discussed in the preceding article contain three arbitrary constants, three independent conditions are needed in order to determine a specific parabola.

Example 1. Find the equation of the parabola with horizontal axis which crosses the x axis at $x = 2$, and the y axis at $y = -1$ and $y = 7$.

Solution: Substituting the coordinates of the points (2,0), (0,−1), and (0,7) in the equation

$$y^2 + Dx + Ey + F = 0,$$

we obtain

$$0 + 2D + 0 \quad + F = 0,$$
$$1 + 0 \quad - \quad E + F = 0,$$
$$49 + 0 \quad + 7E + F = 0.$$

Solving these equations, we find that $D = \frac{7}{2}$, $E = -6$, and $F = -7$. Hence the required equation is

$$2y^2 + 7x - 12y - 14 = 0,$$

whose graph is shown in Figure 104.

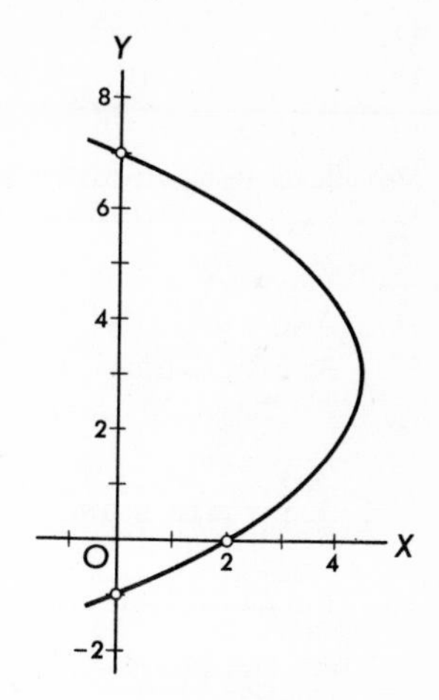

Figure 104

Example 2. Find the equation of the parabola with vertical axis whose focus is the point (2,1) and whose latus rectum has length 4.

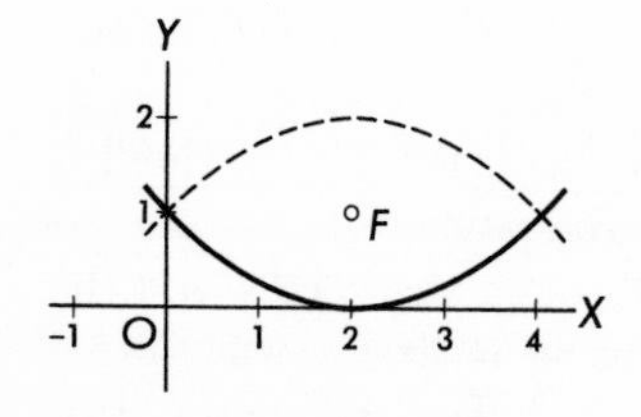

Figure 105

Solution: Since the focal distance is one-fourth the length of the latus rectum, we have $a = 1$. Thus the vertex of the parabola, as shown in Figure 105, is located at the point (2,0) or (2,2), and the corresponding equations are

$$(x - 2)^2 = 4y, \quad \text{or} \quad (x - 2)^2 = -4(y - 2).$$

EXERCISE 33

Find the vertex, focus, and end points of the latus rectum for each of the following parabolas, and sketch the graph.

1. $y^2 + 8x = 0$. *Ans.* $V(0,0)$, $F(-2,0)$, $E(-2, \pm 4)$.
2. $x^2 - 4y + 8 = 0$.
3. $x^2 - 2x - y = 0$. $V(1,-1)$, $F(1,-\frac{3}{4})$, $E(1 \pm \frac{1}{2}, -\frac{3}{4})$.
4. $y^2 - 6x + 3 = 0$.
5. $y^2 + 3x - 2y + 7 = 0$. $V(-2,1)$, $F(-\frac{11}{4},1)$, $E(-\frac{11}{4}, 1 \pm \frac{3}{2})$.
6. $x^2 - 2x - 3y + 10 = 0$.
7. $2y^2 - 5x + 3y - 7 = 0$. $V(-\frac{13}{8}, -\frac{3}{4})$, $F(-1, -\frac{3}{4})$, $E(-1, -\frac{3}{4} \pm \frac{5}{4})$.
8. $9x^2 - 12x - 36y - 8 = 0$.
9. $4y^2 - x + 2y = 0$. $V(-\frac{1}{4}, -\frac{1}{4})$, $F(-\frac{3}{16}, -\frac{1}{4})$, $E(-\frac{3}{16}, -\frac{1}{4} \pm \frac{1}{8})$.
10. $5x^2 - 5x + 7y - 4 = 0$.

In each of the following, find the equation of the parabola determined by the given conditions.

11. Focus (1,0), vertex (2,0). *Ans.* $y^2 + 4x - 8 = 0$.
12. Focus $(1,-1)$, directrix $y = 2$.
13. Vertex (0,3), directrix $x = -1$. $y^2 - 4x - 6y + 9 = 0$.
14. Axis horizontal, vertex (1,2), latus rectum 6.
15. Axis vertical, vertex $(-1,-1)$, and passing through (2,2).
Ans. $x^2 + 2x - 3y - 2 = 0$.
16. Axis horizontal, focus (0,0), latus rectum 8.
17. Axis horizontal, vertex on y axis, and passing through (2,4) and $(8,-2)$.
Ans. $y^2 - 2x - 4y + 4 = 0$, $y^2 - 18x - 20y + 100 = 0$.
18. Axis vertical, latus rectum 4, and passing through (6,4) and $(-4,-1)$.
19. Axis vertical and passing through (0,0), (1,0), and $(5,-20)$.
Ans. $x^2 - x + y = 0$.
20. Focus $(-1,4)$, end point of latus rectum $(-1,1)$.

Find the points of intersection of the following curves.

21. $\begin{cases} y = 2x + 4, \\ y^2 = 4x + 8. \end{cases}$ *Ans.* $(-2,0)$, $(-1,2)$.
22. $\begin{cases} 3x - 7y + 1 = 0, \\ y^2 - 3x + 5y = 0. \end{cases}$
23. $\begin{cases} x^2 - 4y = 1, \\ x^2 + x - 2y = 8. \end{cases}$ (3,2), $(-5,6)$.
24. $\begin{cases} x^2 + x - y = 0, \\ y^2 + 2x = 0. \end{cases}$
25. A chord passing through the focus of the parabola $y^2 = 8x$ has one end at the point (8,8). Where is the other end of the chord? *Ans.* $(\frac{1}{2},-2)$.
26. Find the locus of a point which moves so that its distance from the line $x + y + 1 = 0$ is equal to its distance from the point (1,1).
27. Find the equation of the circle that passes through the vertex and the end points of the latus rectum of the parabola $y^2 = 8x$.
Ans. $x^2 + y^2 = 10x$.
28. Find the length of the chord common to the parabolas $y^2 = 2x + 4y + 6$ and $y^2 = 3x + 3y + 1$.
29. Find the equation of the parabola with vertical axis that passes through the point (0,2) and the points of intersection of the parabolas $x^2 + 2x + 3y + 4 = 0$ and $x^2 - 3x + y + 3 = 0$. *Ans.* $x^2 - 8x - y + 2 = 0$.
30. In triangle ABC if $\tan A \tan \frac{1}{2}B = 2$ and AB is fixed, show that the locus of C is a parabola with its vertex at A and focus at B. *Hint:* Put A at (0,0), B at $(a,0)$, and observe that $\tan A = y/x$.
31. Show that the equation of the line tangent to the parabola $y^2 = 4ax$ at the point (x_1,y_1) is $y_1y = 2a(x + x_1)$.
32. Using the result of Problem 31, show that the equation of the line normal to the parabola $y^2 = 4ax$ at the point (x_1,y_1) is $y_1(x - x_1) + 2a(y - y_1) = 0$.
33. For all parabolas show that the angle between the line segments joining the end points of the latus rectum to the vertex is $2 \operatorname{Tan}^{-1}2$.

34. Show that the circle having the latus rectum of a parabola as diameter is tangent to the directrix.
35. When the load is uniformly distributed horizontally, the cable of a suspension bridge hangs in a parabolic arc. If a bridge is 300 feet long, the towers 60 feet high, and the cable 20 feet above the roadbed at the center, find the distance from the roadbed to the cables at intervals of 50 feet. *Ans.* $37\frac{7}{9}$ ft., $24\frac{4}{9}$ ft.
36. Draw a line from the point $P(0,b)$ to the focus F of the parabola $y^2 = 4ax$. Prove that the line perpendicular to PF at P is tangent to the parabola at the point $(b^2/a,2b)$.

70. The Ellipse

The locus of a point which moves so that the sum of its distances from two fixed points is constant is called an ellipse. The fixed points are called the **foci** of the ellipse, and the line joining them the **principal axis.**

In accordance with this definition, an ellipse can be constructed mechanically, as shown in Figure 106, by placing tacks at the foci F' and F, and putting a loop of string of length $F'F + 2a$ over them, where $2a$ denotes the constant length which is referred to in the definition and which is necessarily greater than $F'F$. If a pencil is placed at P and moved so as to keep the string taut, it will describe an ellipse. This is true since in all positions the point P satisfies the condition $F'P + FP = 2a$.

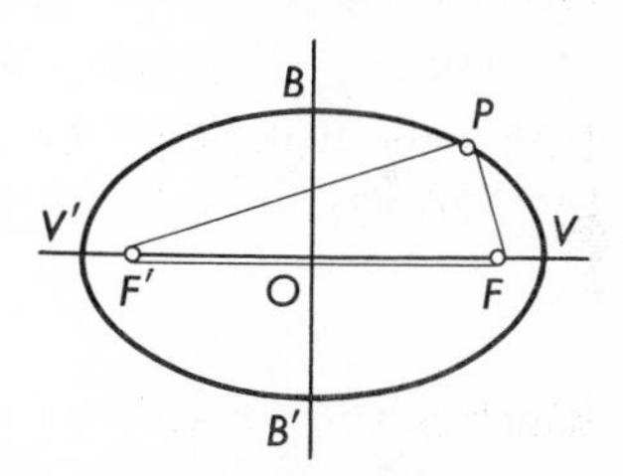

Figure 106

It is evident from the preceding construction that an ellipse is symmetric with respect to its principal axis and also with respect to the line $B'B$, which is the perpendicular bisector of $F'F$. The point of intersection O of $B'B$ and $F'F$ is thus a point of symmetry and is called the **center** of the ellipse. The chords of an ellipse that pass through the center are called **diameters,** and the end points V' and V of the diameter through the foci are called the **vertices.** The diameter $V'V$ has a length equal to $2a$. This follows from the definition, $FV + F'V = 2a$, and the symmetry, $V'F' = FV$; thus $V'F' + F'V = V'V = 2a$. It is also evident by symmetry that the length of BF is a. Thus, if the lengths of OB and OF are denoted by b and c, respectively, we obtain from the right triangle BOF the basic relation

$$a^2 = b^2 + c^2, \tag{1}$$

which connects the lengths of the semiaxes and the so-called **focal distance.** This relation indicates that $b < a$; and $V'V$ and $B'B$ are called, respectively, the **major** and **minor axes** of the ellipse.

In order to develop its analytic properties let us consider an ellipse that has its center at the origin and its foci on the x axis, as shown in Figure 107. If the foci are denoted as $F'(-c,0)$ and $F(c,0)$, the vertices as $V'(-a,0)$ and $V(a,0)$, and the ends of the minor axis as $B'(0, -b)$ and $B(0,b)$, the definition requires that a point $P(x,y)$ on the ellipse satisfy $F'P + FP = 2a$, which in terms of the coordinates is

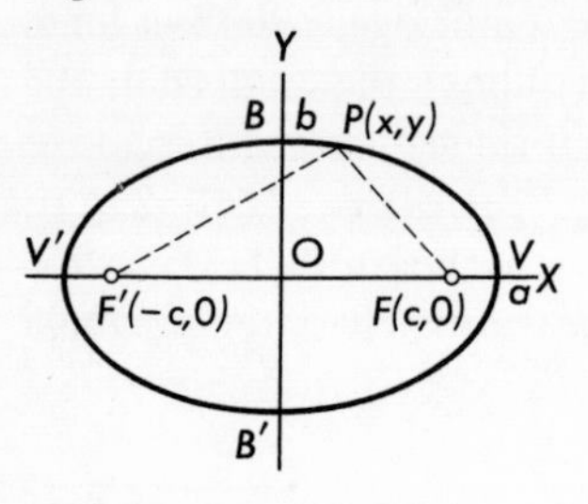

Figure 107

$$\sqrt{(x + c)^2 + y^2} + \sqrt{(x - c)^2 + y^2} = 2a.$$

Transposing the second radical, squaring, and simplifying, we get

$$cx - a^2 = -a\sqrt{(x - c)^2 + y^2}.$$

Squaring again and simplifying, we obtain

$$(a^2 - c^2)x^2 + a^2y^2 = a^2(a^2 - c^2).$$

Now substituting b^2 for $a^2 - c^2$ in accordance with (1), and dividing by a^2b^2, we have

$$\frac{\boldsymbol{x^2}}{\boldsymbol{a^2}} + \frac{\boldsymbol{y^2}}{\boldsymbol{b^2}} = \mathbf{1},$$

which is the equation of the ellipse shown in Figure 107.

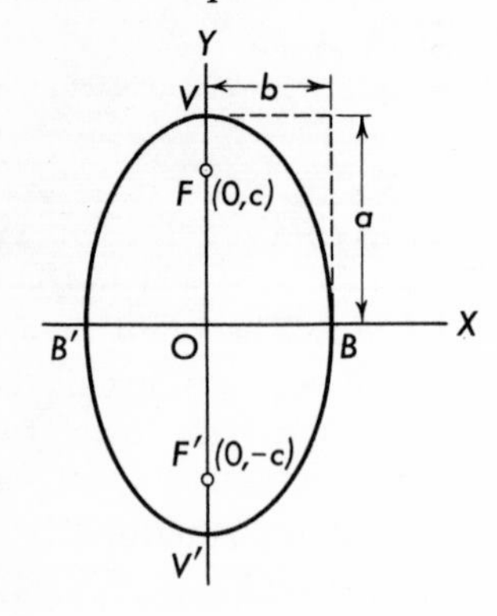

Figure 108

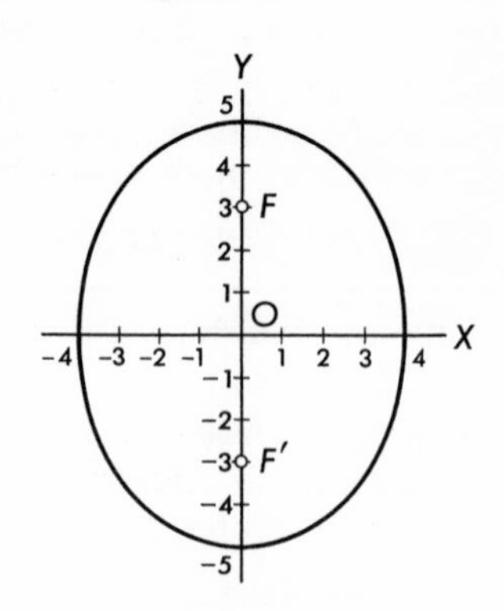

Figure 109

In like manner, when the center is at the origin and the foci are on the y axis, as shown in Figure 108, the equation of the ellipse is

$$\frac{\boldsymbol{y^2}}{\boldsymbol{a^2}} + \frac{\boldsymbol{x^2}}{\boldsymbol{b^2}} = \mathbf{1},$$

where, as before, a and b denote the semimajor and semiminor axes, respectively.

Example. Find the lengths of the semiaxes, locate the foci, and sketch the ellipse whose equation is $25x^2 + 16y^2 = 400$.

Solution: The intercepts on the coordinate axes are $x = \pm\sqrt{\frac{400}{25}} = \pm 4$, and $y = \pm\sqrt{\frac{400}{16}} = \pm 5$. Hence the major axis lies along the y axis, and the semiaxes of the ellipse are $a = 5$ and $b = 4$. Since $c^2 = a^2 - b^2$, we find that $c = 3$. Thus the foci are $(0, \pm 3)$, as shown in Figure 109.

71. Another Construction of an Ellipse

When only the lengths of the semiaxes, a and b, are known, an ellipse can be drawn in the following manner.

On the edge of a straight strip of paper mark three points A, M, and P, so that $AP = a$ and $MP = b$, as shown in Figure 110. Then, as indicated in Figure 111, the strip of paper is placed on two perpendicular lines, L and L', so that A and M fall, respectively, on L and L'. A point is put on the paper opposite the mark P. This is a point of the ellipse. When a sufficient number of points have been plotted in this manner, the ellipse can be drawn.

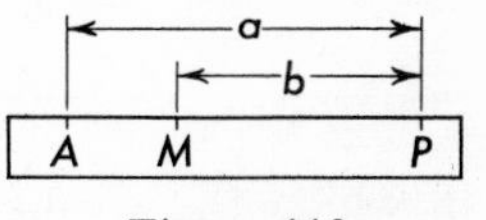

Figure 110

To prove that the locus of point P in Figure 111 is an ellipse, construct AR and PR parallel to the x and y axes respectively. Since $AP = a$ and $MP = b$, by similar triangles, we have

$$\frac{y}{b} = \frac{PR}{a},$$

and from the right triangle ARP we have

$$x^2 + PR^2 = a^2.$$

Eliminating PR from these equations, we obtain

$$\frac{x^2}{a^2} + \frac{y^2}{b^2} = 1,$$

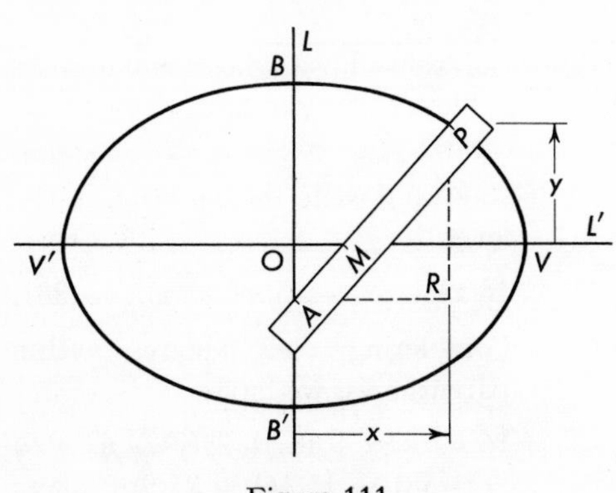

Figure 111

which is the equation of an ellipse.

72. General Equations of an Ellipse

By methods similar to those discussed in Article **70**, we can readily establish the following results which are now summarized for convenience.

The **standard form** *of the equation of an ellipse whose center is the point* **(*h*,*k*)** *is*

$$\frac{(x-h)^2}{a^2}+\frac{(y-k)^2}{b^2}=1, \qquad \textit{for horizontal major axis,}$$

$$\frac{(y-k)^2}{a^2}+\frac{(x-h)^2}{b^2}=1, \qquad \textit{for vertical major axis,}$$

where ***a*** *and* ***b*** *are the lengths of the semimajor and semiminor axes, respectively.*

If we expand the parentheses in either of the above equations and collect terms, we obtain an equation of the form

$$Ax^2 + Cy^2 + Dx + Ey + F = 0,$$

in which the coefficients A and C are positive and unequal. This is called the **general form** of the equation of an ellipse. Not all equations of this form, however, represent ellipses. There are two degenerate cases. When the left member is written as the sum of two squares, the right member may be zero or it may be negative. In the former case the locus is the single point (h,k), and in the latter case there is no locus.

Example. Find the center and foci of the ellipse whose equation is $16x^2 + 25y^2 - 128x - 150y + 381 = 0$. Sketch the graph.

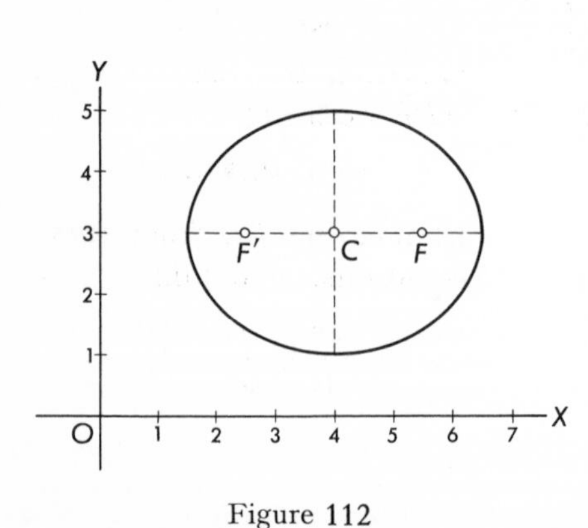

Figure 112

Solution: Transpose the constant and write the equation in the form

$$16(x^2 - 8x) + 25(y^2 - 6y) = -381.$$

Completing the squares within parentheses, we have

$$16(x^2 - 8x + 16) + 25(y^2 - 6y + 9) = -381 + 16(16) + 25(9)$$

$$16(x-4)^2 + 25(y-3)^2 = 100,$$

or

$$\frac{(x-4)^2}{\frac{25}{4}}+\frac{(y-3)^2}{4}=1.$$

Since $\frac{25}{4} > 4$, the major axis is horizontal, and $a = \frac{5}{2}$ and $b = 2$. The center is $(4,3)$, and from $c = \sqrt{a^2 - b^2}$ we have $c = \sqrt{\frac{25}{4} - 4} = \frac{3}{2}$. Hence the foci are $(\frac{5}{2},3)$ and $(\frac{11}{2},3)$. A sketch of the ellipse is shown in Figure 112.

73. Ellipses Determined by Four Conditions

Since the equations discussed in the preceding article contain four arbitrary constants, an ellipse with horizontal and vertical axes is determined by four conditions. These conditions, however, must be consistent with the restrictions placed on the arbitrary constants.

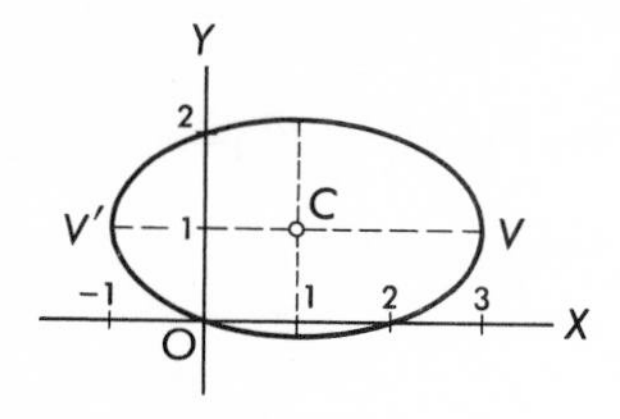

Figure 113

Example 1. Find the general equation of the ellipse that has its center at (1,1), a vertex at (3,1), and that passes through the origin.

Solution: It is evident from the stated conditions that $h = 1$, $k = 1$, and $a = 2$; hence the equation can be written as

$$\frac{(x-1)^2}{4} + \frac{(y-1)^2}{b^2} = 1. \qquad (1)$$

To determine b^2, we substitute $x = 0$ and $y = 0$ in (1); thus

$$\frac{1}{4} + \frac{1}{b^2} = 1; \quad \text{hence} \quad b^2 = \frac{4}{3}.$$

Substituting this value of b^2 in (1) and expanding the parentheses, we obtain the required equation

$$x^2 + 3y^2 - 2x - 6y = 0,$$

whose graph is shown in Figure 113.

Example 2. Find the locus of a point which moves so that its distance from the point $(ae,0)$ is e $(0 < e < 1)$ times its distance from the line $x = a/e$.

Solution: If $P(x,y)$, as shown in Figure 114, is a point on the locus, we have

$$\sqrt{(x-ae)^2 + y^2} = e\left(\frac{a}{e} - x\right) = a - ex$$

$$x^2 - 2aex + a^2e^2 + y^2 = a^2 - 2aex + e^2x^2$$

$$(1 - e^2)x^2 + y^2 = a^2(1 - e^2)$$

$$\frac{x^2}{a^2} + \frac{y^2}{a^2(1-e^2)} = 1.$$

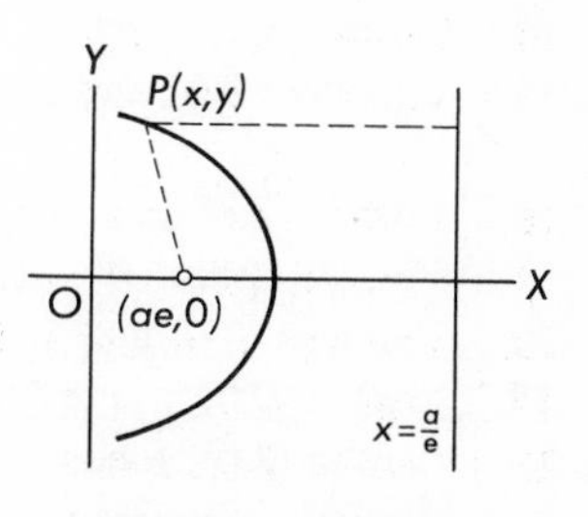

Figure 114

Thus we see that the locus is an ellipse having its center at the origin, its vertices at the points $(\pm a,0)$, and a semiminor axis equal to $a\sqrt{1-e^2}$. It also follows from $c^2 = a^2 - b^2 = a^2 - a^2(1 - e^2) = a^2e^2$ that the points $(\pm ae,0)$ are the foci of the ellipse.

The definition of an ellipse is often given in this form.

The locus of a point which moves so that its distance from a fixed point is a constant fraction e ($e < 1$) of its distance from a fixed line is called an ***ellipse.***

The fixed point and line are called a **focus** and **directrix,** respectively, and the constant e is called the **eccentricity** of the ellipse.

EXERCISE 34

Find the center, foci, and semiaxes for each of the following ellipses, and sketch the graph.

1. $x^2 + 4y^2 = 4$. *Ans.* $C(0,0)$, $F(\pm\sqrt{3},0)$, 2, 1.
2. $9x^2 + 4y^2 = 36$.
3. $4x^2 + y^2 = 8x$. $C(1,0)$, $F(1,\pm\sqrt{3})$, 2, 1.
4. $x^2 + 4y^2 = 4x + 8y$.
5. $2x^2 + y^2 - 4y + 3 = 0$. $C(0,2)$, $F\left(0,2 \pm \frac{1}{\sqrt{2}}\right)$, 1, $\frac{1}{\sqrt{2}}$.
6. $25x^2 + 16y^2 + 200x = 0$.
7. $x^2 + 3y^2 + 4x + 6y + 1 = 0$. $C(-2,-1)$, $F(-2 \pm 2,-1)$, $\sqrt{6}$, $\sqrt{2}$.
8. $9x^2 + 5y^2 - 6x + 10y - 39 = 0$.
9. $16x^2 + 25y^2 + 16x + 4 = 100y$. $C(-\frac{1}{2},2)$, $F(-\frac{1}{2} \pm \frac{3}{2},2)$, $\frac{5}{2}$, 2.
10. $20x^2 + 36y^2 + 9 = 60x + 36y$.

In each of the following, find the equation of the ellipse determined by the given conditions.

11. Center (2,0), focus (5,0), $b = 4$. *Ans.* $16x^2 + 25y^2 - 64x - 336 = 0$.
12. Center $(-1,1)$, focus (1,1), vertex (2,1).
13. Center $(-1,-2)$, vertex $(-1,0)$, $b = 1$. $4x^2 + y^2 + 8x + 4y + 4 = 0$.
14. Center (1,3), vertex $(1,-1)$, and passing through the origin.
15. Vertices (2,6) and $(2,-4)$, $b = 4$.
    Ans. $25x^2 + 16y^2 - 100x - 32y - 284 = 0$.
16. Foci $(-2,3)$ and (4,3), $b = 4$.
17. Foci (2,1) and $(2,-1)$, $a = 2$. $4x^2 + 3y^2 - 16x + 4 = 0$.
18. Vertices (0,0) and (0,8), focus (0,1).
19. Center (0,0), vertex (0,4), eccentricity $\frac{1}{2}$. $4x^2 + 3y^2 - 48 = 0$.
20. Center (2,0), focus (2,6), eccentricity $\frac{2}{3}$.
21. Find the equation of the locus of a point which moves so that the sum of its distances from the points (2,1) and (8,1) is 10.
    Ans. $16x^2 + 25y^2 - 160x - 50y + 25 = 0$.
22. Find the equation of the locus of a point which moves so that the sum of its distances from the points $(-1,-1)$ and $(-1,3)$ is 6.
23. Find the equation of the locus of a point which moves so that its distance from the point (2,0) is two-thirds its distance from the line $y = 5$.
    Ans. $9x^2 + 5y^2 - 36x + 40y - 64 = 0$.

24. Find the equation of the locus of a point which moves so that its distance from the point $(-2,1)$ is one-half its distance from the line $x = 4$.
25. Is the point $(5,3)$ inside or outside the ellipse $4x^2 + 9y^2 - 24x - 36y + 36 = 0$? *Ans.* Inside.
26. Find the length of the chord which is common to the ellipses $x^2 + 4y^2 = 8x$ and $x^2 + 4y^2 = 8y$.
27. Find the eccentricity of an ellipse whose major axis is twice as long as its minor axis. *Ans.* $\frac{1}{2}\sqrt{3}$.
28. Does the origin O lie inside or outside the ellipse that passes through the point $(2,4)$ and has foci at $(5,0)$ and $(0,3)$?
29. In the ellipse $x^2 + 3y^2 + 2x - 6y = 0$, find the length of the diameter which has a slope 1. *Ans.* $2\sqrt{2}$.
30. The arch of a concrete bridge is a semiellipse having a span of 60 feet and a central height of 20 feet. If the roadway is 25 feet above the base, find at 10-foot intervals the distance from the arch to the roadway.
31. Find the equation of the line that is tangent to the ellipse $x^2 + 3y^2 - x + 2y = 0$ at the origin. *Ans.* $x - 2y = 0$.
32. Prove that the rhombus formed by joining the foci of an ellipse to the end points of the minor axis has an area equal to $2abe$.
33. Prove that the distances from a point $P(x,y)$ on $b^2x^2 + a^2y^2 = a^2b^2$ to the foci are $a \pm ex$.
34. Lines are drawn through a point on $b^2x^2 + a^2y^2 = a^2b^2$ from the end points of the minor axis. Prove that the product of their intercepts on the x axis is constant.
35. The chord of an ellipse through a focus perpendicular to the major axis is called a *latus rectum*. Show that its length is $2b^2/a$.
36. Prove that the equations of the lines that are tangent to $b^2x^2 + a^2y^2 = a^2b^2$ and have a slope m are $y = mx \pm \sqrt{b^2 + a^2m^2}$.

74. The Hyperbola

The locus of a point which moves so that the difference of its distances from two fixed points is constant is called a hyperbola. The fixed points are called the **foci** of the hyperbola, and the line joining them the **principal axis.**

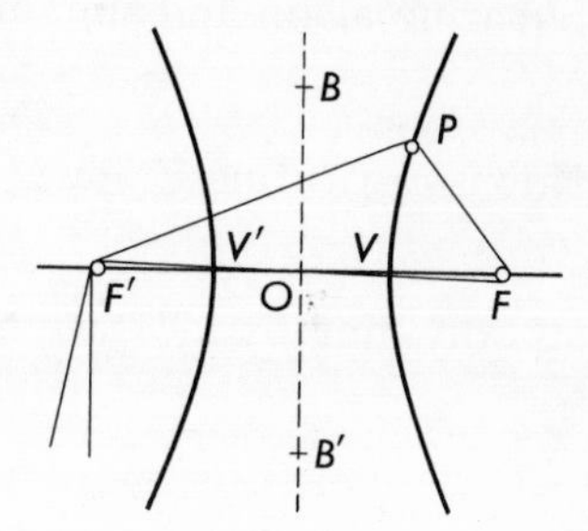

Figure 115

In accordance with this definition, a hyperbola can be constructed as follows. Place tacks at the foci F' and F, fasten a string to a pencil, and loop both ends of the string over F' and one end under F, as shown in Figure 115. Place the pencil at a point V for which $F'V - FV = 2a$, where

$2a$ denotes the constant difference referred to in the definition, tighten the strings, and keep them taut. Then, as the strings below F' are let out together, the pencil will describe a hyperbola. This is true since in any position P the distances $F'P$ and FP are increased by equal amounts. The other branch of the hyperbola can be drawn in a similar manner.

It is evident from the preceding construction that a hyperbola is symmetric with respect to its principal axis and also with respect to the line $B'B$, which is the perpendicular bisector of $F'F$. The point of intersection O of $B'B$ and $F'F$ is thus a point of symmetry and is called the **center** of the hyperbola. The points V' and V where the hyperbola crosses the principal axis are called the **vertices.** The segment $V'V$, called the **transverse axis,** has a length equal to $2a$. This follows from the definition $F'V - VF = 2a$, and the symmetry $F'V' = VF$; thus $F'V - F'V' = V'V = 2a$.

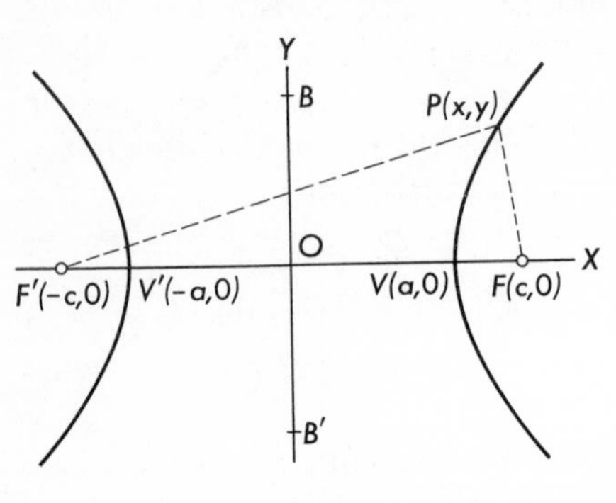

Figure 116

In order to develop its analytic properties, let us consider a hyperbola that has its center at the origin and its foci on the x axis, as shown in Figure 116. If the foci are denoted as $F'(-c,0)$ and $F(c,0)$, and the vertices as $V'(-a,0)$ and $V(a,0)$, the definition requires that a point $P(x,y)$ on the hyperbola satisfy $F'P - FP = \pm 2a$, which in terms of the coordinates is

$$\sqrt{(x + c)^2 + y^2} - \sqrt{(x - c)^2 + y^2} = \pm 2a.$$

Transposing the second radical, squaring, and simplifying, we get

$$cx - a^2 = \pm a\sqrt{(x - c)^2 + y^2}.$$

Squaring again and simplifying, we obtain

$$(c^2 - a^2)x^2 - a^2y^2 = a^2(c^2 - a^2).$$

Now substituting b^2 for $c^2 - a^2$ so that

$$c^2 = a^2 + b^2,$$

and dividing by a^2b^2, we have

$$\frac{x^2}{a^2} - \frac{y^2}{b^2} = 1,$$

which is called the **standard form** of the equation of the hyperbola, shown in Figure 116.

Because of the similarity between this equation and that of an ellipse, the segment BOB', as shown in Figure 116, with $BO = OB' = b$, is given a name and is called the **conjugate axis** of the hyperbola.

In like manner, when the center is at the origin and the foci are on the y axis, as in Figure 117, the equation of the hyperbola in standard form is

$$\frac{y^2}{a^2} - \frac{x^2}{b^2} = 1,$$

where, as before, $b^2 = c^2 - a^2$.

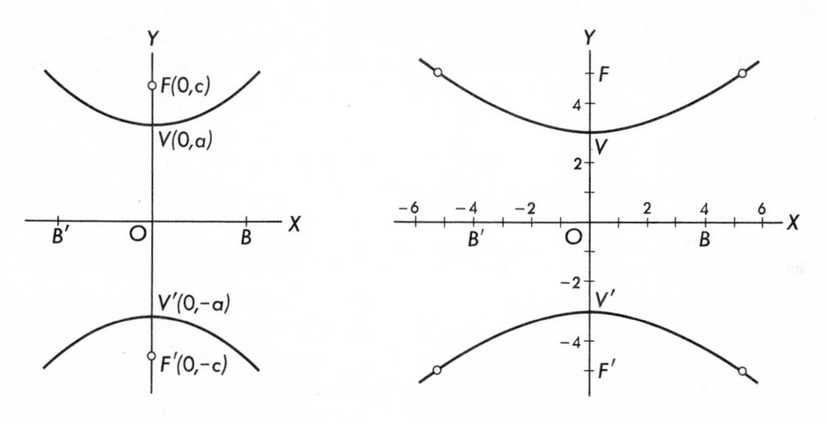

Figure 117

Figure 118

Example. Locate the foci and sketch the hyperbola whose equation is $16y^2 - 9x^2 = 144$.

Solution: Writing the equation in the form

$$\frac{y^2}{9} - \frac{x^2}{16} = 1, \tag{1}$$

we see that the transverse axis lies on the y axis, and $a = 3$ and $b = 4$. Hence $c = \sqrt{a^2 + b^2} = 5$, and the foci are $(0, \pm 5)$. Letting $y = \pm 5$, we obtain from (1) the values $x = \pm \frac{16}{3}$. These points, together with V and V', give the hyperbola shown in Figure 118.

75. Asymptotes

When the hyperbola

$$y = \pm \frac{b}{a} \sqrt{x^2 - a^2} \tag{1}$$

and the lines

$$y = \pm \frac{b}{a} x \tag{2}$$

are drawn on the same coordinate axes, as in Figure 119, the graphs indicate that the distance between the hyperbola and the straight lines gets closer and closer to zero as the distance from the center increases. Curves approaching a line in this manner are said to be **asymptotic** to the line, and the line is called an **asymptote** of the curve.

To prove that (2) are asymptotes of (1), let $x = x_1$, and consider in the first quadrant the difference between the corresponding ordinates, y_l and y_h, of the line and hyperbola, respectively. From equations (1) and (2) we have

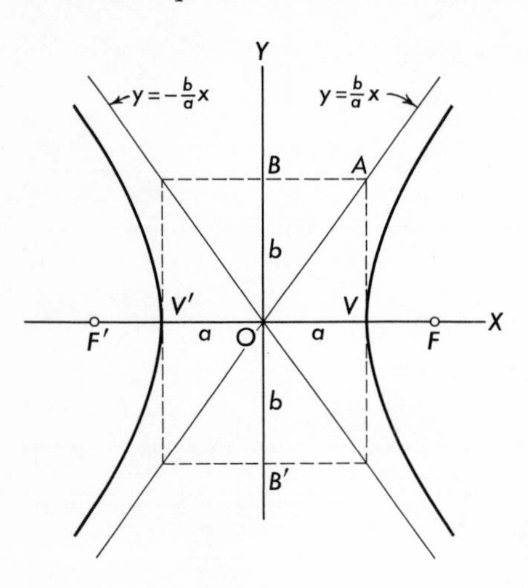

Figure 119

$$y_l - y_h = \frac{b}{a}(x_1 - \sqrt{x_1^2 - a^2}).$$

Multiplying the numerator and denominator of the right side by $x_1 + \sqrt{x_1^2 - a^2}$, we obtain

$$y_l - y_h = \frac{ab}{x_1 + \sqrt{x_1^2 - a^2}}.$$

Since both terms in the denominator are positive and increase without limit as x_1 increases, the fraction on the right side approaches zero. This means then that the line is an asymptote of the hyperbola. A similar proof can be applied in the other three quadrants.

Observe in Figure 119 that the asymptotes of a hyperbola can be readily drawn, because they are the diagonals of a rectangle whose midsections are $V'V$ and $B'B$. Note also that OA, the half-length of a diagonal, is $\sqrt{a^2 + b^2}$, or c, the distance from O to F. This gives a ready means for locating the foci on the graph.

As a final observation, note that equations (2) can be written as $\frac{x}{a} + \frac{y}{b} = 0$ and $\frac{x}{a} - \frac{y}{b} = 0$, or together as $\left(\frac{x}{a} + \frac{y}{b}\right)\left(\frac{x}{a} - \frac{y}{b}\right) = 0$, which is $\frac{x^2}{a^2} - \frac{y^2}{b^2} = 0$. Thus we have the following result.

The equations of the asymptotes of the hyperbolas

$$\frac{x^2}{a^2} - \frac{y^2}{b^2} = 1 \qquad or \qquad \frac{y^2}{a^2} - \frac{x^2}{b^2} = 1$$

are obtained by changing the 1 *to* 0 *in the above equations.*

76. General Equations of a Hyperbola

By methods similar to those discussed in Article **74,** we can readily establish the following results which are now summarized for convenience.

The **standard form** *of the equation of a hyperbola whose center is the point* (h,k) *is*

$$\frac{(x-h)^2}{a^2} - \frac{(y-k)^2}{b^2} = 1, \qquad \textit{for horizontal transverse axis,}$$

$$\frac{(y-k)^2}{a^2} - \frac{(x-h)^2}{b^2} = 1, \qquad \textit{for vertical transverse axis,}$$

where a *and* b *are the lengths of the semitransverse and semiconjugate axes, respectively.*

If we expand the parentheses in either of the above equations and collect terms, we obtain an equation of the form

$$Ax^2 + Cy^2 + Dx + Ey + F = 0, \tag{1}$$

where A and C have unlike signs. This is called the **general form** of the equation of a hyperbola. An equation of this type will always, with one exception, represent a hyperbola. The exception occurs when the left member is written as the difference of two squares and the right member reduces to zero. The locus in this case is two straight lines.

Example. Find the center, vertices, foci, and asymptotes of the hyperbola whose equation is $9x^2 - 4y^2 - 36x + 8y - 4 = 0$. Sketch the graph.

Solution: Transpose the constant and write the equation in the form

$$9(x^2 - 4x) - 4(y^2 - 2y) = 4.$$

Completing the squares within parentheses, we have

$$9(x^2 - 4x + 4) - 4(y^2 - 2y + 1) = 4 + 9(4) - 4(1)$$

$$9(x-2)^2 - 4(y-1)^2 = 36,$$

or

$$\frac{(x-2)^2}{4} - \frac{(y-1)^2}{9} = 1.$$

Since the term in $x - 2$ is positive, the transverse axis is horizontal, and $a = 2$ and $b = 3$. The center is (2,1); hence the vertices are $(2 \pm 2,1)$ or (0,1) and (4,1). Since $c = \sqrt{a^2 + b^2}$, we have $c = \sqrt{4 + 9} = \sqrt{13}$. Hence the foci are $(2 \pm \sqrt{13},1)$.

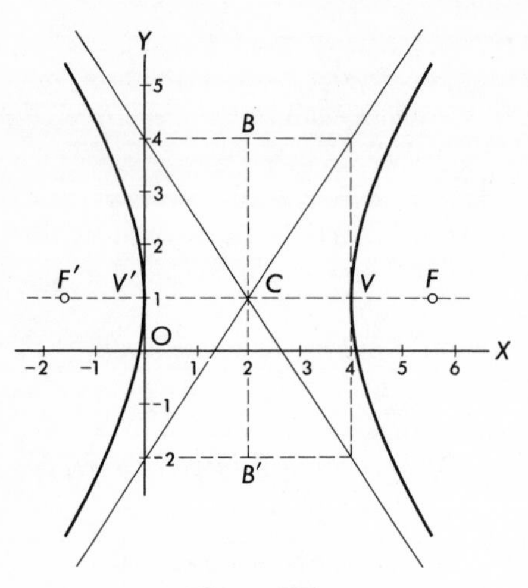

Figure 120

The equations of the asymptotes are given by

$$\frac{(x-2)^2}{4} - \frac{(y-1)^2}{9} = 0,$$

or

$$\left(\frac{x-2}{2} + \frac{y-1}{3}\right)\left(\frac{x-2}{2} - \frac{y-1}{3}\right) = 0,$$

and hence are $3x + 2y - 8 = 0$ and $3x - 2y - 4 = 0$.

The graph is shown in Figure 120.

77. Hyperbolas Determined by Four Conditions

As for the ellipse, a hyperbola with horizontal and vertical axes is determined by four conditions which do not conflict with the restrictions placed on the constants in the preceding article.

Example 1. Find the equation of the hyperbola that has a focus at (5,1) and the lines $y = \pm 2x + 1$ as asymptotes.

Solution: The point of intersection of the asymptotes is (0,1), which is the center of the hyperbola. The distance from the center to the focus gives $c = 5$, and from the slope of the asymptotes we have $\frac{b}{a} = 2$. Thus, using the relation $c^2 = a^2 + b^2$, we find $a = \sqrt{5}$ and $b = 2\sqrt{5}$.

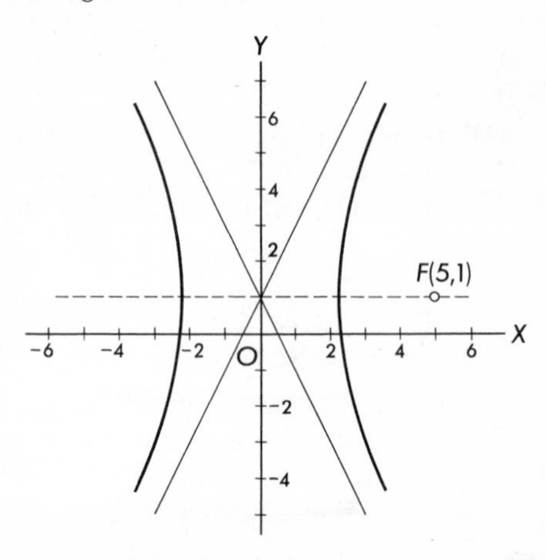

Figure 121

Hence the required equation is

$$\frac{x^2}{5} - \frac{(y-1)^2}{20} = 1,$$

whose graph is shown in Figure 121.

Example 2. Find the locus of a point which moves so that its distance from the point $(ae,0)$ is e $(e > 1)$ times its distance from the line $x = a/e$.

Solution: If $P(x,y)$, as shown in Figure 122, is a point on the locus, we have

$$\sqrt{(x - ae)^2 + y^2} = e\left(x - \frac{a}{e}\right) = ex - a$$

$$x^2 - 2aex + a^2e^2 + y^2 = e^2x^2 - 2aex + a^2$$

$$(e^2 - 1)x^2 - y^2 = a^2(e^2 - 1)$$

$$\frac{x^2}{a^2} - \frac{y^2}{a^2(e^2 - 1)} = 1.$$

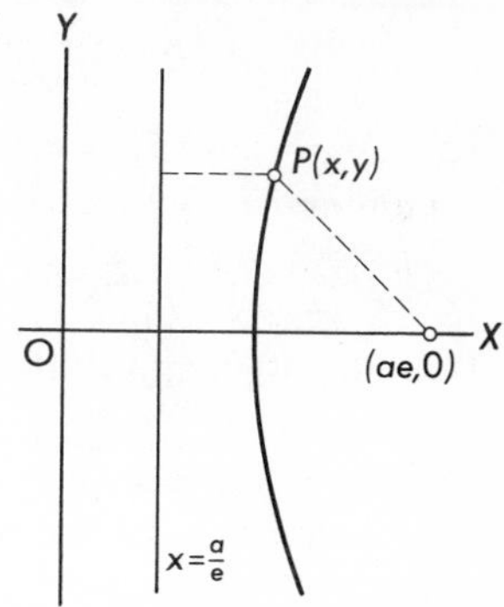

Figure 122

Thus we see that the locus is a hyperbola having its center at the origin, its vertices at $(\pm a,0)$, and a semiconjugate axis equal to $a\sqrt{e^2 - 1}$. It also follows from $c^2 = a^2 + b^2 = a^2 + a^2(e^2 - 1) = a^2e^2$ that the points $(\pm ae,0)$ are the foci of the hyperbola.

The definition of a hyperbola is often given in this form.

The locus of a point which moves so that its distance from a fixed point is a constant e $(e > 1)$ times its distance from a fixed line is called a ***hyperbola.***

The fixed point and line are called a **focus** and **directrix,** respectively, and the constant e is called the **eccentricity** of the hyperbola.

EXERCISE 35

Find the center, vertices, foci, and asymptotes for each of the following hyperbolas, and sketch the graph.

1. $4x^2 - y^2 = 4$. *Ans.* $C(0,0)$, $V(\pm 1,0)$, $F(\pm \sqrt{5},0)$, $y = \pm 2x$.
2. $9y^2 - 4x^2 = 36$.
3. $4x^2 - y^2 = 4y$.
   Ans. $C(0,-2)$, $V(0,-2 \pm 2)$, $F(0,-2 \pm \sqrt{5})$, $y + 2 = \pm 2x$.
4. $x^2 - y^2 = 8x - 10y$.
5. $y^2 - 9x^2 + 2y + 10 = 0$.
   Ans. $C(0,-1)$, $V(\pm 1,-1)$, $F(\pm \sqrt{10},-1)$, $y + 1 = \pm 3x$.
6. $9x^2 - 16y^2 = 72x$.
7. $x^2 - 4y^2 - x + 12y = 9$.
   Ans. $C\left(\frac{1}{2},\frac{3}{2}\right)$, $V\left(\frac{1}{2} \pm \frac{1}{2},\frac{3}{2}\right)$, $F\left(\frac{1}{2} \pm \frac{\sqrt{5}}{4},\frac{3}{2}\right)$, $2y - 3 = \pm\left(x - \frac{1}{2}\right)$.
8. $y^2 - x^2 = \frac{1}{4} + x + y$.
9. $9x^2 - 16y^2 + 18x + 64y = 91$.
   Ans. $C(-1,2)$, $V(-1 \pm 2,2)$, $F(-1 \pm \frac{5}{2},2)$, $y - 2 = \pm\frac{3}{4}(x + 1)$.
10. $3y^2 - x^2 + 4x + 6y = 4$.

In each of the following, find the equation of the hyperbola determined by the given conditions.

11. Vertices $(-3,0)$ and $(3,0)$, $b = 4$. *Ans.* $16x^2 - 9y^2 - 144 = 0$.
12. Vertices $(0,-4)$ and $(0,4)$, focus $(0,5)$.
13. Center $(1,1)$, vertex $(1,5)$, conjugate axis 6.
 Ans. $16x^2 - 9y^2 - 32x + 18y + 151 = 0$.
14. Center $(-2,2)$, focus $(2,2)$, conjugate axis 4.
15. Center $(-\frac{3}{2},\frac{1}{2})$, vertex $(0,\frac{1}{2})$, focus $(\frac{3}{2},\frac{1}{2})$.
 Ans. $12x^2 - 4y^2 + 36x + 4y - 1 = 0$.
16. Vertices $(3,0)$ and $(3,3)$, asymptote $x - 2y = 0$.
17. Foci $(0,0)$ and $(0,10)$, asymptote $x + y = 5$.
 Ans. $2x^2 - 2y^2 + 20y - 25 = 0$.
18. Asymptotes $x + y = 1$ and $x - y = 1$, and passing through $(3,1)$.
19. Center $(1,1)$, vertex $(1,3)$, eccentricity 2.
 Ans. $x^2 - 3y^2 - 2x + 6y + 10 = 0$.
20. Center $(2,0)$, focus $(2,4)$, eccentricity $\sqrt{2}$.
21. Find the equation of the locus of a point which moves so that the difference of its distances from the points $(-3,2)$ and $(7,2)$ is 8.
 Ans. $9x^2 - 16y^2 - 36x + 64y - 172 = 0$.
22. Find the equation of the locus of a point which moves so that the difference of its distances from the points $(-1,-4)$ and $(-1,2)$ is 4.
23. Find the equation of the locus of a point which moves so that its distance from the point $(4,2)$ is twice its distance from the line $x = 1$.
 Ans. $3x^2 - y^2 + 4y - 16 = 0$.
24. Find the equation of the locus of a point which moves so that its distance from the point $(1,-1)$ is three times its distance from the line $y = 3$.
25. Find the points of intersection of the hyperbolas $4x^2 - y^2 = 6x$ and $4x^2 - y^2 = 6y$. *Ans.* $(0,0)$, $(2,2)$.
26. Find the equation of the hyperbola that passes through the points $(0,0)$, $(2,0)$, $(0,4)$, and $(3,-1)$, and has axes parallel to the coordinate axes.
27. For what value of k will the line $y = x + k$ be tangent to the hyperbola $x^2 - 4y^2 = 48$? *Ans.* $k = \pm 6$.
28. Find the equation of the line that is tangent to the hyperbola $x^2 - y^2 = x + 2y$ at the origin.
29. Find the eccentricity of a hyperbola whose transverse and conjugate axes are equal in length. *Ans.* $\sqrt{2}$.
30. A circle is tangent to the circle $x^2 + y^2 + 2rx = 0$ and passes through the point $(r,0)$. Find the locus of its center.
31. Prove that the rhombus formed by joining the foci of a hyperbola to the end points of the conjugate axis has an area equal to $2abe$.
32. Prove that the product of the distances to the asymptotes from any point of a hyperbola is constant.

33. Prove that the distances from a point $P(x,y)$ on $b^2x^2 - a^2y^2 = a^2b^2$ to the foci are $|ex \pm a|$.
34. The chord of a hyperbola through a focus perpendicular to the principal axis is called a *latus rectum*. Show that its length is $2b^2/a$.
35. Prove that the equations of the lines that are tangent to $b^2x^2 - a^2y^2 = a^2b^2$ and have a slope m, are $y = mx \pm \sqrt{a^2m^2 - b^2}$.
36. Two concentric hyperbolas so related that the transverse and conjugate axes of one are, respectively, the conjugate and transverse axes of the other are called *conjugate hyperbolas*. Show that the eccentricities e_1 and e_2 of two conjugate hyperbolas satisfy the relation $e_1^2e_2^2 = e_1^2 + e_2^2$.

78. Translation of Axes

If, at a point (h,k) in the xy plane, new coordinate axes x' and y' are chosen so that they are parallel to the x and y axes, respectively, we say that there has been a *translation of axes* in the plane. In this case each point P in the plane has two sets of coordinates, namely, (x,y) relative to the given axes and (x',y') relative to the new axes; the relationship between them is

$$x = x' + h \qquad \text{and} \qquad y = y' + k. \tag{1}$$

Illustration. The translation of axes $x = x' + 2$, $y = y' + 3$ applied to the parabola $x^2 - 4x - 4y + 16 = 0$ gives

$$(x' + 2)^2 - 4(x' + 2) - 4(y' + 3) + 16 = 0,$$

which reduces to $x'^2 = 4y'$.

Since a translation of axes does not affect the nature of a curve in any manner, it follows that intrinsic properties of the curve remain *invariant* under the transformation. Thus the latus rectum of the parabola given in the preceding illustration is 4, since the latus rectum of the parabola whose equation is $x'^2 = 4y'$ is clearly 4.

If the translation of axes defined by (1) is applied to the equation

$$Ax^2 + 2Bxy + Cy^2 + 2Dx + 2Ey + F = 0, \tag{2}$$

we obtain a new equation

$$Ax'^2 + 2Bx'y' + Cy'^2 + 2D'x' + 2E'y' + F' = 0, \tag{3}$$

where

$$D' = Ah + Bk + D,$$
$$E' = Bh + Ck + E,$$
$$F' = Ah^2 + 2Bhk + Ck^2 + 2Dh + 2Ek + F.$$

When $D' = E' = 0$ in (3), we observe that the equation has symmetry with respect to the origin, and thus represents a central conic or a corresponding degenerate conic. It therefore follows from

$$Ah + Bk + D = 0 \quad \text{and} \quad Bh + Ck + E = 0,$$

that, when $B^2 - AC \neq 0$, the conic represented by (2) is a central conic with center at the point

$$h = (CD - BE)/(B^2 - AC), \qquad k = (AE - BD)/(B^2 - AC).$$

79. Rotation of Axes

If the axes in the xy plane are rotated about the origin through an angle θ, as shown in Figure 123, we say that there has been a *rotation of axes* in the plane.

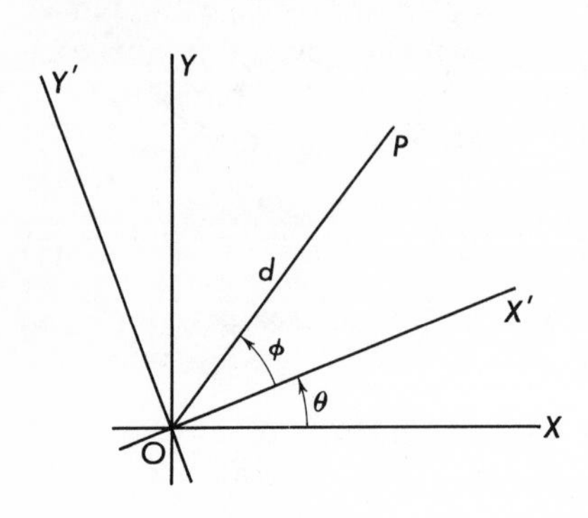

Figure 123

In this case each point P in the plane has two sets of coordinates, namely, (x,y) relative to the given axes and (x',y') relative to the new axes. If ϕ is the angle from OX' to OP and d is the distance from O to P, then

$$x' = d \cos \phi, \qquad y' = d \sin \phi. \quad (1)$$

In the same manner, it follows that

$$x = d \cos (\phi + \theta),$$
$$y = d \sin (\phi + \theta).$$

The latter equations may be written in the form

$$x = d \cos \phi \cos \theta - d \sin \phi \sin \theta,$$
$$y = d \cos \phi \sin \theta + d \sin \phi \cos \theta,$$

whence by (1), we find

$$\begin{aligned} x &= x' \cos \theta - y' \sin \theta, \\ y &= x' \sin \theta + y' \cos \theta. \end{aligned} \quad (2)$$

By solving (2) in the usual way for x' and y', we obtain

$$x' = x \cos \theta + y \sin \theta,$$
$$y' = -x \sin \theta + y \cos \theta,$$

which we observe is equivalent to a rotation of $-\theta$ about the origin.

Illustration. If the axes are rotated 45°, we have $x = (x' - y')/\sqrt{2}$ and $y = (x' + y')/\sqrt{2}$. Hence a curve whose equation is $5x^2 - 6xy + 5y^2 = 8$ in the given system of coordinates has the equation

$$5\left(\frac{x' - y'}{\sqrt{2}}\right)^2 - 6\left(\frac{x' - y'}{\sqrt{2}}\right)\left(\frac{x' + y'}{\sqrt{2}}\right) + 5\left(\frac{x' + y'}{\sqrt{2}}\right)^2 = 8,$$

or

$$x'^2 + 4y'^2 = 4,$$

in the rotated system of coordinates. Since this is the equation of an ellipse with semiaxes 1 and 2, it is apparent that the equation $5x^2 - 6xy + 5y^2 = 8$ represents an ellipse with the same properties.

The procedure of analysis suggested by the preceding illustration can be effected in general. That is, a proper rotation of axes can be found which will transform a general equation of second degree,

$$Ax^2 + 2Bxy + Cy^2 + 2Dx + 2Ey + F = 0, \tag{3}$$

into an equation in x' and y' that has no $x'y'$ term.

In general, by substituting (2) in (3), we obtain an equation of the form

$$A'x'^2 + 2B'x'y' + C'y'^2 + 2D'x' + 2E'y' + F = 0, \tag{4}$$

where

$$\begin{aligned}
A' &= A\cos^2\theta + 2B\sin\theta\cos\theta + C\sin^2\theta,\\
B' &= (C - A)\sin\theta\cos\theta + B(\cos^2\theta - \sin^2\theta),\\
C' &= A\sin^2\theta - 2B\sin\theta\cos\theta + C\cos^2\theta,\\
D' &= D\cos\theta + E\sin\theta,\\
E' &= -D\sin\theta + E\cos\theta.
\end{aligned}$$

Equation (4) will have no $x'y'$ term, provided $B' = 0$. This condition means that $\frac{1}{2}(C - A)\sin 2\theta + B\cos 2\theta = 0$, or

$$\cot 2\theta = \frac{A - C}{2B}, \tag{5}$$

where $B \neq 0$, since otherwise no rotation would be necessary. The equation (5) can be solved for $\tan\theta$ giving

$$\tan\theta = \frac{(C - A) \pm \sqrt{(C - A)^2 + 4B^2}}{2B}. \tag{6}$$

If the arbitrary sign in (6) is chosen so as to make $\tan\theta$ positive, we can then compute the coefficients for (2) from the relations

$$\sin\theta = \tan\theta/\sqrt{1 + \tan^2\theta}, \qquad \cos\theta = 1/\sqrt{1 + \tan^2\theta}.$$

Example. Find the eccentricity of the conic whose equation is $24xy - 7y^2 = 144$.

Solution: We rotate the axes through an angle θ determined by (6), that is,

$$\tan\theta = \frac{-7 + \sqrt{(-7)^2 + 4(12)^2}}{24} = \frac{-7+25}{24} = \frac{3}{4}.$$

By use of this value, we find $\sin\theta = 3/5$, $\cos\theta = 4/5$; and the equations (2) become

$$x = (4x' - 3y')/5 \qquad \text{and} \qquad y = (3x' + 4y')/5.$$

The substitution of these relations in the original equation yields

$$24\left(\frac{4x' - 3y'}{5}\right)\left(\frac{3x' + 4y'}{5}\right) - 7\left(\frac{3x' + 4y'}{5}\right)^2 = 144,$$

which, upon simplification, gives

$$\frac{x'^2}{16} - \frac{y'^2}{9} = 1.$$

For this hyperbola, we observe that $a = 4$ and $b = 3$. Hence it follows from the relation $ae = \sqrt{a^2 + b^2}$ that the eccentricity of the hyperbola is $5/4$.

EXERCISE 36

Determine the nature and position of the following curves.

1. $4xy + 3y^2 - 8x + 16y + 19 = 0.$
   Ans. Hyperbola; $C(-7,2)$, slope of axes 2 and $-\frac{1}{2}$.
2. $x^2 + 2xy + y^2 - 14x + 2y - 7 = 0.$
3. $6x^2 - 5xy - 6y^2 - 46x - 9y + 60 = 0.$
   Ans. Two lines through $(3,-2)$, slopes $\frac{2}{3}$ and $-\frac{3}{2}$
4. $5x^2 - 26xy + 5y^2 + 10x - 26y + 71 = 0.$
5. $13x^2 + 10xy + 13y^2 + 6x - 42y - 27 = 0.$
   Ans. Ellipse; $C(-1,2)$, slope of axes 1 and -1.
6. $x^2 + 6xy + 9y^2 + x + 3y - 2 = 0.$
7. $4x^2 - 4xy + y^2 + 12x - 6y + 10 = 0.$ *Ans.* No curve.
8. $16x^2 - 12xy + 21y^2 - 16x + 6y - 71 = 0.$
9. $x^2 - 4xy + 4y^2 + 36x + 28y + 24 = 0.$
   Ans. Parabola; $V(0,-1)$, slope of axis $\frac{1}{2}$.
10. $2x^2 + 2xy + 5y^2 + 2x - 2y + 1 = 0.$

Show that the following expressions which involve the coefficients of equation (3), Article **79**, remain invariant under rotation of axes.

11. $A + C.$ 12. $B^2 - AC.$ 13. $\begin{vmatrix} A & B & D \\ B & C & E \\ D & E & F \end{vmatrix}.$

14. For a rotation θ that makes $B' = 0$, show that the result of Problem 12 means that the equation (3) represents (*a*) an ellipse when $B^2 - AC < 0$, (*b*) a parabola when $B^2 - AC = 0$, (*c*) a hyperbola when $B^2 - AC > 0$, or one of the corresponding degenerate conics.
15. When $B^2 - AC < 0$, the equation $Ax^2 + 2Bxy + Cy^2 = 1$ represents an ellipse. Show that the area of this ellipse is $\pi/\sqrt{AC - B^2}$. *Hint:* If a and b are the semiaxes, use the fact that the area is πab.
16. When $B^2 - AC > 0$, the equation $Ax^2 + 2Bxy + Cy^2 = 1$ represents a hyperbola. Show that the equations of its asymptotes are given by $Ax^2 + 2Bxy + Cy^2 = 0$.
17. Find the center of the ellipse that passes through the points $(-1,5)$, $(0,2)$, $(1,1)$, $(3,1)$, and $(2,4)$. *Ans.* $(1,3)$.
18. Find the eccentricity of the ellipse that passes through the points $(0,h)$, $(h,0)$, $(0,-h)$, $(-h,0)$, and (h,h). *Hint:* First rotate axes.
19. Find the equation of the asymptotes of the hyperbola that passes through the points $(0,1)$, $(0,-1)$, $(1,0)$, $(-1,0)$, and $(0.3,0.3)$. *Ans.* $x + 9y = 0$, $9x + y = 0$.
20. A point moves so that the sum of the squares of its distances from two intersecting straight lines is constant. Prove that the locus is an ellipse, and find its eccentricity in terms of the acute angle θ between the lines. What is the locus when the lines are perpendicular?

80. Line Tangent to a Conic

Let (x_1,y_1) denote a point on a conic whose equation is

$$Ax^2 + 2Bxy + Cy^2 + 2Dx + 2Ey + F = 0. \tag{1}$$

By differentiation, we find

$$2Ax + 2By + 2Bx\frac{dy}{dx} + 2Cy\frac{dy}{dx} + 2D + 2E\frac{dy}{dx} = 0,$$

whence

$$\frac{dy}{dx} = -\frac{Ax + By + D}{Bx + Cy + E}.$$

Therefore the equation of the tangent line at the point (x_1,y_1) is

$$y - y_1 = -\frac{Ax_1 + By_1 + D}{Bx_1 + Cy_1 + E}(x - x_1), \tag{2}$$

provided $Bx_1 + Cy_1 + E \neq 0$. By clearing fractions in (2) and using the fact that the coordinates (x_1,y_1) satisfy (1), we find that the equation of the tangent line may be written in the form

$$Ax_1x + B(x_1y + xy_1) + Cy_1y + D(x + x_1) + E(y + y_1) + F = 0.$$

This result is easily remembered because of its resemblance to the equation of the conic (1).

Illustration. The equation of the line tangent to the hyperbola $4xy + y^2 - 6y = 15$ at the point (2,3) is $2(2y + 3x) + 3y - 3(y + 3) = 15$ or $3x + 2y = 12$.

81. Poles and Polars

In the preceding article we found that the equation

$$Ax_1x + B(x_1y + xy_1) + Cy_1y + D(x + x_1) + E(y + y_1) + F = 0 \quad (1)$$

represents a line tangent to the conic

$$Ax^2 + 2Bxy + Cy^2 + 2Dx + 2Ey + F = 0, \quad (2)$$

provided the point (x_1,y_1) is on the conic. However, since (1) is of the first degree in x and y regardless of the location of the point (x_1,y_1), it is evident that (1) is a straight line which in some way is related to the conic and the point (x_1,y_1).

This line is called the **polar** *of the point* (x_1,y_1) *with respect to the conic* (2), *and the point is called the* **pole** *of the line.*

When (2) represents one of the degenerate conics, the polar is of little importance. We shall therefore assume in the following discussion that (2) represents either an ellipse, a parabola, or a hyperbola. The properties of poles and polars are basically dependent on the following theorem.

Theorem. *If P_2 is any point on the polar of another point P_1, the polar of P_2 passes through P_1.*

Proof: We know that the polar of $P_1(x_1,y_1)$ with respect to (2) is (1), and if $P_2(x_2,y_2)$ is on this line, we must have

$$Ax_1x_2 + B(x_1y_2 + x_2y_1) + Cy_1y_2 + D(x_2 + x_1) + E(y_2 + y_1) + F = 0. \quad (3)$$

However, the polar of P_2 with respect to (2) is

$$Ax_2x + B(x_2y + xy_2) + Cy_2y + D(x + x_2) + E(y + y_2) + F = 0,$$

and this line passes through $P_1(x_1,y_1)$ because of (3).

82. Tangents to a Conic

An inspection of the conics shows that for a point not on the conic either two tangent lines or no tangent line can be drawn from the point to the conic. In the former case the point is said to be *outside* the conic and in the latter case *inside* the conic.

For a point P outside a conic let PM and PN be the two lines tangent to the conic, as shown in Figure 124. Now the polar of a point on a conic is the tangent line to the conic at that point. Hence PM is the polar of M and PN is the polar of N. Therefore, by the theorem in the preceding article, the polar of P must pass through M and N. Hence the polar of P is the line MN, which is the *chord of contact* of the tangent lines from P. By similar reasoning, the converse can also be established. That is, *if a straight line intersects a conic, its pole is the point of intersection of the tangent lines taken at the points of intersection.*

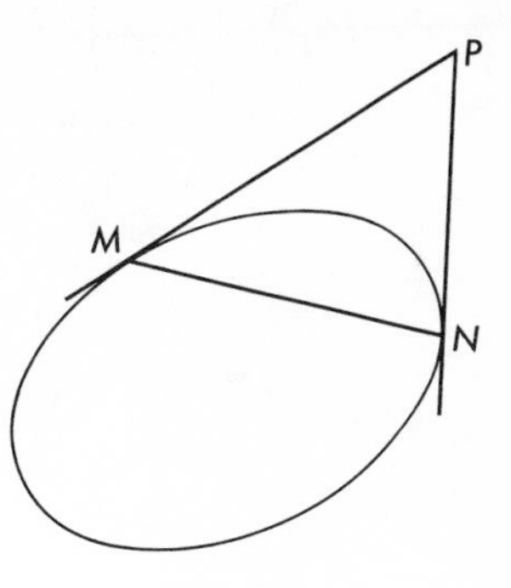

Figure 124

Example. Find the lines which are tangent to the conic $4x^2 - 5xy + 2y^2 + 3x - 2y = 0$ and pass through the point (2,3).

Solution: Since this point is not on the conic, we compute the equation of its polar and find $x = 0$. This line intersects the conic at the points (0,0) and (0,1).

Hence the equations of the two tangent lines are $3x - 2y = 0$ and $x - y + 1 = 0$.

EXERCISE 37

Find the equation of the line tangent to the following conics at the given point.

1. $3x^2 - 3xy + 4x + y - 3 = 0$, $(-1,1)$. *Ans.* $5x - 4y + 9 = 0$.
2. $x^2 + 8xy - 2y^2 - 12x + 6y - 4 = 0$, $(0,2)$.
3. $x^2 - 6xy + 9y^2 - 4x + 7 = 0$, $(2,1)$. $x - y - 1 = 0$.
4. $x^2 + xy + y^2 + 2x + 3y = 0$, $(1,-1)$.

Find the equations of the lines which are tangent to the following conics and pass through the given point.

5. $x^2 + 2xy + y^2 + 2x + 6y + 1 = 0$, $(4,-2)$. *Ans.* $x + 2y = 0$, $2x + 3y = 2$.
6. $2x^2 - 2y^2 - 6x - 6y - 1 = 0$, $(1,-2)$.
7. $5y^2 + 4x - 2y - 3 = 0$, $(2,0)$. $x + 2y = 2$, $x - 3y = 2$.
8. $x^2 + 2xy + 2y^2 - 4x + 5y + 3 = 0$, $(1/8,-1/4)$.
9. Find the pole of the polar line $2x - y = 0$ with respect to the conic whose equation is $x^2 + 8xy - 2y^2 - 12x + 6y - 9 = 0$. *Ans.* (0,3).
10. If m_1 is the slope of the polar of a point P_1 with respect to the ellipse $b^2x^2 + a^2y^2 = a^2b^2$, and m_2 is the slope of the line joining P_1 to the center, show that $m_1m_2 = -b^2/a^2$. Find a similar relation for the hyperbola.
11. Show that for any conic section the polar of the focus is the directrix.

12. Prove that if in any conic the pole of the normal at P lies on the normal at Q, then the pole of the normal at Q lies on the normal at P.
13. If $L_k \equiv a_k x + b_k y + c_k = 0$, $k = 1, 2, 3$, are the equations of three lines, no two of which are parallel, show that the conic whose equation is $AL_1L_2 + BL_1L_3 + CL_2L_3 = 0$ (A, B, C constants) passes through the intersection of $L_1 = 0$ and $L_2 = 0$ and is tangent to the line $BL_1 + CL_2 = 0$ at that point.

CHAPTER 8

Differentiation of Transcendental Functions

83. Transcendental Functions

A function which is not algebraic is called a **transcendental** function. In this chapter differentiation formulas will be derived for the following elementary transcendental functions: trigonometric, inverse trigonometric, logarithmic, and exponential functions.

84. Properties of Trigonometric Functions

In trigonometry, we recall that two different units were used for measuring angles, namely *degrees* and *radians*. By definition a radian is that central angle of a circle whose arc is equal in length to a radius. Hence, from the measure of a straight angle, we have the conversion relation

$$\pi \text{ radians} = 180°.$$

Although degrees are used in many applications, the radian measure is better adapted for theoretical work. For this reason radians are used almost exclusively in calculus.

The **sine curve,** $y = \sin x$, as shown in **51,** page 7, illustrates graphically that the sine function is single-valued, continuous, and *periodic* with **period** 2π and **amplitude** 1.

Illustration 1. To draw a graph of the equation $y = 3 \sin (2x - \frac{1}{2}\pi)$, we first determine the beginning and end of a period by setting the whole angle $2x - \frac{1}{2}\pi$ equal to 0 and 2π, respectively. Doing this, we find $x = \frac{1}{4}\pi$ and $x = \frac{5}{4}\pi$.

Since the multiplicative factor 3 gives the amplitude of the curve, we draw one period of a sine curve as shown in Figure 125. The remainder of the curve is determined by its periodicity.

Note 1: As illustrated in **51** and **52**, page 7, the graph of a cosine curve can always be obtained by moving the graph of the corresponding sine curve to the left a distance equal to one-fourth of a period. Thus, if the curve shown in Figure 125 is shifted to the left a distance $\frac{1}{4}\pi$, its equation will be $y = 3\cos(2x - \frac{1}{2}\pi)$.

The **tangent curve,** $y = \tan x$, as shown in **53,** page 7, illustrates graphically that the tangent function is single-valued, continuous except for $x = \pm(n + \frac{1}{2})\pi$, and periodic with period π. As a branch of the curve recedes to infinity, we observe that it becomes and remains arbitrarily close to one of the vertical lines $x = \pm(n + \frac{1}{2})\pi$. These lines are called **asymptotes** of the curve.

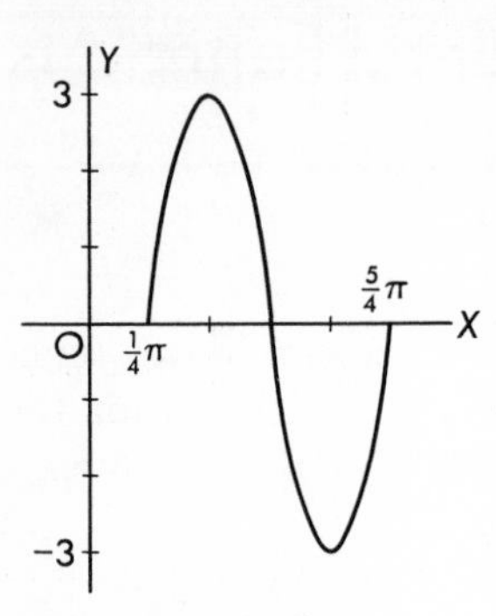

Figure 125

From the relation $\cot x = -\tan(x + \frac{1}{2}\pi)$, it is apparent that a cotangent curve has characteristics similar to those of a tangent curve.

The **secant curve,** $y = \sec x$, as shown in **54,** page 7, illustrates graphically that the secant function is single-valued, continuous except at $x = \pm(n + \frac{1}{2})\pi$, periodic with period 2π, and asymptotic to the vertical lines $x = \pm(n + \frac{1}{2})\pi$.

As for the preceding cofunctions, the cosecant function has properties similar to those of the secant function.

Example. Plot the curve $y = \cos^2 x$.

Solution: Although points on the graph of this curve can be obtained directly by substitution, it is simpler to proceed as follows. First we transform the given equation using the half-angle formula **30**, page 3; thus

$$y = \tfrac{1}{2} + \tfrac{1}{2}\cos 2x.$$

The graph of this equation is readily obtained by **composition of ordinates**. That is, we plot the two curves $y = \frac{1}{2}$ and $y = \frac{1}{2}\cos 2x$, and add their corresponding ordinates. Doing this, we obtain the graph shown in Figure 126.

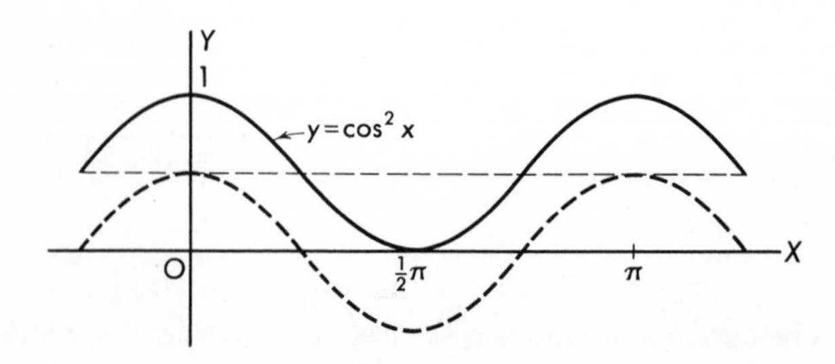

Figure 126

Note 2: The trigonometric formulas **24–34**, pages 2–4, are used frequently in calculus, and it is advisable to memorize *at least* formulas **26** and **29**.

85. Limit of sin θ/θ

In order to develop differentiation formulas for the trigonometric functions we shall need the following theorem.

Theorem. *If the angle* $\boldsymbol{\theta}$ *is expressed in radians, the ratio* $\mathbf{\sin\theta/\theta}$ *approaches unity as* $\boldsymbol{\theta}$ *approaches zero. That is,*

$$\lim_{\theta\to 0} \frac{\sin\theta}{\theta} = 1.$$

Proof: Let θ be a positive acute angle as shown in Figure 127. Construct a circular arc PB of radius r, draw PA perpendicular to OB, and PC tangent to the arc PB. By geometry, it is clear that

$$\text{Area } AOP < \text{Area } BOP < \text{Area } COP. \quad (1)$$

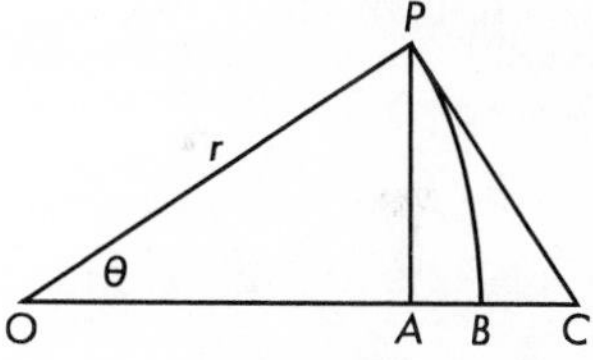

Figure 127

By trigonometry, we have $OA = r\cos\theta$, $AP = r\sin\theta$, and $PC = r\tan\theta$. Hence, by substitution in (1), we obtain

$$\tfrac{1}{2}r\cos\theta\cdot r\sin\theta < \tfrac{1}{2}r^2\theta < \tfrac{1}{2}r\cdot r\tan\theta, \quad (2)$$

when θ, as given in formula **5**, page 1, is measured in radians.

Dividing each term of (2) by $\frac{1}{2}r^2\sin\theta$ and taking reciprocals, we obtain

$$\frac{1}{\cos\theta} > \frac{\sin\theta}{\theta} > \cos\theta.$$

Since $\sin\theta/\theta$ lies between two values both of which approach 1 as θ approaches zero, it follows that

$$\lim_{\theta\to 0} \frac{\sin\theta}{\theta} = 1.$$

If the preceding limit is taken through negative values, it is clear from the relations

$$\lim_{\theta\to 0} \frac{\sin(-\theta)}{(-\theta)} = \lim_{\theta\to 0} \frac{-\sin\theta}{-\theta} = \lim_{\theta\to 0} \frac{\sin\theta}{\theta} = 1$$

that we obtain the same result.

86. Derivatives of Trigonometric Functions

Let $y = \sin x$, where x is measured in radians. By the four-step rule, we have

$$1.\quad y + \Delta y = \sin(x + \Delta x),$$

$$2.\quad \Delta y = \sin(x + \Delta x) - \sin x.$$

Making use of **31,** page 4, we obtain

$$\Delta y = 2\cos(x + \tfrac{1}{2}\Delta x)\sin\tfrac{1}{2}\Delta x;$$

and thus

$$3.\quad \frac{\Delta y}{\Delta x} = \cos(x + \theta)\frac{\sin\theta}{\theta},$$

where $\theta = \frac{1}{2}\Delta x$.

As Δx approaches zero, θ also approaches zero. Hence, by the theorem in the preceding article, we have

$$4.\quad \frac{dy}{dx} = \lim_{\theta\to 0}\cos(x + \theta)\cdot\lim_{\theta\to 0}\frac{\sin\theta}{\theta} = \cos x.$$

If u is any differentiable function of x, it follows by $\boldsymbol{D_7}$ that

$$\boldsymbol{D_{10}}\qquad \frac{d}{dx}\sin u = \cos u\,\frac{du}{dx}.$$

Illustration 1. If $y = \sin 7x$, then $y' = \cos 7x\,\dfrac{d(7x)}{dx} = 7\cos 7x$.

Note: Suppose that an angle is measured in degrees as $x°$. Since $x° = \pi x/180$ radians, we see that

$$\frac{d}{dx}\sin x° = \cos\frac{\pi x}{180}\cdot\frac{d}{dx}\left(\frac{\pi x}{180}\right) = \frac{\pi}{180}\cos x°.$$

To avoid the complication of the factor $\pi/180$ we use radian measure when handling trigonometric functions in calculus.

The derivative of $\cos u$ can also be obtained using the four-step rule. However, it is more readily found by using $\boldsymbol{D_{10}}$. Thus, to differentiate $\cos u$, we have

$$\frac{d}{dx}\cos u = \frac{d}{dx}\sin(\tfrac{1}{2}\pi - u) = \cos(\tfrac{1}{2}\pi - u)\frac{d}{dx}(\tfrac{1}{2}\pi - u);$$

hence

$$\boldsymbol{D_{11}}\qquad \frac{d}{dx}\cos u = -\sin u\,\frac{du}{dx}.$$

By expressing each of the remaining trigonometric functions in terms of the sine and cosine, we can establish the following formulas.

$$\mathbf{D_{12}} \qquad \frac{d}{dx}\tan u = \sec^2 u \frac{du}{dx},$$

$$\mathbf{D_{13}} \qquad \frac{d}{dx}\cot u = -\csc^2 u \frac{du}{dx},$$

$$\mathbf{D_{14}} \qquad \frac{d}{dx}\sec u = \sec u \tan u \frac{du}{dx},$$

$$\mathbf{D_{15}} \qquad \frac{d}{dx}\csc u = -\csc u \cot u \frac{du}{dx}.$$

For example, if $y = \tan u$, we write $y = \sin u/\cos u$, and it follows that

$$\frac{dy}{dx} = \frac{\cos u \dfrac{d}{dx}(\sin u) - \sin u \dfrac{d}{dx}(\cos u)}{\cos^2 u} = \frac{\cos^2 u + \sin^2 u}{\cos^2 u}\frac{du}{dx}$$

$$= \frac{1}{\cos^2 u}\frac{du}{dx} = \sec^2 u \frac{du}{dx}.$$

Example 1. If $y = \tan^3 2x$, find dy/dx.

Solution: Thinking of the given equation as a series of relations in the form $y = u^3$, $u = \tan v$, $v = 2x$, we obtain

$$\frac{dy}{dx} = 3\tan^2 2x \frac{d}{dx}(\tan 2x) \qquad \text{by } \mathbf{D_5}$$

$$= 3\tan^2 2x \cdot \sec^2 2x \frac{d}{dx}(2x) \qquad \text{by } \mathbf{D_{12}}$$

$$= 6\tan^2 2x \sec^2 2x. \qquad \text{by } \mathbf{D_2}$$

Example 2. If $y = \sin 2x \sec x$, find dy/dx.

Solution: Differentiating as a product, we obtain

$$\frac{dy}{dx} = \sin 2x(\sec x \tan x) + \sec x(2\cos 2x).$$

Note: It is advisable to write a given expression in its simplest form before differentiating. Thus, in the above example, since $\sin 2x = 2\sin x \cos x$ and $\sec x = 1/\cos x$, the given equation can be written as $y = 2\sin x$. Hence $y' = 2\cos x$.

Example 3. If $y = \sin 5x \sin^5 x$, find dy/dx.

Solution: In this example, we use **28,** page 3, to simplify the result. Thus

$$\frac{dy}{dx} = (5 \cos 5x) \sin^5 x + \sin 5x\,(5 \sin^4 x \cos x)$$
$$= 5 \sin^4 x\,(\sin x \cos 5x + \cos x \sin 5x)$$
$$= 5 \sin^4 x \sin 6x.$$

Example 4. If $\sin x + \sin y = xy$, find dy/dx.

Solution: Differentiating implicitly, we obtain

$$\cos x + \cos y \frac{dy}{dx} = y + x\frac{dy}{dx};$$

hence

$$\frac{dy}{dx} = \frac{\cos x - y}{x - \cos y}.$$

EXERCISE 38

Simplify each of the following expressions.

1. $\sin 2x \cos 2x$. *Ans.* $\frac{1}{2} \sin 4x$.
2. $(\sin x + \cos x)^2$.
3. $\cos^4 x - \sin^4 x$. $\cos 2x$.
4. $2 \sin x \csc 2x$.
5. $\dfrac{2 \cot x}{1 + \cot^2 x}$. $\sin 2x$.
6. $\dfrac{\cos 3x}{\sin x} + \dfrac{\sin 3x}{\cos x}$.
7. $\cot x - \tan x$. $2 \cot 2x$.
8. $2 \cos^2 (\frac{1}{2}\pi - x) - 1$.
9. $\sin (\frac{1}{4}\pi + x) + \cos (\frac{1}{4}\pi + x)$. *Ans.* $\sqrt{2} \cos x$.
10. $\sin x\,(\cos 4x + 4 \cos^2 x \cos 2x)$.

Plot each of the following equations.

11. $y = \frac{3}{2} \sin 4x$.
12. $y = \tan 2x$.
13. $y = \sin x + \sin 2x$.
14. $y = x - \cos x$.

In each of the following, find dy/dx.

15. $y = 2 \sin 3x$. *Ans.* $6 \cos 3x$.
16. $y = \cos (x^2 + 1)$.
17. $y = 4 \cot (3 - 2x)$. $8 \csc^2 (3 - 2x)$.
18. $y = 2 \sec \sqrt{x}$.
19. $y = \frac{1}{2}x - \frac{1}{4} \sin 2x$. $\sin^2 x$.
20. $y = x \sec x$.
21. $y = 2 \tan \frac{1}{2}x - x$. $\tan^2 \frac{1}{2}x$.
22. $y = \sec x \sec 2x$.
23. $y = \dfrac{\sin x}{2 + \cos x}$. $\dfrac{1 + 2 \cos x}{(2 + \cos x)^2}$.
24. $y = \dfrac{1 + \tan x}{1 - \tan x}$.
25. $y = x \sin x + (1 - \frac{1}{2}x^2) \cos x$. *Ans.* $\frac{1}{2}x^2 \sin x$.
26. $y = x - \tan x + \frac{1}{3} \tan^3 x$.
27. $y = 2 \cos x \sin 2x - \sin x \cos 2x$. $3 \cos x \cos 2x$.
28. $y = \frac{1}{12} \sec^2 3x\,(\tan^2 3x - 1)$.
29. $y = x^3 - x^2 \cos x + 2x \sin x + 2 \cos x$. $x^2(3 + \sin x)$.
30. $y = \sin^m x \cos^n x$.

31. $y = \sin mx \cos nx$. *Ans.* $m \cos mx \cos nx - n \sin mx \sin nx$.
32. $y = \sin (ax + b) \cos (ax - b)$.
33. $x = \sec^2 y$. $\frac{1}{2} \cos^2 y \cot y$.
34. $x = y + \cot y$.
35. $y = \dfrac{1 - u}{1 + u}$, $u = \cos 2x$. $2 \tan x \sec^2 x$.
36. $y = u^2 - 2u + 4$, $u = 1 + \sec^2 x$.
37. $x = \cos u + u \sin u$, $y = \sin u - u \cos u$. $\tan u$.
38. $x = \theta - \sin \theta$, $y = 1 - \cos \theta$.
39. $y = \tan (x + y)$. $-\csc^2 (x + y) = -(1 + y^{-2})$.
40. $y \sin x + x \sin y = 5$.
41. $\sin (x + y) + \sin (x - y) = 1$. $\cot x \cot y$.
42. $y = 2x + \sin (y - 2x)$.

In each of the following, find d^2y/dx^2.

43. $y = x \sin x$. $2 \cos x - x \sin x$.
44. $y = a \sec kx$.
45. $y = \cos^3 2x$. $24 \cos 2x - 36 \cos^3 2x$.
46. $y = x^2 \sin x + 2x \cos x - 2 \sin x$.
47. $y = \sqrt{\dfrac{1 - \cos 4x}{1 + \cos 4x}}$. $8 \sec^2 2x|\tan 2x|$.
48. $y = 2 \sin x \sin 2x$. *Hint:* Write as a sum.
49. Show that $\lim_{\theta \to 0} \dfrac{1 - \cos \theta}{\theta^2} = \frac{1}{2}$. *Hint:* Multiply numerator and denominator by $1 + \cos \theta$.
50. Show that $\sin x/x$ decreases steadily as x increases from 0 to π.
51. Show by mathematical induction that $\dfrac{d^n}{dx^n} (\sin x) = \sin \left(x + \dfrac{n\pi}{2}\right)$, and develop a similar formula for $\dfrac{d^n}{dx^n} (\cos x)$.
52. Using the formula, $\sin 2x = 2 \sin x \cos x$, determine by differentiation the corresponding formula for $\cos 2x$.
53. Derive formula $\boldsymbol{D}_{11}$ using $\boldsymbol{D}_{10}$ and the relation $\cos x = \pm\sqrt{1 - \sin^2 x}$.
54. Derive formula $\boldsymbol{D}_{14}$ using $\boldsymbol{D}_{11}$ and the relation $\sec x = 1/\cos x$.
55. Prove the theorem stated in Article **85** by assuming in Figure 127 that $PA <$ Arc $PB < PC$.

87. Properties of Inverse Trigonometric Functions

If y is a function of x determined by the relation $\sin y = x$, y is called the **inverse sine function** of x and is denoted by

$$\boldsymbol{y = \text{arc} \sin x} \qquad \text{or} \qquad \boldsymbol{y = \sin^{-1} x},$$

where the symbols are read as "the angle whose sine is x."

Similarly we have the definitions*

$$\mathbf{y = cos^{-1} x} \quad \text{if} \quad \mathbf{cos\, y = x,}$$
$$\mathbf{y = tan^{-1} x} \quad \text{if} \quad \mathbf{tan\, y = x,}$$

and so on. These expressions are called the **inverse trigonometric functions.**

The inverse sine curve, as shown in Figure 128, is obtained by taking the reflection of the sine curve, $y = \sin x$, with respect to the line $y = x$, that is, by interchanging x and y. The graph illustrates that the inverse sine function is continuous, multiple-valued, and defined only in the interval from -1 to 1.

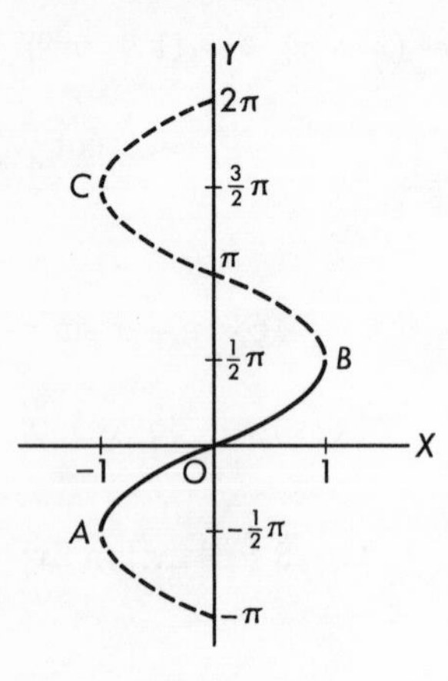

Figure 128

In order to consider the differentiation of a function it is necessary that it be single-valued. For this reason we define the arc AB in Figure 128 to be the **principal branch** of the curve $y = \sin^{-1} x$, and we indicate that we mean the principal branch by capitalizing the first letter in the notation of the function. Thus the equation of the arc AB is $y = \text{Sin}^{-1} x$ or $y = \text{Arc sin } x$, and the single value given by the function $\text{Sin}^{-1} x$ is called the **principal value** of $\sin^{-1} x$.

Illustration. The value of $\text{Sin}^{-1}(-1)$ is $-\frac{1}{2}\pi$ whereas $\sin^{-1}(-1)$ represents any one of an infinite set of numbers including $-\frac{1}{2}\pi, \frac{3}{2}\pi, \frac{7}{2}\pi, \cdots$.

As indicated in **56, 57,** and **58,** page 8, the principal values of the other inverse trigonometric functions are taken in the following intervals:

$$0 \leqq \text{Cos}^{-1} x \leqq \pi, \quad -\tfrac{1}{2}\pi < \text{Tan}^{-1} x < \tfrac{1}{2}\pi, \quad 0 < \text{Cot}^{-1} x < \pi,$$
$$-\pi \leqq \text{Sec}^{-1} x < -\tfrac{1}{2}\pi, \quad x \leqq -1; \qquad 0 \leqq \text{Sec}^{-1} x < \tfrac{1}{2}\pi, \quad x \geqq 1,$$
$$-\pi < \text{Csc}^{-1} x \leqq -\tfrac{1}{2}\pi, \quad x \leqq -1; \qquad 0 < \text{Csc}^{-1} x \leqq \tfrac{1}{2}\pi, \quad x \geqq 1.$$

Thus, for example,

$$\text{Cos}^{-1}(-\tfrac{1}{2}) = \tfrac{2}{3}\pi, \quad \text{Tan}^{-1}(-1) = -\tfrac{1}{4}\pi, \quad \text{Sec}^{-1}(-2) = -\tfrac{2}{3}\pi.$$

Note: In accordance with the above definitions, observe that the equation of the arc BC in Figure 128 is $y = \frac{1}{2}\pi + \text{Cos}^{-1} x$.

---

* In this text we shall use the notation approved by the American Engineering Standards Committee. See "American Standard Mathematical Symbols," *Amer. Math. Monthly*, vol. 35 (1928), pp. 300–304.

Combinations of inverse trigonometric functions may be simplified by use of the formulas listed in **33,** page 4.

Example. Simplify $\text{Tan}^{-1} \frac{1}{2} + \text{Tan}^{-1} (-\frac{1}{3})$.

Solution: Using the third and tenth formulas given in **33**, we obtain

$$\text{Tan}^{-1} \tfrac{1}{2} + \text{Tan}^{-1} (-\tfrac{1}{3}) = \text{Tan}^{-1} \tfrac{1}{2} - \text{Tan}^{-1} \tfrac{1}{3}$$

$$= \text{Tan}^{-1} \left(\frac{\frac{1}{2} - \frac{1}{3}}{1 + \frac{1}{2} \cdot \frac{1}{3}} \right) = \text{Tan}^{-1} \tfrac{1}{7}.$$

88. Derivatives of Inverse Trigonometric Functions

To determine the derivative of the function $y = \text{Sin}^{-1} x$, we first write the equation in the equivalent form

$$\sin y = x, \quad -\tfrac{1}{2}\pi \leqq y \leqq \tfrac{1}{2}\pi.$$

Differentiating with respect to y,* and making use of formula $\boldsymbol{D}_8$, we obtain

$$\cos y = \frac{dx}{dy}, \quad \text{or} \quad \frac{dy}{dx} = \frac{1}{\cos y}.$$

By trigonometry, we have

$$\cos y = +\sqrt{1 - \sin^2 y} = \sqrt{1 - x^2},$$

where the positive sign of the radical is taken since $\cos y$ is positive for all values of y between $-\frac{1}{2}\pi$ and $\frac{1}{2}\pi$. Thus

$$\frac{dy}{dx} = \frac{1}{\sqrt{1 - x^2}},$$

and by $\boldsymbol{D}_7$, we have

$$\boldsymbol{D}_{16} \qquad \frac{d}{dx} \text{Sin}^{-1} u = \frac{1}{\sqrt{1 - u^2}} \frac{du}{dx},$$

where u is a differentiable function of x.

Illustration 1. If $y = \text{Sin}^{-1} 2x$, then by $\boldsymbol{D}_{16}$

$$\frac{dy}{dx} = \frac{1}{\sqrt{1 - (2x)^2}} \frac{d}{dx} (2x) = \frac{2}{\sqrt{1 - 4x^2}}.$$

---

* We differentiate here with respect to y in order to avoid making the assumption that dy/dx exists.

In a similar manner, we derive the following:

$$\mathbf{D_{17}} \qquad \frac{d}{dx}\,\mathrm{Cos}^{-1}\,u = -\frac{1}{\sqrt{1-u^2}}\frac{du}{dx}.$$

$$\mathbf{D_{18}} \qquad \frac{d}{dx}\,\mathrm{Tan}^{-1}\,u = \frac{1}{1+u^2}\frac{du}{dx}.$$

$$\mathbf{D_{19}} \qquad \frac{d}{dx}\,\mathrm{Cot}^{-1}\,u = -\frac{1}{1+u^2}\frac{du}{dx}.$$

$$\mathbf{D_{20}} \qquad \frac{d}{dx}\,\mathrm{Sec}^{-1}\,u = \frac{1}{u\sqrt{u^2-1}}\frac{du}{dx}.$$

$$\mathbf{D_{21}} \qquad \frac{d}{dx}\,\mathrm{Csc}^{-1}\,u = -\frac{1}{u\sqrt{u^2-1}}\frac{du}{dx}.$$

Illustration 2. If $y = \mathrm{Sec}^{-1}\sqrt{1+x^2}$, then by $\mathbf{D_{20}}$

$$\frac{dy}{dx} = \frac{1}{\sqrt{1+x^2}\sqrt{(1+x^2)-1}}\frac{d}{dx}\sqrt{1+x^2} = \frac{1}{1+x^2}, \quad x \geqq 0.$$

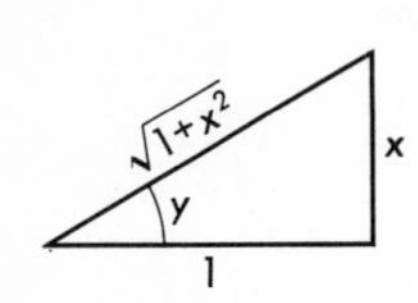

Figure 129

Note: For $x \geqq 0$, we see from Figure 129 that $y = \mathrm{Sec}^{-1}\sqrt{1+x^2} = \mathrm{Tan}^{-1}\,x$; hence the above result could have been obtained by using $\mathbf{D_{18}}$.

Example. If $y = \sqrt{a^2-x^2} - a\,\mathrm{Cos}^{-1}\dfrac{x}{a}$, find $\dfrac{dy}{dx}$.

Solution:

$$\frac{dy}{dx} = \frac{(-2x)}{2\sqrt{a^2-x^2}} - a\left(-\frac{1}{\sqrt{1-\frac{x^2}{a^2}}}\right)\frac{1}{a} = \frac{-x+a}{\sqrt{a^2-x^2}} = \sqrt{\frac{a-x}{a+x}},$$

for $0 < x < a$.

EXERCISE 39

1. Evaluate $\mathrm{Sin}^{-1}(0)$, $\mathrm{Tan}^{-1}(\sqrt{3})$, $\mathrm{Sec}^{-1}(-1)$. *Ans.* 0, $\frac{1}{3}\pi$, $-\pi$.
2. Evaluate $\mathrm{Cos}^{-1}(-\frac{1}{2})$, $\mathrm{Cot}^{-1}(1)$, $\mathrm{Csc}^{-1}(-2)$.
3. Evaluate $\mathrm{Sin}^{-1}(\frac{3}{4})$, $\mathrm{Tan}^{-1}(-5)$. 0.848, -1.373.
4. Evaluate $\mathrm{Cos}^{-1}(-0.1)$, $\mathrm{Sec}^{-1}(3)$.

Simplify the following expressions.

5. $\mathrm{Cos}^{-1}\frac{3}{5} + \mathrm{Cos}^{-1}\frac{4}{5}$. *Ans.* $\frac{1}{2}\pi$.
6. $\mathrm{Tan}^{-1}\frac{1}{2} + \mathrm{Tan}^{-1}\frac{1}{3}$.
7. $\mathrm{Tan}^{-1}2 - \mathrm{Tan}^{-1}(-3)$. $\frac{3}{4}\pi$.
8. $\mathrm{Sin}^{-1}\frac{3}{5} + \mathrm{Cos}^{-1}\frac{12}{13}$.
9. $\mathrm{Sin}^{-1}\frac{12}{13} + \mathrm{Sin}^{-1}(-\frac{5}{13})$. *Ans.* $\mathrm{Sin}^{-1}\frac{119}{169}$.
10. $\mathrm{Tan}^{-1}\frac{1}{3} + \mathrm{Tan}^{-1}\frac{1}{13}$.
11. If $a > 0$, show that $\mathrm{Csc}^{-1}\,a = \mathrm{Sin}^{-1}(1/a)$, $\mathrm{Sec}^{-1}\,a = \mathrm{Cos}^{-1}(1/a)$, and $\mathrm{Cot}^{-1}\,a = \mathrm{Tan}^{-1}(1/a)$.

12. Derive formula $\boldsymbol{D}_{18}$.

13. Derive formula $\boldsymbol{D}_{19}$.

14. Derive formula $\boldsymbol{D}_{20}$.

15. Derive formula $\boldsymbol{D}_{21}$.

16. Derive formula $\boldsymbol{D}_{17}$ using $\boldsymbol{D}_{16}$ and the relation $\text{Cos}^{-1} u = \frac{1}{2}\pi - \text{Sin}^{-1} u$.

Differentiate each of the following functions with respect to x, $(a > 0)$.

17. $\text{Tan}^{-1} 3x$. *Ans.* $\dfrac{3}{1 + 9x^2}$.

18. $\text{Sec}^{-1} \frac{1}{4}x$.

19. $\text{Cos}^{-1} (1 - x)$. $\dfrac{1}{\sqrt{2x - x^2}}$.

20. $\text{Sin}^{-1} (2/x)$.

21. $\text{Csc}^{-1}\sqrt{x}$. $\dfrac{-1}{2x\sqrt{x - 1}}$.

22. $\text{Cot}^{-1}\sqrt{x^2 - 2x}$.

23. $(\text{Sin}^{-1} 4x)^2$. $\dfrac{8 \text{ Sin}^{-1} 4x}{\sqrt{1 - 16x^2}}$.

24. $x \text{ Tan}^{-1} \frac{1}{2}x$.

25. $\text{Cos}^{-1} (\sin x)$. -1 or $+1$.

26. $\text{Tan}^{-1} \sqrt{\dfrac{3x - 4}{4}}$.

27. $\text{Cot}^{-1}\sqrt{x^2 - 1} + \text{Sec}^{-1} x$. 0.

28. $\text{Sin}^{-1} (2\sqrt{x - x^2})$.

29. $\text{Sin}^{-1} \dfrac{x}{\sqrt{x^2 + a^2}}$. *Ans.* $\dfrac{a}{x^2 + a^2}$.

30. $x\sqrt{a^2 - x^2} + a^2 \text{ Sin}^{-1} \dfrac{x}{a}$.

31. $\dfrac{x}{\sqrt{a^2 - x^2}} - \text{Sin}^{-1} \dfrac{x}{a}$. $\dfrac{x^2}{(a^2 - x^2)^{3/2}}$.

32. $\text{Sin}^{-1} \dfrac{x}{a} + \dfrac{\sqrt{a^2 - x^2}}{x}$.

33. $\text{Tan}^{-1} \dfrac{x}{a} + \text{Tan}^{-1} \dfrac{a}{x}$. 0.

34. $\text{Tan}^{-1} \left(\dfrac{a + x}{1 - ax}\right)$.

35. $\text{Tan}^{-1} \dfrac{x}{a - \sqrt{a^2 - x^2}}$. $-\dfrac{1}{2\sqrt{a^2 - x^2}}$.

36. $a \text{ Cos}^{-1} \left(1 - \dfrac{x}{a}\right) + \sqrt{2ax - x^2}$.

Find dy/dx for the given value of x.

37. $y = x \text{ Cos}^{-1} x$; $x = -\frac{1}{2}$. *Ans.* 2.672.

38. $y = x/\text{Tan}^{-1} x$; $x = 1$.

39. $y = x^2 \text{ Sec}^{-1}\sqrt{x}$; $x = 2$. 4.142.

40. $y = \sqrt{x} \text{ Sin}^{-1}\sqrt{x}$; $x = \frac{1}{4}$.

41. $y = \dfrac{1}{x} \text{ Tan}^{-1} \dfrac{1}{x}$; $x = -1$. 1.285.

42. $y = x(\text{Cos}^{-1} 2x)^2$; $x = 0.1$.

43. If $\sqrt{x^2 - y^2} + \text{Sin}^{-1}(y/x) = 0$, find dy/dx.

Ans. $y' = (y \pm x^2)/(x \pm xy),\ x \lessgtr 0$.

44. Find the smallest value attained by the function $\text{Tan}^{-1}(1 + x) + \text{Tan}^{-1}(1 - x)$ in the interval from $x = -1$ to $x = 1$.

45. If $y = \sin(n\,\text{Sin}^{-1} x)$, show that $(1 - x^2)y'' - xy' + n^2y = 0$.

89. Exponential and Logarithmic Functions

A function y defined by the relation,

$$y = a^x, \tag{1}$$

where a is a positive number other than one, is called an **exponential function** of x. The graph, as shown in Figure 130 for $a > 1$, indicates that the function (1) is positive, single-valued, continuous, and asymptotic to the x axis. The function also has these properties when $0 < a < 1$.

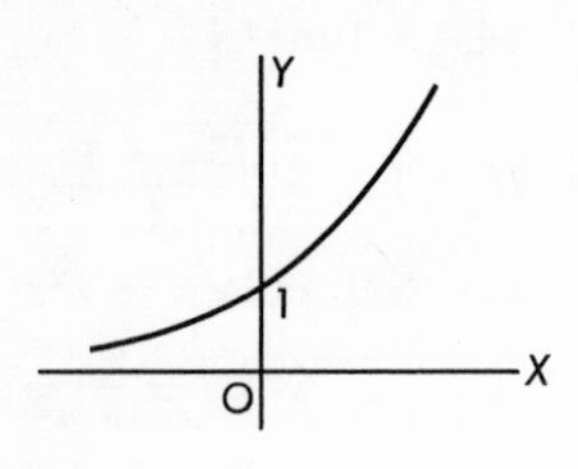

Figure 130

By the definition of a logarithm, the relation (1) is equivalent to

$$x = \log_a y. \tag{2}$$

Thus a^x and $\log_a x$ are inverse functions, and it follows that

$$a^{\log_a x} = x \qquad \text{and} \qquad \log_a a^x = x.$$

Illustration 1. If $y = 2^{\sin 3x}$, we may solve for x by applying a series of inverse operations; thus

$$\sin 3x = \log_2 y,$$

$$3x = \sin^{-1}(\log_2 y),$$

$$x = \tfrac{1}{3}\sin^{-1}(\log_2 y).$$

A function y defined by the relation

$$y = \log_a x, \tag{3}$$

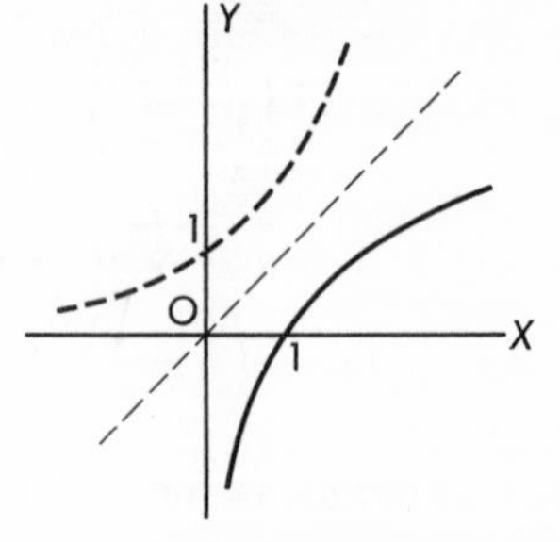

Figure 131

where a is a positive number other than one, is called a **logarithmic function** of x. The graph of (3), as shown in Figure 131, is the reflection of (2) with respect to the line $y = x$. We see from this graph that the logarithmic function is single-valued, continuous, asymptotic to the y axis, and defined only in the interval $0 < x < \infty$.

Operations involving logarithms are governed by the properties listed in **18**, page 2.

Illustration 2. If $\log_{10} x = 1 - 3 \log_{10} 2 + \frac{1}{2} \log_{10} 5$, by use of the laws of logarithms, we obtain

$$\log_{10} x = \log_{10} 10 - \log_{10} 2^3 + \log_{10} \sqrt{5},$$

and

$$\log_{10} x = \log_{10} \frac{10\sqrt{5}}{8};$$

hence

$$x = \tfrac{5}{4}\sqrt{5}.$$

In the next article we will find that the differentiation formula for a logarithmic function involves an irrational number which is denoted by e and is defined by the limit

$$e = \lim_{z \to 0} (1 + z)^{1/z}.$$

A mathematical proof determining the existence of this limit is rather involved, and hence will be omitted. Nevertheless, the accompanying table of values indicates that the limit does exist and that approximately $e = 2.718 \cdots$.

z	$(1 + z)^{1/z}$
0.1	2.5937
0.01	2.7048
0.001	2.7169
0	?
−0.001	2.7196
−0.01	2.7320
−0.1	2.8680

In mathematics two systems of logarithms are particularly important. For computational work, logarithms having the base 10 are the most convenient to use. These are called **common,** or **Briggsian, logarithms.** For theoretical work, logarithms having the base e are usually used. These are called **natural,** or **Napierian, logarithms.** We shall denote the common logarithm of N by **log** N and the natural logarithm* by **ln** N. Thus $y = \log x$ means $x = 10^y$, whereas $y = \ln x$ means $x = e^y$. The relationship between $\log N$ and $\ln N$ can be determined by taking the common and natural logarithms of the expression $N = e^x$; thus

$$\log N = x \log e \qquad \text{and} \qquad \ln N = x \ln e = x.$$

* In some books the symbol $\log N$ is used to denote a natural logarithm.

Hence, on eliminating x,

$$\log N = \ln N \cdot \log e,$$

and since $\log e = \log 2.718 = 0.4343$, we obtain

$$\mathbf{\log N = 0.4343 \ln N} \qquad \text{and} \qquad \mathbf{\ln N = 2.303 \log N.}$$

The coefficient $M = 0.4343$ is called the **modulus** of common logarithms.

Example 1. If $y = e^x - e^{-x}$, find x in terms of y.

Solution: Multiplying by e^x, we have

$$e^{2x} - 1 = ye^x, \qquad \text{or} \qquad (e^x)^2 - y(e^x) - 1 = 0.$$

Solving, by use of the quadratic formula, we obtain

$$e^x = \tfrac{1}{2}(y + \sqrt{y^2 + 4}),$$

where the root $e^x = \frac{1}{2}(y - \sqrt{y^2 + 4})$ is rejected since e^x is never negative. Then, by taking logarithms, we find

$$x = \ln \tfrac{1}{2}(y + \sqrt{y^2 + 4}).$$

Example 2. Show that $\log(\sqrt{x+1} - \sqrt{x}) = -\log(\sqrt{x+1} + \sqrt{x})$.

Solution: Multiplying the numerator and denominator by $\sqrt{x+1} + \sqrt{x}$ and making use of the value $\log 1 = 0$, we have

$$\log(\sqrt{x+1} - \sqrt{x}) = \log \frac{(x+1) - x}{\sqrt{x+1} + \sqrt{x}} = -\log(\sqrt{x+1} + \sqrt{x}).$$

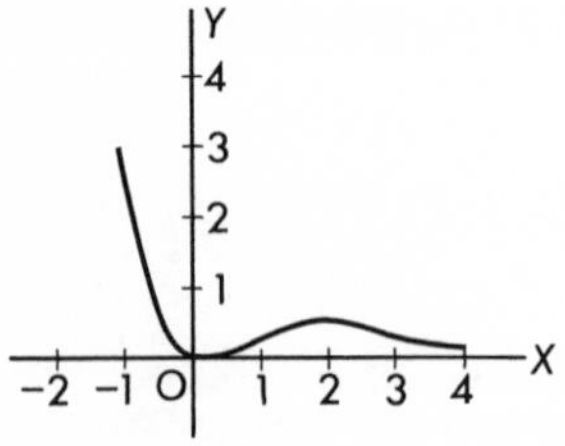

Example 3. Sketch a graph of $y = x^2e^{-x}$.

Solution: We first observe that $y = 0$ when $x = 0$, and that y is positive for all other values of x. Next we observe that $y \to 0$ as $x \to \infty$ and $y \to \infty$ as $x \to -\infty$.

Drawing the curve in accordance with these characteristics and estimating that $y = 2.7$ when $x = -1$, and $y = \frac{1}{2}$ when $x = 2$, we obtain the graph shown in Figure 132.

Figure 132

EXERCISE 40

Solve for x in each of the following.

1. $\log_4 x = -\frac{3}{2}$. *Ans.* $\frac{1}{8}$.
2. $\ln x = 3$.
3. $\log x = 2 - \log 2$. 50.
4. $\log_a x = 0$.
5. $2^x = 4^{x-2}$. 4.
6. $e^x = 3$.

7. $3^{x+1} = 5^x$. *Ans.* 2.150.
8. $(0.015)^{2x} = (0.34)^{x-1}$.
9. $\ln x = 1 + 2 \ln 2$. $4e$.
10. $\ln \ln x = 1$.
11. $4 \ln \tan^{-1} x = 1$. 3.391.
12. $\ln \sin x = 1 + \ln \cos x$.
13. $e^x - 5e^{-x} = 4$. 1.609.
14. $3e^{2x} + 3e^{-2x} = 10$.
15. $2^x + 4^x = 8^x$. 0.694.
16. $4^x + 4^{-x} = 4$.
17. $9^x - 3^{x+1} = 54$. 2.
18. $1 + \ln x = \ln (1 + x)$.
19. $\log x + \ln x = 1$. 2.008.
20. $\ln x + \ln (x + 2) = 2$.
21. If $(\ln x)/x = (\ln 2)/2$ and $(\ln y)/y = (\ln \frac{1}{2})/\frac{1}{2}$, does it necessarily follow that $x = 2$ and $y = \frac{1}{2}$? Justify your answers. *Ans.* $x = 2$ or 4.

In each of the following, solve for x in terms of y.

22. $y = e^{x^2}$.
23. $y = 10^{5x}$. *Ans.* $x = \frac{1}{5} \log y$.
24. $y = e^{\sin x}$.
25. $y = \log 3x$. $x = \frac{1}{3} 10^y$.
26. $y = \ln 9x^2$.
27. $y = \ln \sin x$. $x = \sin^{-1} e^y$.
28. $y = \tan^{-1} (\log 2x)$.
29. $y = \frac{1}{2}(e^x + e^{-x})$. $x = \ln (y \pm \sqrt{y^2 - 1})$.
30. $y = \tan e^x + \cot e^x$.
31. $y = e^{3x} - 3e^{2x} + 3e^x$. $x = \ln (1 + \sqrt[3]{y - 1})$.
32. $y = \ln (x \pm \sqrt{x^2 - 1})$.
33. $y = \ln x + \ln (x - 2)$. $x = 1 + \sqrt{1 + e^y}$.
34. $y = \ln \sin x + \ln \cos x$.

Sketch a graph of each of the following equations.

35. $y = e^{-x^2}$.
36. $y = \ln x^2$.
37. $y^2 = e^x$.
38. $y^2 = \ln x$.
39. $y = e^{1/x}$.
40. $y = \ln (1/x)$.
41. $y = xe^x$.
42. $y = x \ln x$.
43. $y = e^x/x$.
44. $y = (\ln x)/x$.
45. $y = e^{\sin x}$.
46. $y = \ln \sin x$.

90. Derivatives of Logarithmic Functions

Let us apply the four-step rule to the function $y = \log_a x$. Thus, for a fixed value of x, we have

$$1.\quad y + \Delta y = \log_a (x + \Delta x),$$

$$2.\quad \Delta y = \log_a (x + \Delta x) - \log_a x$$

$$= \log_a \frac{x + \Delta x}{x} = \log_a \left(1 + \frac{\Delta x}{x}\right),$$

$$3.\quad \frac{\Delta y}{\Delta x} = \frac{1}{\Delta x} \log_a \left(1 + \frac{\Delta x}{x}\right).$$

Letting $z = \Delta x/x$, 3 may be written in the form

$$\frac{\Delta y}{\Delta x} = \frac{1}{xz} \log_a (1 + z) = \frac{1}{x} \log_a (1 + z)^{1/z}.$$

Since z approaches zero as Δx approaches zero, from the continuity of the logarithmic function and the limit given in the preceding article it follows that

$$4. \qquad \frac{dy}{dx} = \frac{1}{x} \lim_{z \to 0} \log_a (1 + z)^{1/z}$$

$$= \frac{1}{x} \log_a \lim_{z \to 0} (1 + z)^{1/z} = \frac{1}{x} \log_a e.$$

By $\boldsymbol{D_7}$ this result gives

$$\boldsymbol{D_{22}} \qquad \frac{d}{dx} \log_a u = \frac{\log_a e}{u} \frac{du}{dx},$$

and for natural logarithms the above formula becomes

$$\boldsymbol{D_{23}} \qquad \frac{d}{dx} \ln u = \frac{1}{u} \frac{du}{dx}.$$

Illustration. If $y = \log (2x + 1)$, then $\dfrac{dy}{dx} = \dfrac{\log e}{2x + 1} (2) = \dfrac{0.8686}{2x + 1}.$

If $y = \ln \sin x$, then $\dfrac{dy}{dx} = \dfrac{1}{\sin x} \dfrac{d}{dx} (\sin x) = \dfrac{\cos x}{\sin x} = \cot x.$

Example. If $y = \ln \left(x^3 \sqrt{\dfrac{x - 1}{x + 1}} \right)$, find $\dfrac{dy}{dx}$.

Solution: Making use of the properties of logarithms, we may write the given expression in the form

$$y = 3 \ln x + \tfrac{1}{2} \ln (x - 1) - \tfrac{1}{2} \ln (x + 1).$$

Hence, using $\boldsymbol{D_{23}}$, we obtain

$$\frac{dy}{dx} = \frac{3}{x} + \frac{1}{2(x - 1)} - \frac{1}{2(x + 1)} = \frac{3x^2 + x - 3}{x(x^2 - 1)}.$$

Note: When n is any real constant, formula $\boldsymbol{D_5}$ can be proved in the following manner, if we assume that dy/dx exists. Let $y = u^n$, then $\ln y = n \ln u$. Differentiating implicitly, we obtain

$$\frac{1}{y} \frac{dy}{dx} = \frac{n}{u} \frac{du}{dx};$$

hence

$$\frac{dy}{dx} = nu^{n-1} \frac{du}{dx}.$$

EXERCISE 41

Differentiate each of the following functions.

1. $\ln (x - 1)^3$. *Ans.* $3/(x - 1)$.
2. $\log_a (x^2 + 3x)$.
3. $\ln \sqrt[3]{2x^3 - 5}$. $2x^2/(2x^3 - 5)$.
4. $\ln (x\sqrt{x + 1})$.
5. $\log \dfrac{x}{1 + x}$. $\dfrac{\log e}{x(1 + x)}$.
6. $\ln (x + \sqrt{x^2 + 1})$.
7. $\ln \sqrt{\dfrac{x - 1}{x + 1}}$. $\dfrac{1}{x^2 - 1}$.
8. $\ln \dfrac{x^2(x + 1)}{(x + 2)^3}$.
9. $\ln \cos 3x$. $-3 \tan 3x$.
10. $\log (x \sin x)$.
11. $\ln (\sec x + \tan x)$. $\sec x$.
12. $\ln (\ln x)$.
13. $\sqrt{\log x}$. $\dfrac{\log e}{2x\sqrt{\log x}}$.
14. $\dfrac{x}{\ln x}$.
15. $x \operatorname{Tan}^{-1} x - \ln \sqrt{x^2 + 1}$. *Ans.* $\operatorname{Tan}^{-1} x$.
16. $\ln \dfrac{1 + \sin x}{1 + \sin x + \cos x}$.

Find dy/dx for the given value of x.

17. $y = \ln (x^2 - 8)$; $x = 4$. *Ans.* 1.
18. $y = x \ln (1 + x)$; $x = 1$.
19. $y = \log (3x - 2)$; $x = 2$. 0.326.
20. $y = (\ln x)^2$; $x = 2$.
21. $y = (\ln x)/x$; $x = 2$. 0.077.
22. $y = \ln (\sin x)$; $x = \frac{1}{4}\pi$.
23. $y = \sin (\ln x)$; $x = 1$. 1.
24. $y = \sqrt{x} \ln \sqrt{x}$; $x = 4$.
25. $y = \operatorname{Tan}^{-1} (\ln x)$; $x = 1/e$. $\frac{1}{2}e$.
26. $y = \log (\log x)$; $x = 10$.

Find the second derivative of the following functions.

27. $x \ln x$. *Ans.* $1/x$.
28. $x^2 \ln x^2$.
29. $\log (3/x)$. $(\log e)/x^2$.
30. $\ln \cot \frac{1}{2}x$.

Find the maximum and minimum values of the following functions.

31. $x - \ln x$. *Ans.* 1, min.
32. $x + \ln \cos x$.
33. $\log \dfrac{x^3}{x + 2}$. $3 \log 3$, min.
34. $\ln \dfrac{x}{x^2 + 1}$.
35. $\dfrac{1 - \ln x}{x}$. $-\dfrac{1}{e^2}$, min.
36. $x(\ln x)^2$.

91. Derivatives of Exponential Functions

The derivative of the exponential function $y = a^x$, $(a > 0, a \neq 1)$, may be found in the following manner. Taking natural logarithms of both sides, we have

$$\ln y = x \ln a.$$

Differentiating this equation with respect to y, we find

$$\frac{1}{y} = \frac{dx}{dy} \ln a;$$

hence by $\boldsymbol{D}_8$

$$\frac{dy}{dx} = a^x \ln a.$$

Thus by $\boldsymbol{D}_7$ this result gives

$$\boldsymbol{D}_{24} \qquad \frac{d}{dx} a^u = a^u \ln a \frac{du}{dx},$$

and for the base e the above formula becomes

$$\boldsymbol{D}_{25} \qquad \frac{d}{dx} e^u = e^u \frac{du}{dx}.$$

Illustration 1. If $y = 2^{3x}$, then $dy/dx = (2^{3x})(\ln 2)(3) = 2^{3x} \ln 8$. If $y = e^{\tan 5x}$, then $dy/dx = (e^{\tan 5x})(\sec^2 5x)(5) = 5e^{\tan 5x} \sec^2 5x$.

To find the derivative of an exponential function of the form u^v where u and v are both functions of x, we differentiate the logarithm of the function.

Illustration 2. If $y = x^x$, then $\ln y = x \ln x$. Differentiating, we obtain

$$\frac{1}{y}\frac{dy}{dx} = (1)(\ln x) + (x)\left(\frac{1}{x}\right),$$

$$\frac{dy}{dx} = x^x(1 + \ln x).$$

The work involved in differentiating an algebraic function is often simpler if logarithms are used.

Example 1. Find $\dfrac{dy}{dx}$, if $y = \dfrac{(x-1)^{3/2}(x-3)^{1/2}}{(x-2)^2}$.

Solution: Taking natural logarithms, we have

$$\ln y = \tfrac{3}{2} \ln (x - 1) + \tfrac{1}{2} \ln (x - 3) - 2 \ln (x - 2).$$

Differentiating, we obtain

$$\frac{1}{y}\frac{dy}{dx} = \frac{3}{2(x-1)} + \frac{1}{2(x-3)} - \frac{2}{(x-2)}$$

$$= \frac{3(x^2 - 5x + 6) + (x^2 - 3x + 2) - 4(x^2 - 4x + 3)}{2(x-1)(x-2)(x-3)}$$

$$= -\frac{x-4}{(x-1)(x-2)(x-3)}.$$

Multiplying both sides by y and simplifying, we find

$$\frac{dy}{dx} = -\frac{(x-1)^{1/2}(x-4)}{(x-3)^{1/2}(x-2)^3}.$$

A situation frequently encountered in certain problems of biology, chemistry, and economics is one in which the rate of change of a substance with respect to time is proportional to the amount of the substance present at a given time. Such is the case, for example, in considering the decomposition of a radioactive substance or the growth of a bacteria culture under ideal circumstances.

If the positive function $f(t)$ represents the amount of substance present at time t, the preceding law can be stated mathematically as

$$f'(t) = kf(t), \tag{1}$$

where k is a constant and $t \geqq 0$. The function $f(t)$ can be determined explicitly by writing (1) in the form

$$\frac{f'(t)}{f(t)} = k, \quad \text{whence} \quad \ln f(t) = kt + c.$$

By finding the antilogarithm of this latter expression, we obtain

$$f(t) = Ae^{kt}, \tag{2}$$

where $A = e^c$ is a positive constant.

If the constant k is positive, the function $f(t)$ increases in what is called an *exponential law of growth*. If k is negative, $f(t)$ decreases in what is called an *exponential law of decay*.

Example 2. If the half-life of radium is 1600 years and we start with 100 milligrams, find the amount of radium remaining after t years.

Solution: To say that the half-life of radium is 1600 years means that half of the original amount or 50 milligrams will remain after 1600 years. Thus, by substitution in (2), we find

$$100 = Ae^0 \qquad \text{and} \qquad 50 = Ae^{1600k}.$$

Hence $A = 100$, and from $e^{1600k} = \frac{1}{2}$ we have

$$1600k = \ln \tfrac{1}{2}; \qquad \text{therefore} \quad k = \frac{-\ln 2}{1600} = -0.00043.$$

This gives

$$f(t) = 100e^{-0.00043t}$$

as the law of decay for the given quantity of radium.

EXERCISE 42

Differentiate each of the following functions.

1. e^{4x}. *Ans.* $4e^{4x}$.
2. 3^{2x}.
3. e^{-x^2}. $-2xe^{-x^2}$.
4. x^2e^{3x}.
5. e^x/x. $e^x(x-1)/x^2$.
6. $(1 - a^{-x})^2$.
7. $e^x(x^2 - 2x + 2)$. x^2e^x.
8. $e^{3x} \cos 5x$.
9. $e^{\sin x}$. $e^{\sin x} \cos x$.
10. $e^{x+\ln x}$.
11. $\dfrac{e^x - e^{-x}}{e^x + e^{-x}}$. $\dfrac{4}{(e^x + e^{-x})^2}$.
12. $\ln \dfrac{e^x - 1}{e^x + 1}$.
13. $\ln \sin e^x$. $e^x \cot e^x$.
14. $\operatorname{Tan}^{-1} 2^x$.
15. $x^5e^{-3 \ln x}$. $2x$.
16. $x^e e^x$.
17. x^{x^2}. $x^{x^2+1}(2 \ln x + 1)$.
18. $(\cos x)^{\cos x}$.
19. x^{e^x}. $x^{e^x}e^x\left(\ln x + \dfrac{1}{x}\right)$.
20. $(\sin x)^x$.
21. $\sqrt{x+1}/\sqrt[3]{x+2}$. *Ans.* $(x+4)/6(x+1)^{1/2}(x+2)^{4/3}$.
22. $(1-x)^2(1-2x)^2/(1-3x)^4$.
23. Show that $y = e^{ax} \sin bx$ satisfies the differential equation $y'' - 2ay' + (a^2 + b^2)y = 0$.
24. If $e^x + e^y = e^{x+y}$, show that $dy/dx = -e^{y-x}$.

Find dy/dx for the given value of x.

25. $y = e^{2x}(x - \frac{1}{2})$; $x = \frac{1}{4}$. *Ans.* 0.824.
26. $y = \ln (e^x + e^{-x})$; $x = \frac{1}{2}$.
27. $y = e^{3x} \log 2x$; $x = 1$. 26.86.
28. $y = \tan e^x$; $x = 0$.

Find d^2y/dx^2 for the given value of x.

29. $y = e^{3x}$; $x = 0.1$. *Ans.* 12.15.
30. $y = e^{x^2}$; $x = \frac{1}{2}$.
31. $y = x^2e^x$; $x = -1$. -0.368.
32. $y = e^x \cos x$; $x = 1$.

Find the maximum and minimum values of the following functions.

33. e^{x^2-4x}. *Ans.* e^{-4}, min.
34. $x^8e^{-x^2}$.
35. $e^x(x^2 - 3)$. $6e^{-3}$, max., $-2e$, min.
36. $e^{2x} + e^{-2x}$.

37. $xe^{1/x}$. *Ans.* e, min. 38. $\tan(e^x - 3x)$.

39. In the chemical processing of a certain mineral, the rate of change of the amount of mineral present varies as the amount of the mineral remaining. If, after 8 hours, 100 pounds of mineral have been reduced to 70 pounds, what quantity of the mineral will remain after 24 hours? *Ans.* 34.3 lb.

40. If in a certain city the rate of increase in population is proportional to the population at any time, and if in the last ten years the population increased from 100,000 to 120,000, what will be the population of the city ten years from now?

92. Summary and Applications

For convenience in reference the differentiation formulas derived in this chapter are listed below in their differential form.

$\mathbf{D_{10}}$ $d \sin u = \cos u\, du.$ $\mathbf{D_{11}}$ $d \cos u = -\sin u\, du.$

$\mathbf{D_{12}}$ $d \tan u = \sec^2 u\, du.$ $\mathbf{D_{13}}$ $d \cot u = -\csc^2 u\, du.$

$\mathbf{D_{14}}$ $d \sec u = \sec u \tan u\, du.$ $\mathbf{D_{15}}$ $d \csc u = -\csc u \cot u\, du.$

$\mathbf{D_{16}}$ $d\, \mathrm{Sin}^{-1} u = \dfrac{du}{\sqrt{1 - u^2}}.$ $\mathbf{D_{17}}$ $d\, \mathrm{Cos}^{-1} u = \dfrac{-du}{\sqrt{1 - u^2}}.$

$\mathbf{D_{18}}$ $d\, \mathrm{Tan}^{-1} u = \dfrac{du}{1 + u^2}.$ $\mathbf{D_{19}}$ $d\, \mathrm{Cot}^{-1} u = \dfrac{-du}{1 + u^2}.$

$\mathbf{D_{20}}$ $d\, \mathrm{Sec}^{-1} u = \dfrac{du}{u\sqrt{u^2 - 1}}.$ $\mathbf{D_{21}}$ $d\, \mathrm{Csc}^{-1} u = \dfrac{-du}{u\sqrt{u^2 - 1}}.$

$\mathbf{D_{22}}$ $d \log_a u = \log_a e \dfrac{du}{u}.$ $\mathbf{D_{23}}$ $d \ln u = \dfrac{du}{u}.$

$\mathbf{D_{24}}$ $d\, a^u = a^u \ln a\, du.$ $\mathbf{D_{25}}$ $d\, e^u = e^u\, du.$

Example 1. Find an approximate value for $\cos 31°$ using differentials.

Solution: Let $y = \cos x$; then by $\mathbf{D_{11}}$ we have

$$dy = -\sin x\, dx.$$

The formulas $\mathbf{D_{10}}$ through $\mathbf{D_{21}}$ are valid only when the angles are expressed in radians. Hence, taking $x = 30° = \frac{1}{6}\pi$ and $dx = 1° = 0.0175$, we obtain

$$y = \cos \tfrac{1}{6}\pi = \tfrac{1}{2}\sqrt{3} = 0.8660,$$
$$dy = -(\sin \tfrac{1}{6}\pi)(0.0175) = -\tfrac{1}{2}(0.0175) = -0.0087.$$

Thus an approximate value of $\cos 31°$ is given by

$$y + dy = 0.8660 - 0.0087 = 0.8573.$$

Note 1: Four place tables give $\cos 31° = 0.8572$.

Example 2. In the right triangle ABC (Figure 133), $AB = 2$, $BC = 4$, and ED is parallel to AB. Find the angle θ = angle BAD which minimizes the distance $L = AD + ED$.

Solution: Since $AB = 2$, in triangle ABD we find $AD = 2 \sec \theta$ and $BD = 2 \tan \theta$; hence $DC = 4 - 2 \tan \theta$.

By similar triangles we have

$$\frac{ED}{2} = \frac{4 - 2\tan\theta}{4};$$

hence

$$ED = 2 - \tan\theta.$$

Thus the distance L is given by

$$L = 2\sec\theta + 2 - \tan\theta.$$

Differentiating, we obtain

$$\frac{dL}{d\theta} = 2\sec\theta\tan\theta - \sec^2\theta.$$

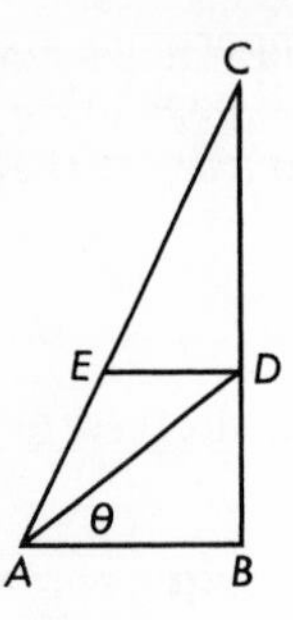

Figure 133

Setting $dL/d\theta = 0$ and solving, we find

$$\sin\theta = \tfrac{1}{2};$$

hence

$$\theta = 30^\circ.$$

Example 3. At what point on the line $y = b$ does the line segment from $(0,0)$ to $(a,0)$ subtend the greatest angle?

Solution: As shown in Figure 134, let $P(x,b)$ be a point on the line $y = b$ such that $0 < x < a$. It follows from the figure that the acute angles AOP and OAP are given by $\text{Cot}^{-1}\frac{x}{b}$ and $\text{Cot}^{-1}\frac{a-x}{b}$, respectively; hence

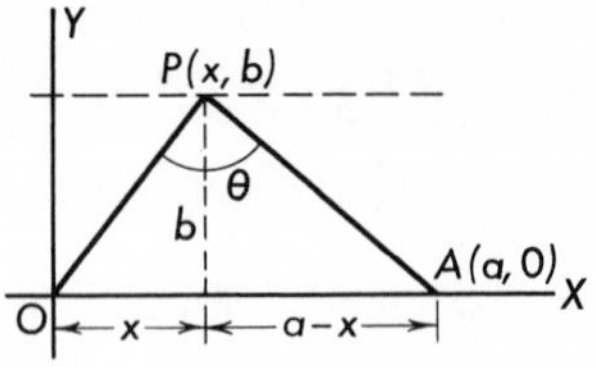

Figure 134

$$\theta = \pi - \text{Cot}^{-1}\frac{x}{b} - \text{Cot}^{-1}\frac{a-x}{b}.$$

Differentiating, we obtain

$$\frac{d\theta}{dx} = \frac{\frac{1}{b}}{1 + \left(\frac{x}{b}\right)^2} + \frac{-\frac{1}{b}}{1 + \left(\frac{a-x}{b}\right)^2}.$$

Setting $d\theta/dx = 0$, it follows that $\frac{x}{b} = \frac{a-x}{b}$. Hence θ is a maximum when $x = \frac{1}{2}a$.

Note 2: Inverse trigonometric functions should be used with caution, since their principal values are defined for different regions. Thus $\text{Tan}^{-1}(-2)$ represents a negative acute angle, whereas $\text{Cot}^{-1}(-2)$ represents a positive obtuse angle. For this reason, whenever possible, it is advisable to consider only positive acute angles.

Example 4. Find the minimum value of the function $f(x) = x + |\ln x|$.

Solution: Since $\ln x$ is negative for $0 < x < 1$, the given function, except for $f(1) = 1$, can be written as

$$f(x) = \begin{cases} x - \ln x, & 0 < x < 1, \\ x + \ln x, & 1 < x. \end{cases}$$

Hence, from

$$f'(x) = \begin{cases} 1 - \dfrac{1}{x}, & 0 < x < 1, \\ 1 + \dfrac{1}{x}, & 1 < x, \end{cases}$$

we conclude that $f(x)$ is decreasing for $0 < x < 1$ and increasing for $1 < x$. Therefore $x = 1$ gives the minimum value 1 for the function.

EXERCISE 43

Find the critical points and sketch the following curves.

1. $y = xe^{-x}$. *Ans.* $(1,1/e)$, max.
2. $y = x \ln x$.
3. $y = \ln(2x - x^2)$. $(1,0)$, max.
4. $y = e^{1/x}$.

Find the angles of intersection of the following pairs of curves.

5. $\begin{cases} y = \ln x, \\ y = \ln(1 - x). \end{cases}$ *Ans.* 53.1°.
6. $\begin{cases} y = \sin x, \\ y = \sin 2x. \end{cases}$
7. $\begin{cases} y = e^{-x}, \\ y = e^{-x^2}. \end{cases}$ 45°, 16.1°.
8. $\begin{cases} y = \text{Tan}^{-1} x, \\ y = \text{Cot}^{-1} x. \end{cases}$

Find the equation of the line tangent to the following curves at the point indicated.

9. $y = xe^{2x}$, $(1,e^2)$. *Ans.* $y = e^2(3x - 2)$.
10. $y = \sin \pi x$, $(-\frac{1}{6}, -\frac{1}{2})$.
11. $y = \ln \cos x$, $(\frac{1}{3}\pi, -\ln 2)$. $3x + \sqrt{3}\,y = \pi - \sqrt{3}\ln 2$.
12. $e^x + e^y = 1$, $(-\ln 2, -\ln 2)$.
13. For the curve $y = \frac{1}{2}x^2 + 2\sin x$, find the first point of inflection to the right of the y axis. *Ans.* $(\frac{1}{6}\pi, \frac{1}{72}\pi^2 + 1)$.
14. Find the point of inflection of the curve $xy = 4 \ln \frac{1}{2}x$.
15. Find d^2y/dx^2 when $\ln(x^2 + y^2) = 2\,\text{Tan}^{-1}(y/x)$.
    Ans. $2(x^2 + y^2)/(x - y)^3$.

16. If $y = \sin x$, show that $\dfrac{d(\ln y)}{d(\ln x)} = x \cot x$.

Find the maximum values attained by the following functions when a and b are positive constants.

17. $\sin (a + x) + \sin (a - x)$. *Ans.* $2|\sin a|$.
18. $a \ln x + b \ln (1 - x)$.
19. $a \sin kx + b \cos kx$. $\sqrt{a^2 + b^2}$.
20. $-(ae^{kx} + be^{-kx})$.

Use differentials to find approximate values for the following expressions.

21. $\sin 32°$, if $\sin 30° = 0.5$. *Ans.* 0.530.
22. $\ln 10.2$, if $\ln 10 = 2.303$.
23. $\text{Sin}^{-1} 0.48$, if $\text{Sin}^{-1} 0.5 = \frac{1}{6}\pi$. 0.501.
24. $e^{3.1}$, if $e^3 = 20$.
25. Prove by mathematical induction that $d^{n+1}(x^n \ln x)/dx^{n+1} = n!/x$.
26. If a particle moves on a straight line so that $s = e^{-t}(\sin t + \cos t)$, find expressions for the velocity and acceleration. Describe the motion.
27. Find the minimum value of $x^2 + |\ln x|$. *Ans.* $\frac{1}{2} + \frac{1}{2} \ln 2$.
28. Find the area of the largest rectangle that has one side on the x axis and two vertices on the curve $y = e^{-x^2}$.
29. Find the area of the largest triangle cut from the first quadrant by a line tangent to the curve $y = e^{-x}$. *Ans.* $2/e$.
30. Find the volume of the largest right circular cone which can be inscribed in a sphere of radius 9 inches. *Hint:* Let θ be the central angle subtending a radius of the base of the cone, then $r = 9 \sin \theta$ and $h = 9 + 9 \cos \theta$.
31. Solve Problem 30 using the same variables, if the lateral surface of the cone is to be a maximum. *Ans.* 288π cu. in.
32. A statue 10 feet high is standing on a base 13 feet high. If an observer's eye is 5 feet above the ground, how far should he stand from the base in order that the angle between his lines of sight to the top and bottom of the statue be a maximum?
33. The range, height, and time of flight of a projectile are given by

$$R = \frac{v^2 \sin 2\theta}{g}, \qquad h = \frac{v^2 \sin^2 \theta}{2g}, \qquad \text{and} \qquad t = \frac{2v \sin \theta}{g},$$

where v and g are constants. Find the angle of projection θ which will make each of these in turn a maximum. *Ans.* 45°, 90°, and 90°.

34. The range of a projectile up an inclined plane is given by

$$R = \frac{2v^2 \cos \theta \sin (\theta - \alpha)}{g \cos^2 \alpha},$$

where v and g are constants and α is the inclination of the plane with the horizontal. Find the angle of projection θ which makes R a maximum.

35. A building is to be braced by means of a beam which must pass over a wall. If the wall is $3\frac{3}{8}$ feet high and stands 8 feet from the building, find the shortest beam that can be used. *Ans.* $15\frac{5}{8}$ ft.

36. A steel girder 27 feet long is to be moved on rollers along a passageway 8 feet in width and into a corridor at right angles to the passageway. If the horizontal width of the girder is neglected, how wide must the corridor be in order that the girder can go around the corner?

37. At what point on the y axis does the line segment joining (1,1) and (9,7) subtend the greatest angle? *Hint:* For $1 < y < 7, \theta = \mathrm{Tan}^{-1}\frac{1}{9}(7 - y) + \mathrm{Tan}^{-1}(y - 1)$. *Ans.* $y = 4$.

38. Two line segments AB and AC of lengths 2 and $2 + 2\sqrt{3}$, respectively, form an angle of 60°. At what angle θ with AB should a line through A be drawn so that the sum of the projections of AB and AC on this line will be a maximum?

39. Prove that the curve $y = 2\cos x$ passes through all the points of inflection of the curve $y = x \sin x$.

40. Show that the segment of the tangent to the tractrix

$$x = \frac{a}{2} \ln \frac{a + \sqrt{a^2 - y^2}}{a - \sqrt{a^2 - y^2}} - \sqrt{a^2 - y^2},$$

included between the point of tangency and the x axis, is constant and equal to a. (See **72**, page 10.)

CHAPTER 9

Parametric Equations, Curvature, and Roots

93. Parametric Representations

If the rectangular coordinates of a point on a plane curve can be expressed as functions of a common variable u in the form

$$x = f(u), \qquad y = g(u), \tag{1}$$

the equations (1) are called **parametric equations** of the curve and the variable u is called a **parameter.** If we eliminate u from the equations in (1), we obtain the *rectangular* or *Cartesian equation* of the curve.

Illustration. Eliminating the parameter θ from the equations $x = 2 \sin \theta$ and $y = 3 \cos \theta$, we obtain the rectangular equation of an ellipse. Thus

$$\left(\frac{x}{2}\right)^2 + \left(\frac{y}{3}\right)^2 = \sin^2 \theta + \cos^2 \theta;$$

hence

$$\frac{x^2}{4} + \frac{y^2}{9} = 1.$$

Note: The elimination of the parameter assures us that any point satisfying the parametric equations will satisfy the rectangular equation, but the converse is not necessarily true. For example, the equations $x = \sin^2 \theta$ and $y = \cos^2 \theta$ represent only the line segment from (0,1) to (1,0), whereas the corresponding rectangular equation $x + y = 1$ represents the whole line.

When the functions $f(u)$ and $g(u)$ in (1) are continuous at a value $u = u_0$, we know from this continuity that for each number $\epsilon > 0$, there exists a number $\delta > 0$ such that

$$|f(u) - f(u_0)| < \epsilon/\sqrt{2}, \qquad \text{and} \qquad |g(u) - g(u_0)| < \epsilon/\sqrt{2},$$

provided $|u - u_0| < \delta$. Thus, if P_0 and P are the points of the curve (1) corresponding to the parametric values u_0 and u, respectively, we find for the distance from P to P_0

$$|PP_0| = \sqrt{[f(u) - f(u_0)]^2 + [g(u) - g(u_0)]^2} < \sqrt{\tfrac{1}{2}\epsilon^2 + \tfrac{1}{2}\epsilon^2} = \epsilon.$$

This means that all points P on the curve are arbitrarily close to P_0 whenever u is close enough to u_0. Thus the curve corresponding to the equations (1) is continuous at those points where $f(u)$ and $g(u)$ are continuous functions.

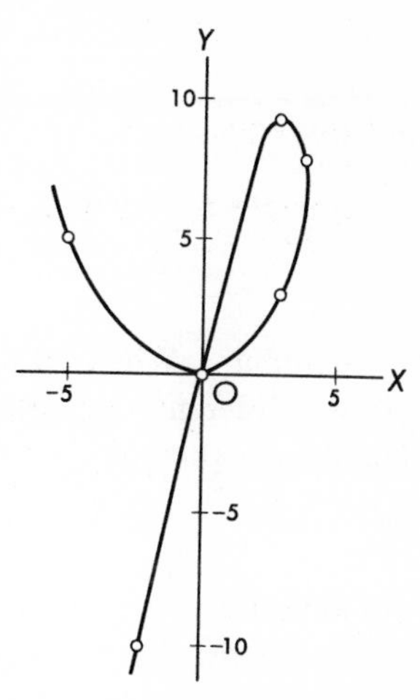

Figure 135

Example 1. Trace the curve whose parametric equations are

$$x = 4t - t^2, \qquad y = 4t^2 - t^3.$$

Solution: Select arbitrary values for t, compute the corresponding values of x and y, and arrange these three numbers in tabular form as indicated.

t	-1	0	1	2	3	4	$4\frac{1}{2}$
x	-5	0	3	4	3	0	$-9/4$
y	5	0	3	8	9	0	$-81/8$

Plotting the points, we obtain the curve shown in Figure 135.

Example 2. The curve traced by a point on the circumference of a circle as it rolls on a straight line is called a **cycloid.** Find parametric equations for a cycloid.

Solution: Consider a circle of radius a starting with the fixed point P at the origin and rolling on the x axis. When the radius CP has turned

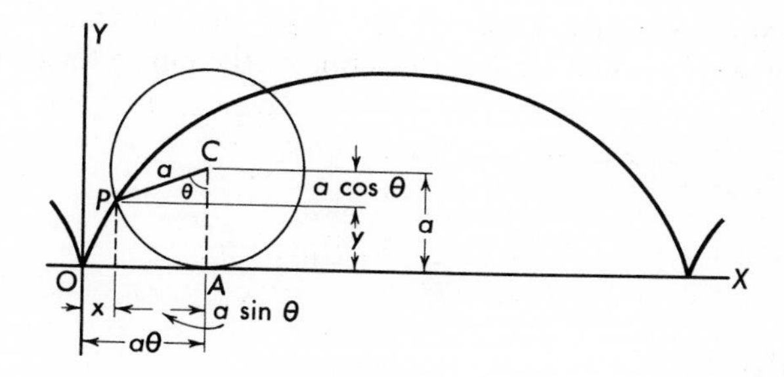

Figure 136

through an angle θ in radians, the circle has rolled to the point A and we have $OA = \text{arc } AP = a\theta$. Hence, from Figure 136, we obtain the coordinates for P,

$$x = a(\theta - \sin\theta), \qquad y = a(1 - \cos\theta).$$

By eliminating θ, the equation of the cycloid becomes

$$x = a \cos^{-1} \frac{a - y}{a} \pm \sqrt{2ay - y^2},$$

but this equation is less convenient to use than the parametric equations.

Example 3. Find parametric equations for the folium of Descartes

$$x^3 + y^3 - 3axy = 0. \tag{2}$$

Solution: When an algebraic equation in x and y contains only terms of two different degrees, an equivalent parametric representation can be found by making the substitution mx for y. When this is done, (2) becomes

$$x^3 + m^3x^3 - 3amx^2 = 0.$$

Dividing by x^2 and solving for x, we obtain

$$x = \frac{3am}{1 + m^3}.$$

Since $y = mx$, it follows that parametric equations of the folium are

$$x = \frac{3am}{1 + m^3}, \qquad y = \frac{3am^2}{1 + m^3}, \tag{3}$$

where m is the parameter.

Graphing equations (3), we obtain curve **67** shown on page 9.

94. Derivatives in Parametric Form

If the equation of a curve is given by the parametric equations $x = f(u)$, $y = g(u)$, then by $\boldsymbol{D}_9$, the slope of the curve for each value of u is given by

$$y' = \frac{dy}{dx} = \frac{\dfrac{dy}{du}}{\dfrac{dx}{du}} = \frac{g'(u)}{f'(u)} \equiv g_1(u),$$

provided that $f'(u) \neq 0$.

Illustration 1. If $x = 3 \sin \theta$ and $y = 5 - 9 \cos \theta$, then

$$\frac{dy}{dx} = \frac{\dfrac{dy}{d\theta}}{\dfrac{dx}{d\theta}} = \frac{9 \sin \theta}{3 \cos \theta} = 3 \tan \theta.$$

Higher derivatives may be found by continuing this process as follows.

$$y'' = \frac{dy'}{dx} = \frac{\dfrac{dy'}{du}}{\dfrac{dx}{du}} = \frac{g_1'(u)}{f'(u)} \equiv g_2(u),$$

$$y''' = \frac{dy''}{dx} = \frac{\dfrac{dy''}{du}}{\dfrac{dx}{du}} = \frac{g_2'(u)}{f'(u)} \equiv g_3(u).$$

The sequence of parametric functions $g_1(u), g_2(u), g_3(u), \cdots$ defined in the above manner gives the respective parametric representations for the derivatives $y', y'', y''', \cdots$.

Illustration 2. For the curve of Illustration 1, we have

$$\frac{d^2y}{dx^2} = \frac{\dfrac{dy'}{d\theta}}{\dfrac{dx}{d\theta}} = \frac{3\sec^2\theta}{3\cos\theta} = \sec^3\theta,$$

$$\frac{d^3y}{dx^3} = \frac{\dfrac{dy''}{d\theta}}{\dfrac{dx}{d\theta}} = \frac{3\sec^3\theta\tan\theta}{3\cos\theta} = \sec^4\theta\tan\theta.$$

Note: The above analysis is sometimes clearer if differentials are used. Thus, in Illustration 1, since $dx = 3\cos\theta\, d\theta$ and $dy = 9\sin\theta\, d\theta$, we have

$$\frac{dy}{dx} = \frac{9\sin\theta\, d\theta}{3\cos\theta\, d\theta} = 3\tan\theta.$$

EXERCISE 44

Trace the following curves by assigning values to the parameter.

1. $x = \dfrac{1}{1+u}, \quad y = \sqrt{u} - 1.$

2. $x = \dfrac{3t}{1+t^3}, \quad y = \dfrac{3t^2}{1+t^3}.$

3. $x = \sec\theta, \quad y = \tan\theta.$

4. $x = \sin\phi, \quad y = \sin 2\phi.$

Find the rectangular equation of each of the following curves.

5. $\begin{cases} x = 3 - t, \\ y = t^2 - 2. \end{cases}$ *Ans.* $x^2 = 6x + y - 7.$

6. $\begin{cases} x = 1 - u^2, \\ y = u + u^3. \end{cases}$

7. $\begin{cases} x = 1/(1 + v), \\ y = v/(1 - v^2). \end{cases}$ $x^2 + 2xy = x + y.$

8. $\begin{cases} x = \sin\phi + \cos\phi, \\ y = \sin\phi. \end{cases}$

9. $\begin{cases} x = \tan\theta, \\ y = \tan 2\theta. \end{cases}$ *Ans.* $x^2y = y - 2x.$ 10. $\begin{cases} x = \sin\theta, \\ y = \cos 2\theta. \end{cases}$

11. $\begin{cases} x = \ln t, \\ y = t^2 - 1. \end{cases}$ $y = e^{2x} - 1.$ 12. $\begin{cases} x = e^v + e^{-v}, \\ y = e^v - e^{-v}. \end{cases}$

Obtain parametric equations equivalent to the following rectangular equations, and trace the curve.

13. $x^2 + y^3 = 4xy.$ *Ans.* $x = \dfrac{4m - 1}{m^3}, \quad y = \dfrac{4m - 1}{m^2}.$

14. $x^2 + y^4 = 4xy.$

15. $x^2 + 2xy + 4y^2 = 8x.$ $x = \dfrac{8}{1 + 2m + 4m^2}, \quad y = \dfrac{8m}{1 + 2m + 4m^2}.$

16. $x^3 + y^3 = x^2 + y^2.$

For each of the following curves, find dy/dx and d^2y/dx^2 in terms of the parameter.

17. $x = u^3 + 1, \quad y = u^2 + 1.$ *Ans.* $2/3u, \quad -2/9u^4.$

18. $x = \dfrac{1}{1 - t}, \quad y = \dfrac{t}{t - 1}.$

19. $x = \dfrac{1}{t - 1}, \quad y = \dfrac{t}{t^2 - 1}.$ $\dfrac{t^2 + 1}{(t + 1)^2}, \quad -2\left(\dfrac{t - 1}{t + 1}\right)^3.$

20. $x = \dfrac{u}{u - 1}, \quad y = \dfrac{u^2}{u^2 - 1}.$

21. $x = \dfrac{2}{1 + v^2}, \quad y = \dfrac{2}{v(1 + v^2)}.$ $\dfrac{1 + 3v^2}{2v^3}, \quad \dfrac{3(1 + v^2)^3}{8v^5}.$

22. $x = \cos^3\theta, \quad y = \sin^3\theta.$

23. $x = \theta - \sin\theta, \quad y = 1 - \cos\theta.$ $\dfrac{\sin\theta}{1 - \cos\theta}, \quad \dfrac{-1}{(1 - \cos\theta)^2}.$

24. $x = \cos\phi + \phi\sin\phi, \quad y = \sin\phi - \phi\cos\phi.$

25. $x = 1 - \ln u, \quad y = u - \ln u.$ $1 - u, \ u.$

26. $x = e^t(\cos t - \sin t), \quad y = e^t(\cos t + \sin t).$

Find the equations of the tangent and the normal to the following curves at the point indicated.

27. $x = t^2 - 2t, \quad y = t^3 - 3t; \quad t = 2.$

Ans. $2y - 9x = 4, \ 9y + 2x = 18.$

28. $x = \sin\theta, \quad y = \tan\theta; \quad \theta = \frac{1}{4}\pi.$

29. $x = e^t, \quad y = 2e^{-t}; \quad t = 0.$ $y + 2x = 4, \ 2y - x = 3.$

30. $x = u^2 - 1, \quad y = u\ln u; \quad u = e.$

Find the parametric coordinates of the maximum and minimum points of the following curves.

31. $x = t^2 + 3t + 2, \quad y = t^2 - 1.$ *Ans.* 0, min.

32. $x = e^v, \quad y = ve^v.$

33. $x = 3\cos\theta, \quad y = 4\sin\theta.$ *Ans.* $\frac{1}{2}\pi$, max.; $\frac{3}{2}\pi$, min.

34. $x = \sin\phi + \cos\phi, \quad y = \sin\phi - \cos\phi.$

35. Show that the parametric equations of the curve traced by a point on the radius CP (Figure 136), or on the radius extended, are

$$x = a\theta - b\sin\theta, \qquad y = a - b\cos\theta,$$

where b is the distance of the tracing point from the center of the circle. When $b \neq a$, the curve is called a **trochoid.**

36. The curve traced by a point on the circumference of a circle of radius b as it rolls on the outside of another circle of radius a is called an **epicycloid.** Let the fixed circle be taken with center at the origin and let the tracing point $P(x,y)$ start at $(a,0)$. If θ denotes the angle between the x axis and the line drawn to the center C of the rolling circle, show that the parametric equations of the epicycloid are

$$x = (a + b)\cos\theta - b\cos\frac{a+b}{b}\theta,$$

$$y = (a + b)\sin\theta - b\sin\frac{a+b}{b}\theta.$$

Hint: Since the arcs of contact are equal, it follows that angle $OCP = a\theta/b$.

95. Differential of Arc Length

Let s denote the length of arc of the plane curve

$$x = f(u), \qquad y = g(u)$$

measured from some initial point $P_0(u_0)$ to the point $P(u)$, and suppose that s increases as u increases. The arc length s is clearly a function of u, and referring to Figure 137, its derivative with respect to u may be obtained from the relation

$$\frac{\Delta s}{\Delta u} = \frac{\Delta s}{\overline{PQ}} \cdot \frac{\overline{PQ}}{\Delta u}$$

$$= \frac{\Delta s}{\overline{PQ}} \cdot \frac{\sqrt{(\Delta x)^2 + (\Delta y)^2}}{\Delta u}$$

$$= \frac{\Delta s}{\overline{PQ}} \cdot \sqrt{\left(\frac{\Delta x}{\Delta u}\right)^2 + \left(\frac{\Delta y}{\Delta u}\right)^2}.$$

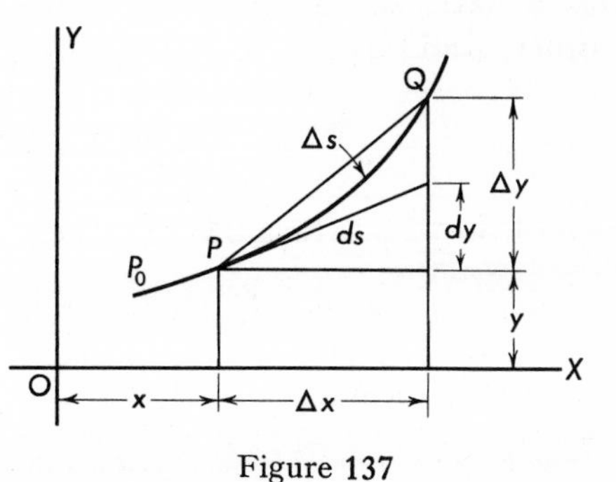

Figure 137

Thus, since the fraction $\Delta s/\overline{PQ}$ approaches unity* as Δu approaches zero, we obtain

$$\frac{ds}{du} = \sqrt{\left(\frac{dx}{du}\right)^2 + \left(\frac{dy}{du}\right)^2}. \tag{1}$$

Multiplying (1) by du, we obtain the differential form for arc length

$$ds = \pm\sqrt{(dx)^2 + (dy)^2}. \tag{2}$$

Thus ds may be considered as the hypotenuse of a right triangle whose sides are dx and dy.

96. Curvature

Let $P(x,y)$ and $Q(x + \Delta x,\ y + \Delta y)$ be two points on the curve $y = f(x)$. When a tangent line describes the arc Δs between P and Q, we see, as indicated in Figure 138, that the tangent line turns through an angle $\Delta\alpha$. The ratio $\Delta\alpha/\Delta s$ is called the *average curvature of the arc PQ*, and we make the following definition.

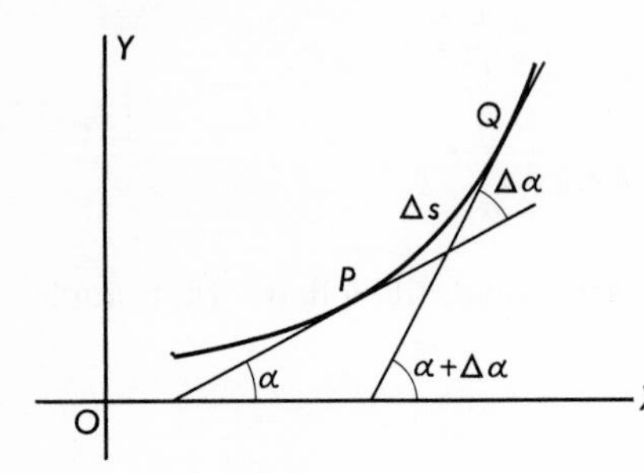

Figure 138

The **curvature** *K at a point P of a curve is the absolute value of the limit of the average curvature of the arc PQ as Q approaches P, that is,*

$$K = \left|\lim_{\Delta s\to 0}\frac{\Delta\alpha}{\Delta s}\right| = \left|\frac{d\alpha}{ds}\right| = \textit{curvature at } P.$$

In order to obtain a more usable formula for K, we calculate $d\alpha/ds$ as a ratio of differentials. Thus, since $\alpha = \operatorname{Tan}^{-1} y'$ we find by differentiation

$$d\alpha = \frac{y''}{1 + (y')^2}\,dx,$$

and from (2), Article **95,** we have

$$ds = \pm\sqrt{1 + (y')^2}\,dx.$$

---

* If the curve has a continuous turning tangent this follows from the definition that a length of arc is equal to the limit approached by the total length of a chain of chords as each chord of the chain approaches zero. See Article **145** for further details.

Hence, by division, the curvature at a point $P(x,y)$ of the curve $y = f(x)$ is

$$\mathbf{K} = \left|\frac{d\alpha}{ds}\right| = \frac{|y''|}{[1 + (y')^2]^{3/2}}. \tag{1}$$

Note: Observe that K is given approximately by $|y''|$ when the slope y' is very small. This approximation is assumed in many formulas used in engineering and physics.

Illustration 1. For the parabola $y = x^2$, we have $y' = 2x$ and $y'' = 2$; hence by (1) the curvature is

$$K = \frac{2}{(1 + 4x^2)^{3/2}},$$

and at the vertex (0,0), by taking $x = 0$, we find $K = 2$ radians per unit length.

When the equation of a curve is given in the form

$$x = f(u), \qquad y = g(u),$$

we have $dy/dx = g'(u)/f'(u)$ and

$$\frac{d^2y}{dx^2} = \frac{f'(u)g''(u) - f''(u)g'(u)}{[f'(u)]^3}.$$

Hence in parametric form the curvature is

$$\mathbf{K} = \frac{|f'g'' - f''g'|}{(f'^2 + g'^2)^{3/2}}. \tag{2}$$

Illustration 2. For the circle $x = r\cos\theta$, $y = r\sin\theta$ of radius r, we have $f' = -r\sin\theta, f'' = -r\cos\theta$, $g' = r\cos\theta$, and $g'' = -r\sin\theta$; hence by (2)

$$K = \frac{r^2\sin^2\theta + r^2\cos^2\theta}{(r^2\sin^2\theta + r^2\cos^2\theta)^{3/2}} = \frac{1}{r}. \tag{3}$$

Thus the curvature at any point of a circle is constant and equal to the reciprocal of the radius of the circle.

97. Circle of Curvature

Consider the curve $y = f(x)$, having at the point P a tangent line L and a curvature K. Let us construct a circle, as shown in Figure 139, so that (*a*) it is tangent to L at P, (*b*) it lies on the same side of L as the curve, and (*c*) it has the curvature K. This circle is called the **circle of**

curvature, its radius the **radius of curvature,** and its center the **center of curvature** of the given curve at the point P. Denoting the radius of curvature by R, it follows from (3) of the preceding article that $R = 1/K$; hence

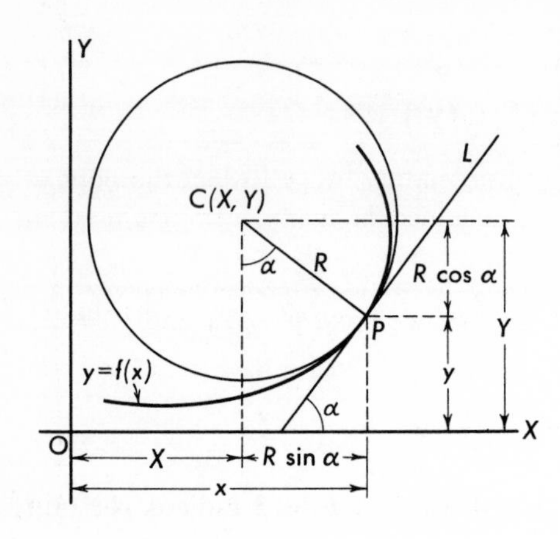

Figure 139

$$R = \frac{(1 + y'^2)^{3/2}}{|y''|}.$$

Illustration. For the curve $y = \ln \sec x$, we have $y' = \tan x$ and $y'' = \sec^2 x$; hence

$$R = \frac{(1 + \tan^2 x)^{3/2}}{\sec^2 x} = \sec x.$$

EXERCISE 45

Find the radius of curvature for each of the following curves at the point indicated.

1. $3y = x^3$; $(1, \frac{1}{3})$. *Ans.* $\sqrt{2}$.
2. $y = x - x^2$; $(0,0)$.
3. $y^2 = x^3$; $(\frac{1}{4}, \frac{1}{8})$. $\frac{125}{96}$.
4. $x^2 - 3y^2 = 1$; $(2,1)$.
5. $y = \sin x$; $(\frac{1}{2}\pi, 1)$. 1.
6. $y = \tan \frac{1}{4}x$; $(\pi, 1)$.
7. $y = e^x$; $(0,1)$. $2\sqrt{2}$.
8. $y = \ln \sin x$; $(\frac{1}{2}\pi, 0)$.
9. $x = u^2 - 2u$, $y = u^3 - u$; $u = 1$. 2.
10. $x = t^2 - 1$, $y = \frac{1}{3}t^3 - t$; $t = 2$.
11. $x = 1/(1 + u)$, $y = 1/(1 - u)$; $u = 0$. $\frac{1}{2}\sqrt{2}$.
12. $x = 4 \sin \theta$, $y = 3 \cos \theta$; $\theta = 0$.
13. $x = \sin \phi$, $y = \sin 2\phi$; $\phi = \frac{1}{2}\pi$. 4.
14. $x = \theta - \sin \theta$, $y = 1 - \cos \theta$; $\theta = \pi$.
15. $x = e^t + e^{-t}$, $y = e^t - e^{-t}$; $t = 0$. 2.
16. $x = 1 + \ln u$, $y = u^2 \ln u$; $u = 1$.

Find the radius of curvature at a general point on each of the following curves.

17. *Inverse sine* $y = \mathrm{Sin}^{-1} x$. *Ans.* $(2 - x^2)^{3/2}/|x|$.
18. *Ellipse* $\dfrac{x^2}{a^2} + \dfrac{y^2}{b^2} = 1$.

19. *Astroid* $x^{2/3} + y^{2/3} = a^{2/3}$. *Ans.* $3|(axy)^{1/3}|$.
20. *Parabolic arc* $x^{1/2} + y^{1/2} = a^{1/2}$.
21. *Catenary* $y = \frac{1}{2}a(e^{x/a} + e^{-x/a})$. y^2/a.
22. *Tractrix* $y = \dfrac{a}{2} \ln \dfrac{a + \sqrt{a^2 - x^2}}{a - \sqrt{a^2 - x^2}} - \sqrt{a^2 - x^2}$.
23. *Cycloid* $x = a(\theta - \sin\theta)$, $y = a(1 - \cos\theta)$. $4a|\sin \frac{1}{2}\theta|$.
24. *Hypocycloid* $x = a\cos^3 t$, $y = a\sin^3 t$.

Find the points of the following curves where the curvature is maximum.

25. $y = 4x - x^2$. *Ans.* (2,4).
26. $y = \sin x$.
27. $y = \ln \sec x$. (0,0).
28. $y = e^x$.
29. $\begin{cases} x = 2u - 3, \\ y = u^2 - 1. \end{cases}$ $u = 0$.
30. $\begin{cases} x = \sin t, \\ y = 2\cos t. \end{cases}$
31. $6y = x^3 + \dfrac{3}{x}$. $(\pm 0.6^{1/4}, \pm 0.6^{3/4})$.
32. $y = \frac{1}{4}x^2 - \frac{1}{2}\ln x$.

98. Center of Curvature

Consider a curve $y = f(x)$ which at the point $P(x,y)$ has a positive slope ($y' > 0$) and is concave upward ($y'' > 0$). It follows from Figure 139 that the coordinates (X,Y) of its center of curvature are

$$X = x - R\sin\alpha, \qquad Y = y + R\cos\alpha. \tag{1}$$

From the preceding article we have

$$R = (1 + y'^2)^{3/2}/y'',$$

and from the relation $\tan\alpha = y'$, we can show that

$$\sin\alpha = \frac{y'}{\sqrt{1 + y'^2}}, \qquad \cos\alpha = \frac{1}{\sqrt{1 + y'^2}}.$$

When these expressions are substituted in (1), we obtain

$$X = x - \frac{y'(1 + y'^2)}{y''}, \qquad Y = y + \frac{1 + y'^2}{y''}. \tag{2}$$

In this way the center of curvature of a curve is determined parametrically in terms of the abscissa of the point P. It can be shown that (2) is valid in all cases, that is, without the restriction that $y' > 0$ and $y'' > 0$.

Illustration. For the parabola $y = 2x - x^2$, we have $y' = 2 - 2x$ and $y'' = -2$. Thus at the point $x = 1$, $y = 1$, we find $y' = 0$ and $y'' = -2$. Substituting these values in (2) we obtain the center of curvature, $X = 1$ and $Y = \frac{1}{2}$.

99. Evolutes

As a point P moves along a curve K_1 the center of curvature corresponding to P describes a second curve K_2. The curve K_2 is called the **evolute** of K_1, and conversely K_1 is called an **involute** of K_2.

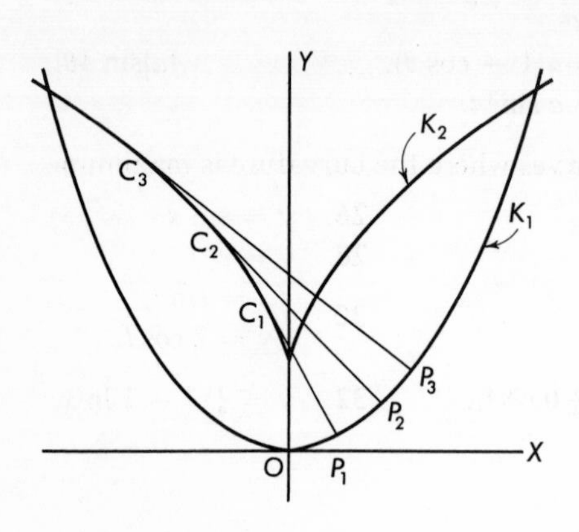

Figure 140

The equation of the evolute corresponding to the curve $y = f(x)$ is given in parametric form by the equation (2) of the preceding article.

Illustration. For the parabola $2y = x^2$, we have $y' = x$ and $y'' = 1$. Substituting in (2), Article **98**, we obtained the following parametric equation for the evolute of the parabola.

$$X = x - x(1 + x^2) = -x^3,$$

$$Y = \tfrac{1}{2}x^2 + (1 + x^2) = \tfrac{3}{2}x^2 + 1.$$

Eliminating the parameter x, we obtain the rectangular equation

$$X^2 = \tfrac{8}{27}(Y - 1)^3.$$

The given parabola and its evolute, the semicubical parabola, are shown in Figure 140.

EXERCISE 46

Find the center of curvature for the following curves at the point indicated.

1. $y = x^4 - x^2$; $(0,0)$. *Ans.* $(0,-\frac{1}{2})$.
2. $y = \sin x$; $(\frac{1}{2}\pi,1)$.
3. $y = \dfrac{x}{x+1}$; $(0,0)$. $(1,-1)$.
4. $y = \dfrac{8a^3}{x^2 + 4a^2}$; $(0,2a)$.
5. $y = e^{-x^2}$; $(0,1)$. $(0,\frac{1}{2})$.
6. $x^{1/2} + y^{1/2} = 3$; $(1,4)$.
7. $x^3 + y^3 = 4xy$; $(2,2)$. $(\frac{7}{4},\frac{7}{4})$.
8. $\begin{cases} x = u + \ln u, \\ y = u \ln u; \quad u = 1. \end{cases}$

Find parametric equations for the evolutes of the following curves.

9. $y = x^3$. *Ans.* $X = \frac{1}{2}x - \frac{9}{2}x^5$, $Y = \frac{5}{2}x^3 + \frac{1}{6}x^{-1}$.
10. $y = x^n$.
11. $y = e^x$. $X = x - 1 - e^{2x}$, $Y = 2e^x + e^{-x}$.
12. $y = \ln \sec x$.
13. $y^3 = a^2x$. $X = (a^4 + 15y^4)/6a^2y$, $Y = (a^4y - 9y^5)/2a^4$.
14. $9y^2 = 4x^3$.
15. $x = \frac{1}{4}t^4$, $y = \frac{1}{5}t^5$. $X = -t^6 - \frac{3}{4}t^4$, $Y = \frac{6}{5}t^5 + t^3$.
16. $x = a(\theta - \sin\theta)$, $y = a(1 - \cos\theta)$.

Find rectangular equations for the evolutes of the following curves.

17. $y^2 = 2ax$. *Ans.* $27aY^2 = 8(X - a)^3$.
18. $b^2x^2 - a^2y^2 = a^2b^2$.
19. $x = a \cos \phi, \quad y = b \sin \phi$. $(aX)^{2/3} + (bY)^{2/3} = (a^2 - b^2)^{2/3}$.
20. $x = a(\cos t + t \sin t), \quad y = a(\sin t - t \cos t)$.

100. Newton's Method

In elementary courses graphical and interpolative methods are given for determining approximate values for the irrational real roots of equations.

Illustration 1. An approximate value for the root of the equation $x = \cos x$ is determined graphically as follows. Plot the curves $y = x$ and $y = \cos x$ (Figure 141). The abscissa of their point of intersection gives us an approximation $x = 0.7$ which is correct to one decimal place. To obtain greater accuracy it is necessary to construct the graphs on a larger scale.

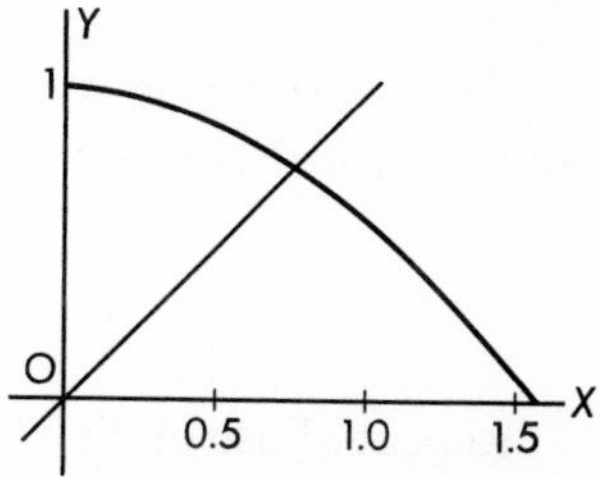

Figure 141

Illustration 2. An approximate value for the root of the equation $x = \cos x$ is determined by interpolation as follows. We write $f(x) = x - \cos x$ and observe in Table IV (page 575) that $f(0.7330) = -0.0101$ and $f(0.7505) = 0.0191$. Then, by interpolation, we obtain

$$\frac{h}{0.0175} = \frac{0.0101}{0.0292};$$

hence,

$$h = 0.006.$$

Thus $x = 0.7330 + 0.006 = 0.739$ gives an approximation which is correct to three decimal places.

x	$f(x)$
0.7330	−0.0101
0.7330 + h	0
0.7505	0.0191

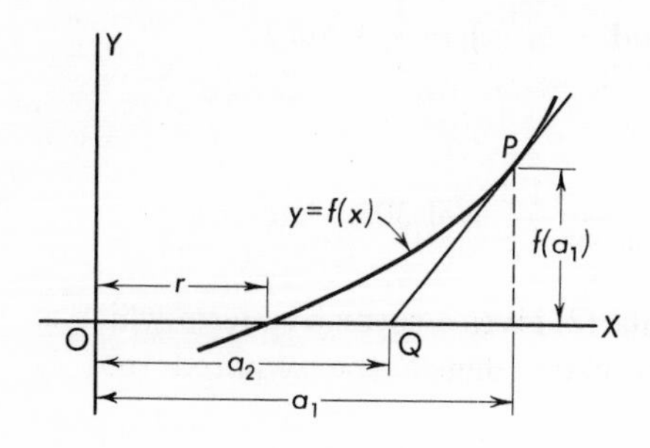

Figure 142

It is the purpose of this article to consider another process, known as **Newton's method,** by means of which the irrational roots can be determined approximately to any desired accuracy.

Consider the curve $y = f(x)$ in Figure 142 and suppose that $x = a_1$ is a first approximation to the root r of the equation $f(x) = 0$.

The equation of the tangent line to the curve at P is

$$y - f(a_1) = f'(a_1)(x - a_1). \tag{1}$$

When a_1 is near to the value r, this tangent line will usually intersect the x axis at a point Q whose abscissa a_2 is a closer approximation to r than is a_1. Thus, setting $x = a_2$ and $y = 0$ in (1), we obtain **Newton's formula**

$$\boldsymbol{a_2 = a_1 - \frac{f(a_1)}{f'(a_1)}}. \tag{2}$$

Now considering a_2 as the initial approximation, by use of (2) we obtain a third approximation

$$a_3 = a_2 - \frac{f(a_2)}{f'(a_2)}.$$

Repeated use of Newton's formula (2) will give a root to any desired accuracy.

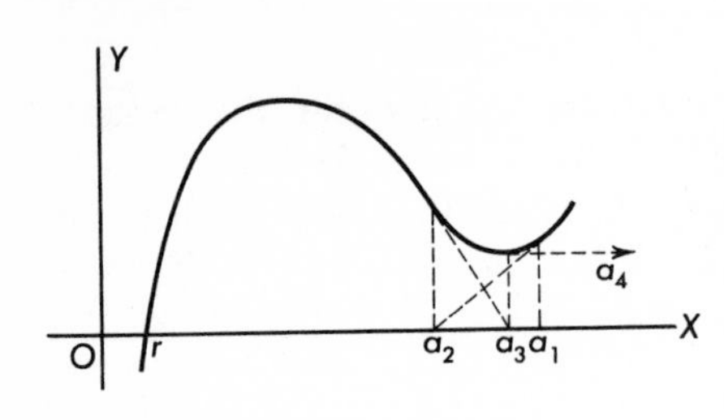

Figure 143

Note: If the initial approximation a_1 is not sufficiently close to r, Newton's formula may lead to an absurd result. Such a situation is indicated in Figure 143.

Example. Find a root of the equation $\ln x - \cos x = 0$ correct to three decimal places.

Solution: A comparison of Tables II and IV (pages 572, 575) indicates that there is a root in the neighborhood of $x = 1.3$. For Newton's formula we have

$$f(x) = \ln x - \cos x \qquad \text{and} \qquad f'(x) = \frac{1}{x} + \sin x.$$

Hence, taking $a_1 = 1.3$, we obtain

$$a_2 = 1.3 - \frac{\ln 1.3 - \cos 1.3}{(1/1.3) + \sin 1.3} = 1.303.$$

The substitution of 1.303 in formula (2) gives a corrective term which is too small to affect the third decimal place; hence the required root is 1.303.

EXERCISE 47

Determine graphically the number of real roots to each of the following equations.

1. $3 \sin x - x = 0$. *Ans.* 3.
2. $\cos 2x - x^2 = 0$.
3. $e^{-x^2} - \ln x = 0$. 1.
4. $\tan x - \ln x = 0$.
5. $e^x + x^3 = 4x$. 3.
6. $x + 1 = x \ln x$.

Each of the following equations has one irrational root. Find it to two decimal places, using Newton's method.

7. $x^3 + 2x - 5 = 0$. *Ans.* 1.33.
8. $x^3 + x^2 + 10 = 0$.
9. $x^4 + x^3 + x^2 = 1$. 0.68.
10. $x^4 - 4x^2 - 4x = 8$.
11. $x^5 + x^3 + 2x = 5$. 1.09.
12. $x^5 + 2x^3 = 17$.

Using Newton's method, find the smallest positive root of the following equations to three decimal places.

13. $\cos x - x = 0$. *Ans.* 0.739.
14. $e^x - 2x^2 = 0$.
15. $e^{-x} - \ln x = 0$. 1.310.
16. $x + \log x = 2$.
17. $2 \sin 2x - x = 1$. 0.381.
18. $x + \text{Tan}^{-1} x = 1$.
19. Find, to two decimal places, the maximum value of the function $x^2 \sin x$ for x between 0 and π. *Ans.* 3.95.
20. Find, to two decimal places, the coordinates of the point of intersection of the hyperbola $xy = 1$ and the catenary $y = \frac{1}{2}(e^x + e^{-x})$.
21. If $y = x^x$, find the value of x to two decimal places when $y = 10$. *Hint:* Consider the common logarithm of y. *Ans.* 2.51.
22. A chord of a circle is 10 inches long and it subtends an arc 12 inches long. Find the central angle which subtends the chord, in radians to two decimal places.
23. The volume of a spherical segment is given by the formula $V = \pi r h^2 - \frac{1}{3}\pi h^3$, where r is the radius of the sphere and h is the height of the segment. Find the height of a segment whose volume is one-third that of the sphere. *Ans.* $0.774r$.
24. If the sum of the sines of two complementary angles is equal to the ratio of the angles, find the angles in radians to two decimal places.

CHAPTER 10

Differentiation with Respect to Time

101. Time-Rates

If the value of a variable x is dependent on the time t, then dx/dt is called its **time-rate** or rate of change with respect to time. If two or more variables are related by an equation and each of the variables depends on the time, a relation among their respective time-rates may be obtained by differentiating the given equation with respect to the time.

Illustration 1. If $xy = 6$, then $x \dfrac{dy}{dt} + y \dfrac{dx}{dt} = 0.$

If at any instant all but one of the variables and all but one of the time-rates are known, we can determine the unknown quantities from the given equation and its derived equation.

Illustration 2. If $dx/dt = 4$ when $x = 2$, in Illustration 1 we obtain $y = 3$ from the given equation and then $dy/dt = -6$ from the derived equation.

A general procedure for solving time-rate problems may be summarized as follows:

1. *Find an equation involving the variables which is true for any time t.*
2. *Differentiate the equation in 1 with respect to t.*
3. *Determine the unknown time-rate from 2, using 1 if needed.*

Example 1. At a certain instant the dimensions of a rectangular parallelepiped are 4, 5, and 6 feet, and they are each increasing, respectively, at the rates 1, 2, and 3 feet per second. At what rate is the volume increasing?

Solution: 1. If x, y, and z denote the dimensions of the parallelepiped, the volume at all times is given by $V = xyz$.

2. Differentiating with respect to time, we have

$$\frac{dV}{dt} = yz\frac{dx}{dt} + xz\frac{dy}{dt} + xy\frac{dz}{dt}. \qquad (1)$$

3. When $x = 4$, $y = 5$, and $z = 6$, it is given that $dx/dt = 1$, $dy/dt = 2$, and $dz/dt = 3$; hence

$$\frac{dV}{dt} = (5)(6)(1) + (4)(6)(2) + (4)(5)(3) = 138 \text{ cu. ft./sec.}$$

Note 1: In applied fields the time-rate of a variable is often denoted by placing a dot above the variable. Thus $\dot{x}$ means dx/dt. Using this notation, (1) would be written as

$$\dot{V} = \dot{x}yz + x\dot{y}z + xy\dot{z}.$$

Example 2. A kite, at a height of 60 feet, is moving horizontally at a rate of 5 feet per second away from the boy who flies it. How fast is the cord being released when 100 feet are out?

Solution: Denoting the horizontal displacement of the kite by x and the length of the cord by y, we see from Figure 144 that

$$y^2 = x^2 + 60^2.$$

Differentiating with respect to the time and dividing by 2, we obtain

$$y\frac{dy}{dt} = x\frac{dx}{dt}. \qquad (2)$$

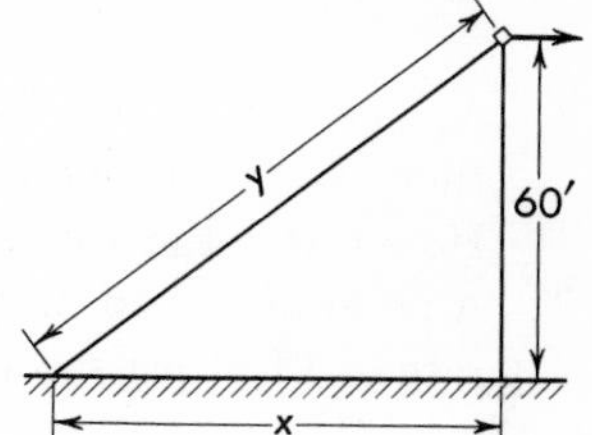

Figure 144

Since $x = \sqrt{100^2 - 60^2} = 80$ and $dx/dt = 5$ when $y = 100$, we find on substitution in (2) that $dy/dt = 4$. Thus the speed at which the cord is being released is 4 feet per second.

Note 2: It is sometimes more convenient to represent the variables of a problem directly in terms of the time t. Thus, in the example above, if x is denoted by $80 + 5t$, then y becomes $\sqrt{(80 + 5t)^2 + 60^2}$, and

$$\frac{dy}{dt} = \frac{5(80 + 5t)}{\sqrt{(80 + 5t)^2 + 60^2}}. \qquad (3)$$

Hence, when $t = 0$, by substitution in (3) we obtain 4 feet per second.

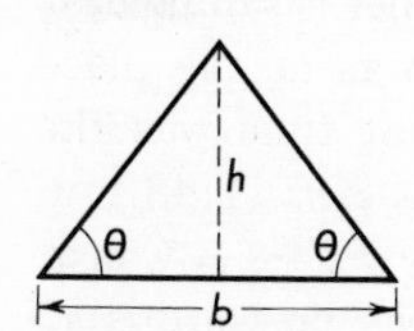

Figure 145

Example 3. The base and the base angles of an isosceles triangle are increasing at the respective rates of 2 feet per second and 5° per second. When the base is 10 feet long and the base angles are 45°, find the rate at which the altitude is increasing.

Solution: If the altitude, base, and base angles are denoted by h, b, and θ, respectively, we see from Figure 145 that

$$h = \tfrac{1}{2}b \tan \theta.$$

Differentiating with respect to the time, we have

$$\frac{dh}{dt} = \frac{1}{2}\tan\theta\frac{db}{dt} + \frac{1}{2}b\sec^2\theta\frac{d\theta}{dt}.$$

Substituting $b = 10$, $db/dt = 2$, $\theta = \pi/4$, $d\theta/dt = \pi/36$, we obtain the required result

$$\frac{dh}{dt} = \frac{1}{2}\left(\tan\frac{\pi}{4}\right)(2) + \frac{1}{2}(10)\left(\sec^2\frac{\pi}{4}\right)\left(\frac{\pi}{36}\right) = 1 + \frac{5\pi}{18} = 1.87 \text{ ft./sec.}$$

EXERCISE 48

1. If the radius of a circle increases at a rate of 0.01 inch per second, find the rate of change of the area when the radius is 3 inches long. *Ans.* 0.19 sq. in./sec.
2. At a certain instant the dimensions of a rectangle are 8 and 12 feet, and they are increasing at the rates 3 and 2 feet per second, respectively. How fast is the area changing?
3. A point moves on the parabola $y = x^2$ so that its abscissa increases at a rate of 3 feet per second. At what rate is the ordinate increasing when $x = 2$? *Ans.* 12 ft./sec.
4. If an angle θ increases uniformly, find the smallest positive value of θ for which $\tan\theta$ increases 8 times as fast as $\sin\theta$.
5. One leg of a right triangle is always 6 feet long, and the other leg is increasing at a rate of 2 feet per second. Find the rate of change of the hypotenuse when it is 10 feet long. *Ans.* 1.6 ft./sec.
6. One end of a ladder 34 feet long slides down a vertical wall while the other end moves away from the wall horizontally at a rate of 3 feet per second. How fast is the top of the ladder descending when its foot is 16 feet from the wall?
7. One ship is sailing south at a rate of 5 knots, and another is sailing east at a rate of 10 knots. At 2 P.M. the second ship was at the place occupied by the first ship one hour before. At what time was the distance between the ships not changing? *Ans.* 1:48 P.M.
8. Air expands adiabatically in accordance with the law $PV^{1.4} = \text{Const.}$ If at a given time the volume is 14 cubic feet and the pressure is 40 pounds per square inch, at what rate is the pressure changing when the volume is decreasing 1 cubic foot per second?
9. The base of an isosceles triangle is 8 feet long. If the altitude is 6 feet long and is increasing 3 inches per minute, at what rate are the base angles changing? *Ans.* $\frac{1}{52}$ rad./min.
10. A triangular trough is 12 feet long, 3 feet wide at the top, and 3 feet deep. If water is poured into the trough at a rate of 10 cubic feet per minute, find how fast the surface is rising when the depth is 2 feet.

11. A light hangs 15 feet directly above a straight walk on which a man 6 feet tall is walking. How fast is the end of the man's shadow traveling when he is walking away from the light at a rate of 3 miles per hour? *Ans.* 5 m.p.h.
12. In Problem 11, how fast is the man's shadow lengthening?
13. If the light in Problem 11 is located 24 feet to one side of the walk, how fast is the man's shadow lengthening when he is 32 feet from the point directly opposite the light? *Ans.* $2\frac{26}{75}$ ft./sec.
14. If $y = 3x - x^3$ and x is increasing at the rate of $\frac{1}{3}$ unit per second, how fast is the slope of the curve changing when $x = 3$?
15. A conical cistern is 10 feet across the top and 12 feet deep. If water is poured into the cistern at the rate of 1 cubic foot per second, how fast is the surface rising when the water is 8 feet deep? *Ans.* 20.6 in./min.
16. The two bases of an isosceles trapezoid are 12 and 20 feet long, respectively. Find the rate at which the area is changing when the equal sides are 5 feet long and are increasing at the rate of 2 feet per minute.
17. A particle travels along the parabola $y = ax^2 + x + b$. At what point do its abscissa and ordinate change at the same rate? *Ans.* $(0,b)$.
18. A man on a pier holds a rope that is attached to a boat at a level 12 feet below the man's hands. If 20 feet of rope are out and the boat is drifting away at a rate of 2 feet per second, find the rate at which the rope is passing through the man's hands.
19. The base of an isosceles triangle is 10 feet long and the base angles are decreasing at a rate of 2° per second. Find the rate of change of the area when the base angles are 45°. *Ans.* -1.75 sq. ft./sec.
20. The area of an ellipse is given by $A = \pi ab$, where a and b are the semi-axes. At a certain instant $a = 6$, $b = 8$, and a is increasing $\frac{1}{3}$ unit each minute. At what rate is b decreasing if the area remains constant?
21. The base diameter and altitude of a right circular cone are observed at a certain instant to be 10 and 20 inches, respectively. If the lateral area is constant and the base diameter is increasing at a rate of 1 inch per minute, find the rate at which the altitude is decreasing. *Ans.* 2.25 in./min.
22. A searchlight revolving once each minute is located at a distance of $\frac{1}{4}$ mile from a straight beach. How fast is the light moving along the beach when the beam makes an angle of 60° with the shore line?
23. A weight is attached to one end of a 33-foot rope which passes over a pulley 18 feet above the ground. The other end is attached to a truck at a point 3 feet above the ground. If the truck moves away at a rate of 2 feet per second, how fast is the weight rising when the truck is 8 feet from the spot directly under the pulley? *Ans.* $\frac{16}{17}$ ft./sec.

24. A man walking 3 miles per hour on a bridge 44 feet above a river is directly over a boat traveling $5\frac{1}{4}$ miles per hour at right angles to the bridge. How fast are the man and the boat separating after 10 seconds?

25. A light is placed on the ground 32 feet from a building. A man 6 feet tall walks from the light toward the building at a rate of 6 feet per second. Find the rate at which his shadow on the building is decreasing when he is 16 feet from the building. *Ans.* $4\frac{1}{2}$ ft./sec.

26. Solve Problem 25 when the light is placed 3 feet above the ground.

27. Each of two sides of a triangle are increasing at the rate of $\frac{1}{2}$ foot per second, and the included angle is decreasing 2° per second. Find the rate of change of the area when the sides and included angle are respectively 5 feet, 8 feet, and 60°. *Ans.* 2.47 sq. ft./sec.

28. In Problem 27, find the rate of change of the third side of the triangle.

29. One ship is 1 mile north of a certain pier and is traveling N 30° E at a rate of 3 miles per hour. Another ship is $\frac{3}{4}$ mile east of the pier and is traveling east at a rate of 7 miles per hour. How fast are the ships separating? *Ans.* 5.4 m.p.h.

30. A particle moves along the curve $y = \ln x$ so that its abscissa is increasing at a rate of 2 units per second. At what rate is the particle moving away from the origin as it passes through the point $(e,1)$?

31. Water drains from a hemispherical basin of diameter 20 inches at the rate of 3 cubic inches per second. How fast is the water level falling when the depth of water is 5 inches? *Ans.* 0.76 in./min.

32. One particle starts at the origin and travels up the line $y = \sqrt{3}\,x$ at a rate of 5 feet per second. Two seconds later another particle starts at the origin and travels up the line $y = x$ at a rate of 10 feet per second. At what rate are they separating 2 seconds after the last particle started?

33. If the x intercept of the tangent to the curve $y = e^{-x}$ is increasing at a rate of 4 units per second, find the rate of change of the y intercept when the x intercept is 6 units. *Ans.* -0.135 un./sec.

34. Starting at the same time from the origin one particle travels up the y axis at a rate of 2 units per second, while another particle travels up the parabola $y = \sqrt{x}$ at a rate such that its abscissa changes 2 units per second. How fast are the particles separating 2 seconds after they start?

35. A clock has hands 1 and $1\frac{3}{5}$ inches long respectively. At what rate are the ends of the hands approaching each other when the time is 2 o'clock? *Ans.* 0.095 in./min.

36. A chord of a circle of diameter 10 feet is decreasing in length 1 foot per minute. Find the rate of change of the smaller arc subtended by the chord when the chord is 8 feet long.

102. Curvilinear Motion

If a particle P moves along the curved arc AB in Figure 146, a vector $\mathbf{v}$ is determined whose horizontal and vertical components are the time rates of change of the abscissa and ordinate of P, respectively. This vector $\mathbf{v}$ is called the **velocity** of the particle P and its magnitude v the **speed.** Since, by definition,

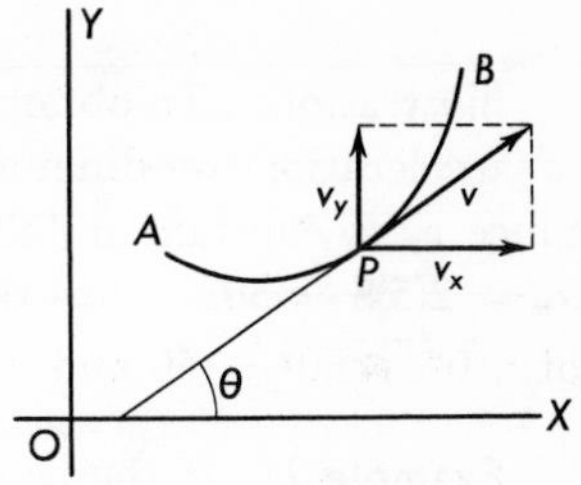

$$\boldsymbol{v_x} = \frac{\boldsymbol{dx}}{\boldsymbol{dt}}, \qquad \text{and} \qquad \boldsymbol{v_y} = \frac{\boldsymbol{dy}}{\boldsymbol{dt}},$$

Figure 146

it follows from the figure and Article **95** that

$$v = \sqrt{v_x^2 + v_y^2} = \sqrt{\left(\frac{dx}{dt}\right)^2 + \left(\frac{dy}{dt}\right)^2} = \left|\frac{ds}{dt}\right|,$$

$$\frac{v_y}{v_x} = \frac{\dfrac{dy}{dt}}{\dfrac{dx}{dt}} = \frac{dy}{dx} = \tan\theta.$$

These relations show that *the velocity of P is directed along a line tangent to the curve with a magnitude equal to the time-rate of P as it moves along the curve.*

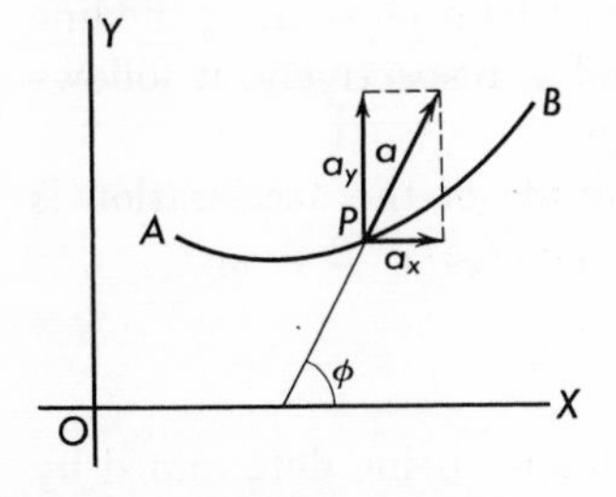

Figure 147

Example 1. A particle moves along the parabola $y = x^2$ so that $v_x = 5$. Find the speed of the particle when its abscissa is $\frac{6}{5}$.

Solution: Differentiating the equation of the parabola with respect to the time t, we obtain

$$\frac{dy}{dt} = 2x\frac{dx}{dt}. \tag{1}$$

When $x = \frac{6}{5}$ and $dx/dt = v_x = 5$, we find $dy/dt = v_y = 12$, so that

$$v = \sqrt{v_x^2 + v_y^2} = \sqrt{5^2 + 12^2} = 13.$$

In a similar manner a vector $\mathbf{a}$ is determined whose horizontal and vertical components are the time rates of change of v_x and v_y, respectively. This vector $\mathbf{a}$, as shown in Figure 147, is called the **acceleration** of the particle P, and its components

$$\boldsymbol{a_x} = \frac{\boldsymbol{d^2x}}{\boldsymbol{dt^2}} \qquad \text{and} \qquad \boldsymbol{a_y} = \frac{\boldsymbol{d^2y}}{\boldsymbol{dt^2}}$$

yield the magnitude a and the direction angle ϕ given by

$$a = \sqrt{a_x^2 + a_y^2}, \qquad \tan\phi = \frac{a_y}{a_x}. \tag{2}$$

Illustration. To obtain a relation in Example 1 between the components of acceleration, we differentiate (1) with respect to t; thus $a_y = 2v_x^2 + 2xa_x$. Since v_x is constant it follows that a_x is zero, and since $v_x = 5$ we obtain $a_y = 2(5)^2 = 50$. Thus the acceleration vector **a** has a constant magnitude of $\sqrt{0^2 + 50^2} = 50$ and is directed vertically upward.

Example 2. If the coordinates at time t of a particle P on a circle are given by $x = k\cos mt$, $y = k\sin mt$, show that the acceleration of P is always directed toward the center of the circle.

Solution: Differentiating twice with respect to t, we obtain

$$a_x = -km^2\cos mt, \qquad a_y = -km^2\sin mt. \tag{3}$$

A comparison of (3) with the given equations shows that

$$a_x = -m^2x, \qquad a_y = -m^2y;$$

hence

$$\frac{a_y}{a_x} = \frac{y}{x}. \tag{4}$$

The relation (4) shows that the direction of the acceleration is along the line OP; since a_x and a_y have signs opposite to x and y, respectively, it follows that the acceleration is directed toward the origin.

In addition we see from (2) that the magnitude of the acceleration is constant and equal to $\sqrt{(-m^2x)^2 + (-m^2y)^2} = m^2\sqrt{x^2 + y^2} = m^2k$.

EXERCISE 49

A particle moves on a plane curve, its coordinates being determined by the following equations where t denotes the time. Find the magnitude and direction of the vectors **v** and **a** at the time indicated.

1. $x = t^2$, $y = 6t + 1$; $t = 3$. *Ans.* $(6\sqrt{2}, \frac{1}{4}\pi)$, $(2,0)$.
2. $x = t^2$, $y = t^3$; $t = \frac{1}{2}$.
3. $x = \sin t$, $y = \sin 2t$; $t = \frac{1}{2}\pi$. $(2, \frac{3}{2}\pi)$, $(1, \pi)$.
4. $x = 2\sin t$, $y = 4\cos t$; $t = \frac{1}{4}\pi$.
5. $x = 2\ln t$, $y = t + t^{-1}$; $t = \frac{1}{3}$.
   Ans. $(10, -\text{Tan}^{-1}\frac{4}{3})$, $(18\sqrt{10}, \pi - \text{Tan}^{-1} 3)$.
6. $x = 2t$, $y = e^t$; $t = 0$.
7. A particle moves along the curve $y = \sqrt{x}$. Find the point at which v_x is twice as large as v_y. *Ans.* $(1,1)$.

8. A particle moves clockwise around the ellipse $x^2 + 4y^2 = 8$ with a constant speed of 5 feet per second. Find v_x and v_y as the particle passes through (2,1).
9. A particle moves along the curve $y = x^3 - x$. If $v_x = 2$ feet per second and $a_x = -3$ feet per second per second as the particle passes through the point (1,0), find v and a at that instant.
   Ans. $2\sqrt{5}$ ft./sec., $3\sqrt{37}$ ft./sec.^{2}.
10. A particle moves clockwise around the ellipse $4x^2 + 9y^2 = 52$ with $v_x = 12$ feet per second. Find a when $x = 2$. *Hint:* $a_x = 0$.
11. A particle moves clockwise around the circle $x^2 + y^2 = 16$ with $v_x = 2$ feet per second. When $x = 2$, find a and ϕ. *Ans.* $(\frac{8}{9}\sqrt{3}, \frac{3}{2}\pi)$.
12. Solve Problem 11 with v instead of v_x equal to 2 feet per second.
13. A particle moves along the sine curve $y = \sin x$. If $v_x = 0$ and $a_x = 2$ feet per second per second as the particle passes through (0,0), find v and a at that instant. *Ans.* 0, $2\sqrt{2}$ ft./sec.^{2}.
14. A particle moves to the right along the parabola $y = 2\sqrt{x}$ with a constant speed of 6 feet per second. Find a as the particle passes through the point (1,2).
15. A ladder 25 feet long has its upper end against a vertical wall and its lower end on a horizontal floor. If the lower end is moved away from the wall at a constant rate of 3 feet per second, find the velocity and acceleration of the middle point of the ladder when its foot is 15 feet from the wall. *Hint:* Express the coordinates of the mid-point of the ladder as functions of the time t. *Ans.* $\frac{15}{8}$ ft./sec., $\frac{45}{128}$ ft./sec.^{2}.
16. Neglecting the resistance of the air, the equation of motion for a projectile is
$$x = v_0 t \cos \phi, \qquad y = v_0 t \sin \phi - 16t^2,$$
where v_0 is the initial velocity in feet per second, ϕ the angle of projection with the horizontal, and t the time of flight in seconds. Find the magnitudes of the velocity and acceleration at any time t.
17. Show that the projectile of Problem 16 attains a minimum velocity of $v_0 \cos \phi$ at the top of its flight.
18. A point moves along a cycloid in accordance with the equations $x = k(t - \sin t)$, $y = k(1 - \cos t)$ where t denotes the time. Show that the magnitude of its acceleration is constant.
19. When a point moves along a curve with constant speed $v = k$, prove that its acceleration is always directed along the normal to the curve. *Hint:* Differentiate the relation $v_x^2 + v_y^2 = k^2$.
20. If a particle moves along the circle $x^2 + y^2 = r^2$ with a constant speed v, show that
$$xa_x + ya_y = -v^2, \qquad ya_x - xa_y = 0;$$
and then determine a as a function of v and r.

103. Tangential and Normal Components of Acceleration

At a given point P of a curve the **tangential component** a_t of the acceleration vector **a** is the projection of **a** on the directed tangent at P, the positive direction of the tangent being the direction of **v** at P. Since the angle from **v** to **a** as shown in Figure 148 is $\phi - \theta$, we have

$$\begin{aligned} a_t &= a \cos (\phi - \theta) = a \cos \phi \cos \theta + a \sin \phi \sin \theta \\ &= a_x \cos \theta + a_y \sin \theta. \end{aligned} \tag{1}$$

Differentiating the equation $v^2 = v_x^2 + v_y^2$ with respect to t and dividing by 2, we obtain

$$\begin{aligned} v\frac{dv}{dt} &= v_x a_x + v_y a_y = (v \cos \theta) a_x + (v \sin \theta) a_y \\ &= v(a_x \cos \theta + a_y \sin \theta). \end{aligned} \tag{2}$$

From (1) and (2) it follows that

$$\boldsymbol{a_t} = \frac{\boldsymbol{dv}}{\boldsymbol{dt}}. \tag{3}$$

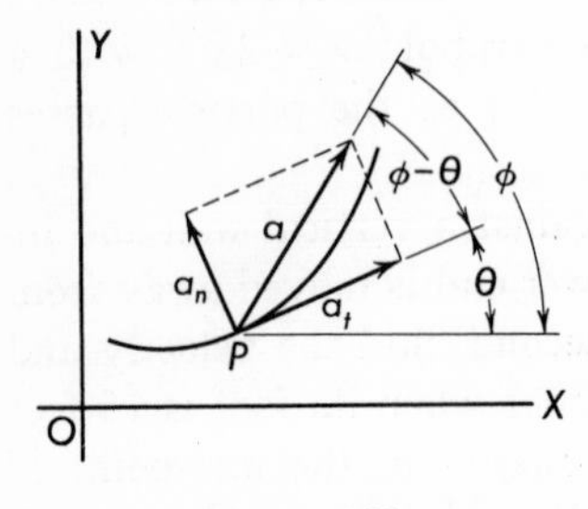

Figure 148

Similarly, the **normal component** a_n of the acceleration vector **a** is the projection of **a** on the directed normal at P, the positive direction of the normal being toward the concave side of the curve. Thus, as for (1), we have

$$\begin{aligned} a_n &= a \sin (\phi - \theta) = a \sin \phi \cos \theta - a \cos \phi \sin \theta \\ &= a_y \cos \theta - a_x \sin \theta. \end{aligned} \tag{4}$$

Differentiating the relation $\tan \theta = v_y/v_x$ with respect to the arc length s, we obtain

$$\begin{aligned} \sec^2 \theta \cdot \frac{d\theta}{ds} &= \frac{v_x a_y - v_y a_x}{v_x^2} \cdot \frac{dt}{ds} \\ &= \frac{(v \cos \theta) a_y - (v \sin \theta) a_x}{v^2 \cos^2 \theta} \cdot \frac{1}{v} \\ &= \frac{a_y \cos \theta - a_x \sin \theta}{v^2 \cos^2 \theta}. \end{aligned} \tag{5}$$

From (4) and (5), and the fact that $\left|\frac{ds}{d\theta}\right|$ is the radius of curvature R of the curve at P, it follows that

$$|\boldsymbol{a_n}| = \frac{\boldsymbol{v^2}}{\boldsymbol{R}}. \tag{6}$$

Example 1. A particle moves along the parabola $y = \frac{1}{2}x^2$ with a constant speed of 5 feet per second. Find a_t and $|a_n|$ as the particle passes through the point $(\frac{4}{3},\frac{8}{9})$,

Solution: Since the speed v is constant, we have $dv/dt = 0$. Hence, by (3), $a_t = 0$.

To find $|a_n|$ we compute the radius of curvature at the point $(\frac{4}{3},\frac{8}{9})$,

$$R = \frac{(1 + y'^2)^{3/2}}{y''} = \frac{(1 + x^2)^{3/2}}{1} = \left(1 + \frac{16}{9}\right)^{3/2} = \frac{125}{27}.$$

Hence, by (6),

$$|a_n| = \frac{5^2}{\frac{125}{27}} = 5.4 \text{ ft./sec.}^2.$$

Note: Substituting $\cos\theta = v_x/v$ and $\sin\theta = v_y/v$ in (1) and (4), we see that the tangential and normal components of the acceleration may also be expressed in the form

$$\boldsymbol{a}_t = \frac{\boldsymbol{v}_x\boldsymbol{a}_x + \boldsymbol{v}_y\boldsymbol{a}_y}{\boldsymbol{v}}, \qquad |\boldsymbol{a}_n| = \left|\frac{\boldsymbol{v}_x\boldsymbol{a}_y - \boldsymbol{v}_y\boldsymbol{a}_x}{\boldsymbol{v}}\right|. \tag{7}$$

Example 2. A particle moves along the parabola $y = \frac{1}{2}x^2$. Find a_t and $|a_n|$ if $v_x = 3$ and $a_x = -3$ as the particle passes through the point $(\frac{4}{3},\frac{8}{9})$.

Solution: Differentiating the equation $y = \frac{1}{2}x^2$ twice with respect to the time t, we obtain

$$\frac{dy}{dt} = x\frac{dx}{dt}, \qquad \text{and} \qquad \frac{d^2y}{dt^2} = \left(\frac{dx}{dt}\right)^2 + x\frac{d^2x}{dt^2},$$

or

$$v_y = xv_x, \qquad \text{and} \qquad a_y = v_x^2 + xa_x. \tag{8}$$

Substituting $x = \frac{4}{3}$, $v_x = 3$, and $a_x = -3$ in (8), we obtain

$$v_y = (\tfrac{4}{3})(3) = 4, \qquad a_y = (3)^2 + (\tfrac{4}{3})(-3) = 5;$$

thus

$$v = \sqrt{v_x^2 + v_y^2} = \sqrt{3^2 + 4^2} = 5.$$

Therefore, by (7), we have

$$a_t = \frac{(3)(-3) + (4)(5)}{5} = 2.2, \qquad |a_n| = \left|\frac{(3)(5) - (4)(-3)}{5}\right| = 5.4.$$

104. Angular Velocity and Acceleration

Consider a point P which moves along a curve in accordance with some law of motion. Since the angle θ between the radius vector OP and the positive x axis is dependent on the position of P, it follows that

θ is a function of the time t. The instantaneous rate at which θ is changing with respect to t is called the **angular velocity** of OP and is denoted by ω; thus

$$\omega = \frac{d\theta}{dt}. \tag{1}$$

The rate at which the angular velocity of OP changes with respect to t is called the **angular acceleration** of OP and is denoted by α; thus

$$\alpha = \frac{d\omega}{dt} = \frac{d^2\theta}{dt^2}. \tag{2}$$

Example. A particle P moves along the parabola $y = x^2$ with $v_x = 5$ and $a_x = 0$. Find the angular velocity and angular acceleration of the radius vector OP as the particle passes through the point (2,4).

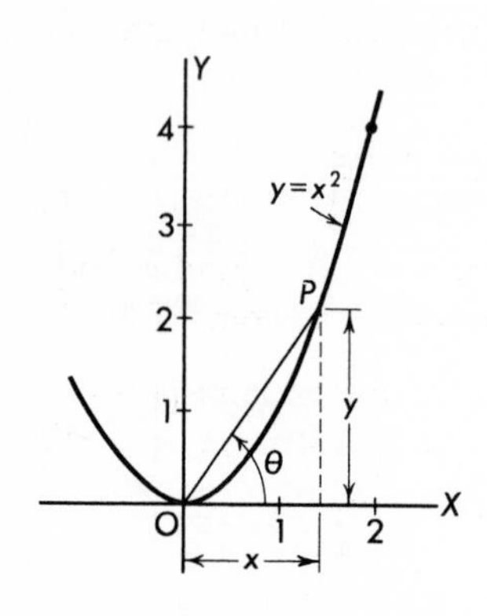

Figure 149

Solution: If θ is the inclination of the radius vector as shown in Figure 149, then

$$\theta = \text{Tan}^{-1}\frac{y}{x} = \text{Tan}^{-1}x.$$

Hence by (1) the angular velocity of OP at time t is

$$\omega = \frac{d\theta}{dt} = \frac{1}{1+x^2}\cdot\frac{dx}{dt} = \frac{v_x}{1+x^2}. \tag{3}$$

By (2) the angular acceleration of OP at time t is

$$\alpha = \frac{d\omega}{dt} = \frac{(1+x^2)a_x - v_x(2xv_x)}{(1+x^2)^2}. \tag{4}$$

When $x = 2$, $v_x = 5$, and $a_x = 0$, by substitution in (3) and (4) we find

$$\omega = 1 \text{ rad./sec.,} \qquad \alpha = -4 \text{ rad./sec.}^2.$$

EXERCISE 50

1. A particle moves to the right along the curve $y = \frac{1}{3}x^3$ with a constant speed of 4 feet per second. Find a_t and $|a_n|$ as it passes through the point $(1,\frac{1}{3})$. *Ans.* 0, 11.3 ft./sec.^{2}.
2. A particle moves to the right along the curve $y = 2\sqrt{x}$ with a constant speed of 5 feet per second. Find a_t and $|a_n|$ as it passes through the point (4,4).
3. A particle moves to the left along the curve $y = e^x$ with a constant speed of 4 feet per second. Find a_t and $|a_n|$ as it passes through the point (0,1). *Ans.* 0, 5.66 ft./sec.^{2}.

4. A particle moves along the curve $y = 4x^{2/3}$. Find a_t and $|a_n|$ if $v_x = 6$ and $a_x = 3$ as the particle passes through the point (8,16).
5. A particle moves clockwise around the circle $x^2 + y^2 = 25$. Find a_t and $|a_n|$ if $v_x = 3$ and $a_x = 0$ as the particle passes through the point (4,3). *Ans.* $6\frac{2}{3}$, 5.
6. A particle moves along the curve $y = \sin x$. Find a_t and $|a_n|$ if $v_x = 4$ and $a_x = 0$ as the particle passes through the point $(\frac{1}{4}\pi, \frac{1}{2}\sqrt{2})$.
7. A particle P moves upward along the line $x = 4$ with a constant speed of 2 units per second. Find the angular velocity and acceleration of the radius vector OP when the particle is 4 units above the x axis. *Ans.* $\frac{1}{4}$ rad./sec., $-\frac{1}{8}$ rad./sec.^{2}.

If P denotes the particle and O the origin of coordinates, find the angular velocity and acceleration of the radius vector OP for the time and conditions stated in the indicated problems.

8. Problem 4.
9. Problem 5. *Ans.* -1, $-\frac{4}{3}$.
10. Problem 2.
11. An airplane traveling at a constant altitude of 1000 feet with a speed of 300 miles per hour is approaching an observer on the ground. At what angular velocity is the observer's line of sight being elevated at the instant when it makes an angle of 30° with the horizon? *Ans.* 0.11 rad./sec.
12. A particle moves on the circle $x^2 + y^2 = r^2$. If the angle $XOP = \theta$ is dependent on the time t, show that

$$\mathbf{v} = \mathbf{r}\boldsymbol{\omega}, \qquad |\mathbf{a}_n| = \mathbf{r}\boldsymbol{\omega}^2, \qquad \mathbf{a}_t = \mathbf{r}\boldsymbol{\alpha}.$$

Hint: Consider the relation $s = r\theta$.
13. A particle moves along the circle $x^2 + y^2 = 9$ in accordance with $\theta = t + t^2$ where t denotes the time. Find the direction and magnitude of its acceleration when $t = 0$. See Problem 12. *Ans.* $3\sqrt{5}$, $\pi - \text{Tan}^{-1} 2$.
14. A particle moves along the circle $x^2 + y^2 = 25$ in accordance with $\theta = te^{-t}$. Find the velocity of the particle when a_n is a minimum. See Problem 12.
15. A particle moves so that its position at time t (seconds) is given by the equation $x = 4 \cos 3t$, $y = 4 \sin 3t$, where x and y are expressed in feet. Show that the particle traverses a circle, and find a_t and $|a_n|$ for the particle. *Ans.* 0, 36 ft./sec.^{2}.
16. Two points that always have the same positive abscissa move in such a manner that each generates one of the curves $y = 2x - x^2$ and $y = 16x - 4x^3$. When are the points moving with equal speed in the

direction of the y axis? What is true of the tangent lines to the curves at these points?

17. A line tangent to the curve $x = \sqrt{y}$ at the point P intersects the x axis at the point Q. If P travels up the curve at a rate of 2 units per second, how fast is the point Q traveling when P passes through (2,4)?

Ans. $1/\sqrt{17}$ un./sec.

18. A man walks across the diameter of a circular courtyard of radius r at a constant rate c. A lamp, at one extremity of the diameter perpendicular to the one on which he walks, throws his shadow on the wall. Find the velocity of the shadow along the wall in terms of some parameter.

CHAPTER 11

Polar Coordinates

105. Polar Coordinates

The analysis of points and curves in a plane is often simplified if some type of coordinate system is used other than rectangular coordinates. There are many such possibilities, and in this chapter we shall study one that is called a system of **polar coordinates.**

If a fixed point O on a line OX is selected, it is evident that the position of any point P in the plane can be described, as shown in Figure 150, by giving the distance OP and the magnitude of the angle XOP. These values denoted by r, the **radius vector,** and θ, the **polar angle,** are called the **polar coordinates** of P and are written (r,θ). The polar angle is *positive* when measured counterclockwise from OX, and *negative* when taken clockwise; the radius vector is *positive* if measured from O along the terminal side of θ, and *negative* when taken in the opposite direction. The fixed line OX is called the **initial line** or **polar axis,** and the point O is the **pole** or **origin.**

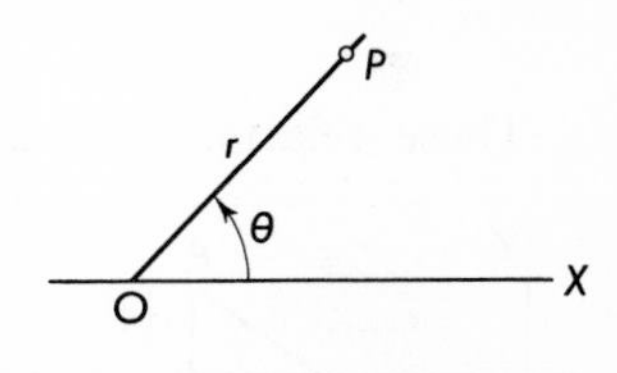

Figure 150

If the polar coordinates of a point are known, the work involved in plotting the point is considerably simplified if a special type of graph paper, called **polar coordinate paper,** is used. The coordinate divisions on this paper consist of a set of radial lines passing through the pole and a set of concentric circles having the pole as center. The points $A(5,30°)$, $B(-7,60°)$, $C(9,-90°)$ and $D(-8,-45°)$ are plotted on such a system in Figure 151.

If the polar axis is taken along the positive x axis, as shown in Figure 152, it is evident that the relations between the polar coordinates (r,θ) of P and the rectangular coordinates (x,y) are

$$x = r\cos\theta, \qquad r = \pm\sqrt{x^2 + y^2},$$

$$y = r\sin\theta, \qquad \theta = \tan^{-1}\frac{y}{x}.$$

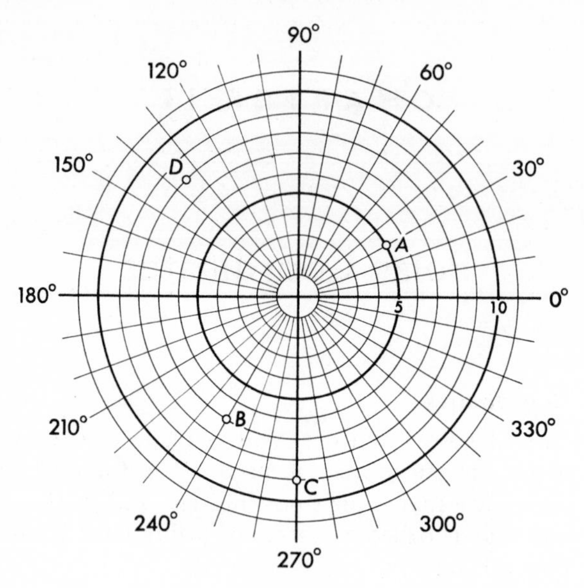

Figure 151

These relations are used when we wish to change from one coordinate system to the other.

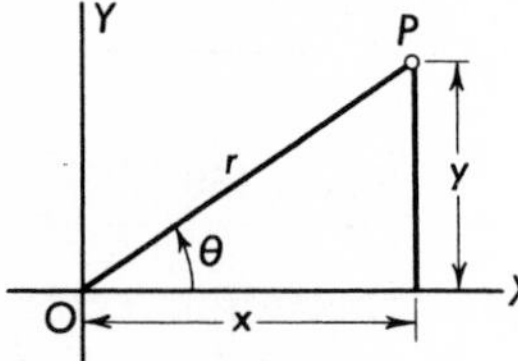

Figure 152

Illustration 1. The polar equation $r = a \cos \theta$, or $r^2 = ar \cos \theta$, becomes $x^2 + y^2 = ax$ in rectangular coordinates.

Illustration 2. The rectangular equation $y^2 = 4ax$ becomes $(r \sin \theta)^2 = 4a(r \cos \theta)$, or $r = 4a \cot \theta \csc \theta$ in polar coordinates.

106. Locus of a Polar Equation

The locus of a polar equation is in general a curve that passes through all points whose coordinates r and θ satisfy the given equation. We can find points that satisfy a polar equation by assigning arbitrary values to θ and computing the related values of r. In order to avoid confusion in graphing a curve, it is advisable to plot the points systematically in increasing order of θ, and to connect them in the same order as you go along.

Example 1. Find the locus of the cardioid $r = 4(1 - \cos \theta)$.

Solution: Observing that $\cos(-\theta) = \cos \theta$, we select arbitrary positive and negative values for θ and compute the corresponding values of r. We thus obtain the pairs of related values given in the accompanying table.

θ	0	$\pm 30°$	$\pm 60°$	$\pm 90°$	$\pm 120°$	$\pm 150°$	$\pm 180°$
r	0	0.5	2	4	6	7.5	8

When the points with positive angles are plotted and joined, we obtain the arc OAB shown in Figure 153. The points with negative angles give arc OCB.

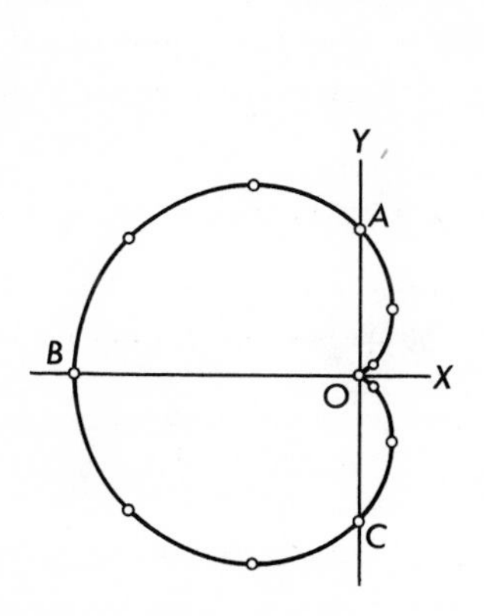

Figure 153

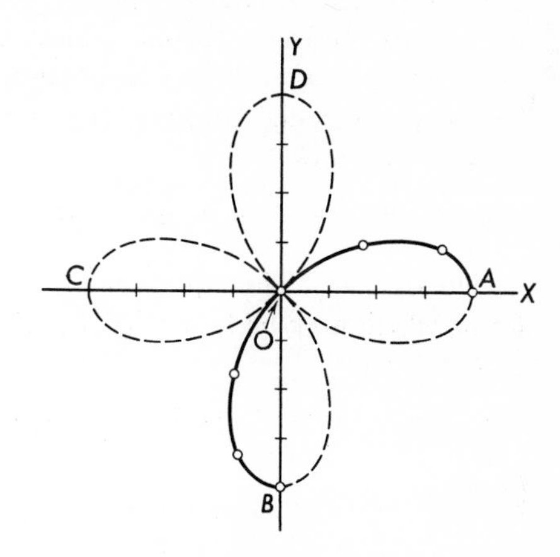

Figure 154

Example 2. Plot the four-leaf rose $r = 4 \cos 2\theta$.

Solution: Choosing values of θ from 0° to 90°, we obtain values of r given in the accompanying table. These points when plotted give arc AOB shown in Figure 154.

θ	0	15°	30°	45°	60°	75°	90°
r	4	$2\sqrt{3}$	2	0	-2	$-2\sqrt{3}$	-4

Because of the periodic character of the cosine function, r takes on the tabular values in reverse order as θ increases from 90° to 180°. These points when plotted give arc BOC. Similarly, arcs COD and DOA are obtained as θ increases through the values 180° to 270° and 270° to 360°, respectively.

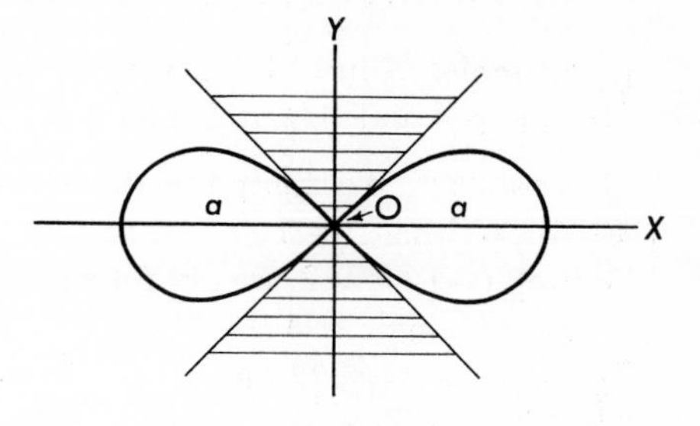

Figure 155

Note: In graphing the lemniscate $r^2 = a^2 \cos 2\theta$, shown in Figure 155, observe that r is imaginary for $45° < \theta < 135°$ and $225° < \theta < 315°$.

107. Intersection of Polar Curves

It is apparent that the polar coordinates of a point may be expressed in various ways. Thus $(2,30°)$, $(2,-330°)$, and $(-2,210°)$ all denote the same point. Because of this indefiniteness in the representation of a point, it follows that the polar equation of a curve may also be written in various alternate forms. Thus the equation of the circle $r = 2$ can be written as $r = -2$. In general, if $F(r,\theta) = 0$ is the equation of a curve in polar coordinates, the curve may be represented by any one of the equations

$$F[(-1)^n r, \theta + n\pi] = 0, \quad \text{where } n = 0, \pm 1, \pm 2, \cdots. \tag{1}$$

Illustration. The equation $r = \sin \frac{1}{2}\theta$ has three other distinct alternate forms which may be found from $(-1)^n r = \sin(\frac{1}{2}\theta + \frac{1}{2}n\pi)$ by taking $n = 1$, 2, and 3; thus

$$(-1)\,r = \sin(\tfrac{1}{2}\theta + \tfrac{1}{2}\pi), \quad \text{or} \quad r = -\cos \tfrac{1}{2}\theta;$$
$$(-1)^2 r = \sin(\tfrac{1}{2}\theta + \pi), \quad \text{or} \quad r = -\sin \tfrac{1}{2}\theta;$$
$$(-1)^3 r = \sin(\tfrac{1}{2}\theta + \tfrac{3}{2}\pi), \quad \text{or} \quad r = \cos \tfrac{1}{2}\theta.$$

The above observation necessitates the following procedure for determining the points of intersection of the two curves

$$F(r,\theta) = 0, \qquad G(r,\theta) = 0. \tag{2}$$

1. *By means of* (1) *determine the distinct equations*

$$F_1 = 0,\ F_2 = 0,\ F_3 = 0,\ \cdots, \tag{3}$$
$$G_1 = 0,\ G_2 = 0,\ G_3 = 0,\ \cdots, \tag{4}$$

   which represent each of the curves in (2).
2. *Solve each equation in* (3) *simultaneously with every equation in* (4).
3. *If values* θ_1 *and* θ_2 *exist such that* $F(0,\theta_1) = 0$ *and* $G(0,\theta_2) = 0$, *the origin* O *is a point of intersection.*

Example. Find the points of intersection of the curve $r = 4 \cos 2\theta$ (Figure 154) and the circle $r = 2$.

Solution: We apply the above procedure.

1. Writing $(-1)^n r = 4\cos(2\theta + 2n\pi)$, we obtain $r = \pm 4 \cos 2\theta$. Writing $(-1)^n r = 2$, we obtain $r = \pm 2$.

2. Solving $r = 4 \cos 2\theta$ and $r = 2$, we find $\theta = 30°$, $150°$, $210°$, and $330°$. Solving $r = 4 \cos 2\theta$ and $r = -2$, we find $\theta = 60°$, $120°$, $240°$, and $300°$. The other pairings in 1 give no new solutions.

3. The origin is not a point of intersection, since r is never zero on the curve $r = 2$.

Thus we find the eight points of intersection $(2, \pm\frac{1}{6}\pi)$, $(2, \pm\frac{1}{3}\pi)$, $(2, \pm\frac{2}{3}\pi)$, and $(2, \pm\frac{5}{6}\pi)$.

Note: In many problems the coordinates of the points of intersection of two curves can be obtained directly from their graphs. If this is the case, it is not necessary to go through the above analysis.

EXERCISE 51

Change the following equations from rectangular to polar coordinates.

1. $x^2 + y^2 = a^2$. *Ans.* $r = a$.
2. $x^2 + y^2 = x + y$.
3. $y = x$. $\theta = \frac{1}{4}\pi$ or $\frac{5}{4}\pi$.
4. $x \sin \alpha + y \cos \alpha = a$.
5. $y^3 = ax^2$. $r = a \cot^2 \theta \csc \theta$.
6. $(x^2 + y^2)^2 = a^2(x^2 - y^2)$.
7. $2xy = a^2$. $r^2 = a^2 \csc 2\theta$.
8. $x\sqrt{x^2 + y^2} = ay$.

Change the following equations from polar to rectangular coordinates.

9. $r = a \sec \theta$. *Ans.* $x = a$.
10. $r^2 = a^2 \cot \theta$.
11. $r = \tan \theta \sec \theta$. $y = x^2$.
12. $r^2 = a^2 \sin 2\theta$.
13. $r^3 = a^3 \csc \theta$. $x^2y + y^3 = a^3$.
14. $r = a \tan^2 \theta$.
15. $r^2 = \theta$. $y = x \tan (x^2 + y^2)$.
16. $\theta = \frac{1}{2}\pi$.

Plot the graph of each of the following equations.

17. *Three-leaf rose.* $r = a \sin 3\theta$.
18. $r = 2 + 4 \sin \theta$.
19. *Spiral of Archimedes.* $r = a\theta$.
20. $r = \tan \theta$.
21. *Cardioid.* $r = a(1 + \cos \theta)$.
22. $r^2 = \sin 2\theta$.
23. *Lemniscate.* $r^2 = a^2 \sin 2\theta$.
24. $r = 2 \sin \frac{1}{2}\theta$.

Find the points of intersection of the following pairs of curves.

25. $\begin{cases} r = 2 \sin \theta, \\ r = 2 \cos \theta. \end{cases}$ *Ans.* $(\sqrt{2}, \frac{1}{4}\pi)$, origin.
26. $\begin{cases} r = \sin \theta, \\ r = \sin 2\theta. \end{cases}$
27. $\begin{cases} r = 4 \cos \theta, \\ r = 4(1 - \cos \theta). \end{cases}$ $(2, \pm\frac{1}{3}\pi)$, origin.
28. $\begin{cases} r = \tan \theta, \\ r = \cot \theta. \end{cases}$
29. $\begin{cases} r = \cos \theta, \\ r^2 = 2 + \cos \theta. \end{cases}$ $(1,0)$.
30. $\begin{cases} r = \sin 2\theta, \\ r = 1 + \cos 2\theta. \end{cases}$
31. $\begin{cases} r^2 \sin 2\theta = 8, \\ r = 2 \sec \theta. \end{cases}$ $(2\sqrt{2}, \frac{1}{4}\pi)$.
32. $\begin{cases} r = \sec \theta \tan \theta, \\ r = \csc \theta \cot^2 \theta. \end{cases}$

108. Angle Between the Radius Vector and Tangent

Let $P(r,\theta)$ be a point on the curve C (Figure 156) whose equation in polar coordinates is

$$r = f(\theta). \tag{1}$$

In order to find the slope of (1) at P ($\tan \alpha$ in the figure), we proceed as follows. Consider the rectangular coordinates of P

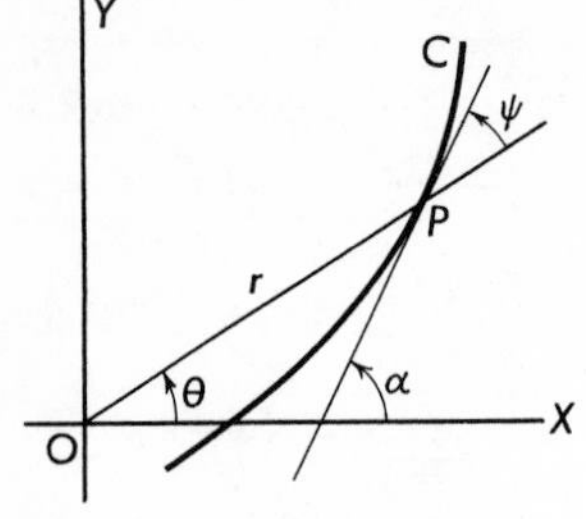

Figure 156

$$x = r \cos \theta, \qquad y = r \sin \theta.$$

Because of (1) these equations may be considered as parametric equations of the curve C, θ being the parameter. Hence we have

$$\frac{dx}{d\theta} = \frac{dr}{d\theta} \cos \theta - r \sin \theta,$$

$$\frac{dy}{d\theta} = \frac{dr}{d\theta} \sin \theta + r \cos \theta.$$

Thus it follows that

$$\textbf{Slope of tangent} = \frac{\dfrac{dy}{d\theta}}{\dfrac{dx}{d\theta}} = \frac{r' \sin \theta + r \cos \theta}{r' \cos \theta - r \sin \theta}, \tag{2}$$

provided that $dx/d\theta \neq 0$.

Illustration. At the point $(1,\frac{1}{6}\pi)$ on the curve $r = 2 \sin \theta$, we have $r = 1$ and $r' = 2 \cos \theta = \sqrt{3}$; hence

$$\text{Slope} = \frac{(\sqrt{3})(\frac{1}{2}) + (1)(\frac{1}{2}\sqrt{3})}{(\sqrt{3})(\frac{1}{2}\sqrt{3}) - (1)(\frac{1}{2})} = \sqrt{3}.$$

If r' and $\cos \theta$ are both different from zero, we may write (2) in the form

$$\tan \alpha = \frac{\tan \theta + (r/r')}{1 - (r/r') \tan \theta}. \tag{3}$$

However, in Figure 156 we observe that $\psi = \alpha - \theta$; hence

$$\tan \psi = \frac{\tan \alpha - \tan \theta}{1 + \tan \alpha \tan \theta}. \tag{4}$$

By substituting (3) in (4) we have the following result.

Theorem. *If ψ is the angle between the radius vector OP and the tangent line at P, then*

$$\tan \psi = \frac{r}{\frac{dr}{d\theta}}. \tag{5}$$

If two curves C and C' intersect at the point P, we see in Figure 157 that their angle of intersection ϕ is given by $|\psi - \psi'|$. Hence we have

$$\tan \phi = \left|\frac{\tan \psi - \tan \psi'}{1 + \tan \psi \tan \psi'}\right|, \tag{6}$$

and if the equations of C and C' are given in polar coordinates, the values $\tan \psi$ and $\tan \psi'$ can be found from (5).

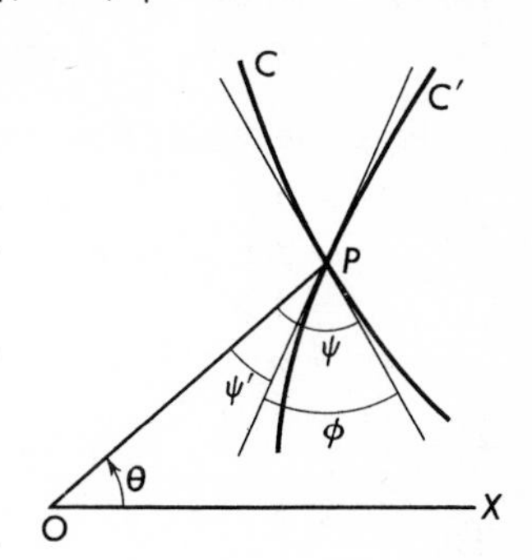

Figure 157

Example. Show that the curves $r = 2 \cos \theta$ and $r = 3 \tan \theta$ pass through the point $(\sqrt{3}, \frac{1}{6}\pi)$, and find their angle of intersection.

Solution: The coordinates $(\sqrt{3}, \frac{1}{6}\pi)$ satisfy the given equations, since for $\theta = \frac{1}{6}\pi$ we have $\cos \theta = \frac{1}{2}\sqrt{3}$ and $\tan \theta = \frac{1}{3}\sqrt{3}$.

To obtain the angle of intersection, we use (5) to compute

$$\tan \psi = \frac{r}{r'} = \frac{2 \cos \theta}{-2 \sin \theta} = -\sqrt{3},$$

$$\tan \psi' = \frac{r}{r'} = \frac{3 \tan \theta}{3 \sec^2 \theta} = \frac{1}{4}\sqrt{3}.$$

Then, substituting in (6), we obtain

$$\tan \phi = \frac{\frac{1}{4}\sqrt{3} - (-\sqrt{3})}{1 + (\frac{1}{4}\sqrt{3})(-\sqrt{3})} = 5\sqrt{3}.$$

Hence the angle of intersection is $\text{Tan}^{-1}(5\sqrt{3})$ or 83.4°.

EXERCISE 52

For each of the following curves, find the angle between the radius vector and the tangent line at the point indicated.

1. $r = a \sec 2\theta;\ \ \theta = \frac{1}{8}\pi.$ *Ans.* 26.6°.
2. $r = a/(1 - \cos \theta);\ \ \theta = \frac{1}{3}\pi.$
3. $r = a \sin \frac{1}{2}\theta;\ \ \theta = \frac{1}{2}\pi.$ 63.4°.
4. $r = a \tan 2\theta;\ \ \theta = \frac{1}{16}\pi.$
5. $r = \theta^2;\ \ \theta = \pi.$ 57.5°.
6. $r = e^{3\theta};\ \ \theta = \theta_1.$

7. Find ψ and α in terms of θ for the circle $r = a \sin \theta$.

Ans. $\psi = \theta, \alpha = 2\theta$.

8. For the parabola $r = a \sec^2 \frac{1}{2}\theta$, show that $\psi + \alpha = \pi$.

Find the slopes of the following curves at the points indicated.

9. $r = \tan \theta$; $\theta = \frac{1}{4}\pi$. *Ans.* 3.
10. $r = \sin 3\theta$; $\theta = \frac{1}{6}\pi$.
11. $r = \sin^2 \theta$; $\theta = \frac{1}{3}\pi$. $-3\sqrt{3}$.
12. $r = 1 - \cos \theta$; $\theta = \frac{1}{4}\pi$.
13. $r = \cos 2\theta$; origin. ± 1.
14. $r = \sec \frac{1}{2}\theta$; $\theta = \frac{1}{2}\pi$.
15. $r^2 = \cos 2\theta$; $\theta = \frac{1}{6}\pi$. 0.
16. $r\theta = 2$; $\theta = \pi$.

Find the angle of intersection of the following pairs of curves.

17. $\begin{cases} r = 6 \cos \theta, \\ r = 2(1 + \cos \theta). \end{cases}$ *Ans.* 30°, 90°.
18. $\begin{cases} r = a \sin \theta, \\ r = a \cos \theta. \end{cases}$
19. $\begin{cases} r = 2 \csc \theta, \\ r = \sec^2 \frac{1}{2}\theta. \end{cases}$ 45°.
20. $\begin{cases} r = \tan \theta, \\ r = \cot \theta. \end{cases}$
21. $\begin{cases} r = 6 \sec \theta, \\ r = 7 + 5 \cos \theta. \end{cases}$ 74.9°.
22. $\begin{cases} r = 2, \\ r = 4 \cos 2\theta. \end{cases}$
23. $\begin{cases} r = 1 + \cos \theta, \\ r = 1 - \cos \theta. \end{cases}$ 90°, 0°.
24. $\begin{cases} r^2 = \sec 2\theta, \\ r^2 = \csc 2\theta. \end{cases}$

109. Differential of Arc

From the relations

$$x = r \cos \theta, \qquad y = r \sin \theta \tag{1}$$

between the rectangular and polar coordinates of a point, we obtain by differentiation

$$\begin{aligned} dx &= \cos \theta \, dr - r \sin \theta \, d\theta, \\ dy &= \sin \theta \, dr + r \cos \theta \, d\theta. \end{aligned} \tag{2}$$

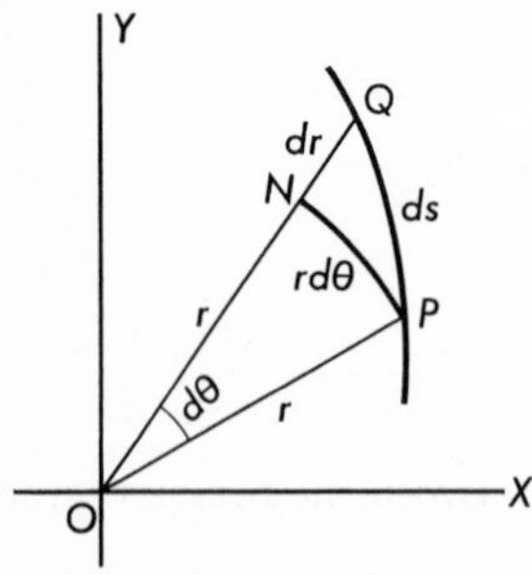

Figure 158

By substituting (2) in $ds = \pm\sqrt{(dx)^2 + (dy)^2}$ and simplifying, we obtain the differential of arc expressed in polar coordinates

$$\boldsymbol{ds = \pm\sqrt{(dr)^2 + r^2(d\theta)^2}} \quad \text{or}$$

$$\boldsymbol{ds = \pm\sqrt{r'^2 + r^2}\, d\theta.} \tag{3}$$

Illustration. For the circle $r = a \sin \theta$, we have $r' = a \cos \theta$; hence

$$ds = \pm\sqrt{a^2 \cos^2 \theta + a^2 \sin^2 \theta}\, d\theta = \pm a \, d\theta.$$

Note: The relation (3) is easily remembered if one *thinks* of the figure PNQ in Figure 158 as forming a right triangle.

110. Curvature

If r and $dr/d\theta$ are not both zero at a point P of the curve $r = f(\theta)$, we have the following result.

Theorem. *The curvature at a point $P(r,\theta)$ of the curve $r = f(\theta)$ is*

$$K = \left|\frac{d\alpha}{ds}\right| = \frac{|r^2 + 2r'^2 - rr''|}{(r^2 + r'^2)^{3/2}}, \tag{1}$$

where r' and r'' are respectively the first and second derivatives of r with respect to θ.

Proof: From (5), Article **108,** we have $\psi = \tan^{-1}(r/r')$; hence

$$d\psi = \frac{1}{1 + (r/r')^2} \cdot \frac{r' \cdot r' - r \cdot r''}{r'^2}\, d\theta = \frac{r'^2 - rr''}{r'^2 + r^2}\, d\theta. \tag{2}$$

In Figure 156, we see that $\alpha = \theta + \psi$. Hence, using (2), we obtain

$$d\alpha = d\theta + d\psi = \frac{r^2 + 2r'^2 - rr''}{r^2 + r'^2}\, d\theta. \tag{3}$$

Dividing (3) by the arc length, $ds = \pm\sqrt{r^2 + r'^2}\, d\theta$, gives the formula (1).

Illustration. For the circle $r = a \sin\theta$, we have $r' = a\cos\theta$ and $r'' = -a\sin\theta$. Hence the radius of curvature $R = 1/K$ at any point of the circle is

$$R = \frac{(a^2 \sin^2\theta + a^2\cos^2\theta)^{3/2}}{a^2\sin^2\theta + 2a^2\cos^2\theta + a^2\sin^2\theta} = \frac{a}{2}.$$

111. Radial and Transverse Components of Velocity and Acceleration

Consider a particle P which moves along the curve $r = f(\theta)$ in a manner determined by the velocity vector $\mathbf{v}$ and the acceleration vector $\mathbf{a}$.

The projection of $\mathbf{v}$ on the directed line OP (Figure 159) is called the **radial component** of the velocity and is denoted by v_r. The projection of $\mathbf{v}$ on the line making a counterclockwise right angle with OP is called the **transverse component** of the velocity and is denoted by v_θ.

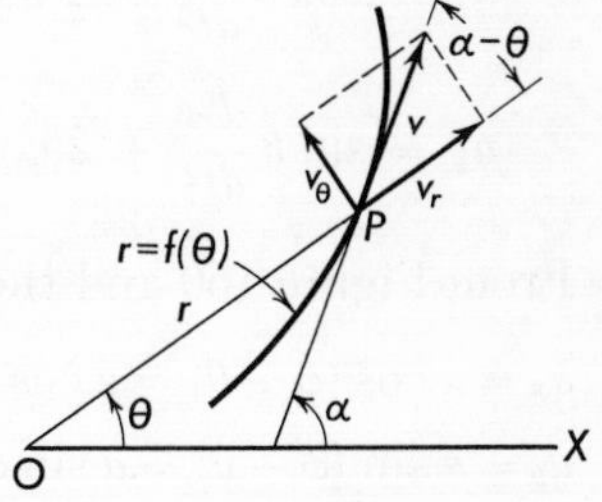

Figure 159

Theorem I. *If a particle moves along the curve $r = f(\theta)$, the radial and transverse components of its velocity at any instant are given by*

$$v_r = \frac{dr}{dt}, \qquad v_\theta = r\frac{d\theta}{dt} = r\omega. \tag{1}$$

Proof: If r and θ are known differentiable functions of the time t, the relations $x = r\cos\theta$ and $y = r\sin\theta$ give

$$\begin{aligned} v_x &= \frac{dx}{dt} = \cos\theta\,\frac{dr}{dt} - r\sin\theta\,\frac{d\theta}{dt}, \\ v_y &= \frac{dy}{dt} = \sin\theta\,\frac{dr}{dt} + r\cos\theta\,\frac{d\theta}{dt}. \end{aligned} \tag{2}$$

From Figure 159 and the relations $v_x = v\cos\alpha$, $v_y = v\sin\alpha$, we have

$$\begin{aligned} v_r &= v\cos(\alpha-\theta) = v\cos\alpha\cos\theta + v\sin\alpha\sin\theta = v_x\cos\theta + v_y\sin\theta, \\ v_\theta &= v\sin(\alpha-\theta) = v\sin\alpha\cos\theta - v\cos\alpha\sin\theta = v_y\cos\theta - v_x\sin\theta. \end{aligned} \tag{3}$$

Substituting (2) in (3) we obtain the result (1).

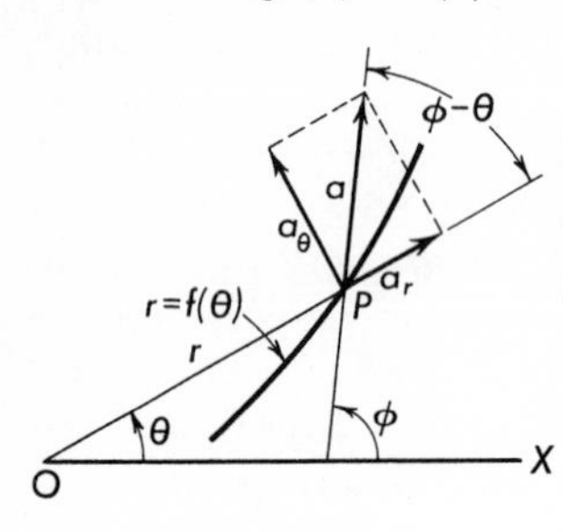

Figure 160

As for **v**, the projections of the acceleration vector **a** on the line OP and its normal are called the **radial** and **transverse components** of the acceleration. They are denoted respectively by a_r and a_θ as shown in Figure 160.

Theorem 2. *If a particle moves along the curve $r = f(\theta)$, the radial and transverse components of its acceleration at any instant are given by*

$$a_r = \frac{d^2r}{dt^2} - r\left(\frac{d\theta}{dt}\right)^2, \qquad a_\theta = 2\,\frac{dr}{dt}\,\frac{d\theta}{dt} + r\,\frac{d^2\theta}{dt^2}. \tag{4}$$

Proof: Differentiating (2) with respect to t gives

$$\begin{aligned} a_x &= \cos\theta\,\frac{d^2r}{dt^2} - 2\sin\theta\,\frac{dr}{dt}\,\frac{d\theta}{dt} - r\cos\theta\left(\frac{d\theta}{dt}\right)^2 - r\sin\theta\,\frac{d^2\theta}{dt^2}, \\ a_y &= \sin\theta\,\frac{d^2r}{dt^2} + 2\cos\theta\,\frac{dr}{dt}\,\frac{d\theta}{dt} - r\sin\theta\left(\frac{d\theta}{dt}\right)^2 + r\cos\theta\,\frac{d^2\theta}{dt^2}. \end{aligned} \tag{5}$$

From Figure 160 and the relations $a_x = a\cos\phi$, $a_y = a\sin\phi$, we have

$$\begin{aligned} a_r &= a\cos(\phi-\theta) = a\cos\phi\cos\theta + a\sin\phi\sin\theta = a_x\cos\theta + a_y\sin\theta, \\ a_\theta &= a\sin(\phi-\theta) = a\sin\phi\cos\theta - a\cos\phi\sin\theta = a_y\cos\theta - a_x\sin\theta. \end{aligned} \tag{6}$$

Substituting (5) in (6), we obtain the result (4).

Example. A particle travels around the limaçon $r = 3 + 2\cos\theta$ with a constant angular velocity of 2 radians per second, that is, $d\theta/dt = 2$. If r is expressed in feet, find v and a at the instant when $\theta = \frac{1}{2}\pi$.

Solution: Since $\frac{d\theta}{dt}$ is constant, we have $\frac{d^2\theta}{dt^2} = 0$, and from the given equation

$$\frac{dr}{dt} = -2\sin\theta\frac{d\theta}{dt} = -4\sin\theta, \qquad \frac{d^2r}{dt^2} = -4\cos\theta\frac{d\theta}{dt} = -8\cos\theta.$$

Substituting in (1) and setting $\theta = \frac{1}{2}\pi$, we obtain

$$v_r = -4\sin\theta = -4, \qquad v_\theta = (3 + 2\cos\theta)\,2 = 6.$$

Hence

$$v = \sqrt{v_r^2 + v_\theta^2} = \sqrt{(-4)^2 + (6)^2} = 7.21 \text{ ft./sec.}$$

Substituting in (4) and setting $\theta = \frac{1}{2}\pi$, we obtain

$$a_r = -8\cos\theta - 4(3 + 2\cos\theta) = -12, \qquad a_\theta = 4(-4\sin\theta) = -16.$$

Hence

$$a = \sqrt{a_r^2 + a_\theta^2} = \sqrt{(-12)^2 + (-16)^2} = 20 \text{ ft./sec}^2.$$

EXERCISE 53

Find the radius of curvature of the following curves at the point indicated.

1. $r = \theta^2;\ \theta = \frac{3}{2}$. *Ans.* $\frac{125}{44}$.
2. $r = 4 + 3\sin\theta;\ \theta = 0$.
3. $r = \tan\theta;\ \theta = \frac{3}{4}\pi$. $\sqrt{5}$.
4. $r = 2/(1 + \cos\theta);\ \theta = \frac{1}{2}\pi$.
5. $r = \cos 2\theta;\ \theta = \frac{1}{6}\pi$. $\frac{13}{58}\sqrt{13}$.
6. $r = 2\sin 3\theta;\ \theta = \frac{1}{6}\pi$.
7. $r^2 = \sin 2\theta;\ \theta = \frac{1}{4}\pi$. $\frac{1}{3}$.
8. $r = \tan\theta\sec\theta;\ \theta = \frac{5}{6}\pi$.
9. $r^2\theta = 4;\ \theta = \frac{2}{3}$. $\frac{125}{28}\sqrt{6}$.
10. $r = e^{2\theta};\ \theta = \ln 2$.

In each of the following, a particle moves along the given curve with a constant angular velocity $\omega = d\theta/dt$ of 2 radians per second. Find the speed and acceleration of the particle when θ has the value indicated.

11. $r = 4;\ \theta = \frac{1}{4}\pi$. *Ans.* 8, 16.
12. $r = 2\theta;\ \theta = \pi$.
13. $r = 5 + 4\sin\theta;\ \theta = \frac{1}{3}\pi$. 17.4, 50.3.
14. $r = 6/(2 + \cos\theta);\ \theta = \frac{2}{3}\pi$.
15. $r = 1 + \sin^2\theta;\ \theta = \frac{1}{2}\pi$. 4, 16.
16. $r = 2\sin^2\frac{1}{2}\theta;\ \theta = \frac{1}{3}\pi$.
17. A particle moves in accordance with the equations $r = t^2 + t$ and $\theta = \frac{1}{6}t^3$ where t denotes the time. Find its position and speed when $t = 2$. *Ans.* $(6,\frac{4}{3})$, 13.

18. A particle moves counterclockwise around the limaçon $r = 4 + 2\cos\theta$ with a constant speed of 14 feet per second. Find v_r and v_θ when $\theta = \frac{1}{3}\pi$.
19. A particle moves to the left on the parabola $r = 4/(1 + \cos\theta)$ with a constant speed of 4 feet per second. Find v_r and v_θ when $\theta = \frac{1}{2}\pi$.

Ans. $2\sqrt{2}$, $2\sqrt{2}$ ft./sec.

20. A particle moves along the curve $r = \sin 2\theta$ with increasing θ. Find its speed and acceleration if $d\theta/dt = 2$ and $d^2\theta/dt^2 = 5$ when $\theta = \frac{1}{4}\pi$.

CHAPTER 12

Indeterminate Forms

112. Limits

Since calculus is primarily concerned with the study of limiting processes, it is important and necessary that we appreciate and understand the various rules that apply to limits. We repeat below the four basic rules on limits that were considered in the second chapter.

If $f(x)$ and $g(x)$ possess limits as x approaches a, then

L_1 $\lim [f(x) \pm g(x)] = \lim f(x) \pm \lim g(x)$.

L_2 $\lim [f(x) \cdot g(x)] = \lim f(x) \cdot \lim g(x)$.

L_3 $\lim [f(x)/g(x)] = \lim f(x)/\lim g(x)$, if $\lim g(x) \neq 0$.

L_4 $\lim F[g(x)] = F[\lim g(x)]$, if $\lim g(x) = c$, and $F(y)$ is continuous at $y = c$.

Thus far, only L_1, L_2, and L_4 have been proved in detail, but it is interesting to note that L_3 can be established by use of L_2 and L_4. For example, let us suppose that $\lim g(x) = c \neq 0$. Since the function $F(y) = 1/y$ is continuous at $y = c$, it follows from L_4 that $\lim [1/g(x)] = 1/\lim g(x)$. Hence by L_2 we have

$$\lim \frac{f(x)}{g(x)} = \lim \left\{ f(x) \cdot \frac{1}{g(x)} \right\} = \lim f(x) \cdot \lim \frac{1}{g(x)} = \frac{\lim f(x)}{\lim g(x)}.$$

Although the proposition L_3 has many uses, the condition that $\lim g(x)$ be different from zero greatly restricts its usefulness in many important limit operations. For example, the definition of a derivative,

$$\lim_{\Delta x \to 0} \frac{f(x + \Delta x) - f(x)}{\Delta x},$$

involves the limit of a quotient, but in all cases L_3 does not apply and other devices must be used to determine whether or not the limit exists.

It is the purpose of this chapter to study the limit L_3 in those cases where $\lim g(x) = 0$. Before doing this, however, it is necessary to establish several fundamental theorems.

113. Rolle's Theorem

If two points A and B on the x axis are connected by a continuous curve, as shown in Figure 161, and if this curve has a non-vertical tangent at each point between A and B, it would appear geometrically evident that there must exist at least one point P between A and B where the tangent at P is parallel to the x axis. This conclusion, as stated in the following theorem, is attributed to the French mathematician Michel Rolle (1652–1719).

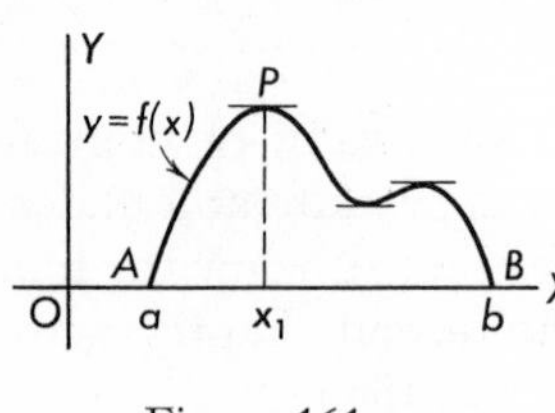

Figure 161

Rolle's Theorem. *If a function $f(x)$ is continuous in the interval $a \leqq x \leqq b$, vanishes at the end points, and has a derivative at every point between a and b, then $f'(x)$ must be zero for at least one value x_1 between a and b.*

Proof: (*a*) If $f(x)$ is zero at all points of the interval, then $f'(x)$ is zero throughout the interval and the theorem is proved.

(*b*) If $f(x)$ is positive or negative in some parts of the interval, then because of continuity the function attains a greatest value M and a least value m, as we know from Theorem 3, Article **23.** If $M \neq 0$ and $f(x_1) = M$, it follows from the theorem on relative maxima, Article **31,** that $f'(x_1)$ must be zero. By a similar argument, if $m \neq 0$ and $f(x_1) = m$, then $f'(x_1) = 0$.

114. Law of the Mean

A situation geometrically similar to that considered in Rolle's theorem is shown in Figure 162. If the curve that connects A and B is continuous and has a non-vertical tangent at each point between A and B, it would appear evident that there must be some point P on the curve between A and B such that the tangent at P is parallel to the chord AB. This generalization of Rolle's theorem is usually known as the **law of the mean.**

Law of the Mean. *If a function $f(x)$ is continuous in the interval $a \leqq x \leqq b$ and has a derivative at every point between a and b, then there is at least one value $x = x_1$ such that*

$$\frac{f(b) - f(a)}{b - a} = f'(x_1), \quad a < x_1 < b. \tag{1}$$

Proof: Consider the function

$$F(x) \equiv f(x) - f(a) - \frac{f(b) - f(a)}{b - a}(x - a), \tag{2}$$

which represents the vertical distance between the arc AB and the chord AB in Figure 162. Since $f(x)$ is continuous for $a \leqq x \leqq b$ and differentiable for $a < x < b$, so too is $F(x)$. Furthermore, we observe that $F(a) = 0$ and $F(b) = 0$. Hence, by Rolle's theorem, there exists a value $x = x_1$ such that $F'(x_1) = 0$. Thus, on differentiating (2) and setting $x = x_1$, we obtain

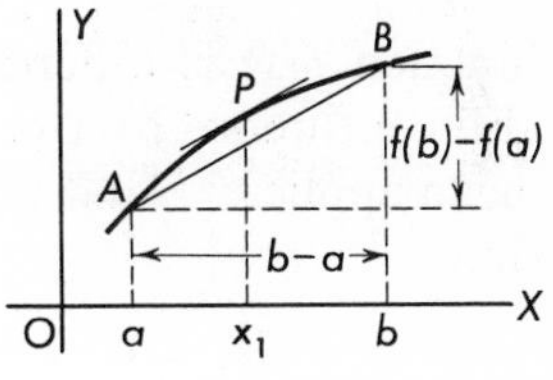

$$F'(x_1) = f'(x_1) - \frac{f(b) - f(a)}{b - a} = 0,$$

Figure 162

which reduces to (1).

Clearing of fractions, we may write (1) in the form

$$f(b) = f(a) + (b - a)f'(x_1). \tag{3}$$

On substituting $a + h$ for b, and $a + \theta h$ for x_1, where θ is a number between 0 and 1, we obtain another form of the law of the mean,

$$\boldsymbol{f(a + h) = f(a) + hf'(a + \theta h), \quad 0 < \theta < 1.} \tag{4}$$

If the maximum and minimum values of the derived function $f'(x)$ in the interval $a < x < b$ are M' and m', respectively, we see that the relation (1) yields the inequality

$$(b - a)m' < f(b) - f(a) < (b - a)M'. \tag{5}$$

Illustration 1. If $f(x) = \sin x$, we get $f'(x) = \cos x$; hence $M' = \max(\cos x) = 1$ and $m' = \min(\cos x) = -1$. Thus, by substitution in (5), we obtain the inequality relation

$$|\sin b - \sin a| < |b - a|$$

for all numbers a and b.

If h in (4) is a sufficiently small number, then $a + \theta h$ is essentially equal to a, and we may write

$$f(a + h) \approx f(a) + hf'(a). \tag{6}$$

which is the same approximation formula that was considered in Article **36**.

Illustration 2. If $f(x) = \sqrt{x}$, we find $f'(x) = 1/2\sqrt{x}$. Thus, by use of (6), an approximation for $\sqrt{102}$ is

$$\sqrt{102} \approx \sqrt{100} + (2)\left(\frac{1}{2\sqrt{100}}\right) = 10 + 0.1 = 10.1.$$

In Article **28** we proved that the derivative of a constant is equal to zero. Using the law of the mean we can now establish the converse of this result.

Theorem. *If a function $f(x)$ has a derivative which is equal to zero for all values of x in the interval $a \leqq x \leqq b$, then $f(x)$ is a constant throughout the interval.*

Proof: Let x' be any point in the interval from a to b. Since the function $f(x)$ is differentiable in the closed interval $a \leqq x \leqq x'$, it is also continuous by the theorem given in Article **27**, and the law of the mean applies. That is, there exists a number x_1 between a and x' such that

$$f(x') - f(a) = f'(x_1)(x' - a).$$

Since $f'(x_1)$ is zero by hypothesis, it follows that $f(x') = f(a)$. This means that $f(x)$ has the same value $f(a)$ throughout the interval, and so is a constant.

115. Cauchy's Theorem

Let the equation of the curve considered in Figure 162 be represented in parametric form as $x = g(u)$ and $y = f(u)$, and let u_A, u_P, and u_B be the parameter values corresponding to the points A, P, and B, respectively. Since the slope of the curve is given by $dy/dx = f'(u)/g'(u)$, it would appear to follow from the law of the mean that

$$\frac{f(u_B) - f(u_A)}{g(u_B) - g(u_A)} = \frac{f'(u_P)}{g'(u_P)}, \quad u_A < u_P < u_B.$$

This extension of the law of the mean, as it is stated in the following theorem, is attributed to the French mathematician Augustin Louis Cauchy (1789–1857).

Cauchy's Theorem. *If the functions $f(x)$ and $g(x)$ are continuous in the interval $a \leqq x \leqq b$, and if the derivatives $f'(x)$ and $g'(x)$ exist, and $g'(x)$ is non-zero, at every point between a and b, then there is at least one value $x = x_1$ such that*

$$\frac{f(b) - f(a)}{g(b) - g(a)} = \frac{f'(x_1)}{g'(x_1)}, \quad a < x_1 < b. \tag{1}$$

Proof: This theorem can be proved in a manner similar to that used in proving the law of the mean. In this case consider the function $F(x)$ defined as

$$F(x) \equiv f(x) - f(a) - \frac{f(b) - f(a)}{g(b) - g(a)}[g(x) - g(a)]. \tag{2}$$

Because $g'(x) \neq 0$ for $a < x < b$, it follows from the law of the mean that $g(b) \neq g(a)$, since otherwise $g'(x)$ would have to vanish for some x in the interval. From the form of $F(x)$ and the hypotheses on $f(x)$ and $g(x)$, it is clear that $F(x)$ is continuous in the interval $a \leqq x \leqq b$ and that its derivative exists at every point within this interval. Furthermore, we observe that $F(a) = 0$ and $F(b) = 0$. Hence, by Rolle's theorem, there exists a value $x = x_1$ such that $F'(x_1) = 0$. Thus, on differentiating (2) and setting $x = x_1$, we find

$$F'(x_1) = f'(x_1) - \frac{f(b) - f(a)}{g(b) - g(a)} g'(x_1) = 0,$$

which reduces to (1) since $g'(x_1) \neq 0$.

EXERCISE 54

For each of the following functions, find a value x_1, if possible, such that $f(b) = f(a) + (b - a)f'(x_1)$. What condition in the law of the mean is violated when no x_1 exists?

1. $f(x) = x^2$; $a = 2$, $b = 3$. *Ans.* $\frac{5}{2}$.
2. $f(x) = \sqrt{x}$; $a = 1$, $b = 4$.
3. $f(x) = \ln x$; $a = 1$, $b = e$. $e - 1$.
4. $f(x) = \sin \pi x$; $a = 0$, $b = \frac{1}{2}$.
5. $f(x) = x^{2/3}$; $a = -1$, $b = 1$. No derivative at $x = 0$.
6. $f(x) = 1/x$; $a = -2$, $b = 1$.
7. $f(x) = \cot \pi x$; $a = -\frac{1}{2}$, $b = \frac{1}{2}$. Discontinuous at $x = 0$.
8. $f(x) = 1 - |x|$; $a = -1$, $b = 1$.
9. $f(x) = x^2$; $a = a$, $b = b$. $\frac{1}{2}(a + b)$.
10. $f(x) = x^3$; $a = a$, $b = b$.

Use the relation (1) or (4) in Article **114** to establish the following inequalities.

11. Show that $|\cos b - \cos a| < |b - a|$ for all a and b.
12. Taking $f(x) = \ln x$ and $a = 1$, show that $\dfrac{h}{1 + h} < \ln(1 + h) < h$ for $-1 < h < 0$ and $h > 0$.
13. Taking $f(x) = e^x$ and $a = 0$, show that $h < e^h - 1 < he^h$ for $h \neq 0$.
14. Taking $f(x) = \text{Sin}^{-1} x$ and $a = 0$, show that $h < \text{Sin}^{-1} h < \dfrac{h}{\sqrt{1 - h^2}}$ for $0 < h < 1$.
15. Taking $f(x) = \text{Tan}^{-1} x$ and $a = 0$, show that $\dfrac{h}{1 + h^2} < \text{Tan}^{-1} h < h$ for $h \neq 0$.
16. Taking $f(x) = x \ln x$ and $a = 1$, show that $\dfrac{1}{b} < \dfrac{\ln b}{b - 1} < 1$ for $b > 1$.
17. Use the law of the mean to prove that $2.024 < \sqrt{4.1} < 2.025$.

18. If $f'(x) > 0$ at all points in the interval $a < x < b$, use the law of the mean to show that $f(x)$ is an increasing function.
19. If the functions $f(x)$ and $g(x)$ are such that $f'(x) = g'(x)$ for every point in the interval $a \leqq x \leqq b$, show that $f(x) = g(x) + C$ where C is a constant.
20. Show that the mean value theorem for a definite integral can be obtained by taking $f(x) = \int_a^x g(t)\,dt$ and $b = x$ in the law of the mean. *Hint:* Use the fact that $f'(x) = g(x)$.

116. The Indeterminate Form 0/0

If two functions $f(x)$ and $g(x)$ are both zero when $x = a$, the fraction $f(a)/g(a)$ is said to assume the indeterminate form $0/0$. In this case the function $F(x) = f(x)/g(x)$ is undefined for $x = a$, since division by zero is not permitted. However, $F(x)$ may approach a limit as x approaches a. The process of determining this limit, if it exists, is called *evaluating the indeterminate form.*

Illustration 1. When $x = 1$, the fraction $(x^2 - 1)/(x - 1)$ has the form $0/0$, and hence is undefined. Evaluating the limit, however, we have

$$\lim_{x\to 1} \frac{x^2 - 1}{x - 1} = \lim_{x\to 1} x + 1 = 2.$$

If the functions $f(x)$ and $g(x)$ satisfy the required conditions of Cauchy's theorem in an interval containing $x = a$, it follows that either

$$\frac{f(a) - f(x)}{g(a) - g(x)} = \frac{f'(x_1)}{g'(x_1)} \quad \text{or} \quad \frac{f(x) - f(a)}{g(x) - g(a)} = \frac{f'(x_2)}{g'(x_2)},$$

where $x < x_1 < a$ or $a < x_2 < x$, respectively. However, when $f(a) = 0$ and $g(a) = 0$, the above relations reduce to

$$\frac{f(x)}{g(x)} = \frac{f'(x_1)}{g'(x_1)} \quad \text{or} \quad \frac{f(x)}{g(x)} = \frac{f'(x_2)}{g'(x_2)},$$

and since x_1 and x_2 must each approach a as x approaches a, we have the following result, named for the French mathematician G. F. A. de L'Hospital (1661–1704).

L'Hospital's Rule. *If the functions $f(x)$ and $g(x)$ are continuous in an interval containing $x = a$, and if their derivatives exist and $g'(x) \neq 0$ in this interval (except possibly at $x = a$), then when $f(a) = 0$ and $g(a) = 0$, we have*

$$\lim_{x\to a} \frac{f(x)}{g(x)} = \lim_{x\to a} \frac{f'(x)}{g'(x)},$$

provided the limit on the right exists.

If the functions $f(x)$ and $g(x)$ are continuous and differentiable for every positive x and if $f(x)/g(x)$ takes the form $0/0$ as $x \to \infty$, it is shown in more advanced books that L'Hospital's rule applies, that is,

$$\lim_{x\to\infty} \frac{f(x)}{g(x)} = \lim_{x\to\infty} \frac{f'(x)}{g'(x)}.$$

It can also be shown that if $f'(x)/g'(x)$ approaches infinity as $x \to a$ (or $x \to \infty$), then $f(x)/g(x)$ approaches infinity.

Example. Evaluate $\lim_{x\to 0} (\tan x)/x$.

Solution: Since the fraction has the form $0/0$ for $x = 0$, we apply L'Hospital's rule and obtain

$$\lim_{x\to 0} \frac{\tan x}{x} = \lim_{x\to 0} \frac{\sec^2 x}{1} = 1.$$

If the application of L'Hospital's rule results in a fraction which is also indeterminate, the process may be repeated. For example,

$$\lim_{x\to 0} \frac{x^3 - 5x^2}{x^3 + 2x^2} = \lim_{x\to 0} \frac{3x^2 - 10x}{3x^2 + 4x} = \lim_{x\to 0} \frac{6x - 10}{6x + 4} = -\frac{5}{2}.$$

Occasionally the limit of an indeterminate expression can be found by evaluating a simpler indeterminate.

Illustration 2. Using the result of the example above, we have

$$\lim_{x\to 0} \frac{2 \tan x \sec x}{xe^x} = \lim_{x\to 0} \frac{2 \sec x}{e^x} \cdot \lim_{x\to 0} \frac{\tan x}{x} = 2\cdot 1 = 2,$$

and

$$\lim_{x\to 0} \frac{\tan^2 x}{x^2} = \left(\lim_{x\to 0} \frac{\tan x}{x}\right)^2 = 1.$$

117. The Indeterminate Form ∞/∞

If $f(x)$ and $g(x)$ both increase without limit as $x \to a$ (or $x \to \pm\infty$), the fraction $f(x)/g(x)$ is undefined and is said to assume the indeterminate form ∞/∞. If the limit of $f(x)/g(x)$ exists as $x \to a$ (or $x \to \pm\infty$), it may be found by L'Hospital's rule. A rigorous proof of this fact is beyond the scope of this book.

Illustration. $\lim_{x\to\infty} \frac{x^2}{e^x} = \lim_{x\to\infty} \frac{2x}{e^x} = \lim_{x\to\infty} \frac{2}{e^x} = 0.$

The application of L'Hospital's rule does not always lead to desirable results.

Example. Evaluate $\lim\limits_{x\to 0+} \dfrac{e^{-(1/x)}}{x}$.

Solution: Applying L'Hospital's rule, we have

$$\lim_{x\to 0+} \frac{e^{-(1/x)}}{x} = \lim_{x\to 0+} \frac{(1/x^2)e^{-(1/x)}}{1} = \lim_{x\to 0+} \frac{e^{-(1/x)}}{x^2}.$$

It is apparent that repeated use of L'Hospital's rule in this case would accomplish nothing, so we try other means. Writing the original expression in a different form and changing variables, we find

$$\lim_{x\to 0+} \frac{1/x}{e^{1/x}} = \lim_{z\to\infty} \frac{z}{e^z} = \lim_{z\to\infty} \frac{1}{e^z} = 0.$$

EXERCISE 55

Evaluate each of the following limits.

1. $\lim\limits_{x\to 2} \dfrac{x^3 - x^2 - 4}{x^2 - 4}$. *Ans.* 2.
2. $\lim\limits_{x\to a} \dfrac{x - a}{x^n - a^n}$.
3. $\lim\limits_{x\to 0} \dfrac{a - \sqrt{a^2 - x^2}}{x}$. 0.
4. $\lim\limits_{x\to 0} \dfrac{\sqrt{4 + x} - \sqrt{4 - x}}{x}$.
5. $\lim\limits_{x\to 0} \dfrac{e^x - e^{-x}}{\tan x}$. 2.
6. $\lim\limits_{x\to 0} \dfrac{a^x - b^x}{x}$.
7. $\lim\limits_{x\to \alpha} \dfrac{\sin x - \sin \alpha}{x - \alpha}$. $\cos \alpha$.
8. $\lim\limits_{x\to \alpha} \dfrac{\tan 2x - \tan 2\alpha}{x - \alpha}$.
9. $\lim\limits_{x\to 0} \dfrac{\tan x - x}{x - \sin x}$. 2.
10. $\lim\limits_{x\to 0} \dfrac{\ln \sec x}{x^2}$.
11. $\lim\limits_{x\to \infty} \dfrac{\ln x}{x^n}$. 0.
12. $\lim\limits_{\theta\to 0} \dfrac{1 - \cos\theta}{\sin\theta}$.
13. $\lim\limits_{\theta\to 0} \dfrac{\tan 2\theta}{2\sin^2\theta}$. ∞.
14. $\lim\limits_{\theta\to \frac{1}{2}\pi} \dfrac{\cos 5\theta}{\cos 7\theta}$.
15. $\lim\limits_{x\to \pi} \dfrac{\ln \cos 2x}{(\pi - x)^2}$. -2.
16. $\lim\limits_{x\to 0} \dfrac{e^x - e^{-x}}{\ln (x + 1)}$.
17. $\lim\limits_{x\to 0} \dfrac{\mathrm{Sin}^{-1} x}{x}$. 1.
18. $\lim\limits_{x\to 0} \dfrac{x - \mathrm{Sin}^{-1} x}{x^3}$.
19. $\lim\limits_{\theta\to \frac{1}{4}\pi} \dfrac{\sec^2\theta - 2\tan\theta}{1 + \cos 4\theta}$. $\frac{1}{2}$.
20. $\lim\limits_{x\to 0} \dfrac{e^x + e^{-x} - 2\cos x}{x \sin x}$.
21. $\lim\limits_{x\to 0} \dfrac{x - \sin x}{x^3}$. $\frac{1}{6}$.
22. $\lim\limits_{x\to 0} \dfrac{1 - \ln x}{e^{1/x}}$.
23. $\lim\limits_{x\to \infty} \dfrac{x}{\sqrt{1 + x^2}}$. 1.
24. $\lim\limits_{x\to \infty} \dfrac{2^x}{e^{x^2}}$.

118. The Indeterminate Form $0 \cdot \infty$

If $f(x) \to 0$ and $g(x) \to \infty$ as $x \to a$ (or $x \to \pm\infty$), the product $f(a) \cdot g(a)$ is undefined and is said to assume the indeterminate form $0 \cdot \infty$. If the limit of $f(x) \cdot g(x)$ exists as $x \to a$ (or $x \to \pm\infty$), it may be found by writing the product as a fraction,

$$\frac{f(x)}{1/g(x)} \quad \text{or} \quad \frac{g(x)}{1/f(x)},$$

and applying L'Hospital's rule.

Illustration. (*a*) $\displaystyle\lim_{x\to\infty} xe^{-x} = \lim_{x\to\infty} \frac{x}{e^x} = \lim_{x\to\infty} \frac{1}{e^x} = 0,$

(*b*) $\displaystyle\lim_{x\to 0} \sin 3x \cot 2x = \lim_{x\to 0} \frac{\sin 3x}{\tan 2x} = \lim_{x\to 0} \frac{3\cos 3x}{2\sec^2 2x} = \frac{3}{2}.$

119. The Indeterminate Form $\infty - \infty$

If $f(x)$ and $g(x)$ both increase without limit as $x \to a$ (or $x \to \pm\infty$), the difference $f(a) - g(a)$ is undefined and is said to assume the indeterminate form $\infty - \infty$. If the limit of $f(x) - g(x)$ exists as $x \to a$ (or $x \to \pm\infty$), it may be found by transforming the difference into a fraction by algebraic means and applying L'Hospital's rule.

Illustration. $\displaystyle\lim_{x\to 0} (\csc x - \cot x) = \lim_{x\to 0} \frac{1 - \cos x}{\sin x} = \lim_{x\to 0} \frac{\sin x}{\cos x} = 0.$

Note 1: Although a simpler fraction is to be preferred, we can always use the fraction

$$f(x) - g(x) = \frac{\dfrac{1}{g(x)} - \dfrac{1}{f(x)}}{\dfrac{1}{f(x)g(x)}}.$$

Note 2: Occasionally an indeterminate of the form $\infty - \infty$ can be evaluated most readily by finding the limit of its exponential. Thus, to evaluate $\displaystyle\lim_{x\to\infty} (x - \ln x)$, we let $y = x - \ln x$, and determine the limit of

$$e^y = e^{x - \ln x} = \frac{e^x}{e^{\ln x}} = \frac{e^x}{x}.$$

Hence

$$\lim_{x\to\infty} e^y = \lim_{x\to\infty} \frac{e^x}{x} = \lim_{x\to\infty} \frac{e^x}{1} = \infty,$$

and since $y \to \infty$ when $e^y \to \infty$, we obtain

$$\lim_{x\to\infty} (x - \ln x) = \infty.$$

EXERCISE 56

Evaluate each of the following limits.

1. $\lim_{x\to 0} x \ln x.$ *Ans.* 0.
2. $\lim_{x\to\infty} x \sin(\pi/x).$
3. $\lim_{x\to 0} x \csc 2x.$ $\frac{1}{2}$.
4. $\lim_{x\to\frac{1}{2}\pi} \sec 5x \cos 3x.$
5. $\lim_{x\to 0+} xe^{1/x}.$ ∞.
6. $\lim_{x\to 1} \dfrac{x^7-1}{x}\cdot\dfrac{x^2}{x^9-1}.$
7. $\lim_{x\to 0} \csc x \operatorname{Sin}^{-1} x.$ 1.
8. $\lim_{x\to 0} \sin x \ln(\tan x).$
9. $\lim_{x\to\frac{1}{2}\pi} \tan x \tan 2x.$ -2.
10. $\lim_{x\to\frac{1}{4}\pi} (1-\tan x)\sec 2x.$
11. $\lim_{x\to\frac{1}{2}\pi} (\sec x - \tan x).$ 0.
12. $\lim_{x\to\infty} [\ln(x-2) - \ln \frac{1}{2}x].$
13. $\lim_{x\to 1} \left(\dfrac{1}{x-1} - \dfrac{1}{\ln x}\right).$ $-\frac{1}{2}$.
14. $\lim_{x\to 1} \left(\dfrac{x}{x-1} - \dfrac{1}{\ln x}\right).$
15. $\lim_{x\to\frac{1}{2}\pi} (\tan 5x - \tan x).$ ∞.
16. $\lim_{x\to 1} \left(\dfrac{x}{\ln x} - \dfrac{1}{x\ln x}\right).$
17. $\lim_{x\to 0} (\csc x - \csc 2x).$ ∞.
18. $\lim_{x\to\frac{1}{2}\pi} (x\tan x - \frac{1}{2}\pi \sec x).$
19. $\lim_{x\to 0} \left(\dfrac{1}{x} - \dfrac{1}{\sin x}\right).$ 0.
20. $\lim_{x\to 0} \left(\dfrac{1}{x\sin x} - \dfrac{1}{x^2}\right).$
21. $\lim_{x\to\infty} (e^x - x).$ ∞.
22. $\lim_{x\to\infty} [\ln x - \ln(\ln x)].$
23. $\lim_{x\to 0} \left(\dfrac{1}{\sin^2 x} - \dfrac{1}{x^2}\right).$ $\frac{1}{3}$.
24. $\lim_{x\to 1} \left(\dfrac{n}{x^n-1} - \dfrac{m}{x^m-1}\right).$

120. The Indeterminate Forms 0^0, ∞^0, 1^∞

If $f(x)\to 0$ and $g(x)\to 0$, or $f(x)\to\infty$ and $g(x)\to 0$, or $f(x)\to 1$ and $g(x)\to\infty$ as $x\to a$ (or $x\to\pm\infty$), the expression $f(a)^{g(a)}$ is undefined and is said to assume the indeterminate form 0^0, ∞^0, or 1^∞, respectively. If the limit of $f(x)^{g(x)}$ exists as $x\to a$ (or $x\to\pm\infty$), it may be found by denoting the expression by y, and investigating the limit approached by the logarithm

$$\ln y = g(x)\ln f(x).$$

If we find that $\lim_{x\to a}\ln y = k$, it follows that $\lim_{x\to a} y = e^k$.

Example 1. Evaluate $\lim_{x\to 0} x^x$.

Solution: When $x = 0$, the function x^x assumes the indeterminate form 0^0. Hence, writing $y = x^x$, we have $\ln y = x\ln x$, and

$$\lim_{x\to 0}\ln y = \lim_{x\to 0}\frac{\ln x}{1/x} = \lim_{x\to 0}\frac{1/x}{-1/x^2} = \lim_{x\to 0} -x = 0.$$

Therefore $\lim_{x\to 0} y = \lim_{x\to 0} x^x = e^0 = 1.$

Example 2. Evaluate $\lim_{x \to 0} (1 - \sin x)^{1/x}$.

Solution: When $x = 0$, the given function assumes the indeterminate form 1^∞. Thus, writing $y = (1 - \sin x)^{1/x}$, we have

$$\lim_{x \to 0} \ln y = \lim_{x \to 0} \frac{\ln (1 - \sin x)}{x} = \lim_{x \to 0} \frac{\dfrac{-\cos x}{1 - \sin x}}{1} = -1.$$

Therefore $\lim_{x \to 0} (1 - \sin x)^{1/x} = e^{-1} = 1/e$.

EXERCISE 57

Evaluate each of the following limits.

1. $\lim_{x \to \infty} x^{1/x}$. *Ans.* 1.
2. $\lim_{x \to 1} x^{1/(1-x)}$.
3. $\lim_{x \to 0} (\sin x)^x$. 1.
4. $\lim_{x \to 0} (\sin x)^{\tan x}$.
5. $\lim_{x \to \infty} \left(\dfrac{x}{x - 2}\right)^x$. e^2.
6. $\lim_{x \to \infty} \left(\dfrac{3}{x} + 1\right)^x$.
7. $\lim_{x \to 0} (1 + \tan x)^{1/x}$. e.
8. $\lim_{x \to 0} (1 - x^2)^{\cot x}$.
9. $\lim_{x \to \infty} \left(1 - \dfrac{1}{x^3}\right)^x$. 1.
10. $\lim_{x \to 0} (1 + 2x)^{(1+2x)/x}$.
11. $\lim_{x \to \infty} (e^x + x)^{1/x}$. e.
12. $\lim_{x \to 0} (e^x + x)^{1/x}$.
13. $\lim_{x \to \infty} \left(\cos \dfrac{2}{x}\right)^{x^2}$. e^{-2}.
14. $\lim_{x \to 0} (\sin x + \cos x)^{\cot x}$.
15. $\lim_{x \to 0} (1 + ax)^{b/x}$. e^{ab}.
16. $\lim_{x \to \infty} (1 + ax)^{b/x}$.
17. $\lim_{x \to 0} (1 + x)^{\ln x}$. 1.
18. $\lim_{x \to 0} (\sin x)^{\ln \cos x}$.
19. $\lim_{x \to 0} (e^{x^2/2} \cos x)^{4/x^4}$. $e^{-1/3}$.
20. $\lim_{x \to 0} \left(\dfrac{\sin x}{x}\right)^{1/x}$.

CHAPTER 13

Curve Tracing

121. Graphs of Curves in Rectangular Coordinates

In elementary work the basic procedure for plotting the graph of any equation, $F(x,y) = 0$, consists in (*a*) finding, when possible, sets of values for x and y which satisfy the equation, (*b*) plotting the points (x,y), and (*c*) connecting the points with a smooth curve. This process, as we learned in analytic geometry, is materially simplified by determining certain general properties of the curve. These properties and their tests are as follows.

1. Extent. To find the extent of a curve means to find those ranges of the variables x and y which are permissible as coordinates of a point on the curve.

Illustration 1. The curve $y^2 = (x - 4) \ln x$ is located in the regions for which $0 < x \leqq 1$ and $x \geqq 4$. This follows since $\ln x$ is undefined for $x \leqq 0$, and y^2 is negative when $1 < x < 4$.

2. Symmetry. If the function $F(x,y)$ satisfies any one of the following identities, the curve $F(x,y) = 0$ is symmetric with respect to the point or line indicated

$$\begin{aligned} F(-x,y) &\equiv F(x,y), \quad y \text{ axis;} \\ F(x,-y) &\equiv F(x,y), \quad x \text{ axis;} \\ F(-x,-y) &\equiv F(x,y), \quad \text{origin;} \\ F(y,x) &\equiv F(x,y), \quad \text{line } y = x. \end{aligned}$$

Illustration 2. Since the substitution of $-x$ for x and $-y$ for y does not alter the equation $y = xe^{x^2}$, its graph is symmetric with respect to the origin. That is, the curve is not changed when it is rotated 180° about the origin.

3. Intercepts. To find where the curve, $F(x,y) = 0$, crosses the coordinate axes, we have

$$x_1 \text{ is an } x \text{ intercept, if } F(x_1,0) = 0,$$
$$y_1 \text{ is a } y \text{ intercept, if } F(0,y_1) = 0.$$

Illustration 3. Setting $y = 0$ in the equation $y = (x - 2) \ln x$, we obtain from $x - 2 = 0$ and $\ln x = 0$ the x intercepts $x = 2$ and $x = 1$. There are no y intercepts since $\ln x$ is undefined when $x = 0$.

4. Vertical and horizontal asymptotes. If the ordinate y of a point on a curve increases or decreases without limit as its abscissa x approaches a value a, the line $x = a$ is a vertical asymptote of the curve. If y approaches the value k as x increases or decreases without limit, the line $y = k$ is a horizontal asymptote of the curve.

Illustration 4. The curve $y = (\ln x)/x$ has the vertical asymptote $x = 0$, since $\lim_{x \to 0^+} (\ln x)/x = -\infty$; and the horizontal asymptote $y = 0$, since $\lim_{x \to \infty} (\ln x)/x = 0$.

Example 1. Discuss and sketch the curve $y = \ln \cos x$.

Solution: We proceed in accordance with the above analysis.

1. Since the curve repeats itself at intervals of 2π, we shall determine the curve in the interval from $x = -\pi$ to $x = \pi$. In this range y is undefined when $\cos x$ is negative; hence the curve is restricted to the interval $-\frac{1}{2}\pi < x < \frac{1}{2}\pi$.

2. Replacing x by $-x$ leaves the equation unaltered. Hence the curve is symmetric with respect to the y axis.

3. When $x = 0$, we find $y = 0$; and when $y = 0$, we find $x = 0$. Thus the curve intersects the axes at (0,0).

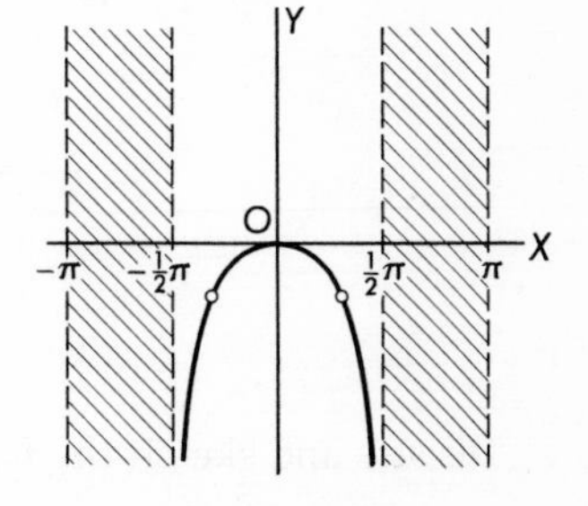

Figure 163

4. As x approaches $\pm\frac{1}{2}\pi$, y decreases without limit. Hence the lines $x = \frac{1}{2}\pi$ and $x = -\frac{1}{2}\pi$ are vertical asymptotes. A periodic function can have no horizontal asymptotes.

Determining one additional point $(\frac{1}{3}\pi, -0.7)$, we have the curve shown in Figure 163.

Example 2. Discuss and sketch the curve $y^2 = \dfrac{x^2}{(x - 1)(x - 2)}$.

Solution: 1. We shade the region $1 < x < 2$ to indicate that it contains no points of the curve.

2. We substitute $-y$ for y and find that the curve is symmetric with respect to the x axis.

3. We find one point of intersection with the axes, (0,0).

4. By inspection we observe that $x = 1$ and $x = 2$ are vertical asymptotes. Also, since

$$\lim_{x \to \pm\infty} \frac{x^2}{(x-1)(x-2)} = 1,$$

we have the horizontal asymptotes $y = \pm 1$.

In order to locate the curve definitely, we substitute $x = -1, \frac{1}{2}$, and 3 in the given equation and determine the corresponding values $y = \pm 0.4$, ± 0.6, and ± 2.1. Plotting these points and using the properties discussed above, we obtain the curve shown in Figure 164.

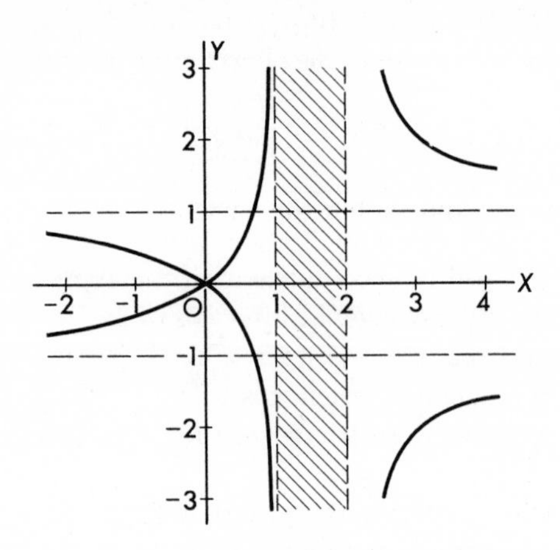

Figure 164

EXERCISE 58

Discuss and sketch the following curves.

1. $y = \dfrac{4}{x^2 + 4}$.
2. $y = \dfrac{x^2}{x^2 - 4}$.
3. $y = \dfrac{x^2}{4 - x}$.
4. $y = \dfrac{x}{(x-1)^3}$.
5. $y = \dfrac{6}{x^3 - x}$.
6. $y = \dfrac{x^3}{x - 2}$.
7. $y = \dfrac{x}{\sqrt{x+1}}$.
8. $y = \dfrac{\sqrt{9 - x^2}}{x}$.
9. $x = \dfrac{y^2}{1 - y^2}$.
10. $x = \dfrac{y + 1}{y^2 + 2}$.
11. $y = (\ln x)^2$.
12. $y = e^{-x^2}$.
13. $y = x^2 e^{-x}$.
14. $y = (\ln x)/x$.
15. $y = \dfrac{\operatorname{Tan}^{-1} x}{x}$.
16. $y = \dfrac{\sin x}{x}$.

17. $y = \ln \tan x$.
18. $y = x \ln (4 - x^2)$.
19. $x = y \ln (1 - y)$.
20. $x = e^{-y^2} \sin y$.
21. $y^2 = \dfrac{x^2}{4 - x^2}$.
22. $y^2 = \dfrac{4}{x + 2}$.
23. $y^2 = \dfrac{4x}{x^3 + 8}$.
24. $y^2 = \dfrac{x^2 - 4}{x^3 + x^2}$.
25. $y^2 = x^3 - 9x$.
26. $y^2 = x - x^{-1}$.
27. $(y + 1)^2 = x(x + 1)^2$.
28. $y^2(4 - x^2) + x^2(4 - y^2) = 0$.
29. $y^2 = e^x - e^{-x}$.
30. $y^2 = xe^{-x}$.
31. $y^2 = \sin x$.
32. $y^2 = x \operatorname{Cos}^{-1} x$.
33. $y^2 = x \ln (2 - x)$.
34. $y^2 = (\ln x)/(x - 2)$.
35. $x^2 = e^y/y$.
36. $x^2 = \ln (4 - y^2)$.

122. Oblique Asymptotes Determined by Inspection

If the equation of a curve can be written in the form

$$y = ax + b + h(x), \tag{1}$$

where a and b are constants, and $h(x)$ satisfies one or both of the conditions

$$\lim_{x \to \infty} h(x) = 0, \qquad \lim_{x \to -\infty} h(x) = 0,$$

then (1) is asymptotic to the line $y = ax + b$. This follows from the fact that the vertical distance between the curve and the line approaches zero as x increases or decreases without limit.

Illustration. (*a*) Writing the equation $xy = (x + 1)^2$ in the form $y = x + 2 + \frac{1}{x}$, it follows that the line $y = x + 2$ is an asymptote of the curve, since $\lim_{x \to \pm\infty} (1/x) = 0$.

(*b*) Writing the equation $e^x(y - x) = 1$ in the form $y = x + e^{-x}$, we find the asymptote $y = x$, since $\lim_{x \to \infty} e^{-x} = 0$.

Note: A curve may have an oblique asymptote even though its equation cannot be written in the form (1). The hyperbola $x^2 - y^2 = 1$, for example, is asymptotic to the line $y = x$.

123. Asymptotes to an Algebraic Curve

If $P(x,y)$ is an irreducible* polynomial of the nth degree in x and y, the equation

$$P(x,y) = 0 \tag{1}$$

* $P(x,y)$ is said to be irreducible when it cannot be expressed as the product of two other polynomials, each of degree less than n. Thus $P(x,y) \equiv x^2 + xy$ is reducible, since $x^2 + xy = x(x + y)$.

is called an **algebraic equation** defining x and y as **algebraic functions** of each other, and the graph of (1) is called an **algebraic curve** of the nth order.

Let (1) be written in descending powers of y as

$$P_0(x)y^p + P_1(x)y^{p-1} + \cdots + P_p(x) = 0, \tag{2}$$

where $p \leqq n$ and $P_0, P_1, \cdots, P_p$ are polynomials in x or constants. If the equation (2) can be solved for y in terms of x, we obtain p equations

$$y = B_1(x), \qquad y = B_2(x), \qquad \cdots, \qquad y = B_p(x), \tag{3}$$

each representing a part, called a **branch,** of the whole curve. Thus the parabola* $y^2 - 4x = 0$ has two branches $y = 2\sqrt{x}$ and $y = -2\sqrt{x}$.

The existence of vertical asymptotes to (1) can be determined by observing in (3) whether or not any values of x make y infinite. Hence we have the following theorem.

Theorem I. *If the equation* (1) *is written in the form* (2), *the real roots of the equation* $\mathbf{P_0(x) = 0}$ *give the vertical asymptotes of* (1).

Proof: Substituting $z = 1/y$ in (2) and multiplying through by z^p, we obtain

$$P_0(x) + P_1(x)z + \cdots + P_p(x)z^p = 0. \tag{4}$$

It is apparent that $y \to \infty$ as $z \to 0$, and the condition $z \to 0$ in (4) requires that $P_0(x) = 0$. Thus, if P_0 is a constant or has no real roots, the curve (1) has no vertical asymptotes. However, if a real value x_1 exists such that $P_0(x_1) = 0$, we see for $x = x_1$ that one root of (4) is $z = 0$. This means that, for at least one of the branches (3), y increases or decreases without limit as x approaches x_1. Hence $x = x_1$ is a vertical asymptote of (1).

Corollary. *If the equation* (1) *is written in the form*

$$\mathbf{Q_0(y)x^q + Q_1(y)x^{q-1} + \cdots + Q_q(y) = 0},$$

where $\mathbf{q \leqq n}$ *and* $\mathbf{Q_0, Q_1, \cdots, Q_q}$ *are polynomials in* $\mathbf{y}$, *the real roots of the equation* $\mathbf{Q_0(y) = 0}$ *give the horizontal asymptotes of* (1).

Illustration. Writing the equation $x^3 + 3x^2y^2 + xy^3 = y^3$ in the forms

$$(x-1)y^3 + (3x^2)y^2 + (x^3) = 0,$$
$$x^3 + (3y^2)x^2 + (y^3)x - (y^3) = 0,$$

we see by the above theorem and its corollary that the curve has the vertical asymptote $x = 1$ and no horizontal asymptotes.

In general an **asymptote** of a curve is defined, when it exists, as a line whose position is approached as a limit by a tangent line to the

* Solving for x, we can also say that the parabola has one branch, namely, $x = \frac{1}{4}y^2$.

curve as the point of tangency recedes indefinitely along the curve. Thus the line $y = mx + b$ will be asymptotic to an algebraic curve $P(x,y) = 0$, provided constants m and b are specifically determined when two of the points of intersection of the line and the curve approach infinity. This latter condition means that $P(x,mx + b) = 0$ must have two infinite roots. Hence the oblique asymptotes of an algebraic curve can be found in accordance with the following theorem. For the sake of brevity we shall omit the proof, as it is in some respects similar to the proof of Theorem 1.

Theorem 2. *Let* $\mathbf{y}$ *in equation* (1) *be replaced by* $\mathbf{mx} + \mathbf{b}$ *and let the resulting equation be written in descending powers of* $\mathbf{x}$ *as*

$$A_0(m)x^n + A_1(m,b)x^{n-1} + \cdots + A_n(b) = 0,$$

where $A_1, A_2, \cdots, A_{n-1}$ *are in general functions of* $\mathbf{m}$ *and* $\mathbf{b}$. *If* m_1 *is a real root of the equation* $A_0(m) = 0$, *and* b_1 *is a real root of the first equation in the sequence* $A_1(m_1,b) = 0, A_2(m_1,b) = 0, \cdots$, *which does not vanish identically, then* $y = m_1x + b_1$ *is an asymptote of* (1).

Example. Find the asymptotes of the curve $x^3 + y^3 = 3axy$.

Solution: By Theorem 1 we observe that the given equation has no horizontal or vertical asymptotes. In accordance with Theorem 2 we substitute $mx + b$ for y and obtain

$$(m^3 + 1)x^3 + (3m^2b - 3am)x^2 + (3mb^2 - 3ab)x + b^3 = 0.$$

From $m^3 + 1 = 0$, we obtain one real root $m = -1$. Substituting -1 for m in the coefficient of x^2, we have

$$3b + 3a = 0; \quad \text{hence} \quad b = -a.$$

Thus the line $y = -x - a$ is the only asymptote of the given curve. See **67**, page 9.

EXERCISE 59

Find the vertical and non-vertical (Article **122**) asymptotes of the following curves.

1. $y = \dfrac{x^2 + 1}{4x}$. *Ans.* $x = 0, y = \frac{1}{4}x$.
2. $y = \dfrac{(x - 2)^2}{x}$.
3. $y = \dfrac{x^3 + 1}{x^2 + 1}$. $y = x$.
4. $y = \dfrac{x^3}{2 - x - x^2}$.
5. $y = \dfrac{(x^2 + 1)^2}{x^3 - 1}$. $x = 1, y = x$.
6. $y = \dfrac{2x\sqrt{x} - 3}{\sqrt{x}}$.
7. $xy = x^2 - \ln x$. $y = x, x = 0$.
8. $xy = 1 - \ln x$.
9. $y = x(4 - e^{-x})$. $y = 4x$.
10. $y = 2 + e^{-x} \sin x$.
11. $y = x + \text{Tan}^{-1} x$. $y = x \pm \frac{1}{2}\pi$.
12. $y = x + x \sin (1/x)$.

Find the asymptotes of the following algebraic curves.

13. $x^2 - 4y^2 = 4$. *Ans.* $2y = \pm x$.
14. $x^2y^2 - y^2 = 4$.
15. $x^2y^2 + y^2 = 4$. $y = 0$.
16. $x^2 - 3xy + 2y^2 = 6$.
17. $x^3 + y^2 = 2x^2y$. $8y = 4x + 1$.
18. $y^2 = x(y^2 - x^2)$.
19. $x^2 + y^2 = x(y^2 - x^2)$. $x = 1,\ \pm y = x + 1$.
20. $x(x - y)(x^2 + y^2) = 6$.
21. $x^4 - 2x^2y^2 + y^4 = y$. $y = \pm x$.
22. $xy^2 - 4x^3 = y$.
23. $x^2y + xy^2 = x^2 + y^2$. $x = 1, y = 1, x + y = -2$.
24. $x^2 + y^2 = x^3 + y^3$.

124. Singular Points of Algebraic Curves

If the equation of an algebraic curve is

$$a_0 + a_1x + b_1y + a_2x^2 + b_2xy + c_2y^2 + \cdots + k_ny^n = 0, \tag{1}$$

we find by implicit differentiation that

$$\frac{dy}{dx} = -\frac{a_1 + 2a_2x + b_2y + \cdots}{b_1 + b_2x + 2c_2y + \cdots}. \tag{2}$$

The slope of the curve (1) at the point (x_1,y_1) is determined by evaluating (2) when $x = x_1$ and $y = y_1$. If this substitution gives a finite or infinite ($dx/dy = 0$) result, the point (x_1,y_1) is called an **ordinary point** of the curve. If the above substitution gives an indeterminate of the form $0/0$, the point (x_1,y_1) is called a **singular point** of the curve.

In the following discussion of singular points, we shall assume that the point in question is located at the origin. We lose no generality in this assumption since, if (x_1,y_1) is a singular point of (1), the transformations

$$x = x' + x_1, \qquad y = y' + y_1$$

will place the singular point at the origin of the new coordinate system.

An inspection of (1) and (2) shows that the point (0,0) will be a singular point of (1), if, and only if, $a_0 = a_1 = b_1 = 0$. In this case (1) has the form

$$a_2x^2 + b_2xy + c_2y^2 + \cdots + k_ny^n = 0. \tag{3}$$

If we cut the curve (3) with the line $y = mx$, the abscissas of the points of intersection are the roots of the equation

$$(a_2 + b_2m + c_2m^2)x^2 + \cdots + k_nm^nx^n = 0. \tag{4}$$

Thus $x = 0$ is a double root when m is chosen to be different from the roots m_1 and m_2 of the quadratic equation

$$a_2 + b_2 m + c_2 m^2 = 0, \quad c_2 \neq 0. \tag{5}$$

However, when $m = m_1$ or $m = m_2$, (4) will have at least three roots equal to zero. Consequently, at least one point of intersection of $y = mx$ with (3) approaches the origin as m approaches either m_1 or m_2. Since such a limit defines a tangent line, it follows that $y = m_1 x$ and $y = m_2 x$ are the equations of the tangents to (3) at the origin. Writing the equations of the tangents in a single equation, we have

$$(y - m_1 x)(y - m_2 x) = 0,$$

or

$$y^2 - (m_1 + m_2)xy + m_1 m_2 x^2 = 0. \tag{6}$$

However, from (5) it follows that $m_1 + m_2 = -b_2/c_2$ and $m_1 m_2 = a_2/c_2$; hence (6) becomes

$$a_2 x^2 + b_2 xy + c_2 y^2 = 0. \tag{7}$$

Although the condition $c_2 \neq 0$ was used in proving (7), by suitable modifications of the proof we obtain the same result when $c_2 = 0$. In fact, a similar argument will establish the following theorem.

Theorem. *If the equation of an algebraic curve contains terms of the rth degree ($r \geqq 2$), but none of lower degree, the origin is a singular point of the curve, and the tangents to branches of the curve which are continuous at the origin are given by equating to zero the group of terms of the rth degree.*

When $r = 2$ in the preceding theorem, the origin is a type of singularity called a **double point.** If two branches of the curve pass through the origin with distinct tangents there, the point is called a **node.** If the two branches have a common tangent at the origin, the point is called a **cusp,** or **tacnode,** according as the branches stop or pass through the origin. If no branch of the curve is continuous at the origin, the point is called an **isolated point.** This latter type of singularity always exists when the roots m_1 and m_2 of (5) are imaginary, and occasionally when $m_1 = m_2$. The various types of double points are shown in Figure 165.

Illustration 1. The origin is a node of the curve $x^2 - y^2 - x^3 = 0$, since the tangent lines $x^2 - y^2 = 0$, or $y = x$ and $y = -x$, are real and different.

Illustration 2. The origin is an isolated point of the curve $x^2 + y^2 - x^3 = 0$, since the tangent lines $x^2 + y^2 = 0$ are imaginary.

Illustration 3. The origin is a cusp of the curve $x^2 - 2xy + y^2 = y^3$, since (*a*) the equation $x^2 - 2xy + y^2 = 0$ gives one tangent line $y = x$, and (*b*) the original equation written in the form $y^3 = (x - y)^2$ shows that y can never be negative, that is, the branches of the curve, namely, $x = y \pm y^{3/2}$, stop at the origin.

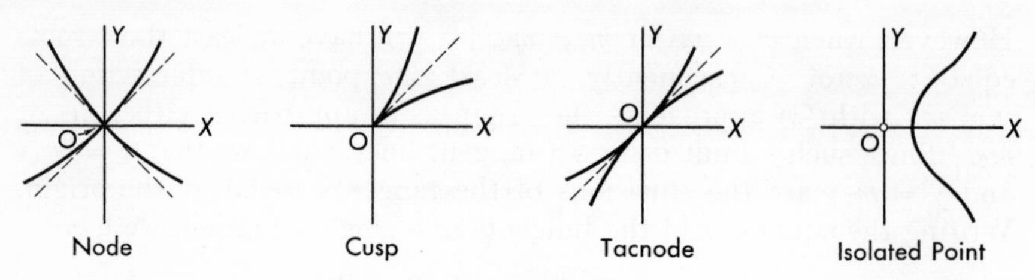

Figure 165

Illustration 4. The origin is a triple point of the curve $x^3 - xy^2 = y^4$. The tangents at the origin are given by $x^3 - xy^2 = 0$, or $x = 0$, $y = x$, and $y = -x$. Hence three branches of the curve pass through the origin.

EXERCISE 60

Classify the singular points of each of the following curves and find the slopes of any branches which are continuous at the point.

1. $y^2 = x^4 + 4x^2$. *Ans.* Node, ± 2.
2. $x^3 + y^3 = 3xy$.
3. $y^3 = x^4 + x^2$. Cusp, ∞.
4. $x^2 = y^5 + 9y^2$.
5. $xy^2 = x^2 + y^2$. Isolated point.
6. $y^4 + x^2 = 2x^2y^2$.
7. $x^4 = y^2(1 - x^2)$. Tacnode, 0.
8. $(x + y)^3 = x^2$.
9. $y^2 + x^4 = 2xy$. Node, 0, 2.
10. $(y - x)^2 = x^4(1 + x^2)$.
11. $y^2 - 2x^3 = xy^2$. Cusp, 0.
12. $x^2 - 2xy = y^3$.
13. $y^2 = x(4 - x)^2$. Node, ± 2.
14. $(y - 2)^2 = (x - 1)^3$.
15. $y^2 = x(x - 2)^3$. Cusp, 0.
16. $y^2 + x(x - 1)^2 = 0$.
17. Show that the curve $y^2 = x(x - 1)^2(x - 2)^4$ has a node at (1,0) and a tacnode at (2,0).
18. The curve $y(y - x)^2 = x^4$ has a triple point at the origin. Find the slopes of any branches which are continuous there.
19. Show that the limaçon $(x^2 + y^2 + bx)^2 = a^2(x^2 + y^2)$ has a node, cusp, or isolated point at the origin, according as $a < b$, $a = b \neq 0$, or $a > b$.
20. Show that the conchoid $(x - a)^2(x^2 + y^2) = b^2x^2$ has a node, cusp, or isolated point at the origin, according as $a < b$, $a = b \neq 0$, or $a > b$.

125. Summary of Curve Tracing

In summarizing the discussion of the preceding articles, we find it advisable when tracing a curve to consider some or all of the following properties.

1. *Extent.*
2. *Symmetry.*
3. *Intercepts.*
4. *Vertical and horizontal asymptotes.*
5. *Oblique asymptotes.*
6. *Singular points.*
7. *Critical points, points of inflection, and concavity.*

The above analysis, when necessary, should be supplemented by additional points of the curve.

Example 1. Trace the curve $y^2 = x^2 \dfrac{x+1}{x-1}$.

Solution: Proceeding with the above analysis we obtain the following results.

1. There are no points of the curve in the regions for which $-1 < x < 0$ and $0 < x < 1$, since y^2 is negative there.

2. The curve is symmetric with respect to the x axis.

3. The curve intersects the axes at $(-1,0)$ and $(0,0)$.

4. The line $x = 1$ is a vertical asymptote.

5. By the analysis in Article **123**, the curve has oblique asymptotes whose equations are $y = x + 1$ and $y = -x - 1$.

6. The origin is an isolated point. This fact follows from 1 and 3 as well as from the analysis in Article **124**.

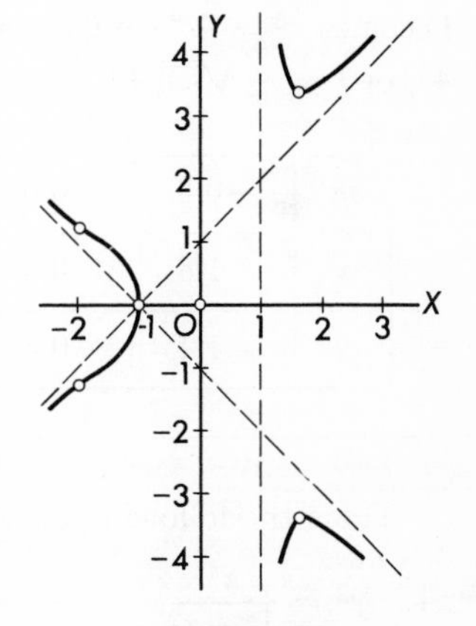

Figure 166

7. At any point on the upper branch of the curve, the first and second derivatives are

$$\frac{dy}{dx} = \frac{x^2 - x - 1}{(x-1)(x^2-1)^{1/2}}, \qquad \frac{d^2y}{dx^2} = \frac{x+2}{(x-1)(x^2-1)^{3/2}}.$$

Thus there is a minimum point at $x = \frac{1}{2} + \frac{1}{2}\sqrt{5} = 1.6$ and a point of inflection at $x = -2$. We also observe that y'' is positive when $x > 1$; hence the upper branch is concave upward in this region.

From the above analysis we obtain the curve shown in Figure 166.

Example 2. Trace the curve $y^2(2x - y) = x^4$.

Solution: In applying the above analysis to the given equation, we learn essentially nothing about the curve except that it has a triple point at the origin and that the slopes of the three branches there are 0, 0, and 2.

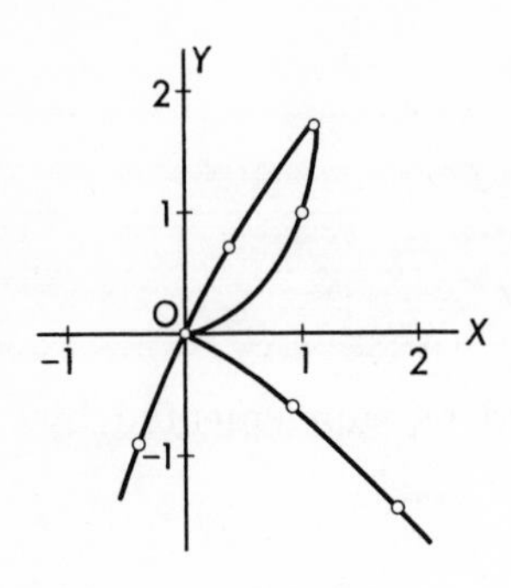

Figure 167

Additional points on the curve can be found in the following manner. As we learned in Article **124**, the line $y = mx$ cuts the given curve three times at the origin and once at a fourth point whose coordinates are given by

$$x = m^2(2 - m), \qquad y = mx = m^3(2 - m).$$

Assigning values to m, we obtain a table of corresponding values for m, x, and y. Plotting these points, we obtain the curve shown in Figure 167.

Note: An algebraic equation is sometimes easier to graph by changing to polar coordinates. For example, in polar coordinates, the equation $(x^2 + y^2)^3 = 4xy(x^2 - y^2)$ becomes $r^6 = 4r^2 \sin\theta \cos\theta(r^2 \cos^2\theta - r^2 \sin^2\theta) = 2r^4 \sin 2\theta \cos 2\theta = r^4 \sin 4\theta$, or $r = \pm\sqrt{\sin 4\theta}$.

m	-0.8	-0.6	0	1	1.5	1.9	2	2.1
x	1.8	0.9	0	1	1.1	0.4	0	-0.4
y	-1.4	-0.6	0	1	1.7	0.7	0	-0.9

EXERCISE 61

Trace the following curves.

1. $y^2 = \dfrac{x^4}{1 - x^2}$.
2. $y^2 = \dfrac{x^3}{x^2 - 1}$.
3. $x^3 + y^3 = 3xy$.
4. $x^3 + y^2 = 2xy$.
5. $y^2 = x^2 \dfrac{4 - x}{1 + x}$.
6. $y^2 = \dfrac{x^2}{x^2 - 1}$.
7. $y^3 = x^2(x + 3)$.
8. $x^4 + y^2 = 2xy$.
9. $y^2 = x(y^2 - x^2)$.
10. $2y^2 - xy = x^2 + x^3$.
11. $y^4 = x^4 + 4x^3$.
12. $x^4 + y^3 = 4x^2y$.
13. $y = xy^2 - 4x^3$.
14. $(x + y)^3 = 8xy$.
15. $x^2 + y^2 = x(y^2 - x^2)$.
16. $(x^2 + y^2)^2 = y^2 - x^2$.

CHAPTER 14

Integration Formulas

126. Introduction

In Chapter 4 indefinite integration was defined as an operation inverse to the operation of differentiation, and we discussed there the integration of powers of a variable. In this and subsequent chapters we shall apply the process of integration to other combinations of elementary functions.

In this connection it is to be noted that the integral of an elementary function cannot always be expressed in terms of elementary functions. As examples, we have the integrals

$$\int \sqrt{1 - x^4}\, dx, \qquad \int \sin x^2\, dx,$$

whose corresponding definite integrals will be discussed in Chapter 18.

For the present we shall consider only those integrals that can be expressed in terms of elementary functions.

127. Formulas of Integration

For reference purposes we have listed below certain standard integration formulas which are frequently used in elementary work. It is strongly advised that the formulas I_1–I_{20} be memorized.

I_1 $$\int du = u + C$$

I_2 $$\int a\, du = au + C, \quad a \text{ constant}$$

I_3 $$\int [f(u) + g(u)]\, du = \int f(u)\, du + \int g(u)\, du$$

I_4 $$\int u^n\, du = \frac{u^{n+1}}{n+1} + C, \quad n \neq -1$$

I_5 $$\int \frac{du}{u} = \ln u + C$$

I_6 $$\int a^u\,du = \frac{a^u}{\ln a} + C, \quad a > 0, a \neq 1$$

I_7 $$\int e^u\,du = e^u + C$$

I_8 $$\int \sin u\,du = -\cos u + C$$

I_9 $$\int \cos u\,du = \sin u + C$$

I_{10} $$\int \sec^2 u\,du = \tan u + C$$

I_{11} $$\int \csc^2 u\,du = -\cot u + C$$

I_{12} $$\int \sec u \tan u\,du = \sec u + C$$

I_{13} $$\int \csc u \cot u\,du = -\csc u + C$$

I_{14} $$\int \tan u\,du = \ln \sec u + C$$

I_{15} $$\int \cot u\,du = \ln \sin u + C$$

I_{16} $$\int \sec u\,du = \ln(\sec u + \tan u) + C$$

I_{17} $$\int \csc u\,du = \ln(\csc u - \cot u) + C$$

I_{18} $$\int \frac{du}{\sqrt{a^2 - u^2}} = \text{Sin}^{-1}\frac{u}{a} + C$$

I_{19} $$\int \frac{du}{a^2 + u^2} = \frac{1}{a}\text{Tan}^{-1}\frac{u}{a} + C$$

I_{20} $$\int \frac{du}{u\sqrt{u^2 - a^2}} = \frac{1}{a}\text{Sec}^{-1}\frac{u}{a} + C$$

I_{21} $$\int \frac{du}{\sqrt{u^2 \pm a^2}} = \ln\left(u + \sqrt{u^2 \pm a^2}\right) + C$$

I_{22} $$\int \frac{du}{a^2 - u^2} = \frac{1}{2a}\ln\frac{a + u}{a - u} + C, \quad u^2 < a^2$$

I'_{22} $$\int \frac{du}{u^2 - a^2} = \frac{1}{2a}\ln\frac{u - a}{u + a} + C, \quad u^2 > a^2$$

I_{23} $$\int \sqrt{a^2 - u^2}\,du = \frac{u}{2}\sqrt{a^2 - u^2} + \frac{a^2}{2}\,\text{Sin}^{-1}\frac{u}{a} + C$$

I_{24} $$\int \sqrt{u^2 \pm a^2}\,du = \frac{u}{2}\sqrt{u^2 \pm a^2} \pm \frac{a^2}{2}\ln\left(u + \sqrt{u^2 \pm a^2}\right) + C$$

Note: The validity of each of the above formulas can be established by showing that the derivative of the integral is equal to the integrand. For example, to prove I_5 we observe that $d(\ln u + C) = du/u$.

128. Integration of Powers

Any power of a function may be integrated by use of formulas I_4 and I_5 provided the integrand contains the exact differential of the function. An adjustment in the constant factor of the integrand is often necessary in order to obtain the exact differential. This can be done as indicated in the following illustrations.

Illustration 1. To evaluate $\int x(x^2 + 1)^2\,dx$, we consider $u = x^2 + 1$. Since $du = 2x\,dx$, by applying I_4 with $n = 2$ we obtain

$$\frac{1}{2}\int (x^2 + 1)^2(2x\,dx) = \frac{1}{2}\frac{(x^2 + 1)^3}{3} + C = \frac{1}{6}(x^2 + 1)^3 + C.$$

Observe that the integral $\int (x^2 + 1)^2\,dx$ cannot be evaluated in the above manner since the factor x in the differential $du = 2x\,dx$ is missing. The latter integral can, however, be evaluated as follows.

$$\int (x^2 + 1)^2\,dx = \int (x^4 + 2x^2 + 1)\,dx = \tfrac{1}{5}x^5 + \tfrac{2}{3}x^3 + x + C.$$

Illustration 2. To evaluate $\displaystyle\int \frac{e^{3x}\,dx}{5 + 2e^{3x}}$, we consider $u = 5 + 2e^{3x}$. Since $du = 6e^{3x}\,dx$, in applying I_5 we obtain

$$\int \frac{e^{3x}\,dx}{5 + 2e^{3x}} = \frac{1}{6}\int \frac{(6e^{3x}\,dx)}{5 + 2e^{3x}} = \frac{1}{6}\ln(5 + 2e^{3x}) + C.$$

The preceding illustrations indicate that it is often helpful when evaluating an integral to consider the integrand in terms of some function of the variable of integration. A change of variable can be made in accordance with the following theorem.

Theorem. *If the substitution $u = \phi(x)$ is such that $f(x)\,dx$ becomes $g(u)\,du$, and if an indefinite integral of $g(u)$ is known to be $G(u)$, then $G[\phi(x)]$ is an indefinite integral of $f(x)$.*

Proof: To prove the theorem, we need to show that

$$\frac{d}{dx}G[\phi(x)] = f(x).$$

By the chain rule of differentiation, this can be written as

$$G'[\phi(x)]\phi'(x) = f(x).$$

It is given, however, that $G'(u) = g(u)$ and $\phi'(x) = du/dx$; hence the preceding equation reduces to

$$g(u)\,du = f(x)\,dx,$$

which is one of the assumptions. Therefore, by reversing the steps in the argument, the theorem is proved.

Illustration 3. To evaluate $\int \frac{x^2\,dx}{\sqrt{x^3 - 1}}$, we make the substitution $u = x^3 - 1$. Since $du = 3x^2\,dx$, we obtain

$$\int \frac{x^2\,dx}{\sqrt{x^3 - 1}} = \int \frac{\frac{1}{3}\,du}{\sqrt{u}} = \frac{1}{3}\int u^{-1/2}\,du = \frac{1}{3}\cdot\frac{u^{1/2}}{\frac{1}{2}} = \frac{2}{3}\sqrt{x^3 - 1}.$$

Since the logarithms of negative numbers have not been defined, formula I_5 is meaningless when u is negative. In this case, however, by writing $u = -v$ we have $du = -dv$ and

$$\int \frac{du}{u} = \int \frac{-dv}{-v} = \int \frac{dv}{v} = \ln v + C = \ln(-u) + C.$$

Hence, when negative numbers are involved, formula I_5 should be considered in the form

$$I_5 \qquad \int \frac{du}{u} = \ln|u| + C.$$

Illustration 4. $\int_{-4}^{-2} \frac{dx}{x} = \Big[\ln|x|\Big]_{-4}^{-2} = \ln 2 - \ln 4 = -\ln 2.$

Example 1. Evaluate $\int_1^3 \frac{2x^2 + 5x + 1}{x + 2}\,dx.$

Solution: Dividing the numerator by the denominator, we obtain

$$\frac{2x^2 + 5x + 1}{x + 2} = 2x + 1 - \frac{1}{x + 2}.$$

Hence, by I_3, I_4, and I_5, we have

$$\begin{aligned}\int_1^3 \frac{2x^2 + 5x + 1}{x + 2}\,dx &= \int_1^3 \left(2x + 1 - \frac{1}{x + 2}\right) dx \\ &= \Big[x^2 + x - \ln(x + 2)\Big]_1^3 \\ &= [9 + 3 - \ln 5] - [1 + 1 - \ln 3] = 9.4892.\end{aligned}$$

Example 2. Find the area A between the curve $y = \sin^2 x \cos x$ and the x axis from $x = 0$ to $x = \frac{1}{2}\pi$.

Solution: Since $A = \int y\,dx$ by Article **40,** we have

$$A = \int_0^{\pi/2} \sin^2 x \cos x\,dx.$$

To evaluate this integral consider $u = \sin x$. Since $du = \cos x\,dx$, by use of I_4, we obtain

$$A = \int_0^{\pi/2} \sin^2 x\,(\cos x\,dx) = \left[\tfrac{1}{3}\sin^3 x\right]_0^{\pi/2} = \tfrac{1}{3}.$$

EXERCISE 62

Evaluate the following integrals.

1. $\int \sqrt{3x}\,dx.$ *Ans.* $\frac{2}{3}\sqrt{3}\,x^{3/2} + C.$
2. $\int \sqrt{3x + 1}\,dx.$
3. $\int x(x^2 - 2)^2\,dx.$ $\frac{1}{6}(x^2 - 2)^3 + C.$
4. $\int (x^2 - 2)^2\,dx.$
5. $\int \frac{dx}{5 - 2x}.$ $-\frac{1}{2}\ln(5 - 2x) + C.$
6. $\int \frac{dx}{(5 - 2x)^2}.$
7. $\int \frac{\sqrt{x}\,dx}{1 + x\sqrt{x}}.$ $\frac{2}{3}\ln(1 + x^{3/2}) + C.$
8. $\int \frac{y^{1/3}\,dy}{(y^{4/3} + 9)^2}.$
9. $\int \left(1 - \frac{1}{z}\right)^2 dz.$ $z - \frac{1}{z} - 2\ln z + C.$
10. $\int \left(1 - \frac{1}{z}\right)^2 \frac{dz}{z^2}.$
11. $\int \cos^3\theta \sin\theta\,d\theta.$ $-\frac{1}{4}\cos^4\theta + C.$
12. $\int \frac{\cos 2x\,dx}{1 + \sin 2x}.$
13. $\int \frac{e^t\,dt}{\sqrt{1 - e^t}}.$ *Ans.* $-2\sqrt{1 - e^t} + C.$
14. $\int (1 + 2e^{3x})^3 e^{3x}\,dx.$
15. $\int \frac{y + 4}{y - 4}\,dy.$ $y + 8\ln(y - 4) + C.$
16. $\int \frac{(x - 1)^3}{x^2}\,dx.$
17. $\int \frac{\sec^2\theta}{\tan\theta}\,d\theta.$ $\ln\tan\theta + C.$
18. $\int \tan\frac{1}{2}x \sec^2\frac{1}{2}x\,dx.$
19. $\int \frac{x^3 + 3x}{x^2 + 1}\,dx.$ $\frac{x^2}{2} + \ln(x^2 + 1) + C.$
20. $\int \frac{x^3 + 1}{x - 1}\,dx.$
21. $\int \frac{\ln x}{x}\,dx.$ $\frac{1}{2}(\ln x)^2 + C.$
22. $\int \frac{dx}{x \ln x}.$
23. $\int \frac{1 + \cos y}{y + \sin y}\,dy.$ $\ln(y + \sin y) + C.$
24. $\int \frac{x + e^{2x}}{x^2 + e^{2x}}\,dx.$
25. $\int_{-1/2}^{1/2} (2y + 1)^7\,dy.$ 16.
26. $\int_8^{10} (\frac{1}{4}x - 1)^{-3}\,dx.$

27. $\displaystyle\int_{-3}^{-2} \frac{y+2}{y^2+4y}\,dy.$ *Ans.* $\frac{1}{2}\ln\frac{4}{3}$.

28. $\displaystyle\int_0^1 x^2\sqrt[3]{1+x^3}\,dx.$

29. $\displaystyle\int_3^5 \frac{(x+2)^2}{x-2}\,dx.$ 37.58.

30. $\displaystyle\int_{-1/3}^0 \frac{2z+3}{3z+2}\,dz.$

31. $\displaystyle\int_0^{\pi/2} \sqrt{\sin x}\cos x\,dx.$ $\frac{2}{3}$.

32. $\displaystyle\int_0^1 \frac{\cos\theta\,d\theta}{\sqrt{1+\sin\theta}}.$

33. $\displaystyle\int_0^1 \frac{\operatorname{Tan}^{-1}x}{1+x^2}\,dx.$ $\pi^2/32$.

34. $\displaystyle\int_1^2 \frac{x-x^{-3}}{x^2+x^{-2}}\,dx.$

35. Evaluate $\displaystyle\int_{-1}^1 |2x-1|\,dx.$ *Ans.* 5/2.

36. If $f(x) = x$ for $x < 1$ and $(x-1)$ for $x \geqq 1$, evaluate $\displaystyle\int_0^2 x^2 f(x)\,dx.$

In each of the following, find the area bounded by the given curves.

37. $y = \dfrac{2}{x-3}$, $y = 0$, $x = 4$, $x = 5$. *Ans.* ln 4.

38. $y = \dfrac{4x}{x^2+5}$, $y = 0$, $x = 1$, $x = 4$.

39. $y = \dfrac{4}{\sqrt{1-2x}}$, $y = 0$, $x = -4$, $x = 0$. 8.

40. $y = \dfrac{e^x}{1+e^x}$, $y = \dfrac{3}{4}$, $x = 0$.

41. $y = \dfrac{x^2+1}{x+1}$, $x + 3y = 7$. $\frac{1}{6}(35 - 12\ln 6)$.

42. $y = \dfrac{x^3}{x+2}$, $y = x^2 - x$.

In each of the following, find the volume generated if the area bounded by the given curves is revolved about the x axis. (Article **47**.)

43. $y = 1 - \dfrac{3}{x}$, $y = 0$, $x = 1$. *Ans.* $(8 - 6\ln 3)\pi$.

44. $y = \dfrac{3x}{\sqrt{x+4}}$, $y = 0$, $x = 4$.

45. $y = \tan x \sec x$, $y = 0$, $x = \frac{1}{4}\pi$. $\frac{1}{3}\pi$.

46. If $a > 0$ and $b > 0$, show that $\displaystyle\int_1^a \frac{du}{u} + \int_1^b \frac{du}{u} = \int_1^{ab} \frac{du}{u}.$

47. If $0 < x < 1$, show that $\frac{1}{4}x^2 < x - \ln(1+x) < \frac{1}{2}x^2$. *Hint:* Show that $\frac{1}{2}x < f'(x) < x$, where $f(x) = x - \ln(1+x)$.

129. Integration of Exponential Functions

Integrating the differential relations $\boldsymbol{D}_{24}$ and $\boldsymbol{D}_{25}$, Article **91,** we obtain the exponential integration formulas

$$\boldsymbol{I}_6 \qquad \int a^u\,du = \frac{a^u}{\ln a} + C, \quad a > 0, a \neq 1,$$

$$\boldsymbol{I}_7 \qquad \int e^u\,du = e^u + C.$$

Illustration 1. $\displaystyle\int 5^{3x}\,dx = \frac{1}{3}\int 5^{3x}\,d(3x) = \frac{5^{3x}}{3\ln 5} + C.$

Illustration 2. $\displaystyle\int xe^{x^2}\,dx = \tfrac{1}{2}\int e^{x^2}\,d(x^2) = \tfrac{1}{2}\,e^{x^2} + C.$

Note: Observe that the integral $\int e^{x^2}\,dx$ cannot be evaluated by $\boldsymbol{I}_7$.

Illustration 3. $\displaystyle\int \frac{dx}{1 - e^{-x}} = \int \frac{e^x\,dx}{e^x - 1} = \int \frac{d(e^x - 1)}{e^x - 1} = \ln(e^x - 1) + C.$

Example. Find the volume generated if the area bounded by the curves $y = e^{-x}$, $y = 0$, $x = 0$, $x = 1$ is revolved about the x axis.

Solution: Since $V = \pi \int y^2\,dx$, Article **47**, we have

$$V = \pi \int_0^1 e^{-2x}\,dx = -\tfrac{1}{2}\pi \int_{x=0}^{x=1} e^{-2x}\,d(-2x)$$
$$= -\tfrac{1}{2}\pi\Big[e^{-2x}\Big]_0^1 = \tfrac{1}{2}\pi(1 - e^{-2}).$$

EXERCISE 63

Evaluate the following integrals.

1. $\int e^{4x}\,dx.$ *Ans.* $\frac{1}{4}e^{4x} + C.$
2. $\int e^{-x/2}\,dx.$
3. $\int 3^{2y}\,dy.$ $3^{2y}/\ln 9 + C.$
4. $\int \sqrt{10^{3x}}\,dx.$
5. $\int x^{-2}e^{1/x}\,dx.$ $-e^{1/x} + C.$
6. $\int t^3e^{t^4}\,dt.$
7. $\int e^{\sin\theta}\cos\theta\,d\theta.$ $e^{\sin\theta} + C.$
8. $\int 3^xe^x\,dx.$
9. $\displaystyle\int \frac{2 + e^x}{e^x}\,dx.$ $x - 2e^{-x} + C.$
10. $\int e^z\sqrt{1 + e^z}\,dz.$
11. $\displaystyle\int_1^4 \frac{e^{\sqrt{x}}\,dx}{\sqrt{x}}.$ 9.342.
12. $\int_{-1}^1 x^2e^{x^3}\,dx.$

13. $\int_0^1 (e^x + x^e)\,dx.$ *Ans.* 1.987.

14. $\int_{\pi/4}^{\pi/2} e^{\cot\theta}\csc^2\theta\,d\theta.$

15. $\int_0^1 (e^x + e^{-x})^2\,dx.$ 5.627.

16. $\int_0^a (e^{x/a} - e^{-x/a})dx.$

17. $\int_0^{\pi/3} \frac{\sec\theta\tan\theta}{\sqrt{e^{\sec\theta}}}\,d\theta.$ 0.477.

18. $\int_1^2 (2 - e^{-t})^2\,dt.$

19. $\int_{-1}^0 \frac{dy}{1 + e^y}.$ 0.620.

20. $\int_{-1}^1 \frac{e^{2x}}{1 + e^x}\,dx.$

21. Find the area between the curve $y = 2^x$ and the chord joining the points (0,1) and (2,4). *Ans.* $5 - 3/\ln 2$.

22. Find the area in the first quadrant bounded by the curve $y = xe^{-x^2}$, its maximum ordinate, and the x axis.

23. Find the volume generated if the area bounded by the curves $y = e^{-x^2}$, $y = 0$, $x = 0$, $x = 1$ is revolved about the y axis. *Hint:* Use $dV = 2\pi xy\,dx$. *Ans.* $\pi(1 - e^{-1})$.

24. Find the volume generated if the area bounded by the curves $y = e^x - e^{-x}$, $y = 0$, $x = 1$ is revolved about the x axis.

25. Use the definition of a definite integral to find, as $n \to \infty$, the limit of $(1 + \sqrt[n]{e} + \sqrt[n]{e^2} + \cdots + \sqrt[n]{e^{n-1}})/n$. See page 104. *Ans.* $e - 1$.

130. Integration of Trigonometric Functions

The six integration formulas $\boldsymbol{I}_8$–$\boldsymbol{I}_{13}$ are derived directly from the corresponding differentiation formulas $\boldsymbol{D}_{10}$–$\boldsymbol{D}_{15}$, Article **86.**

Formula $\boldsymbol{I}_{14}$ can be proved directly as follows.

$$\int \tan u\,du = \int \frac{\sec u \tan u}{\sec u}\,du = \int \frac{d\,(\sec u)}{\sec u} = \ln \sec u + C.$$

Note: The above result may be written in the form $-\ln\cos u + C$, since

$$\ln \sec u = \ln \frac{1}{\cos u} = -\ln \cos u.$$

Formula $\boldsymbol{I}_{16}$ can be proved directly as follows.

$$\int \sec u\,du = \int \frac{\sec^2 u + \sec u \tan u}{\sec u + \tan u}\,du$$

$$= \int \frac{d(\sec u + \tan u)}{\sec u + \tan u}$$

$$= \ln(\sec u + \tan u) + C.$$

Formulas $\boldsymbol{I}_{15}$ and $\boldsymbol{I}_{17}$ can be derived in a similar manner.

Illustration. (a) $\int \sin \frac{1}{2}x\, dx = 2 \int \sin \frac{1}{2}x\, d(\frac{1}{2}x) = -2 \cos \frac{1}{2}x + C,$

(b) $\int e^x \cot e^x\, dx = \int \cot e^x\, d(e^x) = \ln \sin e^x + C,$

(c) $\int \tan^2 \theta\, d\theta = \int (\sec^2 \theta - 1)\, d\theta = \tan \theta - \theta + C.$

131. Transformations of Trigonometric Integrals

Products of the form $\sin au \sin bu$, $\sin au \cos bu$, and $\cos au \cos bu$, where a and b are constants, can be integrated by use of the transformations

$$\sin A \sin B = \tfrac{1}{2} \cos (A - B) - \tfrac{1}{2} \cos (A + B),$$
$$\sin A \cos B = \tfrac{1}{2} \sin (A - B) + \tfrac{1}{2} \sin (A + B),$$
$$\cos A \cos B = \tfrac{1}{2} \cos (A - B) + \tfrac{1}{2} \cos (A + B),$$

and formulas $\boldsymbol{I}_8$ and $\boldsymbol{I}_9$.

Illustration 1. $\int \cos 5x \cos 3x\, dx = \frac{1}{2} \int (\cos 2x + \cos 8x)\, dx$

$= \frac{1}{4} \sin 2x + \frac{1}{16} \sin 8x + C.$

A product of the form $\sin^m u \cos^n u$, where either m or n is a positive odd integer, can be integrated by use of the trigonometric identities

$$\sin^2 u = 1 - \cos^2 u, \qquad \cos^2 u = 1 - \sin^2 u,$$

and formulas $\boldsymbol{I}_8$ and $\boldsymbol{I}_9$.

Illustration 2. $\int \sin^2 x \cos^3 x\, dx = \int \sin^2 x \cos^2 x\, (\cos x\, dx)$

$= \int \sin^2 x(1 - \sin^2 x)\, d(\sin x)$

$= \frac{1}{3} \sin^3 x - \frac{1}{5} \sin^5 x + C.$

A product of the form $\sin^m u \cos^n u$, where m and n are both positive even integers, can be integrated by use of the trigonometric identities

$$\sin^2 u = \tfrac{1}{2} - \tfrac{1}{2} \cos 2u, \qquad \cos^2 u = \tfrac{1}{2} + \tfrac{1}{2} \cos 2u,$$
$$\sin u \cos u = \tfrac{1}{2} \sin 2u,$$

and formulas $\boldsymbol{I}_8$ and $\boldsymbol{I}_9$.

Illustration 3. $\int \sin^2 3x \cos^2 3x\, dx = \frac{1}{4} \int \sin^2 6x\, dx$

$= \frac{1}{8} \int (1 - \cos 12x)\, dx$

$= \frac{1}{8}x - \frac{1}{96} \sin 12x + C.$

A power of the form $\tan^n u$ or $\cot^n u$, where n is a positive integer, can be integrated by use of the trigonometric identities

$$\tan^2 u = \sec^2 u - 1, \qquad \cot^2 u = \csc^2 u - 1,$$

and formulas $\boldsymbol{I}_{10}$, $\boldsymbol{I}_{11}$, $\boldsymbol{I}_{14}$, and $\boldsymbol{I}_{15}$.

Illustration 4. (*a*)
$$\int \tan^3 x\, dx = \int \tan x\,(\sec^2 x - 1)\, dx$$
$$= \tfrac{1}{2}\tan^2 x - \ln \sec x + C,$$

(*b*)
$$\int \tan^4 x\, dx = \int \tan^2 x\,(\sec^2 x - 1)\, dx$$
$$= \int (\tan^2 x \sec^2 x - \sec^2 x + 1)\, dx$$
$$= \tfrac{1}{3}\tan^3 x - \tan x + x + C.$$

A power of the form $\sec^n u$ or $\csc^n u$, where n (>2) is a positive even integer, can be integrated by use of the trigonometric identities

$$\sec^2 u = 1 + \tan^2 u, \qquad \csc^2 u = 1 + \cot^2 u,$$

and formulas $\boldsymbol{I}_{10}$ and $\boldsymbol{I}_{11}$.

Illustration 5.
$$\int \sec^4 x\, dx = \int (1 + \tan^2 x)(\sec^2 x\, dx)$$
$$= \tan x + \tfrac{1}{3}\tan^3 x + C.$$

Note 1: The case in which n is a positive odd integer is discussed in Article **136**.

A product of the form $\tan^m u \sec^n u$, where m and n are positive integers, can be integrated (*a*) as indicated in Illustration 5 when n is even, (*b*) as indicated in Illustration 6 when m is odd, and (*c*) as indicated in Article **136** when m is even and n is odd.

Illustration 6.
$$\int \tan^3 x \sec^3 x\, dx = \int \tan^2 x \sec^2 x\,(\sec x \tan x\, dx)$$
$$= \int (\sec^2 x - 1)\sec^2 x\, d(\sec x)$$
$$= \tfrac{1}{5}\sec^5 x - \tfrac{1}{3}\sec^3 x + C.$$

Note 2: Observe that the methods used in the above illustrations are sometimes applicable even though the exponents are not integers. For example,

$$\int \sin^{1/2} x \cos x\, dx = \int \sin^{1/2} x\, d(\sin x) = \tfrac{2}{3}\sin^{3/2} x + C.$$

Example. Evaluate $\int_0^{\pi/4} \frac{d\theta}{1 - \sin\theta}$.

Solution: Multiplying numerator and denominator by $1 + \sin\theta$, we obtain

$$\int_0^{\pi/4} \frac{d\theta}{1 - \sin\theta} = \int_0^{\pi/4} \frac{1 + \sin\theta}{\cos^2\theta}\, d\theta$$

$$= \int_0^{\pi/4} (\sec^2\theta + \sec\theta\tan\theta)\, d\theta$$

$$= \Big[\tan\theta + \sec\theta\Big]_0^{\pi/4} = \sqrt{2}.$$

EXERCISE 64

Evaluate the following integrals.

1. $\int \cos \frac{3}{2}x\, dx$. *Ans.* $\frac{2}{3}\sin\frac{3}{2}x + C$.
2. $\int \csc^2 (2 - 3x)\, dx$.
3. $\int \frac{1}{x^2}\sin\frac{\pi}{x}\, dx$. $\frac{1}{\pi}\cos\frac{\pi}{x} + C$.
4. $\int \frac{dt}{\cos^2 t}$.
5. $\int \sec 4\theta \tan 4\theta\, d\theta$. $\frac{1}{4}\sec 4\theta + C$.
6. $\int \csc 2y\, dy$.
7. $\int \cot \frac{1}{2}x\, dx$. $2 \ln \sin \frac{1}{2}x + C$.
8. $\int z \tan z^2\, dz$.
9. $\int \sin^3 x \cos^3 x\, dx$. $\frac{1}{4}\sin^4 x - \frac{1}{6}\sin^6 x + C$.
10. $\int \cos^3 3x\, dx$.
11. $\int \cos^2 \frac{1}{2}y\, dy$. $\frac{1}{2}y + \frac{1}{2}\sin y + C$.
12. $\int \sin^4 2x\, dx$.
13. $\int \sec^n \theta \tan\theta\, d\theta$. $\frac{1}{n}\sec^n\theta + C$.
14. $\int \sqrt{\tan x}\, \sec^4 x\, dx$.
15. $\int \tan^2 \frac{3}{4}x\, dx$. $\frac{4}{3}\tan\frac{3}{4}x - x + C$.
16. $\int (\sin x + \cos x)^2\, dx$.
17. $\int \sin 3x \cos 5x\, dx$. *Ans.* $\frac{1}{4}\cos 2x - \frac{1}{16}\cos 8x + C$.
18. $\int \sin 2z \sin 3z\, dz$.
19. $\int \csc^4 \frac{3}{2}\theta\, d\theta$. $-\frac{2}{3}\cot\frac{3}{2}\theta - \frac{2}{9}\cot^3\frac{3}{2}\theta + C$.
20. $\int \cot^3 2\theta\, d\theta$.
21. $\int \tan^4 \frac{1}{2}x\, dx$. $x - 2\tan\frac{1}{2}x + \frac{2}{3}\tan^3\frac{1}{2}x + C$.

22. $\int (\sec\theta - \tan\theta)^2\, d\theta.$

23. $\int \frac{dx}{1+\cos x}.$ *Ans.* $\csc x - \cot x + C.$

24. $\int \frac{\cos(\tan\theta)}{\cos^2\theta}\, d\theta.$

25. $\int \sqrt{1+\cos\theta}\, d\theta.$ $\pm 2\sqrt{1-\cos\theta} + C,\ 0 \leqq \theta \leqq \pi,\ \pi \leqq \theta \leqq 2\pi.$

26. $\int \frac{\cos 2x}{\cos x}\, dx.$

27. $\int \frac{\sin x}{1+\sin x}\, dx.$ $x + \sec x - \tan x + C.$

28. $\int \frac{dx}{(1-\sin x)^2}.$

29. $\int_0^{\pi/2} \sin^3\theta\, d\theta.$ *Ans.* $\frac{2}{3}.$

30. $\int_0^{\pi/4} \cos x \cos 3x\, dx.$

31. $\int_{-\pi/4}^{\pi/4} \sec^6 t\, dt.$ $\frac{56}{15}.$

32. $\int_0^{\pi/2} \sin^2 x \sin 2x\, dx.$

33. $\int_{\pi/6}^{\pi/2} \frac{\sin 2x}{\sin x}\, dx.$ $1.$

34. $\int_0^{\pi/4} \frac{\cos x - \sin x}{\cos x + \sin x}\, dx.$

35. $\int_0^{\pi} \frac{\cos^2 x}{1-\sin x}\, dx.$ $\pi + 2.$

36. $\int_0^{\pi/3} \sin x \sin 2x \sin 3x\, dx.$

37. Find the area between the x axis and one arch of the sine curve $y = \sin x$. *Ans.* 2.

38. Find the area bounded by the curves $y = \sin x$ and $y = \cos x$ between consecutive points of intersection.

39. Find the volume generated if the area of Problem 37 is revolved about the x axis. *Ans.* $\frac{1}{2}\pi^2.$

40. Find the centroid of the area given in Problem 37. (Article **49**.)

41. Find the moment of inertia of the area in Problem 37 with respect to the x axis. *Hint:* Use $dI = \frac{1}{3}y^3\, dx.$ *Ans.* $\frac{4}{9}.$

42. Find the moment of inertia of the volume in Problem 39 with respect to the x axis. *Hint:* Use $dI = \frac{1}{2}\pi y^4\, dx.$

43. Find the area between the x axis and one arch of the cycloid $x = a(\theta - \sin\theta),\ y = a(1-\cos\theta).$ *Ans.* $3\pi a^2.$

44. Find the volume generated if the area of Problem 43 is revolved about the x axis.

45. If n is an integer greater than one, show that

$$\int \tan^n u\, du = \frac{\tan^{n-1} u}{n-1} - \int \tan^{n-2} u\, du.$$

46. Determine constants A and B so that

$$\frac{a \sin \theta + b \cos \theta}{c \sin \theta + d \cos \theta} \equiv A + B \frac{c \cos \theta - d \sin \theta}{c \sin \theta + d \cos \theta},$$

and obtain a formula for the integral

$$\int \frac{a \sin \theta + b \cos \theta}{c \sin \theta + d \cos \theta}\, d\theta.$$

132. Integrals Giving Inverse Trigonometric Functions

The integration formulas

$$I_{18} \qquad \int \frac{du}{\sqrt{a^2 - u^2}} = \mathrm{Sin}^{-1} \frac{u}{a} + C,$$

$$I_{19} \qquad \int \frac{du}{a^2 + u^2} = \frac{1}{a} \mathrm{Tan}^{-1} \frac{u}{a} + C,$$

$$I_{20} \qquad \int \frac{du}{u\sqrt{u^2 - a^2}} = \frac{1}{a} \mathrm{Sec}^{-1} \frac{u}{a} + C,$$

are easily verified by differentiating the right hand members; thus, for example,

$$d\left(\frac{1}{a} \mathrm{Tan}^{-1} \frac{u}{a} + C\right) = \frac{1}{a} \frac{d(u/a)}{1 + (u/a)^2} = \frac{du}{a^2 + u^2}.$$

Illustration 1. $\displaystyle\int \frac{dx}{x\sqrt{4x^2 - 9}} = \int \frac{d(2x)}{(2x)\sqrt{(2x)^2 - 3^2}} = \frac{1}{3} \mathrm{Sec}^{-1} \frac{2x}{3} + C.$

Note 1: Since the use of the differentiation formulas is limited to the principal branches of the curves, the inverse trigonometric functions occurring in the above formulas must be given their principal values as listed in Article **87**.

Illustration 2.

$$\int_{-1}^{1} \frac{dx}{\sqrt{4 - x^2}} = \left[\mathrm{Sin}^{-1} \frac{x}{2}\right]_{-1}^{1}$$
$$= \mathrm{Sin}^{-1} (\tfrac{1}{2}) - \mathrm{Sin}^{-1} (-\tfrac{1}{2})$$
$$= (\tfrac{1}{6}\pi) - (-\tfrac{1}{6}\pi) = \tfrac{1}{3}\pi.$$

Example 1. Evaluate $\displaystyle\int \frac{dx}{2x^2 + 2x + 3}$.

Solution: This integral can be written in the form I_{19} by completing the square in the x terms of the denominator; thus

$$\int \frac{dx}{2x^2 + 2x + 3} = \frac{1}{2} \int \frac{dx}{(x^2 + x + \frac{1}{4}) + \frac{5}{4}} = \frac{1}{2} \int \frac{d(x + \frac{1}{2})}{(x + \frac{1}{2})^2 + (\frac{1}{2}\sqrt{5})^2}$$
$$= \frac{1}{2} \cdot \frac{2}{\sqrt{5}} \mathrm{Tan}^{-1} \frac{x + \frac{1}{2}}{\frac{1}{2}\sqrt{5}} + C = \frac{1}{\sqrt{5}} \mathrm{Tan}^{-1} \frac{2x + 1}{\sqrt{5}} + C.$$

Example 2. Evaluate $\int \frac{(3x - 1)\,dx}{2x^2 + 2x + 3}$.

Solution: Since $d(2x^2 + 2x + 3) = (4x + 2)\,dx$, and $3x - 1 \equiv \frac{3}{4}(4x + 2) - \frac{5}{2}$, the given integral can be written in the form

$$\frac{3}{4}\int \frac{(4x + 2)\,dx}{2x^2 + 2x + 3} - \frac{5}{2}\int \frac{dx}{2x^2 + 2x + 3}.$$

The first integral is $\frac{3}{4} \ln (2x^2 + 2x + 3)$ by I_5, and the second integral is evaluated as in Example 1. Hence the complete integral is

$$\frac{3}{4} \ln (2x^2 + 2x + 3) - \frac{\sqrt{5}}{2} \operatorname{Tan}^{-1} \frac{2x + 1}{\sqrt{5}} + C.$$

Note 2: To express $3x - 1$ as a function of $4x + 2$, we find the coefficients by division; thus

$$\begin{array}{r|l} & \frac{3}{4} \\ 4x + 2 & 3x - 1 \\ & \underline{3x + \frac{3}{2}} \\ & \quad - \frac{5}{2} \end{array}$$

EXERCISE 65

Evaluate the following integrals.

1. $\int \frac{dx}{\sqrt{9 - x^2}}$. *Ans.* $\operatorname{Sin}^{-1} \frac{x}{3} + C$.
2. $\int \frac{dx}{4 + x^2}$.
3. $\int \frac{dx}{x\sqrt{x^2 - 16}}$. $\frac{1}{4} \operatorname{Sec}^{-1} \frac{x}{4} + C$.
4. $\int \frac{dt}{\sqrt{16 - 9t^2}}$.
5. $\int \frac{dy}{25 + 9y^2}$. $\frac{1}{15} \operatorname{Tan}^{-1} \frac{3y}{5} + C$.
6. $\int \frac{dx}{x\sqrt{9x^2 - 4}}$.
7. $\int \frac{x\,dx}{\sqrt{4 - x^2}}$. $-\sqrt{4 - x^2} + C$.
8. $\int \frac{z\,dz}{9 + 4z^2}$.
9. $\int \frac{y\,dy}{\sqrt{16 - 9y^4}}$. $\frac{1}{6} \operatorname{Sin}^{-1} \frac{3y^2}{4} + C$.
10. $\int \frac{x\,dx}{25 + 16x^4}$.
11. $\int \frac{e^x\,dx}{\sqrt{1 - e^{2x}}}$. $\operatorname{Sin}^{-1} e^x + C$.
12. $\int \frac{dx}{\sqrt{e^{2x} - 1}}$.
13. $\int \frac{dy}{(1 + y)\sqrt{y}}$. $2 \operatorname{Tan}^{-1}\sqrt{y} + C$.
14. $\int \frac{\sec^2 \theta\, d\theta}{\sqrt{1 - \tan^2 \theta}}$.
15. $\int \frac{dx}{\sqrt{2x - x^2}}$. $\operatorname{Sin}^{-1} (x - 1) + C$.
16. $\int \frac{dx}{x^2 + 4x + 5}$.
17. $\int \frac{dt}{t^2 - t + 2}$. *Ans.* $\frac{2}{\sqrt{7}} \operatorname{Tan}^{-1} \frac{2t - 1}{\sqrt{7}} + C$.
18. $\int \frac{dx}{\sqrt{8 + 6x - 9x^2}}$.

19. $\int \frac{x\,dx}{\sqrt{3 - 2x - x^2}}$. *Ans.* $-\sqrt{3 - 2x - x^2} - \text{Sin}^{-1} \frac{1}{2}(x + 1) + C$.

20. $\int \frac{(2z - 1)\,dz}{2z^2 - 6z + 5}$.

21. $\int_{-4}^{4} \frac{dy}{16 + y^2}$. *Ans.* $\frac{1}{8}\pi$.

22. $\int_{0}^{1/2} \frac{(1 - x)\,dx}{\sqrt{1 - x^2}}$.

23. $\int_{0}^{1} \frac{x + 1}{x^2 + 1}\,dx$. $\frac{1}{4}\pi + \frac{1}{2}\ln 2$.

24. $\int_{1}^{2} \frac{dx}{(x + 1)\sqrt{2x(x + 2)}}$.

25. $\int_{1}^{e} \frac{dz}{z(1 + \ln^2 z)}$. $\frac{1}{4}\pi$.

26. $\int_{0}^{1} \frac{dx}{e^x + e^{-x}}$.

27. $\int_{2}^{4} \frac{dy}{y\sqrt{y - 1}}$. $\frac{1}{6}\pi$.

28. $\int_{-3}^{1} \frac{(2x + 1)\,dx}{\sqrt{15 - 2x - x^2}}$.

29. Find the first-quadrant area bounded by the curves $y = 20/(4 + x^2)$, $y = 1$, and $x = 0$. *Ans.* 7.07.

30. Find the area between the curves $y(9 + x^2) = 17$ and $y(1 + x^2) = 13$.

31. Find the area between the parabola $x^2 = 4ay$ and the witch $y(x^2 + 4a^2) = 8a^3$. *Ans.* $\frac{2}{3}(3\pi - 2)a^2$.

32. Find the area bounded by the curve $y(x^2 + a^2) = a^2(a - x)$ and the coordinate axes.

33. Find the volume generated by revolving about the x axis the first-quadrant area bounded by the curves $y^2(x^2 + 1) = 4 - x$, $y = 0$, and $x = 0$. *Ans.* 12.2.

34. Find the volume generated by revolving the area bounded by the curves $y^2(e^x + e^{-x}) = 1$, $y = 0$, $x = 0$, and $x = 1$ about the x axis.

35. Find the x coordinate of the centroid of the area given in Problem 29. *Ans.* 1.14.

36. Show that $\int_0^x \frac{dt}{\sqrt{1 - t^3}} < \text{Sin}^{-1} x$, for $0 < x < 1$. *Hint:* For $0 < t < 1$, show that $1/\sqrt{1 - t^3} < 1/\sqrt{1 - t^2}$; and then integrate.

133. Additional Formulas of Integration

The integrals of certain elementary forms of the quadratic expressions $u^2 \pm a^2$ and $a^2 - u^2$ are given in formulas I_{21}–I_{24}. The validity of each of these formulas can be verified by differentiation. Thus for I_{21} we have

$$d[\ln (u + \sqrt{u^2 \pm a^2}) + C] = \frac{d(u + \sqrt{u^2 \pm a^2})}{u + \sqrt{u^2 \pm a^2}}$$

$$= \frac{1}{u + \sqrt{u^2 \pm a^2}}\left[du + \frac{u\,du}{\sqrt{u^2 \pm a^2}}\right]$$

$$= \frac{du}{\sqrt{u^2 \pm a^2}}.$$

Note: Using methods which are discussed in the next chapter, the above formulas can be derived by integration processes.

Illustration. (*a*) $\int \frac{dx}{4 - x^2} = \int \frac{dx}{2^2 - x^2} = \frac{1}{4} \ln \frac{2 + x}{2 - x} + C.$

(*b*) $\int \frac{dx}{\sqrt{9x^2 + 25}} = \frac{1}{3} \int \frac{d(3x)}{\sqrt{(3x)^2 + 5^2}} = \frac{1}{3} \ln (3x + \sqrt{9x^2 + 25}) + C.$

If an integral involves a quadratic of the form $au^2 + bu + c$, the latter can be reduced to one of the above forms by completing the square.

Example 1. Evaluate $\int \sqrt{2x - x^2}\, dx.$

Solution: Writing $2x - x^2$ in the form $1 - (x^2 - 2x + 1)$, by use of I_{23} we obtain

$$\int \sqrt{2x - x^2}\, dx = \int \sqrt{1 - (x - 1)^2}\, d(x - 1)$$

$$= \tfrac{1}{2}(x - 1)\sqrt{2x - x^2} + \tfrac{1}{2} \operatorname{Sin}^{-1} (x - 1) + C.$$

Example 2. Find the area of the ellipse $\frac{x^2}{a^2} + \frac{y^2}{b^2} = 1.$

Solution: It is evident from the symmetry of the curve that one-fourth of the required area is located in the first quadrant. Hence, if A is the total area of the ellipse, by using I_{23} we obtain

$$A = 4 \int_0^a y\, dx = 4 \int_0^a \frac{b}{a} \sqrt{a^2 - x^2}\, dx$$

$$= \frac{2b}{a} \left[x\sqrt{a^2 - x^2} + a^2 \operatorname{Sin}^{-1} \frac{x}{a} \right]_0^a = \pi ab.$$

EXERCISE 66

Evaluate the following integrals.

1. $\int \frac{dx}{\sqrt{x^2 - 4}}$. *Ans.* $\ln (x + \sqrt{x^2 - 4}) + C.$
2. $\int \frac{dy}{y^2 - 4}$.
3. $\int \frac{dz}{9 - 4z^2}$. $\frac{1}{12} \ln \frac{3 + 2z}{3 - 2z} + C.$
4. $\int \frac{dx}{\sqrt{4x^2 + 9}}$.
5. $\int \frac{x\, dx}{\sqrt{9x^2 - 1}}$. $\frac{1}{9}\sqrt{9x^2 - 1} + C.$
6. $\int \frac{x\, dx}{\sqrt{9x^4 - 1}}$.
7. $\int \frac{e^x\, dx}{1 - e^{2x}}$. $\frac{1}{2} \ln \frac{1 + e^x}{1 - e^x} + C.$
8. $\int \frac{\cos \theta\, d\theta}{\sqrt{1 + \sin^2 \theta}}$.

9. $\int \frac{dz}{15 + 2z - z^2}$. *Ans.* $\frac{1}{8} \ln \frac{3 + z}{5 - z} + C$.

10. $\int \frac{dx}{\sqrt{3x^2 - 2x + 1}}$.

11. $\int \frac{(2x - 3)\,dx}{\sqrt{x^2 + x + 2}}$.

Ans. $2\sqrt{x^2 + x + 2} - 4 \ln (2x + 1 + 2\sqrt{x^2 + x + 2}) + C$.

12. $\int \frac{(6y + 1)\,dy}{9y^2 - 6y - 3}$.

13. $\int \frac{dy}{(y - 1)\sqrt{y}}$. *Ans.* $\ln \frac{\sqrt{y} - 1}{\sqrt{y} + 1} + C$.

14. $\int \frac{\sqrt{x + 1}}{\sqrt{x}}\,dx$.

15. $\int \frac{2z^3\,dz}{z^2 - 1}$. $z^2 + \ln (z^2 - 1) + C$.

16. $\int \frac{z^4\,dz}{z^2 - 1}$.

17. $\int_3^5 \sqrt{x^2 - 9}\,dx$. $10 - \frac{9}{2} \ln 3$.

18. $\int_3^4 \sqrt{25 - t^2}\,dt$.

19. $\int_0^1 \frac{dx}{2 - x^2}$. $\frac{1}{2}\sqrt{2} \ln (1 + \sqrt{2})$.

20. $\int_{3/8}^{2/3} \frac{dy}{\sqrt{4y^2 + 1}}$.

21. $\int_{1/2}^1 \sqrt{3 + 4x - 4x^2}\,dx$. $\frac{1}{4}\sqrt{3} + \frac{1}{6}\pi$.

22. $\int_0^2 \sqrt{x^2 - 4x + 8}\,dx$.

23. $\int_{\ln 2}^{\ln 3} \frac{dx}{e^x - e^{-x}}$. $\frac{1}{2} \ln \frac{3}{2}$.

24. $\int_0^4 \frac{x^2\,dx}{\sqrt{x^2 + 9}}$.

25. Find the area bounded by the curves $y = 45/\sqrt{16x^2 - 175}$, $y = 0$, $x = 4$, and $x = 5$. *Ans.* 3.79.

26. Find the area between the curves $x^2y^2 + 9y^2 = 25$ and $y = 1$.

27. Find the area between the hyperbola $x^2 - y^2 = 9$ and the line $y = 2x - 6$. *Ans.* 1.056.

28. Find the centroid of the first-quadrant area bounded by the circle $x^2 + y^2 = a^2$.

29. Find the volume generated if the area of Problem 26 is revolved about the line $y = 1$. *Ans.* 4.66.

30. If $f(x) = \int_1^x \frac{dt}{t + \sqrt{t^2 - 1}}$, $x \geqq 1$, prove that $\frac{1}{2} \ln x \leqq f(x) \leqq \ln x$.

Hint: Use Problem 1, Exercise **20**.

134. Improper Integrals

In defining the definite integral

$$\int_a^b f(x)\,dx, \tag{1}$$

it was assumed that the limits of integration were finite and that the integrand was continuous for every value of x in the range $a \leqq x \leqq b$. If either of these conditions is not fulfilled the integral is called an **improper integral,** and its meaning is defined as follows.

1. Infinite limits. A definite integral, in which one or both limits of integration are infinite, is defined by the relations

$$\int_a^\infty f(x)\,dx = \lim_{b\to\infty} \int_a^b f(x)\,dx,$$

$$\int_{-\infty}^b f(x)\,dx = \lim_{a\to-\infty} \int_a^b f(x)\,dx,$$

$$\int_{-\infty}^\infty f(x)\,dx = \lim_{\substack{b\to\infty \\ a\to-\infty}} \int_a^b f(x)\,dx,$$

provided the limit exists. When the limit exists the integral is said to **converge;** otherwise, it is said to **diverge.**

Illustration 1. (*a*) $\displaystyle\int_{-\infty}^0 e^x\,dx = \lim_{x\to-\infty} (1 - e^x) = 1.$

(*b*) $\displaystyle\int_2^\infty \frac{dx}{x} = \lim_{x\to\infty} (\ln x - \ln 2) = \infty.$

(*c*) $\displaystyle\int_0^\infty \cos x\,dx = \lim_{x\to\infty} (\sin x) = \text{no limit}.$

2. Discontinuous integrand. When $f(x)$ is continuous for all values of x in the domain $a \leqq x \leqq b$ *except* $x = b$ or $x = a$, the integral (1) is defined by the relations

$$\int_a^b f(x)\,dx = \lim_{x\to b^-} \int_a^x f(x)\,dx, \tag{2}$$

or

$$\int_a^b f(x)\,dx = \lim_{x\to a^+} \int_x^b f(x)\,dx, \tag{3}$$

provided the limit exists. The notation $x \to b^-$ is used to mean that x approaches b through values less than b. Similarly, $x \to a^+$ means that x approaches a through values greater than a.

Illustration 2. (*a*) $\displaystyle\int_{-1}^0 \frac{dx}{x^2} = \lim_{x\to 0^-} \left(-\frac{1}{x} - 1\right) = \infty.$

(*b*) $\displaystyle\int_0^a \frac{dx}{\sqrt{a^2 - x^2}} = \lim_{x\to a} \left(\text{Sin}^{-1}\frac{x}{a}\right) = \frac{1}{2}\pi.$

When $f(x)$ is continuous for all values of x in the domain $a \leqq x \leqq b$ *except* $x = c$ (where $a < c < b$), the integral (1) is defined by the relation

$$\int_a^b f(x)\,dx = \int_a^c f(x)\,dx + \int_c^b f(x)\,dx,$$

where the integrals in the right member are evaluated in accordance with (2) and (3), respectively.

Example. Consider $\int_{-1}^{1} \frac{dx}{x^2}$.

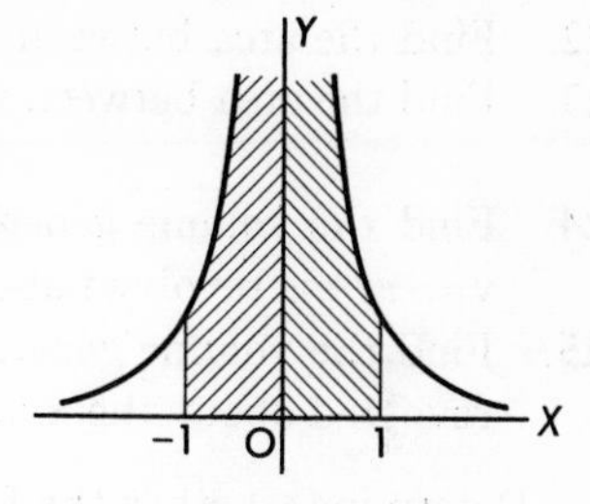

Figure 168

Solution: Since the integrand $1/x^2$ increases without limit as $x \to 0$, we write the integral in two parts to obtain

$$\int_{-1}^{1} \frac{dx}{x^2} = \int_{-1}^{0} \frac{dx}{x^2} + \int_{0}^{1} \frac{dx}{x^2} = \infty + \infty = \infty.$$

Observe that if the above integral is evaluated as an ordinary definite integral, we obtain

$$\int_{-1}^{1} \frac{dx}{x^2} = \left[-\frac{1}{x}\right]_{-1}^{1} = -2,$$

which is an absurd result since the integrand is always positive.

EXERCISE 67

Evaluate the following improper integrals, if they converge.

1. $\int_{1}^{\infty} \frac{dx}{x^3}$. *Ans.* $\frac{1}{2}$.
2. $\int_{1}^{\infty} \frac{dx}{\sqrt[3]{x}}$.
3. $\int_{-\infty}^{1} e^z\, dz$. e.
4. $\int_{0}^{\infty} \sin\theta \cos\theta\, d\theta$.
5. $\int_{5}^{\infty} \frac{dy}{\sqrt{y-1}}$. No value.
6. $\int_{1}^{\infty} \frac{x\, dx}{(1+x^2)^2}$.
7. $\int_{-\infty}^{\infty} \frac{dx}{1+x^2}$. π.
8. $\int_{-\infty}^{\infty} xe^{-x^2}\, dx$.
9. $\int_{0}^{1} \frac{dx}{\sqrt{1-x}}$. 2.
10. $\int_{2}^{3} \frac{dt}{(t-2)^3}$.
11. $\int_{0}^{\pi/2} \tan\theta\, d\theta$. No value.
12. $\int_{-1}^{1} \frac{dx}{1-x^2}$.
13. $\int_{0}^{2} \frac{dx}{(x-1)^{2/3}}$. 6.
14. $\int_{0}^{\pi/4} \frac{\sec^2\theta\, d\theta}{\sqrt{1-\tan\theta}}$.
15. $\int_{1}^{2.6} \frac{dy}{\sqrt{y^2-1}}$. $\ln 5$.
16. $\int_{-\infty}^{1/2} \frac{dy}{(1-2y)^2}$.
17. $\int_{2}^{\infty} \frac{dx}{x\sqrt{x^2-4}}$. $\frac{1}{4}\pi$.
18. $\int_{0}^{1} \frac{1}{x^2} \sin\frac{1}{x}\, dx$.
19. $\int_{0}^{4} \frac{dx}{x^2-2x-3}$. No value.
20. $\int_{0}^{\infty} \frac{dx}{(1+x)\sqrt{x}}$.

21. Find the area bounded by the curve $y = 1/\sqrt{x(2-x)}$, its asymptotes, and the x axis. *Ans.* π.

22. Find the area between the curve $y = 1/(e^x + e^{-x})$ and the x axis.

23. Find the area between the witch $y = 8a^3/(x^2 + 4a^2)$ and its asymptote. *Ans.* $4\pi a^2$.

24. Find the volume generated if the first-quadrant area under the curve $y = e^{-x}$ is revolved about the x axis.

25. Find the volume generated if the area under the curve $y = \sqrt{x}\, e^{-x^2}$ is revolved about the x axis. *Ans.* $\frac{1}{4}\pi$.

Determine whether the following integrals converge or diverge.

26. $\displaystyle\int_0^1 \frac{dx}{\sqrt{x + x^4}}$. *Hint:* Compare with $\displaystyle\int_0^1 \frac{dx}{\sqrt{x}}$.

27. $\displaystyle\int_1^\infty \frac{dx}{\sqrt{x + x^4}}$. *Hint:* Compare with $\displaystyle\int_1^\infty \frac{dx}{x^2}$. *Ans.* Converges.

28. $\displaystyle\int_0^1 \frac{dx}{\sqrt[3]{2x - x^2}}$. *Hint:* Observe that $2 - x > x$, for $0 < x < 1$.

29. If $h > 0$ and the function $f(x)$ is continuous for all x in the domain $a \leqq x \leqq b$ except $x = c$, where $a < c < b$, give an example to show that

$$\lim_{h\to 0}\left[\int_a^{c-h} f(x)\,dx + \int_{c+h}^b f(x)\,dx\right] \neq \lim_{h\to 0}\int_a^{c-h} f(x)\,dx + \lim_{h\to 0}\int_{c+h}^b f(x)\,dx.$$

30. If $h > 0$ and the function $f(x)$ is continuous for all real values of x, give an example to show that

$$\lim_{h\to\infty}\int_{-h}^{h} f(x)\,dx \neq \lim_{h\to\infty}\int_{-h}^{a} f(x)\,dx + \lim_{h\to\infty}\int_{a}^{h} f(x)\,dx.$$

CHAPTER 15

Integration Procedures

135. Introduction

Although some integrals can be evaluated by direct application of the formulas I_1–I_{24}, there are many for which this is not possible. In many instances, however, the integrals can be found by these formulas after suitable transformations have been made. It is the purpose of this chapter to study some of the elementary methods for changing the form of an integral.

136. Integration by Parts

The formula D_4 for the differential of a product may be written in the form

$$u\,dv = d(uv) - v\,du.$$

Integrating both sides of this relation, we obtain

$$I_{25} \qquad \int u\,dv = uv - \int v\,du.$$

This is known as the formula for **integration by parts.**

Illustration. To evaluate $\int \ln x\,dx$, we let $u = \ln x$ and $dv = dx$. Then $du = dx/x$, $v = x$, and substituting in I_{25} we obtain

$$\int \ln x\,dx = x \ln x - \int x \cdot \frac{dx}{x} = x \ln x - x + C.$$

Note: It is not necessary to add a constant of integration when integrating dv, since we obtain the same result in any case. That is,

$$u(v + C) - \int (v + C)\,du \equiv uv - \int v\,du.$$

Occasionally, however, it facilitates the work if a constant is added. As an example, we have

$$\int x \operatorname{Tan}^{-1} x \, dx = \int \operatorname{Tan}^{-1} x \, d\, \tfrac{1}{2}(x^2 + 1)$$

$$= \tfrac{1}{2}(x^2 + 1) \operatorname{Tan}^{-1} x - \int \tfrac{1}{2}(x^2 + 1) \frac{dx}{1 + x^2}$$

$$= \tfrac{1}{2}(x^2 + 1) \operatorname{Tan}^{-1} x - \tfrac{1}{2}x + C.$$

Example 1. Evaluate $\int x^2 \cos 2x \, dx$.

Solution: Let

$$u = x^2 \qquad \text{and} \qquad dv = \cos 2x \, dx;$$

then

$$du = 2x \, dx \qquad \text{and} \qquad v = \tfrac{1}{2} \sin 2x,$$

and by I_{25} we obtain

$$\int x^2 \cos 2x \, dx = \tfrac{1}{2}x^2 \sin 2x - \int x \sin 2x \, dx. \tag{1}$$

To evaluate the new integral we repeat the process. Thus, choosing $u = x$ and $dv = \sin 2x \, dx$, we have

$$\int x \sin 2x \, dx = \int x \, d(-\tfrac{1}{2} \cos 2x)$$

$$= -\tfrac{1}{2} x \cos 2x + \tfrac{1}{2} \int \cos 2x \, dx$$

$$= -\tfrac{1}{2} x \cos 2x + \tfrac{1}{4} \sin 2x.$$

Substituting this result in (1), we obtain

$$\int x^2 \cos 2x \, dx = \tfrac{1}{2}x^2 \sin 2x + \tfrac{1}{2}x \cos 2x - \tfrac{1}{4} \sin 2x + C.$$

Example 2. Evaluate $\int \sec^3 \theta \, d\theta$.

Solution: Let

$$u = \sec \theta \qquad \text{and} \qquad dv = \sec^2 \theta \, d\theta;$$

then

$$du = \sec \theta \tan \theta \, d\theta \qquad \text{and} \qquad v = \tan \theta,$$

and by I_{25} we obtain

$$\int \sec^3 \theta \, d\theta = \sec \theta \tan \theta - \int \sec \theta \tan^2 \theta \, d\theta,$$

or, using $\tan^2\theta = \sec^2\theta - 1$,

$$\int \sec^3\theta\,d\theta = \sec\theta\tan\theta - \int \sec^3\theta\,d\theta + \int \sec\theta\,d\theta.$$

Transposing the first integral in the right member, using I_{16}, and dividing by 2, gives the required result

$$\int \sec^3\theta\,d\theta = \tfrac{1}{2}\sec\theta\tan\theta + \tfrac{1}{2}\ln(\sec\theta + \tan\theta) + C.$$

Example 3. Evaluate $\int_0^\pi e^x \sin x\,dx$.

Solution: Letting $u = \sin x$ and $dv = e^x\,dx$, we obtain

$$\int_0^\pi e^x \sin x\,dx = \Big[e^x \sin x\Big]_0^\pi - \int_0^\pi e^x \cos x\,dx$$
$$= -\int_0^\pi e^x \cos x\,dx.$$

Integrating by parts again, we let $u = \cos x$, $dv = e^x\,dx$, and obtain

$$\int_0^\pi e^x \sin x\,dx = -\Big[e^x \cos x\Big]_0^\pi + \int_0^\pi e^x(-\sin x\,dx)$$
$$= e^\pi + 1 - \int_0^\pi e^x \sin x\,dx.$$

Transposing and dividing by 2 gives the required result

$$\int_0^\pi e^x \sin x\,dx = \tfrac{1}{2}(e^\pi + 1).$$

The method of integration by parts can be used to develop many formulas by means of which a given integral can be reduced in a series of steps to some known integration form. Such formulas are called **reduction formulas.**

Example 4. Derive the reduction formula

$$\int \sin^n x\,dx = -\frac{1}{n}\sin^{n-1} x\cos x + \frac{n-1}{n}\int \sin^{n-2} x\,dx, \quad n > 0. \quad (2)$$

Proof: Let $u = \sin^{n-1} x$ and $dv = \sin x\,dx$; then

$$\int \sin^n x\,dx = \sin^{n-1} x(-\cos x) - \int (-\cos x)(n-1)\sin^{n-2} x\cos x\,dx$$
$$= -\sin^{n-1} x\cos x + (n-1)\int \sin^{n-2} x\cos^2 x\,dx$$
$$= -\sin^{n-1} x\cos x + (n-1)\int \sin^{n-2} x\,dx - (n-1)\int \sin^n x\,dx.$$

Transposing the second integral on the right and dividing by n gives the required formula.

Note: By taking $x = \frac{1}{2}\pi - y$ in (2), we obtain

$$-\int \sin^n (\tfrac{1}{2}\pi - y)\, dy$$
$$= -\frac{1}{n} \sin^{n-1} (\tfrac{1}{2}\pi - y) \cos (\tfrac{1}{2}\pi - y) - \frac{n-1}{n} \int \sin^{n-2} (\tfrac{1}{2}\pi - y)\, dy.$$

This gives the corresponding reduction formula for cosines

$$\int \cos^n y\, dy = \frac{1}{n} \cos^{n-1} y \sin y + \frac{n-1}{n} \int \cos^{n-2} y\, dy.$$

EXERCISE 68

Integrate by parts to evaluate the following integrals.

1. $\int xe^x\, dx.$ *Ans.* $e^x(x - 1) + C.$
2. $\int x^2 \ln x\, dx.$
3. $\int \theta \cos \theta\, d\theta.$ $\cos \theta + \theta \sin \theta + C.$
4. $\int x \sin 2x\, dx.$
5. $\int \mathrm{Sin}^{-1} x\, dx.$ *Ans.* $x\, \mathrm{Sin}^{-1} x + \sqrt{1 - x^2} + C.$
6. $\int \mathrm{Tan}^{-1} y\, dy.$
7. $\int (x^3 + 1) \ln x\, dx.$ $(\frac{1}{4}x^4 + x) \ln x - \frac{1}{16}x^4 - x + C.$
8. $\int \sqrt{x} \ln 2x\, dx.$
9. $\int x\sqrt{x + 1}\, dx.$ $\frac{2}{15}(3x - 2)(x + 1)^{3/2} + C.$
10. $\int x^2\sqrt{x - 1}\, dx.$
11. $\int x^3\sqrt{x^2 + 4}\, dx.$ $\frac{1}{15}(3x^2 - 8)(x^2 + 4)^{3/2} + C.$
12. $\int z\, \mathrm{Sec}^{-1} z\, dz.$
13. $\int x \sec^2 \frac{1}{3}x\, dx.$ $3x \tan \frac{1}{3}x + 9 \ln \cos \frac{1}{3}x + C.$
14. $\int x \sec x \tan x\, dx.$
15. $\int \sin (\ln x)\, dx.$ $\frac{1}{2}x [\sin (\ln x) - \cos (\ln x)] + C.$

16. $\int \sec^5 \theta \, d\theta.$

17. $\int e^{-x} \cos 2x \, dx.$ *Ans.* $\frac{1}{5}e^{-x}(2 \sin 2x - \cos 2x) + C.$

18. $\int \text{Tan}^{-1} \sqrt{x} \, dx.$

19. $\int t^3 e^t \, dt.$ $e^t(t^3 - 3t^2 + 6t - 6) + C.$

20. $\int \theta^3 \sin \theta \, d\theta.$

21. $\int_{-1}^{1} \text{Cos}^{-1} x \, dx.$ *Ans.* $\pi.$

22. $\int_0^{\pi/2} x^2 \sin 2x \, dx.$

23. $\int_0^{\sqrt{7}} \frac{x^3 \, dx}{\sqrt[3]{8 - x^2}}.$ 8.7.

24. $\int_0^4 \frac{x \, dx}{\sqrt{8 - x}}.$

25. $\int_0^{\pi/3} \sin 3\theta \cos \theta \, d\theta.$ $\frac{9}{16}.$

26. $\int_{\pi/4}^{3\pi/4} \csc^3 \theta \, d\theta.$

27. $\int_0^1 \frac{xe^x}{(1 + x)^2} dx.$ $\frac{1}{2}e - 1.$

28. $\int_0^1 \text{Sec}^{-1} \frac{1}{x} \, dx.$

For the area bounded by the curve $y = xe^{-x}$, the x axis, and the maximum ordinate, find the following.

29. The area. *Ans.* $1 - 2e^{-1}.$
30. The centroid of the area.
31. The volume generated if the area is revolved about the x axis. *Ans.* $\frac{1}{4}\pi(1 - 5e^{-2}).$
32. The volume generated if the area is revolved about the y axis.
33. The moment of inertia of the area with respect to the x axis. *Ans.* $\frac{2}{81}(1 - 13e^{-3}).$
34. The moment of inertia of the area with respect to the y axis.

Derive the following reduction formulas.

35. $\int \tan^n x \, dx = \frac{\tan^{n-1} x}{n - 1} - \int \tan^{n-2} x \, dx, \quad n > 1.$

36. $\int \sec^n x \, dx = \frac{\sec^{n-2} x \tan x}{n - 1} + \frac{n - 2}{n - 1} \int \sec^{n-2} x \, dx, \quad n > 1.$

37. $\int x^n \sin ax \, dx = -\frac{x^n \cos ax}{a} + \frac{n}{a} \int x^{n-1} \cos ax \, dx.$

38. $\int x^n \cos ax \, dx = \frac{x^n \sin ax}{a} - \frac{n}{a} \int x^{n-1} \sin ax \, dx.$

39. $\int x^n e^{ax} \, dx = \frac{x^n e^{ax}}{a} - \frac{n}{a} \int x^{n-1} e^{ax} \, dx.$

40. $\int x^m (\ln x)^n \, dx = \frac{x^{m+1}(\ln x)^n}{m + 1} - \frac{n}{m + 1} \int x^m (\ln x)^{n-1} \, dx, \quad m \neq -1.$

137. Algebraic Substitutions

A change in the variable of integration will often reduce an integral to one of the basic integration formulas I_1–I_{24}. Such a change in variable is called a **substitution,** and if the substitution involves only algebraic terms it is called an **algebraic substitution.**

Example 1. Evaluate $\int \frac{x\,dx}{\sqrt{4-x}}$.

Solution: Let $\sqrt{4-x} = z$, and from this we find

$$x = 4 - z^2, \qquad \text{and} \qquad dx = -2z\,dz.$$

Substituting in the given integral and integrating, we obtain

$$\int \frac{x\,dx}{\sqrt{4-x}} = \int \frac{(4-z^2)(-2z\,dz)}{z} = \int (2z^2 - 8)dz = \tfrac{2}{3}z^3 - 8z + C.$$

Expressing this result in terms of the original variable, we have

$$\int \frac{x\,dx}{\sqrt{4-x}} = \tfrac{2}{3}\sqrt{4-x}[(4-x) - 12] + C = -\tfrac{2}{3}(x+8)\sqrt{4-x} + C.$$

Note: Observe that the substitution $\sqrt[n]{a+bx} = z$ will always eliminate radicals when the integrand is a rational function of x and $\sqrt[n]{a+bx}$.

Many integrals may be reduced to the above form by means of an intermediate substitution. Thus, for example, $x^3 = u$ reduces the integral $\int x^5\sqrt[3]{2+x^3}\,dx$ to $\frac{1}{3}\int u\sqrt[3]{2+u}\,du$. Since the latter integral can be evaluated by making the substitution $\sqrt[3]{2+u} = z$, it follows that the original integral could have been evaluated by making the single substitution $\sqrt[3]{2+x^3} = z$.

Example 2. Evaluate $\int \frac{dx}{\sqrt{x} + \sqrt[4]{x^3}}$.

Solution: Letting $x^{1/4} = z$, we have

$$\sqrt{x} = z^2, \qquad \sqrt[4]{x^3} = z^3, \qquad dx = 4z^3\,dz.$$

Hence

$$\int \frac{dx}{\sqrt{x} + \sqrt[4]{x^3}} = \int \frac{4z^3\,dz}{z^2 + z^3} = 4\int \frac{z\,dz}{1+z}$$

$$= 4\int \left(1 - \frac{1}{1+z}\right) dz = 4z - 4\ln(1+z) + C.$$

In terms of x, this becomes

$$\int \frac{dx}{\sqrt{x} + \sqrt[4]{x^3}} = 4\sqrt[4]{x} - 4\ln(1 + \sqrt[4]{x}) + C.$$

If a definite integral is to be evaluated by means of a substitution, the limits of integration are usually changed to correspond with the change in variable. This procedure eliminates the necessity of returning to the original variable of integration.

Example 3. Evaluate $\int_0^4 x\sqrt{x^2+9}\,dx$.

Solution: Letting $\sqrt{x^2+9} = z$ and observing that

$$z = 3 \text{ when } x = 0, \qquad \text{and} \qquad z = 5 \text{ when } x = 4,$$

we have

$$\int_0^4 \sqrt{x^2+9}\,(x\,dx) = \int_3^5 z(z\,dz) = \left[\tfrac{1}{3}z^3\right]_3^5 = \tfrac{98}{3}.$$

The justification for the changing of limits in this manner is contained in the following theorem.

Theorem. *Let $f(x)$ be continuous when $a \leqq x \leqq b$, and let $\phi(u)$ be such that its derivative is continuous and $\phi(\alpha) = a$, $\phi(\beta) = b$, and $a \leqq \phi(u) \leqq b$ when $\alpha \leqq u \leqq \beta$ or $\beta \leqq u \leqq \alpha$. If the substitution $x = \phi(u)$ changes $f(x)\,dx$ to $g(u)\,du$, then*

$$\int_a^b f(x)\,dx = \int_\alpha^\beta g(u)\,du.$$

Proof: Consider the functions

$$F(x) = \int_a^x f(x)\,dx \qquad \text{and} \qquad G(u) = \int_\alpha^u g(u)\,du. \tag{1}$$

By the Fundamental Theorem we obtain $dF(x) = f(x)\,dx$ and $dG(u) = g(u)\,du$. Considering u as the independent variable and $x = \phi(u)$, it follows from the hypothesis, $f(x)\,dx = g(u)\,du$, that $dF(x) = dG(u)$ identically in u. By the theorem in Article **37,** this means that $F(x) = G(u) + C$, where C is a constant. However, for $u = \alpha$ we have $x = a$, and from (1) $F(a) = 0$ and $G(\alpha) = 0$. Hence the constant C is zero, and we have $F(x) = G(u)$. Since $x = b$ when $u = \beta$, we obtain $F(b) = G(\beta)$, which proves the theorem.

EXERCISE 69

Evaluate the following integrals.

1. $\int x\sqrt{x+4}\,dx$. *Ans.* $\frac{2}{15}(3x-8)(x+4)^{3/2} + C$.
2. $\int x\sqrt[3]{x+4}\,dx$.
3. $\int x\sqrt{x^2+4}\,dx$. $\frac{1}{3}(x^2+4)^{3/2} + C$.
4. $\int x^3\sqrt{x^2+4}\,dx$.

5. $\int \frac{dx}{x - \sqrt{x}}$. *Ans.* $2 \ln (\sqrt{x} - 1) + C$.

6. $\int \frac{dy}{\sqrt{y} + \sqrt[4]{y}}$.

7. $\int \frac{dx}{x - \sqrt[3]{x}}$. $\frac{3}{2} \ln (\sqrt[3]{x^2} - 1) + C$.

8. $\int \frac{dx}{x - x^{4/3}}$.

9. $\int \frac{\sqrt{x^2 - 1}}{x} dx$. *Ans.* $\sqrt{x^2 - 1} - \text{Tan}^{-1}\sqrt{x^2 - 1} + C$.

10. $\int \frac{\sqrt{x^3 - 1}}{x} dx$.

11. $\int \frac{t\, dt}{\sqrt[4]{1 + 2t}}$. $\frac{2}{21}(3t - 2)(1 + 2t)^{3/4} + C$.

12. $\int \frac{x^3\, dx}{\sqrt[3]{x^2 + 4}}$.

13. $\int_1^3 x\sqrt[3]{x^2 - 1}\, dx$. *Ans.* 6.

14. $\int_1^2 \frac{(z + 1)\, dz}{z\sqrt{z - 1}}$.

15. $\int_4^9 \frac{dx}{\sqrt{x} - 1}$. $2 + 2 \ln 2$.

16. $\int_0^1 \frac{x^{1/2}\, dx}{1 + x^{3/4}}$.

17. $\int_{-1}^0 x^2\sqrt{x + 1}\, dx$. $\frac{16}{105}$.

18. $\int_0^3 \frac{dx}{(x + 2)\sqrt{x + 1}}$.

19. $\int_0^7 \frac{dy}{1 + \sqrt[3]{y + 1}}$. $\frac{3}{2} + 3 \ln \frac{3}{2}$.

20. $\int_1^\infty \frac{dx}{x\sqrt{x^2 + 4}}$.

21. Find the area bounded by the curves $y = x/(1 + \sqrt{x})$, $y = 0$, and $x = 4$. *Ans.* 3.136.

22. Find the volume generated by revolving the area of the preceding problem about the y axis.

23. Find the volume generated by revolving about the x axis the area bounded by the curves $y = x + \sqrt{x + 1}$, $y = 0$, $x = 0$, and $x = 3$. *Ans.* 100.4.

24. Find the centroid of the volume described in the preceding problem.

25. If $f(x)$ is an **even function,** that is, $f(-x) = f(x)$, prove that

$$\int_{-a}^{a} f(x)\, dx = 2 \int_0^a f(x)\, dx.$$

26. If $f(x)$ is an **odd function,** that is, $f(-x) = -f(x)$, prove that

$$\int_{-a}^{a} f(x)\, dx = 0.$$

27. Show that $\int_0^a f(x)\, dx = 2 \int_0^{a/2} f(x)\, dx$, when $f(a - x) = f(x)$.

28. If $F(x) = \int_1^x f\left(u + \frac{1}{u}\right) \frac{du}{u}$, show that $F\left(\frac{1}{x}\right) = -F(x)$.

29. Show that $\int_0^{\pi/2} f(\sin x)\,dx = \int_0^{\pi/2} f(\cos x)\,dx.$

30. Show that $\int_0^{\pi} f(\sin x)\,dx = 2\int_0^{\pi/2} f(\sin x)\,dx.$

31. Use the identity

$$\int_0^{\pi/2} \ln \sin 2x\,dx = \int_0^{\pi/2} \ln \sin x\,dx + \int_0^{\pi/2} \ln \cos x\,dx + \int_0^{\pi/2} \ln 2\,dx$$

to determine the value of $\int_0^{\pi/2} \ln \sin x\,dx.$ *Ans.* $-\frac{1}{2}\pi \ln 2.$

138. Trigonometric Substitutions

A change of variable involving trigonometric functions is called a **trigonometric substitution.** This type of substitution is particularly useful when an integrand is a rational function of u and one of the following radical expressions. For each of these radicals we use the substitution indicated.

$$\sqrt{a^2 - u^2}, \quad \text{let} \quad u = a \sin \theta, \tag{1}$$

$$\sqrt{a^2 + u^2}, \quad \text{let} \quad u = a \tan \theta, \tag{2}$$

$$\sqrt{u^2 - a^2}, \quad \text{let} \quad u = a \sec \theta. \tag{3}$$

It is clear that each of the above substitutions reduces the corresponding radical to the following rational trigonometric expressions.

$$\sqrt{a^2 - a^2 \sin^2 \theta} = a\sqrt{1 - \sin^2 \theta} = a|\cos \theta|,$$

$$\sqrt{a^2 + a^2 \tan^2 \theta} = a\sqrt{1 + \tan^2 \theta} = a|\sec \theta|,$$

$$\sqrt{a^2 \sec^2 \theta - a^2} = a\sqrt{\sec^2 \theta - 1} = a|\tan \theta|.$$

Example 1. Evaluate $\int \frac{dx}{(9 - x^2)^{3/2}}.$

Solution: In accordance with (1), we let $x = 3 \sin \theta$. Hence, if θ is an acute angle, $\sqrt{9 - x^2} = 3 \cos \theta$, $dx = 3 \cos \theta\, d\theta$, and we have

$$\int \frac{dx}{(9 - x^2)^{3/2}} = \int \frac{3 \cos \theta\, d\theta}{(3 \cos \theta)^3} = \frac{1}{9}\int \sec^2 \theta\, d\theta = \frac{1}{9} \tan \theta + C.$$

The above result may be written in terms of x with the help of Figure 169, which depicts geometrically the relationship $\sin \theta = x/3$. Thus

$$\int \frac{dx}{(9 - x^2)^{3/2}} = \frac{x}{9\sqrt{9 - x^2}} + C.$$

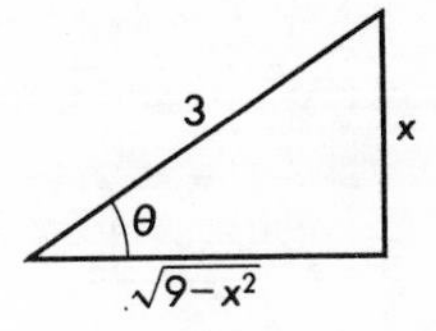

Figure 169

Trigonometric substitutions may be used to

prove the integration formulas I_{21}–I_{24}. For example, to prove

$$I_{21} \qquad \int \frac{du}{\sqrt{a^2 + u^2}} = \ln\,(u + \sqrt{a^2 + u^2}) + C,$$

we let $u = a \tan \theta$ as shown in Figure 170. Then $\sqrt{a^2 + u^2} = a \sec \theta$, $du = a \sec^2 \theta \, d\theta$, and we obtain

$$\int \frac{du}{\sqrt{a^2 + u^2}} = \int \sec \theta \, d\theta = \ln\,(\sec \theta + \tan \theta) + C'$$

$$= \ln \left(\frac{\sqrt{a^2 + u^2}}{a} + \frac{u}{a} \right) + C'$$

$$= \ln\,(u + \sqrt{a^2 + u^2}) + C,$$

Figure 170

where $C = C' - \ln a$.

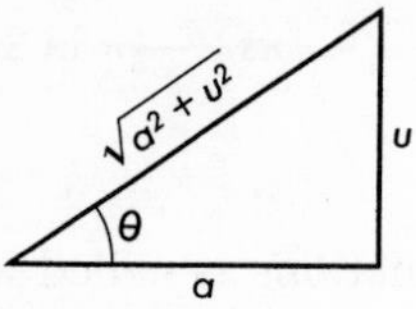

Example 2. Evaluate $\displaystyle\int_0^1 \frac{dx}{\sqrt{x^2 + 2x}}$.

Solution: Since $x^2 + 2x = (x + 1)^2 - 1$, in accordance with (3) we let $x + 1 = \sec \theta$. Making this substitution (Figure 171) and observing that

$$\theta \to 0 \text{ when } x \to 0, \qquad \text{and} \qquad \theta = \tfrac{1}{3}\pi \text{ when } x = 1,$$

we have

$$\int_0^1 \frac{dx}{\sqrt{x^2 + 2x}} = \int_0^{\pi/3} \frac{\sec \theta \tan \theta \, d\theta}{\tan \theta} = \int_0^{\pi/3} \sec \theta \, d\theta$$

$$= \Big[\ln\,(\sec \theta + \tan \theta) \Big]_0^{\pi/3} = \ln\,(2 + \sqrt{3}).$$

Observe in this example that an *improper* integral is transformed into a *proper* integral.

Note: When the trigonometric identities are used to evaluate a definite integral, one must be careful to make a *proper* substitution. For example, the radical $\sqrt{1 - \sin^2 \theta}$ equals $\cos \theta$ when θ varies from 0 to $\frac{1}{2}\pi$ but equals $-\cos \theta$ when θ varies from $\frac{1}{2}\pi$ to π. Thus the integral of $\sqrt{1 - \sin^2 \theta}$ from 0 to π is found as follows.

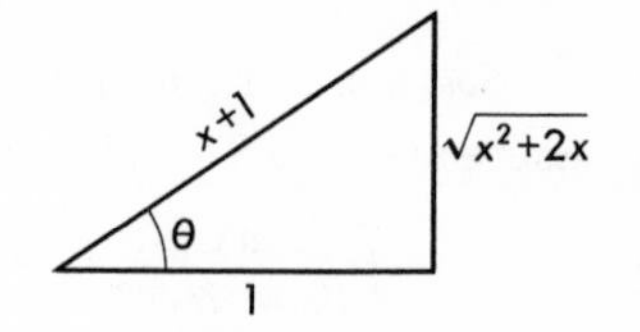

Figure 171

$$\int_0^{\pi} \sqrt{1 - \sin^2 \theta} \, d\theta = \int_0^{\pi/2} \cos \theta \, d\theta + \int_{\pi/2}^{\pi} (-\cos \theta) \, d\theta$$

$$= \Big[\sin \theta \Big]_0^{\pi/2} + \Big[-\sin \theta \Big]_{\pi/2}^{\pi} = 2.$$

EXERCISE 70

Evaluate the following integrals.

1. $\int \frac{dx}{x^2\sqrt{4 - x^2}}$. *Ans.* $-\frac{\sqrt{4 - x^2}}{4x} + C$.

2. $\int \frac{\sqrt{4 - x^2}}{x^2}\, dx$.

3. $\int \frac{dx}{(x^2 + 4)^{3/2}}$. $\frac{x}{4\sqrt{x^2 + 4}} + C$.

4. $\int \frac{y^2\, dy}{\sqrt{y^2 + 4}}$.

5. $\int \frac{dz}{z^2\sqrt{z^2 - 4}}$. $\frac{\sqrt{z^2 - 4}}{4z} + C$.

6. $\int \frac{\sqrt{x^2 - 4}}{x}\, dx$.

7. $\int \frac{\sqrt{9 - x^2}}{x^4}\, dx$. $-\frac{\sqrt{(9 - x^2)^3}}{27x^3} + C$.

8. $\int \frac{dx}{x^4\sqrt{9 - x^2}}$.

9. $\int \frac{dx}{x^2\sqrt{9 + x^2}}$. $-\frac{\sqrt{9 + x^2}}{9x} + C$.

10. $\int \frac{dt}{t^4\sqrt{9 + t^2}}$.

11. $\int \frac{dx}{\sqrt{(4x^2 - 9)^3}}$. $-\frac{x}{9\sqrt{4x^2 - 9}} + C$.

12. $\int x^3\sqrt{x^2 - 9}\, dx$.

13. $\int \sqrt{2x - x^2}\, dx$. *Ans.* $\frac{1}{2}(x - 1)\sqrt{2x - x^2} + \frac{1}{2}\,\mathrm{Sin}^{-1}(x - 1) + C$.

14. $\int \sqrt{y^2 + 4y}\, dy$.

15. $\int \frac{dx}{\sqrt{x^2 + 2x + 2}}$. $\ln(x + 1 + \sqrt{x^2 + 2x + 2}) + C$.

16. $\int \frac{\sqrt{v}\, dv}{\sqrt{2 - v}}$.

17. $\int \frac{dx}{x\sqrt{2ax - x^2}}$. Let $x = 2a \sin^2 \theta$. $-\frac{\sqrt{2ax - x^2}}{ax} + C$.

18. $\int \frac{dx}{x\sqrt{2ax + x^2}}$. Let $x = 2a \tan^2 \theta$.

19. $\int_5^9 \frac{ds}{s\sqrt{s^2 + 144}}$. *Ans.* $\frac{1}{12} \ln \frac{5}{3}$.

20. $\int_0^3 \sqrt{25 - y^2}\, dy$.

21. $\int_0^2 x^2\sqrt{4 - x^2}\, dx$. π.

22. $\int_0^{3/2} \frac{y^2\, dy}{(y^2 + 4)^{3/2}}$.

23. $\int_3^6 \frac{dr}{r^3\sqrt{r^2 - 9}}$. $\frac{3\sqrt{3} + 4\pi}{648}$.

24. $\int_0^{2.4} \frac{x^3\, dx}{\sqrt{(x^2 + 1)^3}}$.

25. $\int_1^\infty \frac{dx}{x^4\sqrt{x^2 + 3}}$. $\frac{4}{27}$.

26. $\int_1^5 \frac{dx}{\sqrt{10x - x^2}}$.

27. Derive formula I_{23} using a trigonometric substitution.

28. Derive formula I_{24} using a trigonometric substitution.

29. Find the area bounded by the curves $y = \sqrt{x^2 - 9}/x^2$, $y = 0$, and $x = 5$. *Ans.* 0.2986.

30. Find the volume generated if the area of the preceding problem is revolved about the y axis.
31. Find the centroid of the area described in Problem 29.

Ans. (4.08, 0.077).

32. Find the centroid of the volume described in Problem 30.

139. Integration of Rational Fractions

We shall now consider the integration of **rational fractions,** that is, fractions in which the numerators and denominators are polynomials in the variable of integration. If the degree of the polynomial in the numerator is *not less* than that in the denominator the fraction is called an **improper fraction,** and such a fraction may always be reduced by division to a mixed fraction consisting of a polynomial and a **proper fraction.** We assume that all fractions considered are **irreducible,** that is, the numerator and denominator have no common factor.

Illustration. $\dfrac{x^2+1}{(x+1)^3}$ is a proper, irreducible, rational fraction.

In the study of algebra one learns the procedure by which two or more fractions may be combined into a single fraction. In the evaluation of integrals, it is important to be able to reverse this procedure, that is, to represent a given fraction as a sum of simpler fractions. This inverse procedure is called the resolving of a given fraction into **partial fractions.** The process of determining these partial fractions is based on the following theorem, whose proof is given in advanced books in algebra.

Theorem. *Any proper rational fraction may be resolved into a sum of partial fractions subject to the classifications listed below.*

I. *If a linear factor* $\mathbf{ax+b}$ *occurs once as a factor of the denominator, there corresponds to this factor one partial fraction* $\dfrac{\mathbf{A}}{\mathbf{ax+b}}$, *where* $\mathbf{A}$ *is a constant and* $\mathbf{A \neq 0}$.

II. *If a linear factor* $\mathbf{ax+b}$ *occurs* $\mathbf{n}$ *times as a factor of the denominator, there corresponds to this factor* $\mathbf{n}$ *partial fractions*

$$\frac{A_1}{ax+b}+\frac{A_2}{(ax+b)^2}+\cdots+\frac{A_n}{(ax+b)^n},$$

where $A_1, A_2, \cdots, A_n$ *are constants and* $A_n \neq 0$.

III. *If a quadratic factor* $\mathbf{ax^2+bx+c}$ *occurs once as a factor of the denominator, there corresponds to this factor one partial fraction* $\dfrac{\mathbf{Ax+B}}{\mathbf{ax^2+bx+c}}$, *where* $\mathbf{A}$ *and* $\mathbf{B}$ *are constants and* $\mathbf{Ax+B \not\equiv 0}$.

IV. *If a quadratic factor* $\boldsymbol{ax^2 + bx + c}$ *occurs* $\boldsymbol{n}$ *times as a factor of the denominator, there corresponds to this factor* $\boldsymbol{n}$ *partial fractions*

$$\frac{A_1x + B_1}{ax^2 + bx + c} + \frac{A_2x + B_2}{(ax^2 + bx + c)^2} + \cdots + \frac{A_nx + B_n}{(ax^2 + bx + c)^n},$$

where the $\boldsymbol{A}$*'s and* $\boldsymbol{B}$*'s are constants and* $\boldsymbol{A_nx + B_n \not\equiv 0}$.

Note: In the statement of the above theorem it is implied that the quadratic factors mentioned cannot be expressed as the product of two real linear factors.

Example 1. Evaluate $\displaystyle\int \frac{x^2 + 2x - 2}{x^3 - 4x}\,dx.$

Solution: In accordance with **I** the integrand can be expressed in the form

$$\frac{x^2 + 2x - 2}{x(x + 2)(x - 2)} = \frac{A}{x} + \frac{B}{x + 2} + \frac{C}{x - 2}, \tag{1}$$

where A, B, and C are constants to be determined. Clearing (1) of fractions, we obtain

$$x^2 + 2x - 2 = A(x + 2)(x - 2) + Bx(x - 2) + Cx(x + 2), \tag{2}$$

or

$$x^2 + 2x - 2 = (A + B + C)x^2 - 2(B - C)x - 4A. \tag{3}$$

There are two general methods for determining the constants A, B, and C.

Method 1: Substitution. Since (2) is true for all values of x, we substitute $x = 0, -2$, and 2 in (2) and obtain the following results.

When $x = 0$, we find $-2 = -4A$; hence $A = \frac{1}{2}$.

When $x = -2$, we find $-2 = 8B$; hence $B = -\frac{1}{4}$.

When $x = 2$, we find $6 = 8C$; hence $C = \frac{3}{4}$.

Method 2: Equating Coefficients. Since (3) is an identity, we equate the coefficients of like powers in the two members, and obtain the simultaneous equations

$$\begin{cases} A + B + C = 1, \\ -2B + 2C = 2, \\ -4A = -2. \end{cases}$$

Solving these equations, we find $A = \frac{1}{2}$, $B = -\frac{1}{4}$, and $C = \frac{3}{4}$.

Now substituting these values in (1), we have

$$\int \frac{x^2 + 2x - 2}{x^3 - 4x}\,dx = \frac{1}{2}\int \frac{dx}{x} - \frac{1}{4}\int \frac{dx}{x+2} + \frac{3}{4}\int \frac{dx}{x-2}$$

$$= \frac{1}{2}\ln x - \frac{1}{4}\ln(x+2) + \frac{3}{4}\ln(x-2) + C$$

$$= \frac{1}{4}\ln\frac{x^2(x-2)^3}{x+2} + C.$$

Example 2. Evaluate $\int \frac{x^3 + x + 2}{x(x^2+1)^2}\,dx.$

Solution: In accordance with **I** and **IV** the integrand can be expressed in the form

$$\frac{x^3 + x + 2}{x(x^2+1)^2} = \frac{A}{x} + \frac{Bx + C}{x^2+1} + \frac{Dx + E}{(x^2+1)^2}. \tag{4}$$

Clearing of fractions, we obtain

$$x^3 + x + 2 = A(x^2+1)^2 + (Bx + C)x(x^2+1) + (Dx + E)x. \tag{5}$$

Although the coefficients A, B, C, D, and E may be found by the methods indicated in Example 1, they are more easily determined in the following manner. Setting $x = 0$ in (5), we find $A = 2$. Transposing the first term on the right side of (5), putting $A = 2$, and dividing through by x gives

$$-2x^3 + x^2 - 4x + 1 = (Bx + C)(x^2+1) + (Dx + E). \tag{6}$$

In (6) we see that if the left side is divided by $x^2 + 1$, the quotient obtained is $Bx + C$ and the remainder is $Dx + E$. Hence, by division, we find

$$\begin{array}{r|l}
 & -2x + 1 \qquad\qquad\quad = Bx + C \\
x^2 + 1 & -2x^3 + x^2 - 4x + 1 \\
 & \underline{-2x^3 \qquad\quad - 2x} \\
 & x^2 - 2x \\
 & \underline{x^2 \qquad\quad + 1} \\
 & -2x \qquad\quad = Dx + E.
\end{array}$$

Substituting in (4), we have

$$\int \frac{x^3 + x + 2}{x(x^2+1)^2}\,dx = 2\int \frac{dx}{x} - \int \frac{2x - 1}{x^2+1}\,dx - \int \frac{2x\,dx}{(x^2+1)^2}$$

$$= 2\ln x - \ln(x^2+1) + \mathrm{Tan}^{-1}\,x + \frac{1}{x^2+1} + C.$$

In order to facilitate the integration the constants in **III** may be taken in the form

$$\frac{A(2ax + b) + B}{ax^2 + bx + c}.$$

Example 3. Evaluate $\int \frac{x^2 + 2x - 10}{x^2(x^2 + 4x + 5)} dx.$

Solution: In accordance with **II** and **III** we have

$$\frac{x^2 + 2x - 10}{x^2(x^2 + 4x + 5)} = \frac{A}{x} + \frac{B}{x^2} + \frac{C(2x + 4) + D}{x^2 + 4x + 5};$$

hence

$$x^2 + 2x - 10 = Ax(x^2 + 4x + 5) + B(x^2 + 4x + 5) + Cx^2(2x + 4) + Dx^2.$$

Equating coefficients, we find

$$\begin{aligned} 5B &= -10; &\text{hence}\quad B &= -2,\\ 5A + 4B &= 2; &\text{hence}\quad A &= 2,\\ A + 2C &= 0; &\text{hence}\quad C &= -1,\\ 4A + B + 4C + D &= 1; &\text{hence}\quad D &= -1. \end{aligned}$$

Thus the given integral becomes

$$\int \frac{x^2 + 2x - 10}{x^2(x^2 + 4x + 5)} dx = 2\int \frac{dx}{x} - 2\int \frac{dx}{x^2} - \int \frac{[(2x + 4) + 1]}{x^2 + 4x + 5} dx$$

$$= 2 \ln x + \frac{2}{x} - \ln (x^2 + 4x + 5) - \text{Tan}^{-1} (x + 2) + C.$$

EXERCISE 71

Evaluate the following integrals.

1. $\int \frac{dx}{x^2 + 2x}.$ *Ans.* $\frac{1}{2} \ln \frac{x}{x + 2} + C.$

2. $\int \frac{(x - 8)\, dx}{x^2 - x - 6}.$

3. $\int \frac{x^2 + x + 2}{x^2 - 1} dx.$ $x + \ln \frac{(x - 1)^2}{x + 1} + C.$

4. $\int \frac{dx}{x(a^2 - x^2)}.$

5. $\int \frac{3y^2 - y + 1}{y^3 - y^2} dy.$ *Ans.* $\frac{1}{y} + 3 \ln (y - 1) + C.$

6. $\int \frac{x^2\, dx}{(x + 1)^3}.$

7. $\int \frac{(x - 1)\, dx}{x(x + 1)^2}.$ $\frac{-2}{x + 1} + \ln \frac{x + 1}{x} + C.$

8. $\int \frac{7t^2 - 20t - 20}{(4 - t^2)^2} dt.$

9. $\int \frac{dz}{z + z^3}.$ $\frac{1}{2} \ln \frac{z^2}{z^2 + 1} + C.$

10. $\int \frac{(2x + 1)\, dx}{x^2(x^2 + 1)}.$

11. $\int \frac{4\, dx}{x^4 - 1}.$ $\ln \frac{x - 1}{x + 1} - 2\, \text{Tan}^{-1} x + C.$

12. $\displaystyle\int \frac{y^2 + 6y + 4}{y^4 + 5y^2 + 4}\, dy.$

13. $\displaystyle\int \frac{(x^2 - 4x - 4)\, dx}{(x - 2)(x^2 + 4)}.$ *Ans.* $\displaystyle \ln \frac{x^2 + 4}{x - 2} + C.$

14. $\displaystyle\int \frac{dx}{x^3(1 + x^2)}.$

15. $\displaystyle\int \frac{8\, dt}{t(t^2 + 2)^2}.$ $\displaystyle \frac{2}{t^2 + 2} + \ln \frac{t^2}{t^2 + 2} + C.$

16. $\displaystyle\int \frac{dx}{x(x^2 + a^2)}.$

17. $\displaystyle\int \frac{x^3 - 6x^2 + 1}{x(x^2 - 1)}\, dx.$ $x - \ln x(x - 1)^2(x + 1)^3 + C.$

18. $\displaystyle\int \frac{z^4\, dz}{(z^2 - 1)^2}.$

19. $\displaystyle\int \frac{(8t^3 + 13)\, dt}{(t + 2)(4t^2 + 1)}.$ $2t - \frac{1}{2} \ln (t + 2)^6(4t^2 + 1) + 3\, \mathrm{Tan}^{-1}\, 2t + C.$

20. $\displaystyle\int \left(\frac{x + 2}{x^2 + 2x + 2}\right)^2 dx.$

21. $\displaystyle\int_2^4 \frac{x\, dx}{(x + 1)(x + 2)}.$ *Ans.* $\ln \frac{27}{20}.$

22. $\displaystyle\int_3^5 \frac{x^2 - 2}{(x - 2)^2}\, dx.$

23. $\displaystyle\int_1^2 \frac{5x^2 - 3x + 18}{x(9 - x^2)}\, dx.$ $13 \ln 2 - 4 \ln 5.$

24. $\displaystyle\int_1^2 \frac{2y^2 + 1}{y(y + 1)^2}\, dy.$

25. $\displaystyle\int_2^3 \frac{4y\, dy}{(y - 1)(y^2 - 1)}.$ $1 + \ln \frac{3}{2}.$

26. $\displaystyle\int_0^1 \frac{x^5\, dx}{(x^2 + 4)^2}.$

27. $\displaystyle\int_0^1 \frac{dx}{1 + x^3}.$ $\frac{1}{9}(\ln 8 + \pi\sqrt{3}).$

28. $\displaystyle\int_1^\infty \frac{dx}{x + x^2 + x^3}.$

29. $\displaystyle\int_0^\infty \frac{dt}{e^{3t} + e^t}.$ $1 - \frac{1}{4}\pi.$

30. $\displaystyle\int_{\pi/6}^{\pi/2} \frac{\cos \theta\, d\theta}{\sin \theta + \sin^3 \theta}.$

31. $\displaystyle\int_0^1 \frac{x^2 + 3x + 1}{x^4 + x^2 + 1}\, dx.$ $\pi/\sqrt{3}.$

32. $\displaystyle\int_5^\infty \frac{(9y - 13)\, dy}{y^3 - 7y + 6}.$

33. Derive formulas I_{22} and I'_{22}, using partial fractions.

34. Find the area in the first quadrant bounded by the curve $(x + 2)^2 y = 4 - x.$

35. Find the volume generated if the area of Problem 34 is revolved about the x axis. *Ans.* $\frac{4}{9}\pi.$

36. Find the volume generated if the area of Problem 34 is revolved about the y axis.

37. Find the area in the first quadrant bounded by the curve $(x^2 + 1)y = 5 - x.$ *Ans.* 5.24.

38. Find the centroid of the area described in Problem 37.

39. Find the volume generated if the area of Problem 37 is revolved about the x axis. *Ans.* 48.2.
40. Find the centroid of the volume described in Problem 39.

140. Miscellaneous Substitutions

If an integrand is a rational function of the trigonometric functions, the substitution $\mathbf{z} = \tan \frac{1}{2}\mathbf{u}$, *or its equivalent,*

$$\sin u = \frac{2z}{1 + z^2}, \qquad \cos u = \frac{1 - z^2}{1 + z^2}, \qquad du = \frac{2dz}{1 + z^2}, \tag{1}$$

will give an integrand which is rational in $\mathbf{z}$.

To establish (1) we observe by formula **29**, page 3, that

$$\tan u = \frac{2 \tan \frac{1}{2}u}{1 - \tan^2 \frac{1}{2}u} = \frac{2z}{1 - z^2}.$$

This relation, as shown in Figure 172, gives the above substitutions for $\sin u$ and $\cos u$. By differentiating $u = 2 \operatorname{Tan}^{-1} z$, we obtain the third relation in (1).

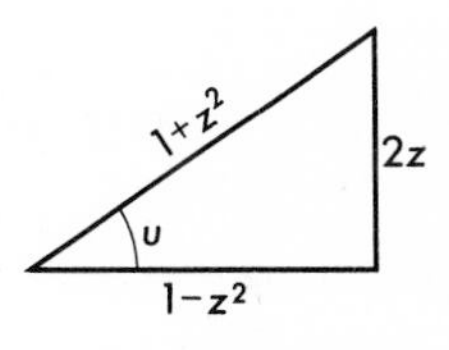

Figure 172

Example 1. Evaluate $\displaystyle\int \frac{dx}{3 + 5 \cos x}$.

Solution: Using the substitution (1), we have

$$\int \frac{dx}{3 + 5 \cos x} = \int \frac{\dfrac{2\,dz}{1 + z^2}}{3 + 5\left(\dfrac{1 - z^2}{1 + z^2}\right)} = \int \frac{dz}{4 - z^2}.$$

Hence, by I_{22} and $z = \tan \frac{1}{2}x$, we obtain

$$\int \frac{dx}{3 + 5 \cos x} = \frac{1}{4} \ln \frac{2 + z}{2 - z} + C = \frac{1}{4} \ln \frac{2 + \tan \frac{1}{2}x}{2 - \tan \frac{1}{2}x} + C.$$

Another substitution which is helpful is

$$u = \frac{1}{z}, \qquad du = -\frac{1}{z^2}\,dz, \tag{2}$$

called the **reciprocal substitution.**

Example 2. Evaluate $\displaystyle\int \frac{dx}{x\sqrt{2x - x^2}}$.

Solution: Using the substitution (2), we have

$$\int \frac{dx}{x\sqrt{2x - x^2}} = \int \frac{-\frac{1}{z^2}\, dz}{\frac{1}{z}\sqrt{\frac{2}{z} - \frac{1}{z^2}}} = \int \frac{-dz}{\sqrt{2z - 1}}.$$

Hence, by I_4 and $z = 1/x$, we obtain

$$\int \frac{dx}{x\sqrt{2x - x^2}} = -\sqrt{2z - 1} + C = -\sqrt{\frac{2 - x}{x}} + C.$$

Note: In using a substitution to evaluate a definite integral, one should be sure that the substitution is single-valued and defined for all values of the variable of integration. For example, in making the substitution $x = 1/z$, $dx = -dz/z^2$, it would appear that

$$\int_{-1}^{1} \frac{dx}{(1 + x^2)^{3/2}} = -\int_{-1}^{1} \frac{z\, dz}{(z^2 + 1)^{3/2}} = \left[\frac{1}{\sqrt{z^2 + 1}}\right]_{-1}^{1} = 0.$$

This result is absurd since the integrand of the original integral is always positive. The difficulty here is that the variable z does not vary continuously from -1 to 1 as x varies from -1 to 1; in fact, z is not even defined when $x = 0$.

EXERCISE 72

Evaluate the following integrals using the half-angle substitution.

1. $\int \frac{dx}{5 + 4 \cos x}$. *Ans.* $\frac{2}{3} \operatorname{Tan}^{-1} (\frac{1}{3} \tan \frac{1}{2}x) + C$.
2. $\int \frac{dx}{2 + \sin x}$.
3. $\int \frac{dx}{13 - 5 \cos x}$. $\frac{1}{6} \operatorname{Tan}^{-1} (\frac{3}{2} \tan \frac{1}{2}x) + C$.
4. $\int \frac{d\theta}{\sin \theta - \cos \theta}$.
5. $\int \frac{dx}{1 + \sin x + \cos x}$. $\ln (1 + \tan \frac{1}{2}x) + C$.
6. $\int \frac{dy}{5 \sec y + 4}$.
7. $\int_0^{\pi/4} \frac{2\, d\theta}{1 + \tan \theta}$. $\frac{1}{4}(\pi + \ln 4)$.
8. $\int_{\pi/3}^{\pi/2} \frac{dx}{\tan x - \sin x}$.
9. $\int_0^{1/4} \frac{dx}{3 - 5 \sin 2x}$. 0.17.
10. $\int_0^{\pi} \frac{dt}{3 + 2 \sin t + \cos t}$.

Evaluate the following integrals using the reciprocal substitution.

11. $\int \frac{dx}{x\sqrt{x^2 + 2x - 1}}$. *Ans.* $\operatorname{Sin}^{-1} \left(\frac{x - 1}{x\sqrt{2}}\right) + C$.
12. $\int \frac{dx}{x\sqrt{3x^2 - 2x - 1}}$.
13. $\int \frac{dx}{x^2\sqrt{2x - x^2}}$. $-\left(\frac{x + 1}{3x^2}\right)\sqrt{2x - x^2} + C$.

14. $\int \frac{(x^2 - x^3)^{1/3}}{x^3}\,dx.$

15. $\int_{1/2}^{2} \frac{dx}{x\sqrt{5x^2 + 4x - 1}}.$ *Ans.* $\frac{1}{6}\pi.$

16. $\int_{1/2}^{2} \frac{dx}{x^2\sqrt{5x^2 + 4x - 1}}.$

Evaluate the following integrals using the indicated substitution.

17. $\int \frac{dx}{x\sqrt{x^2 + 2x - 1}}.$ Let $\sqrt{x^2 + 2x - 1} = z - x.$

Ans. $2\,\text{Tan}^{-1}(x + \sqrt{x^2 + 2x - 1}) + C.$

18. $\int \frac{dx}{x\sqrt{x^2 + x - 2}}.$ Let $\sqrt{x^2 + x - 2} = (x - 1)z.$

19. $\int_{2}^{5} \frac{dx}{x\sqrt{x^2 - 2x + 5}}.$ Let $\sqrt{x^2 - 2x + 5} = z - x.$ *Ans.* $\frac{1}{5}\sqrt{5}\ln 2.$

20. $\int_{1}^{4} \frac{dx}{x\sqrt{x^2 + x - 2}}.$ Let $\sqrt{x^2 + x - 2} = (x + 2)z.$

141. Use of Integration Tables

Thus far the integration processes which we have studied have been used to reduce a given integral to one of the elementary integration formulas $\boldsymbol{I}_1$–$\boldsymbol{I}_{24}$. This procedure is often very laborious, and to facilitate the work of integration it is customary in general practice to use a more extensive set of integration formulas. The Table of Integrals on pages 561–567 is such a set, and the following examples illustrate its use.

Example 1. Evaluate $\int \frac{dx}{x(2 + x)^2}.$

Solution: Using **9**, with $a = 2$, $b = 1$, and $u = x$, we have

$$\int \frac{dx}{x(2 + x)^2} = \frac{1}{2(2 + x)} - \frac{1}{4}\ln\frac{2 + x}{x} + C.$$

Example 2. Evaluate $\int \frac{dx}{x(2 + x^2)^2}.$

Solution: Using **9**, with $a = 2$, $b = 1$, and $u = x^2$, we have

$$\int \frac{dx}{x(2 + x^2)^2} = \frac{1}{2}\int \frac{(2x\,dx)}{x^2(2 + x^2)^2} = \frac{1}{4(2 + x^2)} - \frac{1}{8}\ln\frac{2 + x^2}{x^2} + C.$$

Example 3. Evaluate $\int \sin^4 x\,dx.$

Solution: Using the reduction formula **56** with $n = 4$ and $u = x$, we have

$$\int \sin^4 x\,dx = -\tfrac{1}{4}\sin^3 x\cos x + \tfrac{3}{4}\int \sin^2 x\,dx.$$

Then, using **54,** we obtain

$$\int \sin^4 x\,dx = -\tfrac{1}{4}\sin^3 x \cos x + \tfrac{3}{4}(\tfrac{1}{2}x - \tfrac{1}{2}\sin x \cos x) + C$$
$$= \tfrac{3}{8}x - \tfrac{3}{8}\sin x \cos x - \tfrac{1}{4}\sin^3 x \cos x + C.$$

When evaluating definite integrals, remember (Article **128**) that $\ln f(u)$ means $\ln |f(u)|$.

Example 4. Evaluate $\displaystyle\int_3^4 \frac{x\,dx}{(1-x)^2}$.

Solution: Using **7,** with $a = 1$, $b = -1$, and $u = x$, we have

$$\int_3^4 \frac{x\,dx}{(1-x)^2} = \left[\frac{1}{1-x} + \ln(1-x)\right]_3^4$$
$$= \left[-\frac{1}{3} + \ln 3\right] - \left[-\frac{1}{2} + \ln 2\right] = \frac{1}{6} + \ln\frac{3}{2}.$$

If there is any doubt concerning the principal values of inverse trigonometric functions over negative ranges it is advisable to change the sign of the variable of integration before evaluating the integral.

Example 5. Evaluate $\displaystyle\int_{-2}^{-1} \frac{\sqrt{x^2-1}}{x}\,dx$.

Solution: Setting $x = -z$, we have $dx = -dz$ and

$$\int_{-2}^{-1} \frac{\sqrt{x^2-1}}{x}\,dx = \int_2^1 \frac{\sqrt{z^2-1}}{z}\,dz.$$

Using **29,** with $a = 1$ and $u = z$, we obtain

$$\int_2^1 \frac{\sqrt{z^2-1}}{z}\,dz = \left[\sqrt{z^2-1} - \operatorname{Sec}^{-1} z\right]_2^1 = \frac{1}{3}\pi - \sqrt{3}.$$

EXERCISE 73

Using the Table of Integrals on page 561, evaluate the following integrals.

1. $\displaystyle\int \frac{dx}{x(2+3x)}$. *Ans.* $-\dfrac{1}{2}\ln\dfrac{2+3x}{x} + C.$

2. $\displaystyle\int \frac{x\,dx}{2x+5}$.

3. $\displaystyle\int \frac{dx}{x^2\sqrt{x^2-4}}$. $\dfrac{\sqrt{x^2-4}}{4x} + C.$

4. $\displaystyle\int \frac{x^2\,dx}{\sqrt{x^2+4}}$.

5. $\displaystyle\int \frac{dx}{(4-x^2)^{3/2}}$. $\dfrac{x}{4\sqrt{4-x^2}} + C.$

6. $\displaystyle\int (x^2+8)^{3/2}\,dx$.

7. $\displaystyle\int x\,e^{3x}\,dx$. $\tfrac{1}{9}e^{3x}(3x-1) + C.$

8. $\displaystyle\int \cos^3 2x\,dx$.

9. $\displaystyle\int \frac{dx}{x\sqrt{4x^2+1}}$. *Ans.* $\ln\left(\dfrac{x}{1+\sqrt{4x^2+1}}\right) + C$. 10. $\displaystyle\int \frac{x^3\,dx}{\sqrt{1+x^2}}$.

11. $\displaystyle\int \frac{dx}{x^2\sqrt{x-1}}$. *Ans.* $\dfrac{\sqrt{x-1}}{x} + \mathrm{Tan}^{-1}\sqrt{x-1} + C$.

12. $\displaystyle\int \sec^4\theta\, d\theta$.

13. $\displaystyle\int_0^4 \frac{x^2\,dx}{\sqrt{x^2+9}}$. *Ans.* $10 - \frac{9}{2}\ln 3$. 14. $\displaystyle\int_0^4 x\sqrt{3x+4}\,dx$.

15. $\displaystyle\int_0^3 \frac{x^2\,dx}{(4-x)^2}$. $15 - 16\ln 2$. 16. $\displaystyle\int_{3/4}^{3/2} \frac{\sqrt{9-4x^2}}{x^2}\,dx$.

17. $\displaystyle\int_2^{5/2} x^2\sqrt{x^2-4}\,dx$. $\frac{255}{64} - \ln 4$. 18. $\displaystyle\int_0^1 x\sqrt{8x^2+1}\,dx$.

19. $\displaystyle\int_0^\pi \sin^2\tfrac{1}{2}\theta\,d\theta$. $\frac{1}{2}\pi$. 20. $\displaystyle\int_0^{\pi/6} \tan^3 2\theta\,d\theta$.

21. $\displaystyle\int_0^{1/2} \frac{x^2\,dx}{\sqrt{1-4x^2}}$. $\frac{1}{32}\pi$. 22. $\displaystyle\int_{-\infty}^{-\sqrt{2}} \frac{dx}{x(x^2-1)^{3/2}}$.

23. $\displaystyle\int_2^4 \sqrt{x^2+2x-8}\,dx$. $10 - \frac{9}{2}\ln 3$. 24. $\displaystyle\int_0^{1/5} (2x-x^2)^{3/2}\,dx$.

25. $\displaystyle\int_1^2 x^4\ln x\,dx$. $\frac{32}{5}\ln 2 - \frac{31}{25}$. 26. $\displaystyle\int_0^1 x^2 e^{2x}\,dx$.

27. $\displaystyle\int_0^2 \frac{x^3\,dx}{\sqrt{2-x}}$. $\frac{256}{35}\sqrt{2}$. 28. $\displaystyle\int_0^1 e^{-x}\sin \pi x\,dx$.

29. $\displaystyle\int_0^{\pi/2} \sin^3\theta\cos^2\theta\,d\theta$. $\frac{2}{15}$. 30. $\displaystyle\int_0^{\pi/2} \sin 3\theta\cos 2\theta\,d\theta$.

31. Using the Wallis formulas and the fact that

$$\int_0^{\pi/2} \sin^{2n+1}x\,dx < \int_0^{\pi/2} \sin^{2n}x\,dx < \int_0^{\pi/2} \sin^{2n-1}x\,dx,$$

show that

$$\lim_{n\to\infty} \frac{1}{n}\left[\frac{2\cdot 4\cdot 6\cdots(2n)}{1\cdot 3\cdot 5\cdots(2n-1)}\right]^2 = \pi.$$

142. Approximate Integration. Trapezoidal Rule

In the preceding articles we have learned that the definite integral

$$\int_a^b f(x)\,dx \tag{1}$$

may be evaluated by finding the indefinite integral $F(x)$ and computing $F(b) - F(a)$. We shall now establish two methods for evaluating (1) *approximately*. These methods are particularly useful when the determination of $F(x)$ is difficult or impossible in terms of elementary functions.

Since the *value* of the integral (1) is numerically equal to the area between the curve $y = f(x)$ and the x axis from $x = a$ to $x = b$, any approximation of this area will give an approximation to (1). One method of doing this is to add trapezoids as follows.

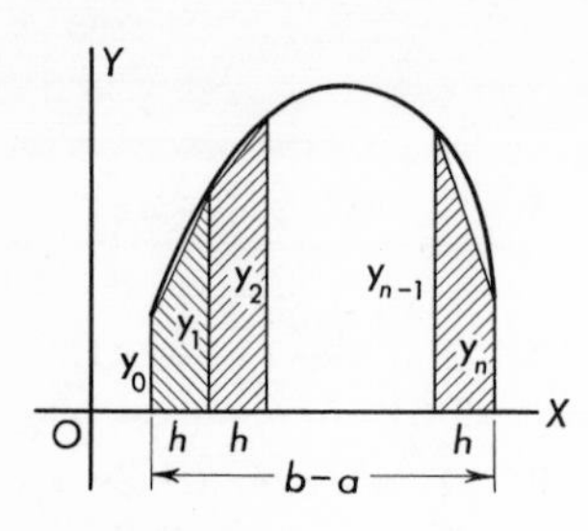

Figure 173

Divide the interval from a to b on the x axis into n equal parts so that each part has a length $h = (b - a)/n$. At each point of division let $y_0, y_1, y_2, \cdots, y_n$ be the respective ordinates of $y = f(x)$ as shown in Figure 173. Joining the ends of the successive ordinates and recalling that the area of a trapezoid is one-half the sum of its bases multiplied by its altitude, we obtain

$$\tfrac{1}{2}h(y_0 + y_1) + \tfrac{1}{2}h(y_1 + y_2) + \cdots + \tfrac{1}{2}h(y_{n-1} + y_n)$$

as the sum of the areas of the n trapezoids.

Thus for (1) we have the approximation

$$\int_a^b y\,dx \approx h(\tfrac{1}{2}y_0 + y_1 + \cdots + y_{n-1} + \tfrac{1}{2}y_n), \qquad (2)$$

which is known as the **trapezoidal rule.** It is geometrically apparent that, in general, a greater number of intervals will give a closer approximation.

Example 1. Calculate $\int_0^{10} x^2\,dx$ by the trapezoidal rule, using 10 intervals.

Solution: Here $h = (10 - 0)/10 = 1$. Substituting the abscissas $x = 0, 1, 2, \cdots, 10$ in the equation $y = x^2$, we obtain the corresponding ordinates $y = 0, 1, 4, \cdots, 100$. Hence, by (2), we have

$$\int_0^{10} x^2\,dx \approx (0 + 1 + 4 + 9 + 16 + \cdots + 81 + \tfrac{1}{2}\cdot 100) = 335.$$

By integration we find that the exact value of the integral is $333\tfrac{1}{3}$. Hence the above result is in error by $\tfrac{1}{2}$ of one per cent. Using 20 intervals instead of 10 gives the result $333\tfrac{3}{4}$.

Example 2. Find the approximate value of $\int_0^2 \sqrt{1 + x^3}\,dx$ taking $n = 4$.

Solution: Here $h = (2 - 0)/4 = \frac{1}{2}$. Substituting $x = 0, \frac{1}{2}, 1, \frac{3}{2}, 2$ in the equation $y = \sqrt{1 + x^3}$, we obtain the corresponding ordinates $y = 1, 1.061, 1.414, 2.092, 3$. Hence, by (2), we have

$$\int_0^2 \sqrt{1 + x^3}\, dx \approx \tfrac{1}{2}(0.5 + 1.061 + 1.414 + 2.092 + 1.5) = 3.284.$$

When $n = 20$, we obtain 3.243, a closer approximation.

143. Simpson's Rule

Instead of joining the ends of successive ordinates by chords and forming trapezoids, we can usually obtain a closer approximation by joining them with arcs of parabolas. This method of approximation depends on the following theorem.

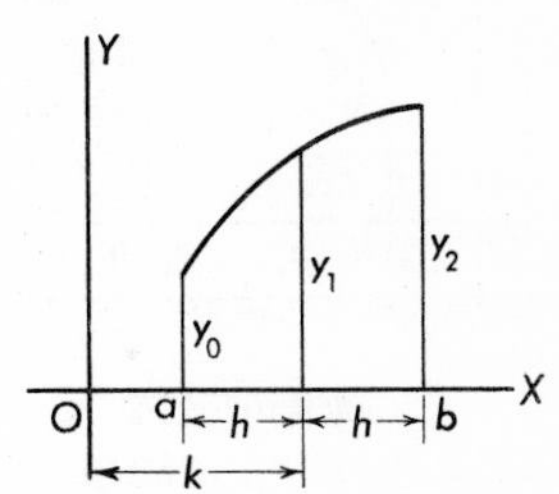

Figure 174

Prismoidal Theorem. *The area* $\boldsymbol{K}$ *between a parabola and the* $\boldsymbol{x}$ *axis from* $\boldsymbol{x = a}$ *to* $\boldsymbol{x = b}$ *is given by the* **prismoidal formula**

$$\boldsymbol{K = \tfrac{1}{3}h(y_0 + 4y_1 + y_2)}, \tag{1}$$

where $\boldsymbol{h = \frac{1}{2}(b - a)}$ *and* $\boldsymbol{y_0, y_1, y_2}$ *are the respective ordinates at* $\boldsymbol{x_0 = a, x_1 = \frac{1}{2}(a + b)}$, *and* $\boldsymbol{x_2 = b}$.

Proof: Let the equation of the parabola shown in Figure 174 be written in the form

$$y = A + B(x - k) + C(x - k)^2. \tag{2}$$

Integrating to find the area, we have

$$K = \int_{k-h}^{k+h} [A + B(x - k) + C(x - k)^2]\, dx$$

$$= 2Ah + \frac{2}{3}Ch^3 = \frac{1}{3}h(6A + 2Ch^2).$$

Finally, to find $6A + 2Ch^2$ in terms of y_0, y_1, and y_2, we substitute $x = k - h, k$, and $k + h$ in (2), and obtain

$$\begin{cases} y_0 = A - Bh + Ch^2, \\ y_1 = A, \\ y_2 = A + Bh + Ch^2. \end{cases}$$

Hence $y_0 + 4y_1 + y_2 = 6A + 2Ch^2$, and the theorem is proved.

Now let us divide the area shown in Figure 175 into an *even* number n of vertical strips each of width $h = (b - a)/n$. Applying the prismoidal formula to each successive double strip, we obtain the area

$$\tfrac{1}{3}h(y_0 + 4y_1 + y_2) + \tfrac{1}{3}h(y_2 + 4y_3 + y_4) + \cdots + \tfrac{1}{3}h(y_{n-2} + 4y_{n-1} + y_n).$$

Simplifying, we obtain the approximation formula

$$\int_a^b y\, dx \approx \frac{h}{3}(y_0 + 4y_1 + 2y_2 + 4y_3 + 2y_4 + \cdots + 4y_{n-1} + y_n), \quad (3)$$

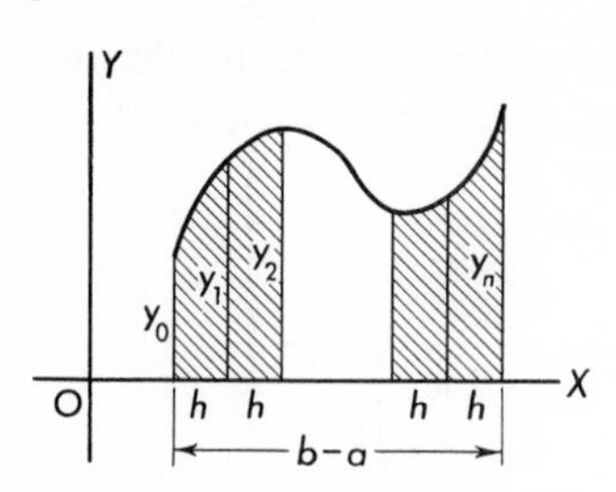

Figure 175

which is named for the English mathematician Thomas Simpson (1710–1761) and called **Simpson's rule.**

Example 1. Calculate $\int_0^2 \sqrt{1 + x^3}\, dx$ by Simpson's rule, taking $n = 4$.

Solution: Using the ordinates as given in Example 2 of the preceding article,. we obtain

$$\int_0^2 \sqrt{1 + x^3}\, dx \approx \frac{0.5}{3}(1 + 4.244 + 2.828 + 8.368 + 3) = 3.240.$$

Observe in this case that Simpson's rule gives a better approximation than the trapezoidal rule. When $n = 20$, Simpson's rule gives 3.241.

Example 2. Determine by Simpson's rule the volume generated by revolving the area $OABC$ of Figure 176 about the x axis.

Solution: Since the formula for a volume of revolution about the x axis is $\int_a^b \pi Y^2\, dx$, we let y in (3) represent πY^2 and obtain $y_0 = 9\pi$, $y_1 = 25\pi$, $y_2 = 36\pi$, $y_3 = 16\pi$, and $y_4 = 25\pi$. Substituting these values and $h = 1$ in Simpson's rule, we obtain

$$V \approx \tfrac{1}{3}(9\pi + 100\pi + 72\pi + 64\pi + 25\pi) = 90\pi.$$

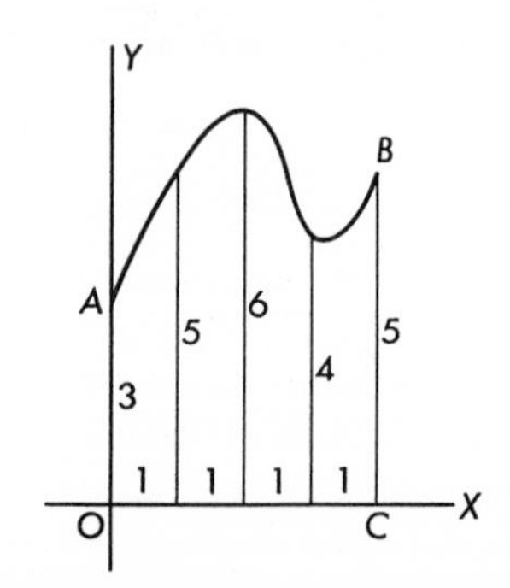

Figure 176

Note: It is shown in more advanced works that Simpson's approximation for the integral $\int_a^b f(x)\, dx$ is in error by an amount which is less than $\frac{(b - a)^5}{180n^4} \max |f^{(4)}(x)|$, $a \leq x \leq b$. Thus, in computing ln 2 from

$\int_1^2 x^{-1}\,dx$, we have $a = 1, b = 2, f(x) = x^{-1}$, and $f^{(4)}(x) = 24x^{-5}$. Hence $\max |f^{(4)}(x)| = 24$, and when $n = 8$ we obtain

$$\text{Error} \leqq \frac{(2-1)^5}{180(8)^4}(24) = 0.00003.$$

Thus, in this case, Simpson's rule gives a value for ln 2 that is correct to four decimal places.

EXERCISE 74

Using the trapezoidal rule, find approximate values for the following integrals. Check your results by integration.

1. $\int_2^7 \frac{dx}{x^2}$; $n = 5$. *Ans.* 0.377.
2. $\int_0^9 \sqrt{x}\,dx$; $n = 9$.
3. $\int_3^6 \frac{dx}{\sqrt{x-2}}$; $n = 6$. 2.009.
4. $\int_0^{3/4} \frac{x\,dx}{\sqrt{1+x^2}}$; $n = 3$.

Using Simpson's rule, find approximate values for the following integrals. Check your results by integration.

5. $\int_2^8 x^3\,dx$; $n = 2$. *Ans.* 1020.
6. $\int_1^9 \frac{dx}{\sqrt{x}}$; $n = 8$.
7. $\int_0^4 \frac{x\,dx}{\sqrt{x^2+9}}$; $n = 4$. 2.001.
8. $\int_0^2 \frac{x^2\,dx}{\sqrt{1+x^3}}$; $n = 4$.

Using both the trapezoidal and Simpson's rules, find approximate values for the following integrals.

9. $\int_0^4 \sqrt{4+x^3}\,dx$; $n = 4$. *Ans.* $\begin{cases}16.39,\\16.13.\end{cases}$
10. $\int_0^2 \sqrt{1+x^4}\,dx$; $n = 4$.
11. $\int_2^8 \sqrt[3]{1+x^2}\,dx$; $n = 4$. $\begin{cases}17.557,\\17.581.\end{cases}$
12. $\int_0^3 \sqrt{3+2x^3}\,dx$; $n = 6$.
13. $\int_0^{0.6} e^{-x^2}\,dx$; $n = 6$. $\begin{cases}0.5345,\\0.5352.\end{cases}$
14. $\int_{0.6}^1 \frac{e^x}{x}\,dx$; $n = 4$.
15. $\int_0^{0.8} \sin x^2\,dx$; $n = 4$. $\begin{cases}0.170,\\0.166.\end{cases}$
16. $\int_0^\pi \sqrt{\sin x}\,dx$; $n = 6$.
17. $\int_2^3 \frac{dx}{\ln x}$; $n = 4$. $\begin{cases}1.122,\\1.118.\end{cases}$
18. $\int_{\pi/4}^{\pi/3} \ln \tan x\,dx$; $n = 4$.
19. Find the value of ln 2 to four decimal places by evaluating $\int_{1/2}^1 \frac{dx}{x}$ by Simpson's rule with $n = 4$. *Ans.* 0.6933.
20. Find the value of π to four decimal places by evaluating $\int_0^1 \frac{dx}{1+x^2}$ by Simpson's rule with $n = 4$.

In Problems 21–23 find by Simpson's rule the area under the curve determined by the given data.

21.

x	0	2	4	6	8
y	5	6	4	2	3

Ans. 32.

22.

x	1	2	3	4	5	6	7
y	0.8	1.3	1.2	1.1	1.2	1.8	2.1

23.

x	2	5	8	11	14	17	20
y	4.16	3.98	3.31	2.86	3.02	3.61	4.34

Ans. 62.96.

24. Find by Simpson's rule the volume generated if the area of Problem 21 is revolved about the x axis.
25. Find by Simpson's rule the moment of inertia with respect to the x axis of the area of Problem 21. *Ans.* $261\frac{1}{3}$.
26. Find by Simpson's rule the moment of inertia with respect to the x axis of the volume of Problem 24.
27. Find the area of the loop of the curve $y^2 = 8x^2 - x^5$. Use Simpson's rule with $n = 8$. *Ans.* 8.217.
28. Prove that the prismoidal formula gives an exact result when y is a polynomial of the third degree in x. *Hint:* Add $D(x - k)^3$ to equation (2) in Article **143** and continue the proof given there.
29. Prove that the trapezoidal rule is in error by an amount that is less than $\frac{(b - a)^3}{12n^2} \max |f''(x)|$, $a \leqq x \leqq b$. *Hint:* Consider the function

$$E_k(t) = \int_{c_k-t}^{c_k+t} f(x)\,dx - t[f(c_k - t) + f(c_k + t)], \quad 0 \leqq t \leqq \tfrac{1}{2}h,$$

which for $t = \frac{1}{2}h$ represents the error associated with the kth trapezoid. Differentiate and apply the law of the mean to obtain $E_k'(t) = -2t^2 f''(x_1)$, $c_k - t \leqq x_1 \leqq c_k + t$. If M_k denotes the maximum value of $f''(x_1)$ in the interval $c_k - \frac{1}{2}h \leqq x_1 \leqq c_k + \frac{1}{2}h$, show that $|E_k(t)| \leqq \frac{2}{3}t^3 M_k$ and deduce the result.
30. Use the procedure suggested in the preceding problem to derive the error formula given in the note of Article **143**.

REVIEW EXERCISE 75

A. Indefinite Integrals

Evaluate the following integrals.

1. $\displaystyle\int \frac{dx}{x + x^3}$. *Ans.* $\displaystyle\frac{1}{2} \ln \frac{x^2}{1 + x^2} + C$.

2. $\displaystyle\int \frac{dx}{1 - x^4}$.

3. $\displaystyle\int \frac{(1 - \sin x)\, dx}{x + \cos x}$. *Ans.* $\ln (x + \cos x) + C$.

4. $\displaystyle\int \tan^3 2\theta \sec 2\theta\, d\theta$.

5. $\displaystyle\int \frac{dv}{v + 4\sqrt{v}}$. *Ans.* $2 \ln (4 + \sqrt{v}) + C$.

6. $\displaystyle\int \frac{x\, dx}{\sqrt{x^2 + 2x + 2}}$.

7. $\displaystyle\int t^2 \ln 2t\, dt$. $\frac{1}{9}t^3(3 \ln 2t - 1) + C$.

8. $\displaystyle\int (t + \sin t)^2\, dt$.

9. $\displaystyle\int \frac{2 + e^z}{1 + e^z}\, dz$. $2z - \ln (1 + e^z) + C$.

10. $\displaystyle\int \sec \theta \tan^2 \theta\, d\theta$.

11. $\displaystyle\int \frac{dx}{x^{2/3}(x^{2/3} + 1)}$. $3 \operatorname{Tan}^{-1} x^{1/3} + C$.

12. $\displaystyle\int \frac{\sqrt{x} + 1}{\sqrt{x} - 1}\, dx$.

13. $\displaystyle\int \frac{\cot \theta\, d\theta}{\ln \sin \theta}$. $\ln \ln \sin \theta + C$.

14. $\displaystyle\int \frac{dx}{1 - \sin 3x}$.

15. $\displaystyle\int \frac{2(2x + 1)\, dx}{x(x + 1)(x + 2)}$. *Ans.* $\displaystyle\ln \frac{x(x + 1)^2}{(x + 2)^3} + C$.

16. $\displaystyle\int (x \ln x)^2\, dx$.

17. $\displaystyle\int \frac{dx}{(x - 2)\sqrt{x + 2}}$. *Ans.* $\displaystyle\ln \left(\frac{\sqrt{x + 2} - 2}{\sqrt{x - 2}}\right) + C$.

18. $\displaystyle\int e^{-x} \sin^2 x\, dx$.

19. $\displaystyle\int \frac{d\theta}{5 - 3 \cos \theta}$. $\frac{1}{2} \operatorname{Tan}^{-1} (2 \tan \frac{1}{2}\theta) + C$.

20. $\displaystyle\int x \operatorname{Sin}^{-1} x\, dx$.

B. Definite Integrals

Evaluate the following integrals.

1. $\displaystyle\int_0^2 x^5\sqrt{1 + x^3}\, dx$. *Ans.* $\frac{1192}{45}$.

2. $\displaystyle\int_2^5 \frac{x\, dx}{(x - 1)^{3/2}}$.

3. $\displaystyle\int_0^{\pi/4} \frac{\cos 2\theta\, d\theta}{1 + \sin 2\theta}$. $\frac{1}{2} \ln 2$.

4. $\displaystyle\int_1^8 \frac{dx}{x + \sqrt[3]{x}}$.

5. $\displaystyle\int_1^2 \frac{8(x + 1)\, dx}{x^2(x^2 + 4)}$. 1.594.

6. $\displaystyle\int_1^6 \frac{dy}{y\sqrt{y^2 + 2y}}$.

7. $\displaystyle\int_1^4 \frac{(\sqrt{x} + 1)\, dx}{\sqrt{x}(x + 1)}$. *Ans.* $\ln \frac{5}{2} + 2 \operatorname{Tan}^{-1} \frac{1}{3}$.

8. $\displaystyle\int_{-1}^{8} \frac{dx}{\sqrt{1+\sqrt{1+x}}}$.

9. $\displaystyle\int_{1/4}^{5/4} \frac{dy}{\sqrt{y+1}-\sqrt{y}}$. *Ans.* $\frac{13}{6}$.

10. $\displaystyle\int_{16}^{25} \frac{dz}{z-2\sqrt{z}-3}$.

11. $\displaystyle\int_{0}^{\ln 3} \frac{e^{2t}\,dt}{\sqrt{1+e^t}}$. $\frac{2}{3}(2+\sqrt{2})$.

12. $\displaystyle\int_{\pi/6}^{\pi/3} \frac{d\theta}{\sin^2\theta\cos\theta}$.

13. $\displaystyle\int_{3}^{7} \frac{dx}{x^2\sqrt{x^2-4}}$. $\sqrt{5}/42$.

14. $\displaystyle\int_{2}^{4} \frac{10x^2\,dx}{x^4+3x^2-4}$.

15. $\displaystyle\int_{5/4}^{3} \frac{dz}{\sqrt{z^2+4z-5}}$. $\ln 2$.

16. $\displaystyle\int_{0}^{2} y^2\sqrt{4-y^2}\,dy$.

17. $\displaystyle\int_{0}^{\pi/2} (\sin\theta+\sin 2\theta)^2\,d\theta$. *Ans.* $\frac{1}{6}(3\pi+8)$.

18. $\displaystyle\int_{0}^{\pi} \sin\tfrac{1}{2}\theta\cos\tfrac{1}{3}\theta\,d\theta$.

19. $\displaystyle\int_{1}^{2} \frac{y^4-3}{y^3+y^2}\,dy$. *Ans.* $\ln\frac{32}{9}-1$.

20. $\displaystyle\int_{2}^{8/3} \sqrt{x^4-2x^3}\,dx$.

C. Improper Integrals

Evaluate the following integrals, if they converge.

1. $\displaystyle\int_{1}^{3} \frac{dx}{\sqrt{x^2-1}}$. *Ans.* $\ln(3+2\sqrt{2})$.

2. $\displaystyle\int_{1}^{3} \frac{x\,dx}{\sqrt{x^2-1}}$.

3. $\displaystyle\int_{0}^{2} \frac{dy}{y^2+2y-3}$. No value.

4. $\displaystyle\int_{-1}^{0} \frac{z^3\,dz}{\sqrt{z+1}}$.

5. $\displaystyle\int_{0}^{a} \frac{dx}{\sqrt{ax-x^2}}$. π.

6. $\displaystyle\int_{0}^{4} \sqrt{\frac{4-x}{x}}\,dx$.

7. $\displaystyle\int_{-\infty}^{\ln 2} \frac{dt}{e^t+4e^{-t}}$. $\frac{1}{8}\pi$.

8. $\displaystyle\int_{0}^{\infty} \frac{dt}{\sqrt{e^t+1}}$.

9. $\displaystyle\int_{0}^{1} \sqrt{\frac{x}{1-x^3}}\,dx$. $\frac{1}{3}\pi$.

10. $\displaystyle\int_{0}^{1} \frac{\mathrm{Sin}^{-1}x}{x^2}\,dx$.

D. Areas $\int y\,dx$, $\int x\,dy$, etc.

In each of the following, find the area bounded by the given curves.

1. $x^2y^2(x+4)=1$, $x=5$, and $x=12$. *Ans.* $\ln\frac{5}{3}$.
2. $y^3=x^3(7x+1)$, $y=0$, and $x=1$.
3. $4y^2-x^2=4$ and $y=2$. $4\sqrt{3}-2\ln(2+\sqrt{3})$.
4. $x^2y^2=y^2+9$, $x=2$, and $x=3$.
5. $4y=x^2-2\ln x$, $y=0$, $x=1$, and $x=4$. $\frac{27}{4}-4\ln 2$.
6. $y=(4-x)\ln x$ and $y=0$.

7. The loop of the curve $y^2 = x^2(4 - x)$. *Ans.* $\frac{256}{15}$.
8. The loop of the curve $y^2 = x^4(4 - x)$.
9. $y = x^2 e^{-x}$, $y = 0$, and $x = 1$. $2 - 5e^{-1}$.
10. Arch of $y = x \cos x$ from $x = 0$ to $x = \frac{1}{2}\pi$.
11. $y = 1/(1 + \sqrt[3]{x})$, $y = 1$, and $x = 8$. $8 - 3 \ln 3$.
12. $xy(x + 1) = x^2 - 4$, $y = 0$, and $x = 3$.
13. $x^2y^4 = y^2 - 16$ and $y = 5$. $\ln 4 - \frac{6}{5}$.
14. $y^2(x + 3) = x - 2$ and $x = 6$.
15. Arch of $y = \sin^3 x$ from $x = 0$ to $x = \pi$. $\frac{4}{3}$.
16. $x^2y^2 + 16x^2 = y^4$ and $y = 3$.
17. $x^{1/2} + y^{1/2} = a^{1/2}$ and $x + y = a$. $\frac{1}{3}a^2$.
18. The loop of the strophoid $y^2(a + x) = x^2(a - x)$.
19. The ellipse $x = a \cos \phi$, $y = b \sin \phi$. πab.
20. The cardioid $x = a(2 \cos t - \cos 2t)$, $y = a(2 \sin t - \sin 2t)$. *Hint:* Evaluate $2 \int y\, dx$ from $t = \pi$ to $t = 0$.

E. Volumes $\pi \int y^2\, dx$, $2\pi \int xy\, dx$, etc.

Find the volume of the solid generated by revolving about the indicated axis the area bounded by the given curves.

1. $xy = x - y$, $y = 0$, and $x = 4$; about x axis. *Ans.* $\pi(\frac{24}{5} - 2 \ln 5)$.
2. $y = \cos x$, $y = 0$, and $x = 0$; about y axis.
3. $y^2(x + 3) = x - 2$ and $x = 6$; about x axis. $\pi(4 + 5 \ln \frac{5}{9})$.
4. Arch of $y = \sin^2 x$ from $x = 0$ to $x = \pi$; about x axis.
5. $x^2y^2 + xy^2 = x - 1$, $y = 0$, and $x = 2$; about x axis. $\pi \ln \frac{9}{8}$.
6. $y = \ln x$, $y = 0$, and $x = 4$; about $x = 4$.
7. The loop of the curve $y^4 = x(4 - x)$; about x axis. $2\pi^2$.
8. The loop of the curve $y^6 = x^3(8 - x)$; about x axis.
9. The ellipse $x = a \cos \phi$, $y = b \sin \phi$; about x axis. $\frac{4}{3}\pi ab^2$.
10. The loop of the curve $x = t^2$, $y = 4t - t^3$; about x axis.
11. $x^3y^2 - xy^2 = x^2 + 1$, $x = 2$, and $x = 4$; about x axis. $\pi \ln \frac{5}{2}$.
12. $x^2 + y^4 = 25$; about x axis.
13. $y = x e^x$, $y = 0$, and $x = 2$; about $x = 2$. 8π.
14. Arch of $y = x \sin x$ from $x = 0$ to $x = \pi$; about y axis.
15. $y = x \ln x$ and $y = 0$; about x axis. $\frac{2}{27}\pi$.
16. $y = (6 - x) \ln x$ and $y = 0$; about y axis.
17. $y(4 + x^2) = 8$ and $y = 1$; about $y = 1$. $2\pi(4 - \pi)$.
18. $y^2x^2 = x^2 - 9$ and $x = 5$; about $x = 5$.
19. $y = x \operatorname{Tan}^{-1} x$, $y = 0$, and $x = 1$; about y axis. *Ans.* $\frac{1}{6}\pi(\pi - 2 + \ln 4)$.
20. $(x^2 + 4)y = 6 - x$, $x = 0$, and $y = 0$; about y axis.

F. Centroids $\bar{x} = \int x_c\, dA \Big/ \int dA, \quad \bar{y} = \int y_c\, dA \Big/ \int dA,$ etc.

Find the centroid of the area bounded by the given curves.

1. $y = x\sqrt{4 - x}$ and $y = 0$. *Ans.* $(\frac{16}{7}, \frac{5}{4})$.
2. $y^2 = 2x$ and $x - y = 4$.
3. Arch of $y = \sin x$ from $x = 0$ to $x = \pi$. $(\frac{1}{2}\pi, \frac{1}{8}\pi)$.
4. $x^2y^2 + 9y^2 = x^2$ and $x = 4$.
5. The loop of the curve $4x^2 = y(9 - y)^2$. $(0, \frac{27}{7})$.
6. $y = \ln x$, $y = 0$, and $x = 2$.
7. $y = e^x$, $y = 0$, $x = 0$, and $x = 1$. $\left(\frac{1}{e - 1}, \frac{e + 1}{4}\right)$.
8. Arch of $x = a(\theta - \sin\theta)$, $y = a(1 - \cos\theta)$ from $\theta = 0$ to $\theta = 2\pi$.
9. $x^2 - y^2 = 9$ and $x = 5$. *Ans.* $\bar{x} = 128/(60 - 27 \ln 3)$.
10. $xy(x + 1) = 2x + 1$, $y = 0$, $x = 1$, and $x = 2$.

Find the centroid of the solid generated by revolving about the indicated axis the area bounded by the given curves.

11. $y^2 = 4ax$ and $x = a$; about x axis. *Ans.* $\bar{x} = \frac{2}{3}a$.
12. $y = 2x\sqrt{3 - x}$ and $y = 0$; about x axis.
13. First-quadrant area of $x^2 + y^4 = 16$; about x axis. $\bar{x} = 16/3\pi$.
14. $(x + 1)y^2 = 4 - x$ and $x = 0$; about x axis.
15. $y = \cos x$, $y = 0$, and $x = 0$; about y axis. $\bar{y} = \frac{1}{16}(\pi + 2)$.
16. The loop of the curve $x = 4t - t^3$, $y = t^2$; about y axis.
17. $y = e^{-x}$, $y = 0$, $x = 0$, and $x = 1$; about y axis.
    Ans. $\bar{y} = (e^2 - 3)/8e(e - 2)$.
18. $x^2y^2 + xy^2 = 2 - x$ and $x = 1$; about x axis.
19. $y^3 = x^3(1 - x)$ and $y = 0$; about x axis. $\bar{x} = \frac{9}{14}$.
20. $y^2 = 1 - \ln x$ and $x = 1$; about x axis.

G. Moments of Inertia $I_x = \int y_r^2\, dA, \quad I_y = \int x_r^2\, dA,$ etc.

For each of the areas bounded by the following curves, find the moment of inertia with respect to the axis indicated.

1. $x^2 = 4ay$ and $y = a$; axis OX. *Ans.* $\frac{8}{7}a^4$.
2. $y^3 = x\,e^{-3x}$, $y = 0$, and $x = 1$; axis OX.
3. $x^2 + y^3 = 64$ and $y = 0$; axis OX. $227\frac{5}{9}$.
4. $x^2y = 8 - 4y$, $x = 0$, $y = 0$, and $x = 2$; axis OY.
5. Arch of $y = \sin x$ from $x = 0$ to $x = \pi$; axis OX. $\frac{4}{9}$.
6. $xy = (4 - x)\ln x$ and $y = 0$; axis OY.
7. $x^3y(y + 2) = y + 4$, $x = 0$, $y = 1$, and $y = 3$; axis OY.
    Ans. $\frac{1}{3}\ln\frac{27}{5}$.

8. First-quadrant area of the ellipse $x = a \cos \phi$, $y = b \sin \phi$; axis OX.
9. $x^2 - y^2 = 16$ and $x = 5$; axis OY. *Ans.* $\frac{255}{2} - 64 \ln 2$.
10. The circle $x^2 + y^2 = 2ay$; axis OX. (Compare your result with Problem 27, Exercise **25**.)

If the areas bounded by the following curves are revolved about the axis indicated, find the moment of inertia of the solid generated with respect to the axis of revolution.

11. $x^2 - y^2 = 3$, $y = 2$, and $y = -2$; about y axis. *Ans.* $\frac{202}{5}\pi$.
12. The loop of the curve $y^4 = x(4 - x)$; about x axis.
13. $y(x^2 + 4) = 8$ and $y = 1$; about y axis. $8\pi(3 - 4 \ln 2)$.
14. Arch of $y = \sin x$ from $x = 0$ to $x = \pi$; about x axis.
15. $y = \sqrt{x}\, e^{x/4}$, $y = 0$, and $x = 1$; about x axis. $\frac{1}{2}\pi(e - 2)$.
16. $y = \cos x$, $x = 0$ and $y = 0$; about y axis.
17. $y^2(1 + x) = 1 - x$ and $x = 0$; about y axis. $\frac{1}{12}\pi(32 - 9\pi)$.
18. The loop of the curve $y^4(x + 1) = x(2 - x)$; about x axis.
19. $y^2 = \ln x$ and $x = 4$; about x axis. *Ans.* $\pi[2(\ln 4)^2 - 4 \ln 4 + 3]$.
20. Arch of $x = a(\theta - \sin \theta)$, $y = a(1 - \cos \theta)$ from $\theta = 0$ to $\theta = 2\pi$; about x axis.

H. Work and Pressure $W = \int F\, ds$, $P = w \int h\, dA$, etc.

1. A horizontal cylindrical tank 6 feet in radius is half full of oil weighing 60 pounds per cubic foot. Find the force on one end of the tank. *Ans.* 8640 lb.
2. A water tank is in the form of a hemisphere, 12 feet in diameter, surmounted by a cylinder of the same diameter and 8 feet high. If the tank is filled to a height 2 feet below the top, find the work done in pumping the water to the top of the tank.
3. Find the force on one side of a circular plate of radius 4 feet, if the plate is submerged vertically in water with its center 4 feet below the surface. *Ans.* $64\pi w$ lb.
4. Solve Problem 3 when the center is 2 feet below the surface.
5. A tank in the shape of a paraboloid of revolution is 10 feet deep and 10 feet across the top. If the tank is filled with oil weighing 60 pounds per cubic foot, find the work required to pump the oil to the top of the tank. *Ans.* 12.5π ft-tons.
6. The vertical end of a water trough is 3 feet wide at the top, 2 feet deep, and has the form of the area bounded by the x axis and one arch of the curve $y = 2 \sin \frac{1}{3}\pi x$. Find the force on the end when the trough is full of water.
7. Solve Problem 6 if the end is a semiellipse. *Ans.* $4w$ lb.

8. A semiellipsoidal tank has axes of 10 feet and 20 feet across the top and is 6 feet deep. If the tank is full of water, find the work required to pump the water to the top of the tank.
9. Solve Problem 8 if the tank has the form of an inverted elliptical cone with the same dimensions. *Ans.* $150\pi w$ ft-lb.
10. Solve Problem 8 if the tank has the form of an elliptical paraboloid with the same dimensions.

CHAPTER 16

Additional Applications of Integration

144. Area in Polar Coordinates

Consider the area AOB in Figure 177 which is bounded by the radial lines $\theta = \alpha$ and $\theta = \beta$, and the curve $r = f(\theta)$ where $f(\theta)$ is a continuous and single-valued function.

If the angle AOB is divided into n equal parts $d\theta$ by means of radial lines from O, the area is divided into n **increments of area,** such as OPQ. Approximating each of these increments by **elements of area** dA in the form of circular sectors, such as OPP', we find by **5,** page 1, that $dA = \frac{1}{2}r^2\,d\theta$. Hence, by the Fundamental Theorem, it follows that

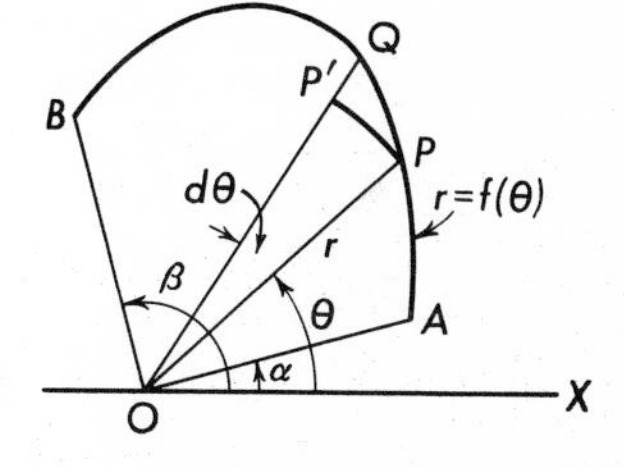

Figure 177

$$A = \frac{1}{2}\int_{\alpha}^{\beta} \boldsymbol{r^2\,d\theta}. \tag{1}$$

Example 1. Find the area of one leaf of the rose $r = a\cos 2\theta$.

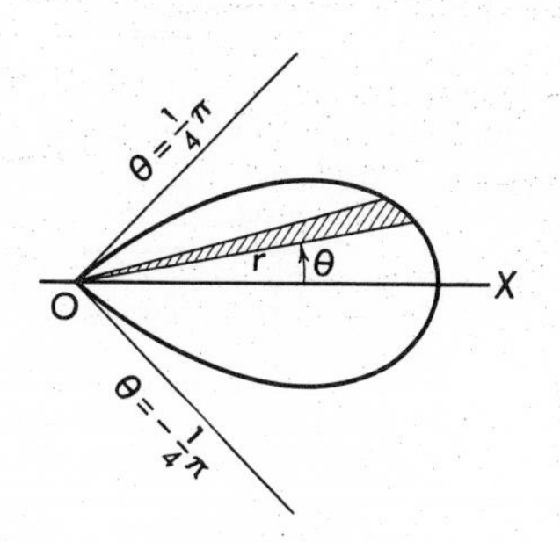

Figure 178

Solution: One leaf of the rose is generated as θ varies from $-\frac{1}{4}\pi$ to $\frac{1}{4}\pi$, as shown in Figure 178. Hence, using these limits and formula (1), we obtain

$$A = \frac{1}{2}\int_{-\pi/4}^{\pi/4} a^2\cos^2 2\theta\,d\theta$$

$$= \frac{1}{2}a^2\int_{-\pi/4}^{\pi/4} \frac{1}{2}(1 + \cos 4\theta)\,d\theta$$

$$= \frac{1}{4}a^2\Big[\theta + \frac{1}{4}\sin 4\theta\Big]_{-\pi/4}^{\pi/4} = \frac{1}{8}a^2\pi.$$

Note: Because of the symmetry of the curve in the above example, we could just as well have integrated from 0 to $\frac{1}{4}\pi$ and doubled the result.

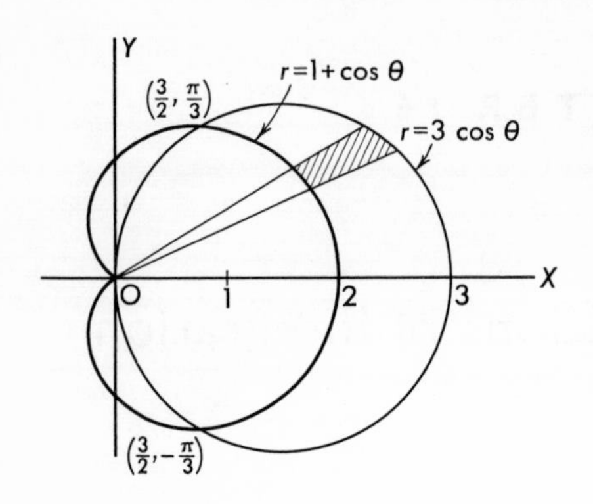

Figure 179

Example 2. Find the area which is inside the circle $r = 3\cos\theta$ and outside the cardioid $r = 1 + \cos\theta$.

Solution: Solving the given equations simultaneously, we find the points of intersection as indicated in Figure 179.

Since the required area is the difference in area between the circle and cardioid as θ increases from $-\frac{1}{3}\pi$ to $\frac{1}{3}\pi$, we find, on taking symmetry into account,

$$A = 2\int_0^{\pi/3} [\tfrac{1}{2}(3\cos\theta)^2 - \tfrac{1}{2}(1 + \cos\theta)^2]\, d\theta$$

$$= \int_0^{\pi/3} [8\cos^2\theta - 2\cos\theta - 1]\, d\theta$$

$$= \Big[8(\tfrac{1}{2}\theta + \tfrac{1}{2}\sin\theta\cos\theta) - 2\sin\theta - \theta\Big]_0^{\pi/3} = \pi.$$

EXERCISE 76

Find the area enclosed by each of the following curves.

1. $r = 4\sin\theta$. *Ans.* 4π.
2. $r = 4 - 3\sin\theta$.
3. $r = 2\cos 3\theta$. π.
4. $r = 1 + \cos\theta$.
5. $r = 8\sin^2\frac{1}{2}\theta$. 24π.
6. $r = 2\sin 4\theta$.
7. $r = 2 - \cos\theta$. $\frac{9}{2}\pi$.
8. $r\cos\theta = \cos 2\theta$.
9. $r^2 = 4\cos 2\theta$. 4.
10. $r^2 = 4\cos 4\theta$.
11. $r = 4\sin^2\theta\cos\theta$. $\frac{1}{2}\pi$.
12. $r = \tan\frac{1}{2}\theta$.

Find the common area enclosed by the following pairs of curves.

13. $\begin{cases} r = 3\cos\theta, \\ r = 1 + \cos\theta. \end{cases}$ *Ans.* $\frac{5}{4}\pi$.
14. $\begin{cases} r = 5\sin\theta, \\ r = 5\cos\theta. \end{cases}$
15. $\begin{cases} r = 3 - 2\cos\theta, \\ r = 2. \end{cases}$ $\frac{19}{3}\pi - \frac{11}{2}\sqrt{3}$.
16. $\begin{cases} r^2 = 6\cos 2\theta, \\ r = 2\cos\theta. \end{cases}$

For each of the following pairs of curves, find the area which is inside the first curve and outside the second.

17. $\begin{cases} r = 5\sin\theta, \\ r = 2 + \sin\theta. \end{cases}$ *Ans.* $\frac{8}{3}\pi + \sqrt{3}$.
18. $\begin{cases} r = 4(1 + \sin\theta), \\ r = 4. \end{cases}$
19. $\begin{cases} r^2 = 2\cos 2\theta, \\ r = 1. \end{cases}$ $\sqrt{3} - \frac{1}{3}\pi$.
20. $\begin{cases} r = 2\sin\theta, \\ r = \sin\theta + \cos\theta. \end{cases}$

Find the area bounded by the following curves.

21. $\begin{cases} r = 2/(1 + \cos\theta), \\ r = 2/(1 - \cos\theta). \end{cases}$ *Ans.* $\frac{16}{3}$.

22. $\begin{cases} r = \csc\theta, \\ r = \tan\theta \sec\theta. \end{cases}$

23. $\begin{cases} r = \tan\theta, \\ r = \cot\theta. \end{cases}$ $4 - \pi$.

24. $\begin{cases} r^2 = 6 \sec 2\theta, \\ r = 3 \sec\theta. \end{cases}$

25. Find the area of the smaller loop of the trisectrix $r = a(1 - 2\cos\theta)$. *Ans.* $\frac{1}{2}a^2(2\pi - 3\sqrt{3})$.

26. Find the area enclosed by the loop of the strophoid $r = a(\sec\theta - \tan\theta)$.

27. Find the area of the loop of the curve $r^2 = a^2 \cos 2\theta \cos\theta$ which is bisected by the initial line. *Ans.* $\frac{1}{3}a^2\sqrt{2}$.

28. Find the area between the inner and outer loops of the curve $r^2 = a^2(1 + \sin\theta)$.

29. Changing to polar coordinates find the area enclosed by the curve $(x^2 + y^2)^3 = 4a^2x^2y^2$. *Ans.* $\frac{1}{2}\pi a^2$.

30. Changing to polar coordinates find the area enclosed by the ellipse $b^2x^2 + a^2y^2 = a^2b^2$.

145. Length of a Plane Curve

Let the equation of the curve shown in Figure 180 be $y = f(x)$ where the function $f(x)$ has a continuous derivative in the interval $a \leqq x \leqq b$. If we divide the curve into n segments by the points $P_k(x_k, y_k)$ in such a way that $a = x_0 < x_1 < \cdots < x_{n-1} < x_n = b$, we define the length of the curve to be the limit of the sum of the n line segments

$$AP_1 + P_1P_2 + \cdots + P_{n-1}B \quad (1)$$

as the greatest of the differences $x_k - x_{k-1}$ approaches zero.

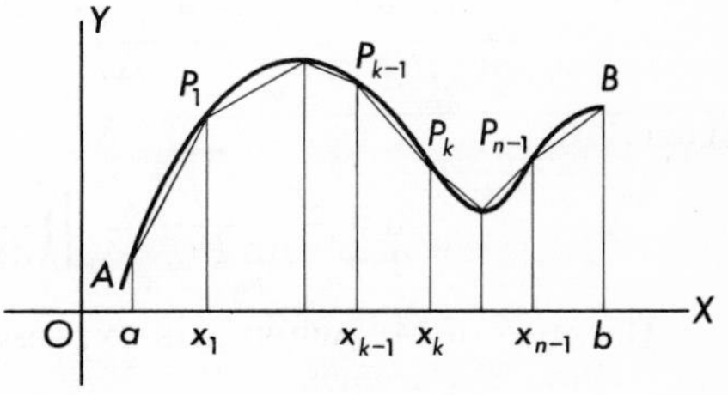

Figure 180

We observe that the kth line segment in (1) has a length given by

$$P_{k-1}P_k = [(x_k - x_{k-1})^2 + (y_k - y_{k-1})^2]^{1/2},$$

and by the law of the mean we know that

$$y_k - y_{k-1} = f(x_k) - f(x_{k-1}) = f'(x_k')(x_k - x_{k-1})$$

where $x_{k-1} \leqq x_k' \leqq x_k$. Hence (1) can be written as

$$\sum_{k=1}^{n} \{1 + [f'(x_k')]^2\}^{1/2} \Delta x_k \quad (2)$$

where $\Delta x_k = x_k - x_{k-1}$. By taking the limit of (2) as $n \to \infty$ and every $\Delta x_k \to 0$, in accordance with the Fundamental Theorem we can express the length of arc as a definite integral in either of the following forms.

$$s = \int_a^b \sqrt{1 + [f'(x)]^2}\, dx, \qquad \text{or} \qquad s = \int_a^b \sqrt{1 + \left(\frac{dy}{dx}\right)^2}\, dx. \quad (3)$$

Illustration. For the curve $y = \frac{2}{3}x^{3/2}$, we have $y' = x^{1/2}$. Hence the length of the curve from $x = 0$ to $x = 3$ is

$$s = \int_0^3 \sqrt{1 + (x^{1/2})^2}\, dx = \left[\frac{2}{3}(1 + x)^{3/2}\right]_0^3 = \frac{14}{3}.$$

Basically, we observe that a length of arc is determined by the integral $\int ds$, where

$$(ds)^2 = (dx)^2 + (dy)^2. \quad (4)$$

Note: In Article **95** we made the assumption,

$$\lim_{Q \to P} \frac{\text{chord } PQ}{\text{arc } PQ} = 1, \quad (5)$$

in order to establish the relationship (4). Since (4) has now been established without this assumption, we can verify the validity of (5). Referring to Figure 137 for the notation used, we have

$$\frac{\text{chord } PQ}{\text{arc } PQ} = \frac{[(\Delta x)^2 + (\Delta y)^2]^{1/2}}{\Delta s} = \left[\left(\frac{\Delta x}{\Delta s}\right)^2 + \left(\frac{\Delta y}{\Delta s}\right)^2\right]^{1/2}.$$

Therefore

$$\lim_{Q \to P} \frac{\text{chord } PQ}{\text{arc } PQ} = \left[\left(\frac{dx}{ds}\right)^2 + \left(\frac{dy}{ds}\right)^2\right]^{1/2} = 1.$$

Because of (4), when x is expressed in terms of y, we use

$$s = \int_{y_1}^{y_2} \sqrt{1 + \left(\frac{dx}{dy}\right)^2}\, dy. \quad (6)$$

When x and y are given in terms of a parameter t, and the derivatives dx/dt and dy/dt are continuous functions in $c \leqq t \leqq d$, we use

$$s = \int_c^d \sqrt{\left(\frac{dx}{dt}\right)^2 + \left(\frac{dy}{dt}\right)^2}\, dt. \quad (7)$$

It is interesting to note that the formula (7) can be derived by a procedure similar to that used in deriving (3). In this case, when $x = f(t)$ and $y = g(t)$, we have by the law of the mean

$$x_k - x_{k-1} = f(t_k) - f(t_{k-1}) = f'(t_k')\, \Delta t_k,$$
$$y_k - y_{k-1} = g(t_k) - g(t_{k-1}) = g'(t_k'')\, \Delta t_k,$$

where t'_k and t''_k are two suitably chosen values of t between t_{k-1} and t_k. Thus (1) becomes

$$\sum_{k=1}^{n} \left\{[f'(t'_k)]^2 + [g'(t''_k)]^2\right\}^{1/2} \Delta t_k. \tag{8}$$

Since t'_k and t''_k are distinct values in the interval Δt_k, the Fundamental Theorem is not applicable to the limit of (8). For this reason it is necessary to proceed in a different way. This we can do by observing that $\sqrt{[f'(t)]^2 + [g'(t)]^2}$ is a continuous function of t, and so by Theorem 3, Article **23,** there are values $\underline{t}_k$ and $\bar{t}_k$ that minimize and maximize the function in each of the intervals Δt_k, that is,

$$\{[f'(\underline{t}_k)]^2 + [g'(\underline{t}_k)]^2\}^{1/2} \leqq \{[f'(t'_k)]^2 + [g'(t''_k)]^2\}^{1/2}$$
$$\leqq \{[f'(\bar{t}_k)]^2 + [g'(\bar{t}_k)]^2\}^{1/2}.$$

Now by the Fundamental Theorem we know that

$$\lim_{n\to\infty} \sum_{k=1}^{n} \left\{[f'(\underline{t}_k)]^2 + [g'(\underline{t}_k)]^2\right\}^{1/2} \Delta t_k = \int_c^d \sqrt{[f'(t)]^2 + [g'(t)]^2}\, dt$$

and

$$\lim_{n\to\infty} \sum_{k=1}^{n} \left\{[f'(\bar{t}_k)]^2 + [g'(\bar{t}_k)]^2\right\}^{1/2} \Delta t_k = \int_c^d \sqrt{[f'(t)]^2 + [g'(t)]^2}\, dt;$$

hence it follows by Theorem 2, Article **22,** that

$$\lim_{n\to\infty} \sum_{k=1}^{n} \left\{[f'(t'_k)]^2 + [g'(t''_k)]^2\right\}^{1/2} \Delta t_k = \int_c^d \sqrt{[f'(t)]^2 + [g'(t)]^2}\, dt.$$

If the equation of the curve is given in polar coordinates, we can show in the same manner as for equation (2) that

$$s = \int_{\theta_1}^{\theta_2} \sqrt{r^2 + \left(\frac{dr}{d\theta}\right)^2}\, d\theta. \tag{9}$$

Example 1. Find the length of the curve $x = 2(2t + 3)^{3/2}$, $y = 3(t + 1)^2$ from $t = -1$ to $t = 3$.

Solution: For the given curve, we have $dx/dt = 6(2t + 3)^{1/2}$ and $dy/dt = 6(t + 1)$; hence by (7)

$$s = \int_{-1}^{3} \sqrt{36(2t + 3) + 36(t^2 + 2t + 1)}\, dt$$
$$= \int_{-1}^{3} 6(t + 2)\, dt = \Big[3(t + 2)^2\Big]_{-1}^{3} = 72.$$

Example 2. Find the length of the cardioid $r = a \cos^2 \frac{1}{2}\theta$.

Solution: Since the entire curve is traced as θ increases from 0 to 2π, we have $r' = -a \sin \frac{1}{2}\theta \cos \frac{1}{2}\theta$ and by (9)

$$s = \int_0^{2\pi} \sqrt{a^2 \cos^4 \tfrac{1}{2}\theta + a^2 \sin^2 \tfrac{1}{2}\theta \cos^2 \tfrac{1}{2}\theta}\, d\theta$$

$$= a\int_0^{2\pi} \sqrt{\cos^2 \tfrac{1}{2}\theta}\, d\theta = a \int_0^{\pi} \cos \tfrac{1}{2}\theta\, d\theta + a \int_{\pi}^{2\pi} (-\cos \tfrac{1}{2}\theta)\, d\theta = 4a.$$

EXERCISE 77

Find the length of each of the following curves.

1. $y = x\sqrt{x}$ from $x = 0$ to $x = \frac{4}{3}$. *Ans.* $\frac{56}{27}$.
2. $3y = 2(x - 1)^{3/2}$ from $x = 1$ to $x = 4$.
3. $3y = 2(x^2 + 1)^{3/2}$ from $x = 0$ to $x = 3$. 21.
4. $y = \ln \sec x$ from $x = 0$ to $x = \frac{1}{3}\pi$.
5. $x = \ln y$ from $y = \frac{3}{4}$ to $y = \frac{4}{3}$. $\frac{5}{12} + \ln \frac{3}{2}$.
6. $2x = y^2$ from $y = 0$ to $y = 2.4$.
7. $8x = y^4 + 2y^{-2}$ from $y = 1$ to $y = 2$. $\frac{33}{16}$.
8. $x = \ln \sin y$ from $y = \frac{1}{3}\pi$ to $y = \frac{2}{3}\pi$.
9. $x = t^3 - 3t,\quad y = 3t^2$ from $t = 0$ to $t = 1$. 4.
10. $x = \frac{1}{3}t^3 + t^{-1},\quad y = 2t$ from $t = 1$ to $t = 3$.
11. One arch of the cycloid $x = a(\phi - \sin \phi),\quad y = a(1 - \cos \phi)$. $8a$.
12. $x = \sin \phi - \phi \cos \phi,\quad y = \cos \phi + \phi \sin \phi$ from $\phi = 0$ to $\phi = \frac{1}{4}\pi$.
13. The circle $r = a \sin \theta + b \cos \theta$. *Ans.* $\pi\sqrt{a^2 + b^2}$.
14. The cardioid $r = a(1 + \cos \theta)$.
15. The entire curve $r = a \sin^3 \frac{1}{3}\theta$. $\frac{3}{2}\pi a$.
16. $r = a \sec^2 \frac{1}{2}\theta$ from $\theta = 0$ to $\theta = \frac{1}{2}\pi$.
17. $4y = 2x^2 - \ln x$ from $x = 1$ to $x = 3$. $4 + \frac{1}{4} \ln 3$.
18. $y = \ln (x^2 - 1)$ from $x = 2$ to $x = 3$.
19. $6xy = x^4 + 3$ from $x = 1$ to $x = 3$. $4\frac{2}{3}$.
20. $2y = \sin x - \ln (\sec x + \tan x)$ from $x = 0$ to $x = \frac{1}{4}\pi$.
21. $y = \ln (e^x + 1) - \ln (e^x - 1)$ from $x = 1$ to $x = 2$. $\ln (1 + e^2) - 1$.
22. The catenary $y = \frac{1}{2}a(e^{x/a} + e^{-x/a})$ from $x = -a$ to $x = a$.
23. The entire hypocycloid $x^{2/3} + y^{2/3} = a^{2/3}$. $6a$.
24. Solve Problem 23, using the parametric equations of the curve $x = a \cos^3 \phi$, $y = a \sin^3 \phi$.
25. The loop of the curve $9y^2 = x(x - 3)^2$. *Ans.* $4\sqrt{3}$.
26. The loop of the curve $9y^2 = x^2(2x + 3)$.
27. $y = \sqrt{1 - x^2} + \ln (1 - \sqrt{1 - x^2}) - \ln x$ from $x = \frac{1}{2}$ to $x = 1$. *Ans.* $\ln 2$.
28. $y = \frac{1}{2}x\sqrt{x^2 - 1} - \frac{1}{2} \ln (x + \sqrt{x^2 - 1})$ from $x = 1$ to $x = 3$.
29. $x = \ln (\sec \phi + \tan \phi),\quad y = \ln (\csc \phi - \cot \phi)$ from $\phi = \frac{1}{6}\pi$ to $\phi = \frac{1}{3}\pi$. *Ans.* $\ln 3$.

30. $r = a \sec\theta \tan\theta$ from $\theta = 0$ to $\theta = \frac{1}{4}\pi$.
31. Show that the total length of the ellipse $x = 2\cos\phi$, $y = \sin\phi$ is given by $2\int_0^{\pi/2} \sqrt{10 - 6\cos 2\phi}\, d\phi = \int_0^{\pi} \sqrt{10 - 6\cos\theta}\, d\theta$. Evaluate the latter integral by Simpson's rule with $n = 6$. *Ans.* 9.69.
32. Using Simpson's rule, find the length of one arch of $y = \sin x$.
33. What is the length from $x = 0$ to $x = \frac{1}{2}\pi$ of the curve whose slope in this region is given by $dy/dx = \sqrt{\cos x}$? *Ans.* 2.
34. Find a curve that passes through the origin and is such that the length of the curve from the origin to the point $P(x,y)$ of the curve is given by $s = x^2 + 2x - y$.

146. Centroid and Moment of Inertia of Arc

Let the arc AB of a curve be divided into n parts as shown in Figure 180, and let (x_k,y_k) be any point on the kth segment of arc Δs_k. In accordance with the definition of centroids for areas and volumes, we define the **centroid of an arc** as the point $(\bar{x},\bar{y})$ determined by the relations

$$s\bar{x} = \lim_{n\to\infty} \sum_{k=1}^{n} x_k\,\Delta s_k = \int_A^B x\,ds,$$
$$s\bar{y} = \lim_{n\to\infty} \sum_{k=1}^{n} y_k\,\Delta s_k = \int_A^B y\,ds, \qquad (1)$$

where A and B refer to appropriate end point limits and ds assumes one of the arc length forms discussed in the preceding article.

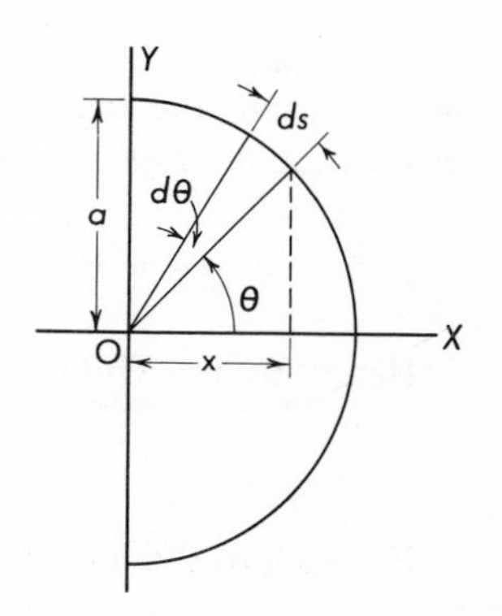

Figure 181

Illustration. Consider the semicircular arc of radius a as shown in Figure 181. Selecting for the circle the polar equation $r = a$, we have $dr/d\theta = 0$; hence $ds = \sqrt{r^2 + r'^2}\, d\theta = a\, d\theta$. Substituting in the first equation of (1), we obtain

$$(\pi a)\bar{x} = \int_{-\pi/2}^{\pi/2} (a\cos\theta)(a\, d\theta) = 2a^2.$$

Thus $\bar{x} = \dfrac{2a^2}{\pi a} = \dfrac{2a}{\pi}$, and, because of symmetry, $\bar{y} = 0$.

In the same manner the **moments of inertia of an arc** with respect to the coordinate axes are defined by the relations

$$I_x = \lim_{n\to\infty} \sum_{k=1}^{n} y_k^2 \, \Delta s_k = \int_A^B y^2 \, ds,$$
$$I_y = \lim_{n\to\infty} \sum_{k=1}^{n} x_k^2 \, \Delta s_k = \int_A^B x^2 \, ds, \tag{2}$$

where A, B, and ds are selected as for (1).

Example. Find I_x for one arch of the cycloid $x = a(\phi - \sin\phi)$, $y = a(1 - \cos\phi)$.

Solution: Since $dx/d\phi = a(1 - \cos\phi)$ and $dy/d\phi = a\sin\phi$, we obtain

$$ds = \sqrt{a^2(1 - \cos\phi)^2 + a^2\sin^2\phi}\, d\phi = a\sqrt{2(1 - \cos\phi)}\, d\phi.$$

Thus, using (2) for one half of the cycloid and doubling the result, we have

$$I_x = 2\int_0^{\pi} [a(1 - \cos\phi)]^2[a\sqrt{2(1 - \cos\phi)}\, d\phi].$$

Now using the trigonometric identity $1 - \cos\phi \equiv 2\sin^2 \frac{1}{2}\phi$, and then substituting θ for $\frac{1}{2}\phi$, we obtain

$$I_x = 16a^3 \int_0^{\pi} \sin^5 \tfrac{1}{2}\phi \, d\phi = 32a^3 \int_0^{\pi/2} \sin^5\theta \, d\theta.$$

Hence, by the Wallis formula, page 567, we find $I_x = \frac{256}{15} a^3$.

EXERCISE 78

For each of the following arcs find the centroidal coordinate indicated.

1. $3y = 4x$ from $x = 0$ to $x = 3$; $\bar{y}$. *Ans.* 2.
2. $9y^2 = 4x^3$ from $x = 0$ to $x = 3$; $\bar{x}$.
3. The first-quadrant arc of the circle $r = a$; $\bar{x}$. $2a/\pi$.
4. $8y = x^4 + 2x^{-2}$ from $x = 1$ to $x = 2$; $\bar{x}$.
5. $3x = 2(y - 1)^{3/2}$ from $y = 1$ to $y = 4$; $\bar{y}$. $\frac{93}{35}$.
6. $6xy = x^4 + 3$ from $x = 1$ to $x = 2$; $\bar{y}$.
7. The first-quadrant arc of the hypocycloid $x = a\cos^3\phi$, $y = a\sin^3\phi$; $\bar{x}$. *Ans.* $2a/5$.
8. $x = t^3 + 3t^{-1}$, $y = 6t$ from $t = 1$ to $t = 3$; $\bar{y}$.
9. $x = t^3 - 12t$, $y = 6t^2$ from $t = 0$ to $t = 1$; $\bar{y}$. $\frac{138}{65}$.
10. The catenary $y = \frac{1}{2}a(e^{x/a} + e^{-x/a})$ from $x = -a$ to $x = a$; $\bar{y}$.

For each of the following arcs find the moment of inertia indicated.

11. Arc of Problem 1; I_y. *Ans.* 15.
12. $3y = (2 + x^2)^{3/2}$ from $x = 0$ to $x = 1$; I_y.

13. $4x = 2y^2 - \ln y$ from $y = 2$ to $y = 4$; I_x. *Ans.* $\frac{123}{2}$.
14. Arc of Problem 3; I_x.
15. $y = e^x$ from $x = 0$ to $x = \ln 7$; I_x. $248\sqrt{2}/3$.
16. Arc of Problem 6; I_y.
17. Arc of Problem 5; I_x. $\frac{254}{7}$.
18. Arc of Problem 8; I_x.
19. Arc of Problem 7; I_y. $3a^3/8$.
20. $y = \sqrt{1 - x^2} + \ln(1 - \sqrt{1 - x^2}) - \ln x$ from $x = 1$ to $x = 3$; I_y.

147. Area of a Surface of Revolution

Let the arc AB of the curve shown in Figure 180 be revolved about the x axis generating a *surface of revolution.* In a manner similar to that used in defining the length of the arc AB, we define the area S of the surface of revolution to be the limit of the area generated by the broken line $AP_1P_2 \cdots P_{n-1}B$ as $n \to \infty$ and each segment tends toward zero.

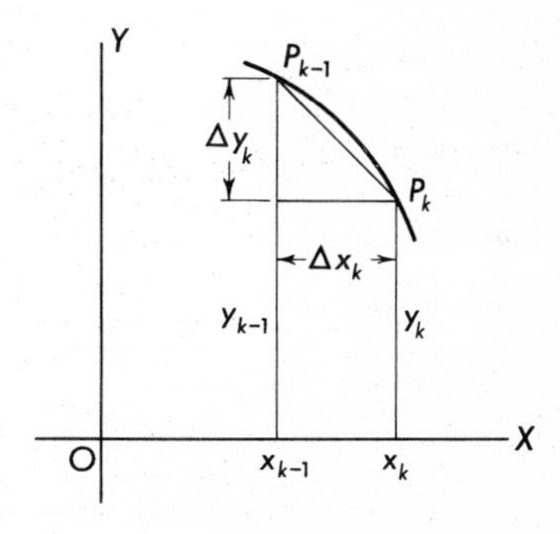

Figure 182

Let the interval from a to b be divided into n parts $\Delta x_1, \Delta x_2, \cdots, \Delta x_n$, and let ordinates $y_k = f(x_k)$ be erected at the points of division. Then construct the broken line joining the points where these ordinates meet the curve. When the arc AB is revolved about the x axis, each of the chords, such as the one shown in Figure 182, will generate the lateral area of a frustum of a cone. Since the lateral area of a frustum of a right circular cone is

$$\pi(r_1 + r_2)l, \tag{1}$$

where r_1, r_2 are the radii of the bases, and l is the slant height, it follows from (1) that the area generated by $P_{k-1}P_k$ has the value

$$\pi(y_{k-1} + y_k)\left[(\Delta x_k)^2 + (\Delta y_k)^2\right]^{1/2}. \tag{2}$$

However, by the law of the mean, $\Delta y_k = f(x_k) - f(x_{k-1}) = f'(x_k')\,\Delta x_k$, where $x_{k-1} \leqq x_k' \leqq x_k$. Hence (2) can be written

$$\pi[f(x_{k-1}) + f(x_k)]\left\{1 + [f'(x_k')]^2\right\}^{1/2} \Delta x_k. \tag{3}$$

The sum of the expressions (3) for $k = 1, 2, \cdots, n$ can be written in two parts as

$$S_n = \sum_{k=1}^{n} \pi f(x_{k-1}) \left\{1 + [f'(x_k')]^2\right\}^{1/2} \Delta x_k$$
$$+ \sum_{k=1}^{n} \pi f(x_k) \left\{1 + [f'(x_k')]^2\right\}^{1/2} \Delta x_k.$$

Each of these is a sum to which the theorem of Bliss applies, and they each have the same limit; therefore

$$S = \lim_{n\to\infty} S_n = 2\pi \int_a^b f(x)\sqrt{1 + [f'(x)]^2}\, dx. \tag{4}$$

The formula (4) can be written in the more general form

$$\boldsymbol{S = 2\pi \int_A^B y\, ds,} \tag{5}$$

where A and B refer to appropriate end point limits and ds assumes one of the arc length forms discussed in Article **145.**

In a similar manner the area of a surface of revolution about the y axis is given by the integral

$$\boldsymbol{S = 2\pi \int_A^B x\, ds.} \tag{6}$$

Example. Find the area of the surface of revolution generated by revolving one arch of the curve $y = \sin x$ about the x axis.

Solution: Since $y = \sin x$, we have $y' = \cos x$ and $ds = \sqrt{1 + \cos^2 x}\, dx$. Observing that the limits $A = 0$ and $B = \frac{1}{2}\pi$ give one-half of the required area, by means of (5) and the substitution $\cos x = z$, we obtain

$$S = 4\pi \int_0^{\pi/2} \sin x\sqrt{1 + \cos^2 x}\, dx = -4\pi \int_1^0 \sqrt{1 + z^2}\, dz$$
$$= 4\pi\left[\tfrac{1}{2}z\sqrt{1 + z^2} + \tfrac{1}{2}\ln\left(z + \sqrt{1 + z^2}\right)\right]_0^1 = 2\pi[\sqrt{2} + \ln(1 + \sqrt{2})].$$

A comparison of (5) and (6) with equation (1) of the preceding article gives the following result.

First Theorem of Pappus. *If a plane arc is revolved about a coplanar axis not crossing the arc, the area of the surface generated is equal to the product of the length of the arc by the circumference of the circle described by the centroid of the arc. Symbolically, for surfaces of revolution about the coordinate axes, we have*

$$\boldsymbol{S_x = 2\pi\bar{y}s, \qquad S_y = 2\pi\bar{x}s.}$$

Illustration. Revolving a circle of radius a about a tangent line, we generate a surface whose area is $S = 2\pi(a)(2\pi a) = 4\pi^2a^2$.

EXERCISE 79

Find the area of the surface generated by revolving each of the following arcs about the x axis.

1. $3y = 4x$ from $x = 0$ to $x = 3$. *Ans.* 20π.
2. $9y = x^3$ from $x = 0$ to $x = 2$.
3. The circle $x^2 + y^2 = a^2$. $4\pi a^2$.
4. $y^2 = 4x$ from $x = 0$ to $x = 3$.
5. $x = t^3 - 3t, \quad y = 3t^2$ from $t = 0$ to $t = 1$. $\frac{48}{5}\pi$.
6. The hypocycloid $x = a\cos^3\phi, \quad y = a\sin^3\phi$.

Find the area of the surface generated by revolving each of the following arcs about the y axis.

7. $y = x^2$ from $x = 0$ to $x = \frac{6}{5}$. *Ans.* $\frac{1036}{375}\pi$.
8. $y = \frac{2}{3}(1 + x^2)^{3/2}$ from $x = 0$ to $x = 2$.
9. $4y = 2x^2 - \ln x$ from $x = 1$ to $x = 4$. $\frac{87}{2}\pi$.
10. $y = \ln(x^2 - 1)$ from $x = 2$ to $x = 3$.
11. $x = 3t(t - 2), \quad y = 8t^{3/2}$ from $t = 0$ to $t = 1$. 39π.
12. $x = \cos\phi + \phi\sin\phi, \quad y = \sin\phi - \phi\cos\phi$ from $\phi = 0$ to $\phi = \frac{1}{2}\pi$.

Using the theorem of Pappus, find the total area generated by revolving the following arcs about the indicated axis.

13. A rectangle of sides a and b about side a. *Ans.* $2\pi b(a + b)$.
14. An equilateral triangle of side a about an altitude.
15. A square with sides a about a line $b\ (> a)$ units from its center. *Ans.* $8\pi ab$.
16. A circle of radius a about a line $2a$ units from its center.
17. The hypocycloid $x^{2/3} + y^{2/3} = a^{2/3}$ about the line $x + y = a$. (See Problem 23, Exercise **77**.) *Ans.* $6\sqrt{2}\pi a^2$.
18. The semicircle $x = \sqrt{a^2 - y^2}$ about the line $x = a$. (See illustration, Article **146**.)

Find the area of the surface generated by revolving the given arcs about the axis indicated.

19. Lemniscate $r^2 = 2a^2\cos 2\theta$ about the x axis. *Ans.* $4\pi a^2(2 - \sqrt{2})$.
20. Lemniscate $r^2 = 2a^2\cos 2\theta$ about the y axis.
21. Cardioid $r = a(1 + \cos\theta)$ about the x axis. $\frac{32}{5}\pi a^2$.
22. Arc of the spiral $r = e^\theta$ from $\theta = 0$ to $\theta = \pi$ about the x axis.
23. Loop of $9y^2 = x(3 - x)^2$ about the x axis. 3π.
24. Loop of $3y^2 = x^2(1 - x)$ about the x axis.
25. $4x^2 + 3y^2 = 3$ about the x axis. $\frac{1}{2}\pi(4 + 3\ln 3)$.

26. $6xy = x^4 + 3$ from $x = 1$ to $x = 2$ about the x axis.

27. $y = \frac{1}{2}a(e^{x/a} + e^{-x/a})$ from $x = 0$ to $x = a$ about the y axis. *Ans.* $2\pi a^2(1 - e^{-1})$.

28. $x = 3 \cos \phi, \quad y = 5 \sin \phi$ from $\phi = 0$ to $\phi = \pi$ about the x axis.

29. One arch of the cycloid $x = a(\theta - \sin \theta), \quad y = a(1 - \cos \theta)$ about the x axis. *Ans.* $\frac{64}{3}\pi a^2$.

30. The arc of Problem 29 from $\theta = 0$ to $\theta = \pi$ about the y axis.

31. Using Simpson's rule, find the area of the surface generated by revolving $y = \cos x$ from $x = 0$ to $x = \frac{1}{2}\pi$ about the y axis. *Ans.* 10.07.

32. Using Simpson's rule, find the area of the surface generated by revolving $y = \frac{1}{4}x^4$ from $x = 0$ to $x = 1$ about the y axis.

148. Volumes of Solids with Known Cross Sections

Let us consider a solid which has bases in the planes $x = a$ and $x = b$, and has other bounding surfaces such that the cross-sectional area of the solid in a plane perpendicular to the x axis is a function $A(x)$ of the distance x.

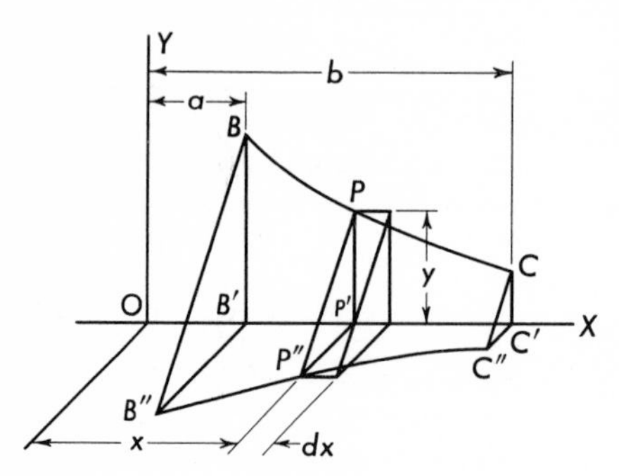

Figure 183

If we divide the solid into n slices by planes perpendicular to the x axis, we see as in Article **47** that the volume of an intermediate slice is approximately

$$dV = A(x)\,dx,$$

and by the Fundamental Theorem, we obtain

$$\boldsymbol{V = \int_a^b A(x)\,dx.}$$

Illustration. If in Figure 183 the equation of BC is $xy = 4$ and $PP'P''$ is an isosceles right triangle, it follows that $A(x) = \frac{1}{2}y^2$ and the volume of the solid from $x = 1$ to $x = 4$ is

$$V = \frac{1}{2}\int_1^4 \left(\frac{4}{x}\right)^2 dx = 8\left[-\frac{1}{x}\right]_1^4 = 6.$$

Example 1. A solid has a circular base of radius a. Find the volume of the solid if every plane section perpendicular to one diameter of the base is a square.

Solution: Placing the solid as shown in Figure 184 with the known sections perpendicular to the y axis, we obtain $A(y) = 4x^2 = 4(a^2 - y^2)$ and

$$V = \int_{-a}^{a} A(y)\, dy = 4 \int_{-a}^{a} (a^2 - y^2)\, dy = \tfrac{16}{3}a^3.$$

Example 2. Find the volume of the solid bounded by the paraboloid $x^2 + 4y^2 = z$ and the plane $z = 4$.

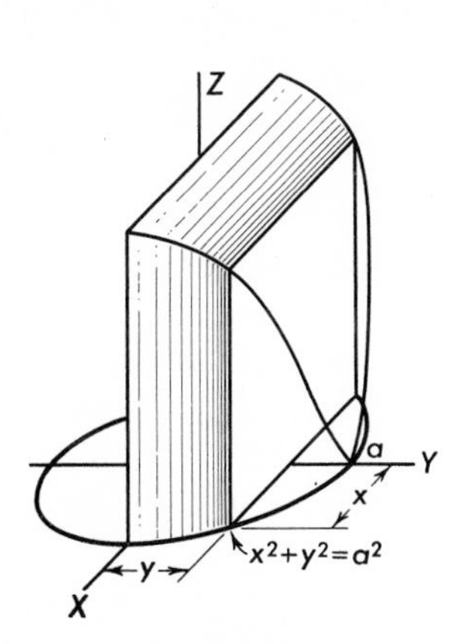

Figure 184

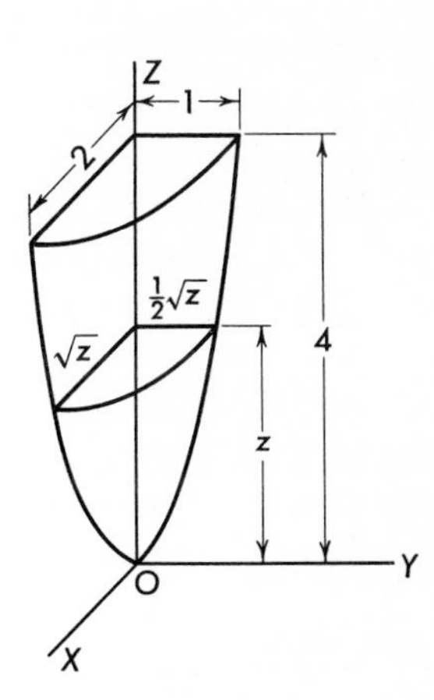

Figure 185

Solution: One quarter of the given solid is shown in Figure 185. We observe that every section perpendicular to the z axis is an ellipse, and at height z the semiaxes of the ellipse are $\sqrt{z}$ and $\frac{1}{2}\sqrt{z}$.

Since the area of an ellipse is π times the product of the semiaxes, we have $A(z) = \pi(\sqrt{z})(\frac{1}{2}\sqrt{z})$ and

$$V = \int_0^4 A(z)\, dz = \tfrac{1}{2}\pi \int_0^4 z\, dz = 4\pi.$$

EXERCISE 80

1. A variable square whose plane is perpendicular to the x axis has one vertex on the x axis and the opposite vertex on the curve $xy = 4$. Find the volume of the solid generated as the square moves from $x = 1$ to $x = 4$. *Ans.* 6.
2. A variable square whose plane is perpendicular to the x axis has two adjacent vertices on the circle $x^2 + y^2 = a^2$. Find the volume of the solid generated as the square moves from $x = -a$ to $x = a$.
3. Solve Problem 2 if the square is replaced by an equilateral triangle. *Ans.* $\frac{4}{3}\sqrt{3}\, a^3$.

4. A variable square whose plane is perpendicular to the y axis has one vertex on the y axis and the opposite vertex on the parabola $y^2 = 4x$. Find the volume of the solid generated as the square moves from $y = 0$ to $y = 4$.
5. A solid has an elliptical base with a major axis of 18 inches and a minor axis of 12 inches. Find the volume of the solid if every section perpendicular to the major axis is (*a*) a square, (*b*) an equilateral triangle.
Ans. (*a*) 1728 cu. in., (*b*) $432\sqrt{3}$ cu. in.
6. A solid has a circular base of radius 10 inches. Find the volume of the solid if every section perpendicular to one diameter is an isosceles triangle whose base is a chord of the circle and whose height is 8 inches.
7. A variable square whose plane is perpendicular to the x axis has two adjacent vertices on the parabola $y^2 = 4ax$. Find the volume of the solid generated as the square moves from $x = 0$ to $x = a$. *Ans.* $8a^3$.
8. Solve Problem 7 if the plane of the square is perpendicular to the y axis and the adjacent vertices are on the curves $y^2 = 4ax$ and $x = a$, respectively.
9. A variable square whose plane is perpendicular to the x axis has one vertex on the curve $y = \sin x$ and an adjacent vertex on the parabola $y = x(\pi - x)$. Find the volume of the solid generated as the square moves from $x = 0$ to $x = \pi$. *Ans.* $\frac{1}{30}(\pi^5 + 15\pi - 240)$.
10. Find the volume of the wedge-shaped solid cut from a right circular cylinder of radius 10 inches by a plane passing through a diameter of the base at an angle of 45° with the base.
11. A variable square whose plane is perpendicular to the x axis has the mid-points of two opposite sides on the curve $x^{2/3} + y^{2/3} = a^{2/3}$. Find the volume of the solid generated as the square moves from $x = 0$ to $x = a$. *Ans.* $\frac{64}{105}a^3$.
12. The axes of two right circular cylinders of equal radius a intersect at right angles. Find the volume common to the cylinders.

Find the volumes bounded by the following surfaces.*

13. $y^2 + 4z^2 = x, \quad x = 2.$ *Ans.* π.
14. $4x^2 + 9z^2 = 36y, \quad y = 4.$
15. $x^2 + y^2 + z^2 = a^2, \quad z = \frac{1}{2}a, \quad z = a.$ $\frac{5}{24}\pi a^3$.
16. $4x^2 + y^2 = z^2 + 16, \quad z = 0, \quad z = 3.$
17. $4x^2 + y^2 = z^2 - 16, \quad z = 5.$ $\frac{13}{6}\pi$.
18. $x^2 + 4y^2 = z^2, \quad z = 0, \quad z = 4.$
19. $x^2 + 4y^2 + 9z^2 = 36.$ 48π.
20. $x + y = z^2, \quad x = 0, \quad y = 0, \quad z = 0, \quad z = 2.$
21. Find the volume of the solid of Problem 13, using the prismoidal formula. *Ans.* π.

---

* See Article **185** for the sketching of surfaces.

22. Find the volume of the solid of Problem 19, using the prismoidal formula.
23. Find the volume of the solid bounded by the surface $x^2 + 4y^2 + z^4 = 1$.
Ans. $\frac{4}{5}\pi$.

24. Show that the volume of the ellipsoid $\frac{x^2}{a^2} + \frac{y^2}{b^2} + \frac{z^2}{c^2} = 1$ is $\frac{4}{3}\pi abc$.

149. Average Value

Consider the curve $y = f(x)$ with ordinates $y_1, y_2, y_3, \cdots, y_n$ spaced at intervals of width Δx from $x = a$ to $x = b$. The arithmetic average of these ordinates is

$$\frac{y_1 + y_2 + y_3 + \cdots + y_n}{n}, \tag{1}$$

and the limit $\bar{y}_x$ approached by this expression as n increases without limit is called the *average value* of y with respect to x for the interval (a,b). Multiplying the numerator and denominator of (1) by Δx and using the Fundamental Theorem, we obtain the formula

$$\bar{y}_x = \frac{\int_a^b y\,dx}{\int_a^b dx} = \frac{\int_a^b y\,dx}{b - a}.$$

Illustration. The average ordinate for one arch of the curve $y = \sin x$ with respect to x is

$$\bar{y}_x = \frac{1}{\pi - 0}\int_0^\pi \sin x\,dx = \frac{2}{\pi}.$$

In general the **average value** of one variable u with respect to another variable v is defined by the relation

$$\bar{u}_v = \frac{\int_A^B u\,dv}{\int_A^B dv}, \tag{2}$$

where u and v are to be expressed in terms of a common variable, and A and B refer to appropriate limits.

Note: Observe that $(\bar{x}_s,\bar{y}_s)$ and $(\bar{x}_A,\bar{y}_A)$ are the coordinates of the respective centroids for an arc s and an area A.

Example. The velocity of a body falling from rest is given by $v = 32t$ or $v = \sqrt{64s}$, where $s = 16t^2$. As v increases from 0 to 96 feet per second, find the average velocity with respect to (*a*) the time t, (*b*) the distance s.

Solution: (*a*) From $v = 32t$ and $v = 96$, we find $t = 3$. Hence, by substitution in (2), we obtain

$$\bar{v}_t = \frac{1}{3 - 0}\int_0^3 (32t)\,dt = 48 \text{ ft./sec.}$$

(*b*) From $v = \sqrt{64s}$ and $v = 96$, we find $s = 144$. Hence, by substitution in (2), we obtain

$$\bar{v}_s = \frac{1}{144 - 0}\int_0^{144} (\sqrt{64s})\,ds = 64 \text{ ft./sec.}$$

EXERCISE 81

1. Find the average ordinate of the curve $y = x^2$, from $x = 0$ to $x = 6$, with respect to x. *Ans.* 12.
2. In Problem 1, find the average abscissa with respect to y.
3. Find the average ordinate of the curve $y = \text{Sin}^{-1} x$, from $x = 0$ to $x = 1$, with respect to x. *Ans.* $\frac{1}{2}\pi - 1$.
4. Find the average ordinate of the curve $x = t^3 - 3t$, $y = 3t^2$, from $t = 0$ to $t = 3$, with respect to x.
5. In Problem 4, find the average ordinate with respect to s, the distance along the curve. *Ans.* 14.4.
6. Find the average slope of the curve $y = \sin x$, from $x = 0$ to $x = \frac{1}{2}\pi$, with respect to x.
7. Find the average volume of a sphere with respect to the radius as the radius increases from 3 feet to 6 feet. *Ans.* 135π cu. ft.
8. At constant temperature the relation between the volume and pressure of a gas is given by $PV = C$, where C is a constant. Find the average pressure with respect to the volume as the volume changes from V_1 to V_2.
9. The position of a moving particle on a straight line is given by $s = t^3 + 3t^2$, where t denotes the time. Find the average velocity and the average acceleration of the particle with respect to t, during the time interval $t = 1$ to $t = 3$. *Ans.* 25, 18.
10. A particle moves along a straight line with a velocity given by $v = t^2 + 1$, where t denotes the time. Find the average velocity with respect to the distance traversed during the interval $t = 0$ to $t = 3$.
11. Find the average width of the loop of $y^2 = x^2(9 - x)$ with respect to x. *Ans.* $\frac{72}{5}$.
12. If the loop of Problem 11 is revolved about the x axis, find the average cross-sectional area with respect to x.
13. Find the average cross section of a sphere with respect to a diameter. *Ans.* $\frac{2}{3}\pi r^2$.
14. For the cardioid $r = a(1 + \cos\theta)$, find the average value of r with respect to θ.

15. For one leaf of the rose $r = 2 \sin 2\theta$, find the average value of r with respect to θ. *Ans.* $4/\pi$.
16. For one arch of the cycloid $x = a(\theta - \sin\theta)$, $y = a(1 - \cos\theta)$, find the average ordinate with respect to (*a*) x, (*b*) s.
17. Rectangles are inscribed in the circle $x^2 + y^2 = a^2$. Find the average value of their areas, if their vertical sides are equally spaced along the x axis. *Ans.* $\frac{4}{3}a^2$.
18. A solid semiellipsoid has a base with semiaxes of 2 and 3, and an altitude of 4. Find its centroid.
19. When a liquid flows through a pipe of radius a, the velocity v of the liquid at a distance x from the axis of the pipe is $v_0(1 - x^2/a^2)$, where v_0 is the velocity along the axis. What is the average value of the velocity with respect to the cross-sectional area? *Ans.* $\frac{1}{2}v_0$.
20. A particle of mass m moves on a straight line in simple harmonic motion, $x = a \cos \omega t$, where a and ω are constants. For one oscillation, find the average value of its kinetic energy, $\frac{1}{2}mv^2$, with respect to the time t. Show that this result equals one-half the maximum kinetic energy.

CHAPTER 17

Infinite Series

150. Sequences and Series

A succession of numbers formed according to some fixed rule is called a **sequence** of numbers. Thus

$$1, 4, 9, 16, 25, \cdots$$

is a sequence having the rule that the nth term is given by n^2.

The indicated sum of a sequence of numbers is called a **series.** Thus, for the sequence $u_1, u_2, u_3, \cdots, u_n, \cdots$, the corresponding series is

$$u_1 + u_2 + u_3 + \cdots + u_n + \cdots. \tag{1}$$

A series is said to be **finite** if the number of terms is limited, and **infinite** if the number of terms is unlimited.

A **general term** of a series is an expression involving n, such that by taking $n = 1, 2, 3, \cdots$, one obtains the first, second, third, $\cdots$ term of the series.

Illustration. If $u_n = n/(2n - 1)$, we have

$$u_1 = \frac{1}{2(1) - 1}, \quad u_2 = \frac{2}{2(2) - 1}, \quad u_3 = \frac{3}{2(3) - 1}, \quad u_{n+1} = \frac{n + 1}{2(n + 1) - 1},$$

and the infinite series is

$$1 + \frac{2}{3} + \frac{3}{5} + \cdots + \frac{n}{2n - 1} + \frac{n + 1}{2n + 1} + \cdots.$$

If the first few terms of a series are known, a form of the general term may be found by expressing the terms $u_1, u_2, u_3, \cdots$ as functions of the indices $1, 2, 3, \cdots$.

Example. Find an nth term of the series

$$1 - \frac{x}{2!} + \frac{x^2}{3!} - \frac{x^3}{4!} + \cdots.$$

Solution: Since

$$u_1 = \frac{(-x)^{(1)-1}}{(1)!}, \quad u_2 = \frac{(-x)^{(2)-1}}{(2)!}, \quad u_3 = \frac{(-x)^{(3)-1}}{(3)!}, \quad u_4 = \frac{(-x)^{(4)-1}}{(4)!},$$

it follows that

$$u_n = \frac{(-x)^{n-1}}{n!}.$$

Note: A few terms of a series cannot determine the general term *uniquely*. Thus, in the above example, if $f(n)$ is an arbitrary function of n subject to the conditions that $f(1) = f(2) = f(3) = f(4) = 0$, for example, $f(n) \equiv (n-1)(n-2)(n-3)(n-4)$, the general term could be

$$u_n = \frac{(-x)^{n-1}}{n!} + f(n).$$

151. Convergent and Divergent Series

Let the sequence $S_1, S_2, \cdots, S_n, \cdots$ denote the respective partial sums of the series (1) of the preceding article, that is,

$$S_1 = u_1, \qquad S_2 = u_1 + u_2, \qquad S_3 = u_1 + u_2 + u_3, \cdots.$$

An infinite series is said to **converge** or **be convergent** if the partial sums S_n have a definite limit S as $n \to \infty$; otherwise the series is said to **diverge** or **be divergent.** The limiting value S for a convergent series is called the "**sum**" of the series.

Illustration 1. For the infinite geometric series

$$a + ar + ar^2 + \cdots + ar^{n-1} + \cdots, \tag{1}$$

we have by **22,** page 2,

$$S_n = a + ar + \cdots + ar^{n-1} = \frac{a}{1-r} - \frac{ar^n}{1-r}.$$

If $|r| < 1$, as n increases without limit, r^n approaches zero, S_n approaches the limit $a/(1-r)$, and hence the series (1) is convergent.

Illustration 2. Consider the series $1 - 1 + 1 - 1 + - \cdots$. If n is even, S_n is 0. If n is odd, S_n is 1. As n increases without limit S_n does not approach a definite limit, but oscillates between 0 and 1. Hence the series diverges. Such a series is called an **oscillating series.**

152. Theorems on Convergence

In developing practicable methods for establishing the convergence and divergence of series, considerable use is made of the following theorem, often called the *fundamental theorem on convergence.*

Theorem 1. *If an infinite series of positive terms is such that S_n always remains less than some constant K, the series converges and its sum S is not greater than K.*

We are not in a position to prove this theorem rigorously, but some intuitive considerations may help in understanding and appreciating the result. Since the terms of the series are positive, we know that the partial sums increase as n increases, that is, $S_{n+1} > S_n$. Since, however, S_n is always less than K, it appears evident that there must exist some smallest value S such that no S_n is greater than S, but that some integer N exists such that S_N is greater than $S - \epsilon$, where ϵ is any positive number. However, S_n is an increasing sequence, so if $S_N > S - \epsilon$, then $S_n > S - \epsilon$ for all $n \geqq N$. By the definition of a limit, this means that

$$\lim_{n \to \infty} S_n = S,$$

and hence that the series converges.

For a convergent series we have the following result.

Theorem 2. *If a series is convergent, the nth term must approach zero as n increases without limit.*

Proof: Let the convergent series

$$u_1 + u_2 + u_3 + \cdots + u_n + \cdots$$

have the sum S. Since $u_n = S_n - S_{n-1}$, it follows that

$$\lim_{n \to \infty} u_n = \lim_{n \to \infty} (S_n - S_{n-1}) = S - S = 0.$$

The above theorem states a *necessary* condition for convergence, but not a *sufficient* condition. That is, the fact that the nth term of a series approaches zero as n increases without limit does not mean that the series is convergent.

Illustration 1. Consider the **harmonic series**

$$1 + \frac{1}{2} + \frac{1}{3} + \frac{1}{4} + \cdots + \frac{1}{n} + \cdots. \tag{1}$$

It is apparent that

$$1 + \frac{1}{2} > \frac{1}{2} = \frac{1}{2},$$

$$\frac{1}{3} + \frac{1}{4} > \frac{2}{4} = \frac{1}{2},$$

$$\frac{1}{5} + \frac{1}{6} + \frac{1}{7} + \frac{1}{8} > \frac{4}{8} = \frac{1}{2},$$

$$\frac{1}{9} + \frac{1}{10} + \cdots + \frac{1}{15} + \frac{1}{16} > \frac{8}{16} = \frac{1}{2},$$

$$\cdots\cdots\cdots$$

Adding the corresponding sides for k groups, we have

$$1 + \frac{1}{2} + \frac{1}{3} + \cdots + \frac{1}{2^k} > \frac{k}{2}. \tag{2}$$

Taking the limit as $k \to \infty$, it follows from (2) that (1) increases without limit. Thus the harmonic series is divergent even though its nth term does approach zero as $n \to \infty$.

Corollary. *If the nth term of an infinite series does not approach zero as n increases without limit, the series is divergent.*

Proof: Since $\lim u_n = 0$ is a necessary condition for convergence, $\lim u_n = c \neq 0$ implies that the series is divergent.

Illustration 2. The series $1 + \frac{2}{3} + \frac{3}{5} + \cdots + \frac{n}{2n-1} + \cdots$ is divergent, since

$$\lim_{n\to\infty} u_n = \lim_{n\to\infty} \frac{n}{2n-1} = \frac{1}{2}.$$

It follows from the definitions that the convergence or divergence of a series is not changed when each term is multiplied by a constant non-zero number. Thus the series $\frac{1}{2} + \frac{1}{4} + \frac{1}{6} + \cdots$ is divergent, since it equals $\frac{1}{2}(1 + \frac{1}{2} + \frac{1}{3} + \cdots)$ and the series $1 + \frac{1}{2} + \frac{1}{3} + \cdots$ is divergent.

Example. If $\sum_{k=1}^{\infty} u_k$ is a series of positive numbers converging to S, show that $\sum_{k=1}^{\infty} u_k^2$ converges.

Solution: Since $\sum_{k=1}^{\infty} u_k$ converges, it follows by Theorem 2 that $u_n \to 0$ as $n \to \infty$. This means that there must exist some number N such that, for all $n \geqq N$, we have $u_n < 1$. Hence, for $n \geqq N$, we obtain

$$\sum_{k=N}^{n} u_k^2 < \sum_{k=N}^{n} 1 \cdot u_k < S.$$

Since the partial sums $S_n = \sum_{k=1}^{n} u_k^2$ increase as n increases, and are never greater than $S + \sum_{k=1}^{N-1} u_k^2$, it follows by Theorem 1 that $\sum_{k=1}^{\infty} u_k^2$ converges.

153. The Integral Test

If $u(n)$ denotes the nth term u_n of the series of positive terms

$$u_1 + u_2 + u_3 + \cdots + u_n + \cdots, \tag{1}$$

and if $u(x)$ is a positive, decreasing, continuous function for x greater than *some positive integer m, then the series* (1) *converges or diverges according as the integral,*

$$\int_m^\infty u(x)\,dx \tag{2}$$

does or does not exist.

Proof: If the integral (2) exists and equals U, we can prove the convergence of the series (1) as follows. Draw a graph of $y = u(x)$ and inscribe rectangles of unit width as shown in Figure 186.

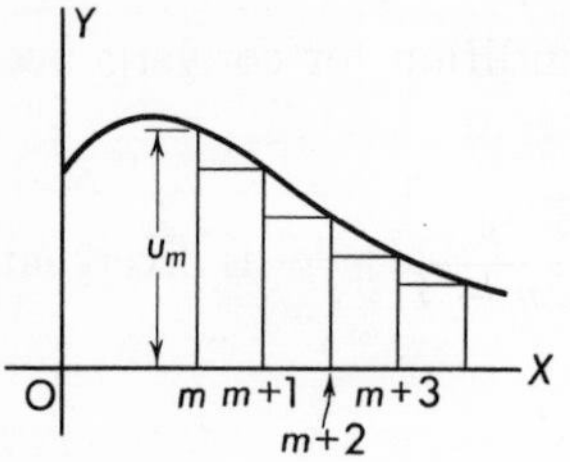

Figure 186

It follows from this construction that the areas of the rectangles are u_{m+1}, u_{m+2}, u_{m+3}, $\cdots$, and if A_k denotes the sum of the first k rectangles, we have

$$A_k \leqq \int_m^{m+k} u(x)\,dx \leqq \int_m^\infty u(x)\,dx = U.$$

Since A_k increases as k increases but is never greater than U, by Theorem 1, Article **152,** we have

$$\lim_{k\to\infty} A_k = A \leqq U.$$

Hence (1) converges and has the sum $S = u_1 + u_2 + \cdots + u_m + A$.

The second part of the theorem may be proved in a similar manner by using a series of circumscribed rectangles of unit width.

Illustration. The series $\frac{1}{2} + \frac{2}{5} + \cdots + \frac{n}{n^2+1} + \cdots$ is divergent, since $u(n) = n/(n^2+1)$ and

$$\int_1^\infty \frac{x\,dx}{x^2+1} = \frac{1}{2}\lim_{x\to\infty} \ln(x^2+1) - \frac{1}{2}\ln 2 = \infty.$$

Example. Investigate the convergence of the ***p* series**

$$1 + \frac{1}{2^p} + \frac{1}{3^p} + \frac{1}{4^p} + \cdots + \frac{1}{n^p} + \cdots. \quad (p > 0.)$$

Solution: Since $u(n) = 1/n^p$, we have

$$\int_1^\infty \frac{dx}{x^p} = \frac{1}{1-p}\lim_{x\to\infty} x^{1-p} - \frac{1}{1-p}.$$

When $p > 1$, $(1-p)$ is negative and x^{1-p} approaches zero as $x \to \infty$. Hence in this case the integral has a definite value and the series converges. When $p < 1$, $(1-p)$ is positive and $x^{1-p} \to \infty$ as $x \to \infty$. Hence the series diverges for $p < 1$.

When $p = 1$, we have from

$$\int_1^\infty \frac{dx}{x} = \lim_{x\to\infty} \ln x = \infty.$$

another proof (see Article **152**) that the harmonic series is divergent.

EXERCISE 82

Find the first three terms and the $(n + 1)$st term of the series whose nth term is as follows.

1. $\dfrac{2^n}{n(n+1)}$. *Ans.* $1, \dfrac{2}{3}, \dfrac{2}{3}, \dfrac{2^{n+1}}{(n+1)(n+2)}$.
2. $\dfrac{1}{\sqrt{3n-1}}$.
3. $(-1)^{n-1}\dfrac{x^n}{(2n)!}$. $\dfrac{x}{2!}, -\dfrac{x^2}{4!}, \dfrac{x^3}{6!}, (-1)^n\dfrac{x^{n+1}}{(2n+2)!}$.
4. $(-1)^{n-1}\dfrac{2n-1}{n(n+2)}$.

Find an nth term for each of the following series.

5. $1 + \frac{1}{4} + \frac{1}{9} + \frac{1}{16} + \cdots$. *Ans.* $1/n^2$.
6. $\dfrac{3}{0!} + \dfrac{4}{1!} + \dfrac{5}{2!} + \dfrac{6}{3!} + \cdots$.
7. $\dfrac{3}{1\cdot 2} - \dfrac{5}{3\cdot 4} + \dfrac{7}{5\cdot 6} - \dfrac{9}{7\cdot 8} + \cdots$. $(-1)^{n-1}\dfrac{2n+1}{(2n-1)2n}$.
8. $1 - \dfrac{x}{4!} + \dfrac{x^2}{7!} - \dfrac{x^3}{10!} + \cdots$.

Determine a general term for each of the following series, and test your series for divergence, using the corollary in Article **152.**

9. $\frac{1}{2} + \frac{3}{5} + \frac{5}{8} + \frac{7}{11} + \cdots$.
10. $1 + \frac{1}{4} + 1 + \frac{1}{9} + \cdots$.
11. $\frac{3}{7} + \frac{4}{9} + \frac{5}{11} + \frac{6}{13} + \cdots$.
12. $\frac{1}{2} - \frac{4}{5} + \frac{9}{10} - \frac{16}{17} + \cdots$.

Using the integral test, determine which of the following series are convergent.

13. $1 + \dfrac{1}{3} + \dfrac{1}{5} + \cdots + \dfrac{1}{2n-1} + \cdots$. *Ans.* Divergent.
14. $\dfrac{1}{4} + \dfrac{1}{16} + \dfrac{1}{36} + \cdots + \dfrac{1}{4n^2} + \cdots$.
15. $1 + \dfrac{1}{\sqrt{2}} + \dfrac{1}{\sqrt{3}} + \cdots + \dfrac{1}{\sqrt{n}} + \cdots$. Divergent.
16. $\dfrac{1}{2} + \dfrac{1}{5} + \dfrac{1}{10} + \cdots + \dfrac{1}{1+n^2} + \cdots$.

17. $\frac{1}{2} + \frac{1}{6} + \frac{1}{12} + \cdots + \frac{1}{n(n+1)} + \cdots.$ *Ans.* Convergent.

18. $e^{-1} + 2e^{-2} + 3e^{-3} + \cdots + ne^{-n} + \cdots.$

19. $\frac{1}{3} + \frac{1}{15} + \frac{1}{35} + \cdots + \frac{1}{4n^2 - 1} + \cdots.$ Convergent.

20. $\frac{5}{3} + \frac{7}{15} + \frac{9}{35} + \cdots + \frac{2n+3}{4n^2 - 1} + \cdots.$

21. $1 + \frac{1}{2\sqrt{2}} + \frac{1}{3\sqrt{3}} + \cdots + \frac{1}{n\sqrt{n}} + \cdots.$ Convergent.

22. $1 + \frac{\sqrt{3}}{2} + \frac{\sqrt{5}}{3} + \cdots + \frac{\sqrt{2n-1}}{n} + \cdots.$

23. $\frac{\ln 2}{2} + \frac{\ln 3}{3} + \frac{\ln 4}{4} + \cdots + \frac{\ln n}{n} + \cdots.$ Divergent.

24. $\frac{1}{2} + \frac{2}{9} + \frac{3}{28} + \cdots + \frac{n}{n^3 + 1} + \cdots.$

25. $\frac{1}{2} + \frac{4}{9} + \frac{9}{28} + \cdots + \frac{n^2}{n^3 + 1} + \cdots.$ Divergent.

26. $\frac{2}{3} + \frac{5}{24} + \frac{1}{10} + \cdots + \frac{n+3}{n(n+1)(n+2)} + \cdots.$

27. $\frac{2}{3} + 2(\frac{2}{3})^2 + 3(\frac{2}{3})^3 + \cdots + n(\frac{2}{3})^n + \cdots.$ Convergent.

28. $\frac{1}{2 \ln 2} + \frac{1}{3 \ln 3} + \frac{1}{4 \ln 4} + \cdots + \frac{1}{n \ln n} + \cdots.$

29. $\sin \pi + \frac{1}{4} \sin \frac{\pi}{2} + \frac{1}{9} \sin \frac{\pi}{3} + \cdots + \frac{1}{n^2} \sin \frac{\pi}{n} + \cdots.$ Convergent.

30. $\sin \pi + \frac{1}{2} \sin \frac{\pi}{2} + \frac{1}{4} \sin \frac{\pi}{4} + \cdots + \frac{1}{2^n} \sin \frac{\pi}{2^n} + \cdots.$

31. If $u_n > 0$ for all n and $\sum_{n=1}^{\infty} u_n$ converges, give examples for which the following series diverge: (*a*) $\sum_{n=1}^{\infty} \sqrt{u_n}$, (*b*) $\sum_{n=1}^{\infty} nu_n$.

32. If $u_n > 0$, $u_n \neq 1$ for all n and $\sum_{n=1}^{\infty} u_n$ converges, prove that the following series are convergent: (*a*) $\sum_{n=1}^{\infty} \frac{u_n}{1 + u_n}$, (*b*) $\sum_{n=1}^{\infty} \frac{u_n}{1 - u_n}$.

33. If $u_n > 0$ for all n, $\sum_{n=1}^{\infty} u_n$ converges and $c_n \to 0$ as $n \to \infty$, show that $\sum_{n=1}^{\infty} c_n u_n$ converges.

34. If $u_n > 0$ for all n and $\sum_{n=1}^{\infty} u_n^2$ converges, show that $\sum_{n=1}^{\infty} u_n/n$ converges. *Hint:* Consider $(u_n - 1/n)^2 \geqq 0$.

35. Use the methods of proof of the integral test for $p > 1$ to show that

$$\frac{1}{(p-1)n^{p-1}} < \sum_{k=n}^{\infty} \frac{1}{k^p} < \frac{1}{(p-1)(n-1)^{p-1}}.$$

36. Let $S_1 = 1, S_2 = 3$, and $S_n = \frac{1}{2}(S_{n-1} + S_{n-2}), n = 3, 4, 5, \cdots$. Is the sequence S_n increasing or decreasing? To what value does S_n converge? *Hint:* Show that $S_{n+1} + \frac{1}{2}S_n$ is invariant.

37. For every integer $n > 1$, show that $\frac{n}{2} < 1 + \frac{1}{2} + \frac{1}{3} + \cdots + \frac{1}{2^n - 1} < n$. *Hint:* Use the method of Illustration 1, Article **152.**

38. If $\{a_n\}$ is a sequence of numbers such that for $n \geqq 1$, $(2 - a_n)a_{n+1} = 1$, prove that $a_n \to 1$ as $n \to \infty$.

154. Comparison Tests

Another procedure for determining the convergence or divergence of a series is to compare the given series with a series whose convergence or divergence is known.

Consider the following two series of positive terms:

$$(A) \qquad a_1 + a_2 + a_3 + \cdots + a_n + \cdots,$$

$$(U) \qquad u_1 + u_2 + u_3 + \cdots + u_n + \cdots.$$

Theorem 1. *If (A) converges to a limit A and if each term of (U) is less than or equal to the corresponding term of (A), then (U) converges.*

Proof: Let $A_n = a_1 + a_2 + \cdots + a_n$ and $U_n = u_1 + u_2 + \cdots + u_n$. Since $u_m \leqq a_m$ for $m = 1, 2, 3, \cdots$, we have $U_n \leqq A_n$ for all values of n. Hence, taking the limit as $n \to \infty$, we obtain

$$\lim_{n\to\infty} U_n \leqq \lim_{n\to\infty} A_n = A.$$

Thus (U) converges by Theorem 1, Article **152.**

Theorem 2. *If (A) diverges and if each term of (U) is greater than or equal to the corresponding term of (A), then (U) diverges.*

Proof: If (U) were a convergent series, then, since $u_n \geqq a_n$, it would follow from Theorem 1 that (A) converges. This, however, contradicts the hypothesis that (A) diverges. Hence (U) must be divergent.

Note: Observe that the convergence or divergence of a series is unaffected by the omission or addition of a finite number of terms, since such an alteration merely changes the limiting value by a constant amount.

Although any series whose convergence or divergence is known may be used as a comparison series, the following are particularly useful.

Comparison series for convergence:

$$a + ar + ar^2 + \cdots + ar^{n-1} + \cdots \quad (a > 0,\ 0 < r < 1).$$

$$1 + \frac{1}{2^p} + \frac{1}{3^p} + \cdots + \frac{1}{n^p} + \cdots \quad (p > 1).$$

Comparison series for divergence:

$$a + ar + ar^2 + \cdots + ar^{n-1} + \cdots \quad (a > 0,\ r \geqq 1).$$

$$1 + \frac{1}{2} + \frac{1}{3} + \cdots + \frac{1}{n} + \cdots.$$

Example 1. Determine the convergence or divergence of the following series by a comparison test

$$\frac{1}{1\cdot 3} + \frac{1}{2\cdot 4} + \frac{1}{3\cdot 5} + \cdots + \frac{1}{n(n+2)} + \cdots.$$

Solution: Consider the p series which, for $p = 2$, is known to converge

$$1 + \frac{1}{2^2} + \frac{1}{3^2} + \cdots + \frac{1}{n^2} + \cdots.$$

Comparing the respective nth terms of the series, we see that

$$\frac{1}{n^2 + 2n} < \frac{1}{n^2}.$$

for all positive integral values of n. Hence, by Theorem 1, the given series converges.

Example 2. Determine the convergence or divergence of the following series by a comparison test

$$\frac{2}{1\cdot 3} + \frac{3}{2\cdot 4} + \frac{4}{3\cdot 5} + \cdots + \frac{n+1}{n(n+2)} + \cdots.$$

Solution: Considering the nth term of the given series, we see that for all positive integral values of n

$$\frac{n+1}{n(n+2)} = \frac{n+1}{n}\cdot\frac{1}{n+2} > \frac{1}{n+2}.$$

However, the series

$$\frac{1}{3} + \frac{1}{4} + \frac{1}{5} + \cdots + \frac{1}{n+2} + \cdots$$

is known to diverge. Hence, by Theorem 2, the given series diverges.

Example 3. Prove that the series $\sum_{n=2}^{\infty} \left\{ \int_{n-1}^{n} \frac{dx}{x} - \frac{1}{n} \right\}$ is convergent.

Solution: Since $1/x$ is a decreasing function of x for $x > 0$, it follows, as in the proof of the integral test, that

$$\frac{1}{n} < \int_{n-1}^{n} \frac{dx}{x} < \frac{1}{n-1}. \tag{1}$$

Subtracting $1/n$ from each term of (1), we have

$$0 < \int_{n-1}^{n} \frac{dx}{x} - \frac{1}{n} < \frac{1}{n(n-1)} < \frac{1}{(n-1)^2}.$$

Thus, by comparison with the p series for $p = 2$, the given series is convergent.

155. Ratio Test

In a series of positive terms

$$u_1 + u_2 + u_3 + \cdots + u_n + u_{n+1} + \cdots \tag{1}$$

suppose that

$$\lim_{n\to\infty} \frac{u_{n+1}}{u_n} = R.$$

Then

$$\begin{aligned} &\text{I.} \quad \textit{if} \quad R < 1, \quad \textit{the series converges,} \\ &\text{II.} \quad \textit{if} \quad R > 1, \quad \textit{the series diverges,} \\ &\text{III.} \quad \textit{if} \quad R = 1, \quad \textit{the test fails.} \end{aligned}$$

Proof: I. Since $R < 1$, there exists some number r between R and 1. Also since the ratio u_{n+1}/u_n approaches R as n increases without limit, there must be a term in the series, say the kth, such that for $n \geqq k$ all ratios u_{n+1}/u_n are less than r. Thus we have

$$\frac{u_{k+1}}{u_k} < r, \quad \text{or} \quad u_{k+1} < ru_k,$$

$$\frac{u_{k+2}}{u_{k+1}} < r, \quad \text{or} \quad u_{k+2} < ru_{k+1} < r^2u_k,$$

$$\frac{u_{k+3}}{u_{k+2}} < r, \quad \text{or} \quad u_{k+3} < ru_{k+2} < r^3u_k,$$

$$\cdots\cdots\cdots\cdots\cdots\cdots\cdots\cdots\cdots$$

Hence each term of the series

$$u_{k+1} + u_{k+2} + u_{k+3} + \cdots + u_{k+m} + \cdots \tag{2}$$

is less than the corresponding term of

$$u_kr + u_kr^2 + u_kr^3 + \cdots + u_kr^m + \cdots. \tag{3}$$

However, (3) is convergent, since it is a geometric series with $r < 1$. Therefore, by comparison, (2) is also convergent, as is (1) by the addition of the constant sum $u_1 + u_2 + \cdots + u_k$.

II. When $R > 1$, it follows from the definition of a limit that there is a term in the series (1), say the kth, such that for $n \geqq k$ all ratios u_{n+1}/u_n are greater than 1; that is, the terms get larger. Hence $\lim_{n\to\infty} u_n$ is not zero and the series diverges.

Note: Observe that the above proof is valid when u_{n+1}/u_n increases without limit as $n \to \infty$. Hence a series is divergent if

$$\lim_{n\to\infty} u_{n+1}/u_n = \infty.$$

III. The failure of the test when $R = 1$ is illustrated by the p series. For this series the test ratio is

$$\frac{u_{n+1}}{u_n} = \left(\frac{n}{n+1}\right)^p = \left(1 - \frac{1}{n+1}\right)^p,$$

and its limit as $n \to \infty$ is always 1 regardless of the fixed value of p. We know, however, that the p series converges when $p > 1$ and diverges when $p \leqq 1$. Hence, when $R = 1$, the ratio test fails to determine whether the series is convergent or divergent, and other tests must be used.

Illustration 1. The series $\frac{3}{2} + \frac{4}{2^2} + \frac{5}{2^3} + \cdots + \frac{n+2}{2^n} + \cdots$ is convergent since

$$u_n = \frac{n+2}{2^n}, \qquad u_{n+1} = \frac{n+3}{2^{n+1}},$$

and

$$\lim_{n\to\infty} \frac{u_{n+1}}{u_n} = \lim_{n\to\infty} \frac{1}{2}\cdot\frac{n+3}{n+2} = \frac{1}{2}.$$

Illustration 2. The series $\frac{1!}{10} + \frac{2!}{10^3} + \frac{3!}{10^5} + \cdots + \frac{n!}{10^{2n-1}} + \cdots$ is divergent, since

$$u_n = \frac{n!}{10^{2n-1}}, \qquad u_{n+1} = \frac{(n+1)!}{10^{2n+1}},$$

and

$$\lim_{n\to\infty} \frac{u_{n+1}}{u_n} = \lim_{n\to\infty} \frac{n+1}{100} = \infty.$$

EXERCISE 83

Determine the convergence or divergence of the following series, using a comparison test.

1. $\frac{1}{1\cdot 2} + \frac{1}{2\cdot 2^2} + \frac{1}{3\cdot 2^3} + \cdots + \frac{1}{n\cdot 2^n} + \cdots.$ *Ans.* Convergent.

2. $1 + \frac{1}{3} + \frac{1}{5} + \cdots + \frac{1}{2n-1} + \cdots.$

3. $\frac{1}{2} + \frac{1}{4^2} + \frac{1}{6^3} + \cdots + \frac{1}{(2n)^n} + \cdots.$ Convergent.

4. $\frac{1}{1\cdot 2} + \frac{1}{3\cdot 4} + \frac{1}{5\cdot 6} + \cdots + \frac{1}{(2n-1)2n} + \cdots.$

5. $\frac{1}{\sqrt{2}} + \frac{1}{\sqrt{4}} + \frac{1}{\sqrt{6}} + \cdots + \frac{1}{\sqrt{2n}} + \cdots.$ Divergent.

6. $\frac{3}{1\cdot 2} + \frac{4}{2\cdot 3} + \frac{5}{3\cdot 4} + \cdots + \frac{n+2}{n(n+1)} + \cdots.$

7. $1 + \frac{1}{\ln 2} + \frac{1}{\ln 3} + \cdots + \frac{1}{\ln n} + \cdots.$ Divergent.

8. $\frac{1}{1\cdot 2\cdot 3} + \frac{1}{2\cdot 3\cdot 4} + \frac{1}{3\cdot 4\cdot 5} + \cdots + \frac{1}{n(n+1)(n+2)} + \cdots.$

9. $\frac{1}{2} + \frac{1}{3\sqrt{2}} + \frac{1}{4\sqrt{3}} + \cdots + \frac{1}{(n+1)\sqrt{n}} + \cdots.$ Convergent.

10. $\frac{1}{2}\sin\pi + \frac{1}{2^2}\sin\frac{\pi}{2} + \frac{1}{2^3}\sin\frac{\pi}{3} + \cdots + \frac{1}{2^n}\sin\frac{\pi}{n} + \cdots.$

Determine the convergence or divergence of the following series, using the ratio test. If the ratio test fails, use a comparison test.

11. $1 + \frac{1}{2!} + \frac{1}{3!} + \cdots + \frac{1}{n!} + \cdots.$ *Ans.* Convergent.

12. $\frac{2}{3} + \frac{3}{3^2} + \frac{4}{3^3} + \cdots + \frac{n+1}{3^n} + \cdots.$

13. $\frac{1}{1\cdot 3} + \frac{1}{3\cdot 5} + \frac{1}{5\cdot 7} + \cdots + \frac{1}{(2n-1)(2n+1)} + \cdots.$ Convergent.

14. $\frac{2}{\pi} + \frac{4}{3\pi^2} + \frac{6}{5\pi^3} + \cdots + \frac{2n}{(2n-1)\pi^n} + \cdots.$

15. $\frac{1}{\sqrt{1\cdot 2}} + \frac{1}{\sqrt{2\cdot 3}} + \frac{1}{\sqrt{3\cdot 4}} + \cdots + \frac{1}{\sqrt{n(n+1)}} + \cdots.$ Divergent.

16. $\frac{4}{1\cdot 2\cdot 3} + \frac{5}{2\cdot 3\cdot 4} + \frac{6}{3\cdot 4\cdot 5} + \cdots + \frac{n+3}{n(n+1)(n+2)} + \cdots.$

17. $\frac{2!}{(1!)^2} + \frac{4!}{(2!)^2} + \frac{6!}{(3!)^2} + \cdots + \frac{(2n)!}{(n!)^2} + \cdots.$ Divergent.

18. $\dfrac{1}{1+1^2}+\dfrac{1}{1+2^2}+\dfrac{1}{1+3^2}+\cdots+\dfrac{1}{1+n^2}+\cdots.$

19. $\dfrac{1}{1+e}+\dfrac{1}{1+\sqrt{e}}+\dfrac{1}{1+\sqrt[3]{e}}+\cdots+\dfrac{1}{1+\sqrt[n]{e}}+\cdots.$ *Ans.* Divergent.

20. $\dfrac{1}{1}+\dfrac{1\cdot 2}{1\cdot 3}+\dfrac{1\cdot 2\cdot 3}{1\cdot 3\cdot 5}+\cdots+\dfrac{n!}{1\cdot 3\cdot 5\cdots(2n-1)}+\cdots.$

21. Prove the following theorem which is known as the **limit test.**

Theorem. *If $\sum u_n$ is a series of positive terms and if a real constant p exists such that*

$$\lim_{n\to\infty} n^p u_n = K > 0, \tag{1}$$

the given series will be convergent when $p > 1$ and divergent when $p \leqq 1$.

Hint: Consider first the case $p > 1$. Let k be a constant greater than K. From (1) it follows that there is some term of the series, say the rth, such that for $n \geqq r$ we have $n^p u_n < k$. Hence $u_n < k/n^p$. Since $p > 1$, it follows by a comparison test that $\sum u_n$ converges. Give a similar proof for the case $p \leqq 1$.

22. Use the limit test (Problem 21) to determine the convergence or divergence of the series given in Problems 6, 9, 15, and 18.

23. Using the fact that $\dfrac{1}{m(m+1)}=\dfrac{1}{m}-\dfrac{1}{m+1}$, find a simpler expression for $S_n=\dfrac{1}{1\cdot 2}+\dfrac{1}{2\cdot 3}+\cdots+\dfrac{1}{n(n+1)}$, and hence find the limit of S_n as $n\to\infty$. *Ans.* 1.

24. Prove that $\dfrac{1}{n+1}+\dfrac{1}{(n+1)(n+2)}+\cdots<\dfrac{1}{n}$. *Hint:* Consider $\sum\limits_{k=1}^{\infty}(n+1)^{-k}$.

25. If $u_n \geqq u_{n+1} > 0$ and $u_2+u_4+u_8+u_{16}+\cdots$ diverges, show that $\sum\limits_{n=1}^{\infty} u_n/n$ diverges.

26. If $u_n > 0$ and $\sqrt[n]{u_n} \leqq k < 1$ for all n, prove that $\sum\limits_{n=1}^{\infty} u_n$ converges.

27. If the series in Example 3, Article **154,** converges to S, show that

$$\lim_{n\to\infty}\left(1+\frac{1}{2}+\frac{1}{3}+\cdots+\frac{1}{n}-\ln n\right)=1-S.$$

156. Alternating Series

A series whose terms are alternately positive and negative is called an **alternating series.**

Alternating Series Test. *If $u_1, u_2, u_3, \cdots$ are positive numbers, the alternating series*

$$u_1 - u_2 + u_3 - \cdots - u_{2k} + u_{2k+1} - \cdots$$

is convergent, provided that

$$(a)\ u_1 \geqq u_2 \geqq u_3 \geqq \cdots, \qquad \text{and} \qquad (b)\ \lim_{n\to\infty} u_n = 0.$$

Proof: The sum of $2k$ terms of the series may be written in either of the following forms:

$$S_{2k} = (u_1 - u_2) + (u_3 - u_4) + \cdots + (u_{2k-1} - u_{2k}), \tag{1}$$

$$S_{2k} = u_1 - (u_2 - u_3) - \cdots - (u_{2k-2} - u_{2k-1}) - u_{2k}. \tag{2}$$

Since $u_n \geqq u_{n+1}$ for all n, each difference within parentheses in (1) and (2) is either positive or zero. Hence (1) shows that S_{2k} is positive or zero, and (2) shows that $S_{2k} \leqq u_1$ for all positive integral values of k. Therefore, by Theorem 1, Article **152,** S_{2k} approaches a definite limit, say S, as $k \to \infty$.

Now consider an odd number of terms

$$S_{2k+1} = S_{2k} + u_{2k+1}.$$

By hypothesis, u_{2k+1} approaches zero as $k \to \infty$; hence

$$\lim_{k\to\infty} S_{2k+1} = \lim_{k\to\infty} S_{2k} + \lim_{k\to\infty} u_{2k+1} = S + 0 = S.$$

This part of the proof is necessary, since otherwise the series might be an oscillating series such as $1 - 1 + 1 - 1 + \cdots$. Therefore, since S_n approaches the same limit S whether n is even or odd, it follows that the given series is convergent.

Example. Test for convergence:

$$1 - \frac{1}{2} + \frac{1}{3} - \frac{1}{4} + \cdots + (-1)^{n-1}\frac{1}{n} + \cdots.$$

Solution: The given series is alternating with

$$u_n = \frac{1}{n} \qquad \text{and} \qquad u_{n+1} = \frac{1}{n+1}.$$

Since (a) $\dfrac{1}{n} > \dfrac{1}{n+1}$ for all n and (b) $\lim\limits_{n\to\infty} \dfrac{1}{n} = 0$, it follows from the alternating series test that the series is convergent.

As a direct consequence of the above theorem, we have the following corollary.

Corollary. *In a convergent alternating series, the error made in taking S_n as an approximation for the value S is less than the absolute value of u_{n+1}.*

Illustration. In the example above, the sum of the first nine terms is 0.746 and the value of the series differs from this by less than $u_{10} = 0.1$. That is, the value of the series lies between 0.645 and 0.746.

157. Absolute and Conditional Convergence

A convergent series

$$u_1 + u_2 + u_3 + \cdots + u_n + \cdots, \tag{1}$$

where the terms u_1, u_2, u_3, $\cdots$ may have different signs, is said to be **absolutely convergent** *if the series of absolute values,*

$$|u_1| + |u_2| + |u_3| + \cdots + |u_n| + \cdots, \tag{2}$$

is convergent.

Illustration 1. The series $1 - \frac{1}{2} + \frac{1}{4} - \frac{1}{8} + \cdots$ is absolutely convergent, since $1 + \frac{1}{2} + \frac{1}{4} + \frac{1}{8} + \cdots$ is convergent.

If a series is convergent but not absolutely convergent, it is said to be **conditionally convergent.**

Illustration 2. The series $1 - \frac{1}{2} + \frac{1}{3} - \frac{1}{4} + \cdots$ is conditionally convergent, since $1 + \frac{1}{2} + \frac{1}{3} + \frac{1}{4} + \cdots$ is divergent.

Theorem 1. *A series is convergent if the series of its absolute values is convergent.*

Proof: Denote by S_n the sum of n terms of (1), by P_n the sum of the positive terms in S_n, and by N_n the sum of the absolute values of the negative terms in S_n; then $S_n = P_n - N_n$. Likewise, let S'_n denote the sum of n terms of (2); then $S'_n = P_n + N_n$.

By hypothesis, (2) converges; therefore S'_n approaches a limit, say S', as $n \to \infty$. Since all terms in (2) are positive, we have $S'_n = P_n + N_n < S'$; hence $P_n < S'$ and $N_n < S'$. Moreover, since P_n and N_n never decrease as n increases, it follows from Theorem 1, Article **152,** that they approach limits, say P and N, respectively. Hence we have

$$\lim_{n\to\infty} S_n = \lim_{n\to\infty} (P_n - N_n) = P - N.$$

Therefore the series (1) is convergent.

Using Theorem 1, an evident extension to the ratio test may be made, as summarized in the following theorem.

Theorem 2. *If in a series whose terms are not all positive the absolute value of the ratio of the $(n + 1)$st term to the nth term approaches a limit R*

as n increases without limit, the series is absolutely convergent if $R < 1$ and divergent if $R > 1$. If $R = 1$, the test fails to determine the convergence or divergence of the series.

In order to determine the convergence or divergence of a given series, the following procedure of testing is suggested.

TESTS FOR CONVERGENCE

1. *If* $\lim u_n \neq 0$ *as* $n \to \infty$, *the series diverges.*
2. *If* $\lim u_n = 0$ *as* $n \to \infty$, *then try*

   (*a*) *The alternating series test. If this test does not apply, try*
   (*b*) *The ratio test. If this fails, try for absolute convergence with*
   (*c*) *The comparison test. If this is difficult, try*
   (*d*) *The integral test.*

EXERCISE 84

Determine a series with the given beginning terms, and test for divergence, absolute convergence, or conditional convergence. (Answers may vary.)

1. $\frac{1}{2} - \frac{3}{2^2} + \frac{5}{2^3} - \frac{7}{2^4} + \cdots$. *Ans.* Abs. conv.
2. $\frac{1}{2\cdot 3} - \frac{1}{4\cdot 5} + \frac{1}{6\cdot 7} - \frac{1}{8\cdot 9} + \cdots$.
3. $\frac{2}{3} - \frac{3}{5} + \frac{4}{7} - \frac{5}{9} + \cdots$. Divergent.
4. $\frac{1}{6} - \frac{1}{8} + \frac{1}{10} - \frac{1}{12} + \cdots$.
5. $1 - \frac{1}{\sqrt{3}} + \frac{1}{\sqrt{5}} - \frac{1}{\sqrt{7}} + \cdots$. Cond. conv.
6. $\frac{3}{2!} - \frac{3^2}{4!} + \frac{3^3}{6!} - \frac{3^4}{8!} + \cdots$.
7. $2(\frac{2}{3}) - 4(\frac{2}{3})^2 - 6(\frac{2}{3})^3 + 8(\frac{2}{3})^4 - - \cdots$. Abs. conv.
8. $1 - \frac{1}{1.1} + \frac{1}{1.2} - \frac{1}{1.3} + \cdots$.
9. $2^{-1} - 2^{-3} + 2^{-5} + 2^{-7} - + \cdots$. Abs. conv.
10. $\frac{1}{3} - \frac{2}{7} + \frac{3}{11} - \frac{4}{15} + \cdots$.
11. $\frac{1}{9} + \frac{2!}{9^2} + \frac{3!}{9^3} + \frac{4!}{9^4} + \cdots$. Divergent.
12. $\frac{1}{\log 2} - \frac{1}{\log 3} + \frac{1}{\log 4} - \frac{1}{\log 5} + \cdots$.
13. $\frac{1}{10} - \frac{2^2}{30} + \frac{3^3}{50} - \frac{4^4}{70} + \cdots$. Divergent.
14. $10 - \frac{10^2}{3!} + \frac{10^3}{5!} - \frac{10^4}{7!} + \cdots$.

15. $\frac{3}{1\cdot 2} - \frac{4}{2\cdot 3} + \frac{5}{3\cdot 4} - \frac{6}{4\cdot 5} + \cdots$. *Ans.* Cond. conv.

16. $\frac{1}{2\sqrt{3}} - \frac{1}{3\sqrt{5}} + \frac{1}{4\sqrt{7}} - \frac{1}{5\sqrt{9}} + \cdots$.

17. $e - e^{1/2} + e^{1/3} - e^{1/4} + \cdots$. Divergent.

18. $1 + \frac{1}{2} - \frac{1}{3} - \frac{1}{4} + + - - \cdots$.

19. $1 - \frac{2}{2^2 + 1} + \frac{3}{3^2 + 1} - \frac{4}{4^2 + 1} + \cdots$. Cond. conv.

20. $\text{Sin}^{-1} 1 - \frac{1}{2!} \text{Sin}^{-1} \frac{1}{2} + \frac{1}{3!} \text{Sin}^{-1} \frac{1}{3} - \frac{1}{4!} \text{Sin}^{-1} \frac{1}{4} + \cdots$.

21. If $u_n > u_{n+1} > 0$ for all n, and $\sum_{n=1}^{\infty} (-1)^{n-1} u_n = S$, show that the partial sums satisfy the inequality $S_{2k} < S < S_{2k+1}$.

22. If $u_n > u_{n+1} > 0$ for all n, and $u_n \to 0$ as $n \to \infty$, prove that $\sum_{n=1}^{\infty} \frac{(-1)^{n-1} u_n}{1 + u_n}$ converges.

23. If $\sum_{n=1}^{\infty} c_n$ is convergent and $\sum_{n=1}^{\infty} u_n$ is absolutely convergent, prove that $\sum_{n=1}^{\infty} c_n u_n$ is absolutely convergent. *Hint:* Convergence implies $|c_n| < M < \infty$ for all n.

24. If $0 < a < 1$ and $\sum_{n=1}^{\infty} c_n$ is convergent, prove that $\sum_{n=1}^{\infty} c_n a^n$ is absolutely convergent. *Hint:* Convergence implies $\lim_{n\to\infty} |c_{n+1}/c_n| \leqq 1$.

158. Power Series

An infinite series of the form

$$a_0 + a_1 x + a_2 x^2 + \cdots + a_n x^n + \cdots, \tag{1}$$

in which $a_0, a_1, a_2, \cdots, a_n, \cdots$ are constants and x is a variable, is called a **power series in x.** The totality of values of x for which a power series converges is called its **interval of convergence.** This interval always includes the value $x = 0$, and its range is determined by the ratio test as illustrated in the following examples.

Example 1. Find the interval of convergence of the series

$$x - \frac{x^2}{2} + \frac{x^3}{3} - \cdots + (-1)^{n-1} \frac{x^n}{n} + \cdots.$$

Solution: By the ratio test, we find

$$\lim_{n\to\infty} \left|\frac{u_{n+1}}{u_n}\right| = \lim_{n\to\infty} \left|\frac{x^{n+1}}{n+1} \cdot \frac{n}{x^n}\right| = \lim_{n\to\infty} \left|\frac{n}{n+1} \cdot x\right| = |x|.$$

Hence the series converges when x is numerically less than 1, and diverges when x is numerically greater than 1. When $x = 1$ or $x = -1$, the ratio test fails, and the corresponding numerical series

$$1 - \tfrac{1}{2} + \tfrac{1}{3} - \tfrac{1}{4} + \cdots, \qquad -1 - \tfrac{1}{2} - \tfrac{1}{3} - \tfrac{1}{4} - \cdots$$

must be tested by other means. Thus the first of these is convergent by the alternating series test, and the second is divergent since it is the negative of the harmonic series. Hence the interval of convergence is $-1 < x \leqq 1$.

Example 2. Find the interval of convergence of the series

$$x + \frac{x^2}{2!} + \frac{x^3}{3!} + \cdots + \frac{x^n}{n!} + \cdots.$$

Solution: Using the ratio test, we have

$$\lim_{n\to\infty}\left|\frac{u_{n+1}}{u_n}\right| = \lim_{n\to\infty}\left|\frac{x^{n+1}}{(n+1)!}\cdot\frac{n!}{x^n}\right| = \lim_{n\to\infty}\left|\frac{x}{n+1}\right| = 0.$$

Hence the series converges for all values of x.

If the power series (1) is convergent in the interval $-r < x < r$, and possibly also at one or both end points, the positive number r is called the *radius of convergence* of the power series.

Theorem. *If r is the radius of convergence of the power series* (1), *then the series is absolutely convergent for all x such that $|x| < r$.*

Proof: It follows from the ratio test that $\lim_{n\to\infty}\left|\frac{a_{n+1}}{a_n}\right| r \leqq 1$, since otherwise there would exist values of x within the interval where the series is divergent. Hence, for any x_0 within the interval, it follows from $|x_0| < r$ that

$$\lim_{n\to\infty}\left|\frac{a_{n+1}}{a_n}x_0\right| < 1.$$

In accordance with the ratio test this means that (1) is absolutely convergent for $x = x_0$, and the theorem is proved.

EXERCISE 85

Find the interval of convergence for each of the following series.

1. $1 + x + x^2 + \cdots + x^{n-1} + \cdots.$ *Ans.* $-1 < x < 1.$
2. $x - 2x^2 + 3x^3 - \cdots + (-1)^{n-1} nx^n + \cdots.$
3. $x + 2!x^2 + 3!x^3 + \cdots + n!x^n + \cdots.$ $x = 0.$
4. $x + \dfrac{x^2}{2} + \dfrac{x^3}{3} + \cdots + \dfrac{x^n}{n} + \cdots.$

5. $x - \frac{x^3}{3!} + \frac{x^5}{5!} - \cdots + (-1)^{n-1}\frac{x^{2n-1}}{(2n-1)!} + \cdots.$ *Ans.* All values of x.

6. $x - \frac{x^3}{2} + \frac{x^5}{3} - \cdots + (-1)^{n-1}\frac{x^{2n-1}}{n} + \cdots.$

7. $2x + 4x^2 + 8x^3 + \cdots + 2^n x^n + \cdots.$ $-\frac{1}{2} < x < \frac{1}{2}.$

8. $1 - x + \frac{x^2}{2^2} - \cdots + (-1)^{n-1}\frac{x^{n-1}}{(n-1)^2} + \cdots.$

9. $1 + \frac{x}{\sqrt{2}} + \frac{x^2}{\sqrt{3}} + \cdots + \frac{x^{n-1}}{\sqrt{n}} + \cdots.$ $-1 \leqq x < 1.$

10. $x + \frac{x^2}{3} + \frac{x^3}{3^2} + \cdots + \frac{x^n}{3^{n-1}} + \cdots.$

11. $\frac{x}{1\cdot 2} + \frac{x^2}{2^2\cdot 2^2} + \frac{x^3}{3^2\cdot 2^3} + \cdots + \frac{x^n}{n^2\cdot 2^n} + \cdots.$ $-2 \leqq x \leqq 2.$

12. $x + \frac{x^2}{2^2} + \frac{x^3}{3^3} + \cdots + \frac{x^n}{n^n} + \cdots.$

13. $x - \frac{x^3}{3} + \frac{x^5}{5} - \frac{x^7}{7} + \cdots.$ $-1 \leqq x \leqq 1.$

14. $\frac{x}{1\cdot 5} + \frac{x^2}{2\cdot 5^2} + \frac{x^3}{3\cdot 5^3} + \frac{x^4}{4\cdot 5^4} + \cdots.$

15. $1 - \frac{3x}{2} + \frac{5x^2}{4} - \frac{7x^3}{8} + \cdots.$ $-2 < x < 2.$

16. $1 - \frac{x^2}{2a^2} + \frac{x^4}{4a^4} - \frac{x^6}{6a^6} + \cdots, \quad (a > 0).$

17. $(x-1) + \frac{1}{2}(x-1)^2 + \frac{1}{3}(x-1)^3 + \cdots.$ $0 \leqq x < 2.$

18. $(x-2) - 2(x-2)^2 + 3(x-2)^3 - \cdots.$

19. $1 + \frac{x+3}{2^2} + \frac{(x+3)^2}{3^2} + \cdots.$ $-4 \leqq x \leqq -2.$

20. $\left(\frac{x+1}{2}\right) + \left(\frac{x+1}{2}\right)^3 + \left(\frac{x+1}{2}\right)^5 + \cdots.$

21. $\left(\frac{x-1}{x}\right) + \frac{1}{2}\left(\frac{x-1}{x}\right)^2 + \frac{1}{3}\left(\frac{x-1}{x}\right)^3 + \cdots.$ $x \geqq \frac{1}{2}.$

22. $2\sin x + \frac{2^2\sin^2 x}{2^2} + \frac{2^3\sin^3 x}{3^2} + \cdots.$

23. $e^x + e^{2x} + e^{3x} + \cdots.$ $x < 0.$

24. $(\log x)^2 + (\log x)^4 + (\log x)^6 + \cdots.$

25. If r is the radius of convergence of $\sum_{n=0}^{\infty} a_n x^n$, show that the limit approached by $|a_{n+1}r/a_n|$ as $n \to \infty$ cannot be greater than 1. *Hint:* If $\lim |a_{n+1}r/a_n| \to 1 + 2h$, where $h > 0$, prove that the series diverges at the point $x_0 = r/(1+h)$ by showing that $\lim |a_{n+1}x_0/a_n| > (1+2h)/(1+h) > 1$.

CHAPTER 18

Expansion of Functions

159. Introduction

By ordinary long division, we may obtain quotients such as

$$\frac{1}{1 - x} = 1 + x + x^2 + x^3 + \cdots. \tag{1}$$

The series on the right side of (1) is convergent in the interval $-1 < x < 1$, and for values of x in this interval it can be shown that the *sum* of the series equals the value of the function from which it was obtained. Accordingly, we say that the right member of (1) is a power-series **expansion** or **development** of the function $1/(1 - x)$ for values of x in the interval $-1 < x < 1$.

The question now arises as to whether other functions such as $\sqrt{1 + x}$ and $\sin x$ can be similarly represented by power series. In the next article we will show how, in certain circumstances, this may be done. To do this, however, we shall need the following theorem which will be proved in Article **162.**

Theorem. *A power series which represents a function $f(x)$ may be differentiated term by term for all values of x within its interval of convergence, and the power series thus obtained equals $f'(x)$.*

Illustration. Differentiating both sides of (1), we find

$$\frac{1}{(1 - x)^2} = 1 + 2x + 3x^2 + \cdots, \quad -1 < x < 1.$$

Observe that the same result is obtained when the function $(1 - x)^{-2}$ is expanded in accordance with the binomial theorem; thus

$$(1 - x)^{-2} = 1 - (-2)x + \frac{(-2)(-3)}{1 \cdot 2} x^2 - \frac{(-2)(-3)(-4)}{1 \cdot 2 \cdot 3} x^3 + \cdots$$

$$= 1 + 2x + 3x^2 + 4x^3 + \cdots.$$

160. Maclaurin's Series

Let us assume that a function $f(x)$ can be represented within a certain interval of convergence by a power series of the form

$$f(x) = c_0 + c_1x + c_2x^2 + \cdots + c_nx^n + \cdots, \tag{1}$$

where the c's are constants to be determined.

Setting $x = 0$ in (1), we see at once that

$$c_0 = f(0).$$

Also, from the successive derivatives of (1),

$$\begin{aligned} f'(x) &= c_1 + 2c_2x + 3c_3x^2 + \cdots, \\ f''(x) &= 2!c_2 + 3!c_3x + 4\cdot 3\, c_4x^2 + \cdots, \\ f'''(x) &= 3!c_3 + 4!c_4x + 5\cdot 4\cdot 3\, c_5x^2 + \cdots, \\ &\cdots\cdots\cdots\cdots\cdots\cdots \end{aligned}$$

when $x = 0$, we find

$$\begin{aligned} f'(0) &= c_1, \\ f''(0) &= 2!c_2, \\ f'''(0) &= 3!c_3, \\ &\cdots\cdots \end{aligned}$$

Solving for the c's and substituting in (1), we obtain

$$\boldsymbol{f(x) = f(0) + f'(0)\, x + \frac{f''(0)}{2!}\, x^2 + \cdots + \frac{f^{(n)}(0)}{n!}\, x^n + \cdots.} \tag{2}$$

This series is called **Maclaurin's series,** or the *power-series expansion of $f(x)$ about $x = 0$.* It is named for the Scottish mathematician Colin Maclaurin (1698–1746).

In order to obtain (2), observe that $f(x)$ and all of its derivatives must exist at $x = 0$. Thus, $\ln x$, $\cot x$, and $\sqrt{x^3}$ have no Maclaurin's series.

Example 1. Obtain the Maclaurin's series for $\sin x$.

Solution: Letting $f(x) = \sin x$, we obtain the derivatives $f'(x) = \cos x$, $f''(x) = -\sin x$, $f'''(x) = -\cos x$, $f^{(4)}(x) = \sin x$, $\cdots$. Thus, when $x = 0$, we find $f(0) = 0, f'(0) = 1, f''(0) = 0, f'''(0) = -1, f^{(4)}(0) = 0$, $\cdots$. Hence, by substitution in (2), we obtain the result

$$\sin x = x - \frac{x^3}{3!} + \frac{x^5}{5!} - \frac{x^7}{7!} + \cdots. \tag{3}$$

Using the ratio test this series may be shown to be convergent for all values of x. As a result, when $x = 2$, we find on substitution in (3) that

$$\begin{aligned}\sin 2 &= 2 - (1.3333) + (0.2667) - (0.0254) + (0.0014) - \cdots \\ &= 0.909.\end{aligned}$$

Note: To find the Maclaurin's series for a function such as $\sin x^2$, it is simpler to obtain the expansion for $\sin y$ and then substitute x^2 for y. The direct procedure of computing the derivatives of $f(x) = \sin x^2$ leads to involved computations.

Example 2. Obtain the Maclaurin's series for $(1 + x)^p$ where p is a real number other than $0, 1, 2, 3, \cdots$.

Solution: By taking $f(x) = (1 + x)^p$, we find

$$f'(x) = p(1 + x)^{p-1}; \quad \text{hence } f'(0) = p,$$

$$f''(x) = p(p - 1)(1 + x)^{p-2}; \quad \text{hence } f''(0) = p(p - 1),$$

$$\cdots\cdots\cdots\cdots\cdots$$

$$f^{(n)}(x) = p(p - 1)\cdots(p - n + 1)(1 + x)^{p-n}; \quad \text{hence}$$

$$\cdots\cdots\cdots\cdots\cdots$$

$$f^{(n)}(0) = p(p - 1)\cdots(p - n + 1).$$

$$\cdots\cdots\cdots\cdots\cdots$$

By substitution in (2), we obtain the familiar **binomial series**

$$(1 + x)^p = 1 + px + \frac{p(p - 1)}{2!}x^2 + \cdots + \frac{p(p - 1)\cdots(p - n + 1)}{n!}x^n + \cdots,$$

which by the ratio test converges for $-1 < x < 1$.

EXERCISE 86

Obtain the following Maclaurin's series and establish their convergence for the intervals indicated.

1. $e^x = 1 + x + \dfrac{x^2}{2!} + \dfrac{x^3}{3!} + \cdots$, all values.
2. $\cos x = 1 - \dfrac{x^2}{2!} + \dfrac{x^4}{4!} - \dfrac{x^6}{6!} + \cdots$, all values.
3. $\ln(1 + x) = x - \dfrac{x^2}{2} + \dfrac{x^3}{3} - \dfrac{x^4}{4} + \cdots$, $-1 < x \leqq 1$.
4. $\dfrac{1}{1 + x} = 1 - x + x^2 - x^3 + \cdots$, $-1 < x < 1$.
5. $\text{Sin}^{-1} x = x + \dfrac{1}{2}\cdot\dfrac{x^3}{3} + \dfrac{1\cdot 3}{2\cdot 4}\cdot\dfrac{x^5}{5} + \cdots$, $-1 < x < 1$. *Note:* It can be shown by advanced methods that this series is convergent for $x = \pm 1$.
6. $\text{Tan}^{-1} x = x - \dfrac{x^3}{3} + \dfrac{x^5}{5} - \dfrac{x^7}{7} + \cdots$, $-1 \leqq x \leqq 1$.

Verify the following expansions.

7. $\sqrt{1 + x} = 1 + \frac{1}{2}x - \frac{1}{8}x^2 + \frac{1}{16}x^3 - \cdots.$
8. $\sqrt[3]{1 + x} = 1 + \frac{1}{3}x - \frac{1}{9}x^2 + \frac{5}{81}x^3 - \cdots.$
9. $\sin\left(\frac{\pi}{4} + x\right) = \frac{1}{\sqrt{2}}\left(1 + x - \frac{x^2}{2!} - \frac{x^3}{3!} + + \cdots\right).$
10. $\frac{1}{2}(e^x + e^{-x}) = 1 + \frac{x^2}{2!} + \frac{x^4}{4!} + \frac{x^6}{6!} + \cdots.$
11. $\tan x = x + \frac{1}{3}x^3 + \frac{2}{15}x^5 + \frac{17}{315}x^7 + \cdots.$
12. $\sec x = 1 + \frac{1}{2}x^2 + \frac{5}{24}x^4 + \frac{61}{720}x^6 + \cdots.$
13. $\ln \cos x = -\frac{1}{2}x^2 - \frac{1}{12}x^4 - \frac{1}{45}x^6 - \cdots.$
14. $1/\sqrt{4 - x} = \frac{1}{2} + \frac{1}{16}x + \frac{3}{256}x^2 + \frac{5}{2048}x^3 + \cdots.$
15. $\cos x^2 = 1 - \frac{x^4}{2!} + \frac{x^8}{4!} - \frac{x^{12}}{6!} + \cdots.$
16. $\sin 2x = 2x - \frac{2^3x^3}{3!} + \frac{2^5x^5}{5!} - \frac{2^7x^7}{7!} + \cdots.$

Using the above Maclaurin's series, compute the following numbers to three decimal places.

17. $\sqrt{e}$. *Ans.* 1.649.
18. $\ln 1.2$.
19. $\sin 1$. 0.841.
20. $\cos 10°$.
21. $\text{Sin}^{-1} \frac{1}{4}$. 0.253.
22. $\sqrt[3]{1.1}$.
23. $\sec \frac{1}{3}$. 1.058.
24. $\text{Tan}^{-1} 0.4$.
25. Using the identity $\frac{1}{4}\pi = \text{Tan}^{-1} \frac{1}{7} + 2\,\text{Tan}^{-1} \frac{1}{3}$, find the value of π to four decimal places. *Ans.* 3.1416.
26. If two power series have the same radius of convergence $r \neq 0$, and if

$$\sum_{n=0}^{\infty} a_n x^n = \sum_{n=0}^{\infty} b_n x^n$$

for every x in the interval $|x| < r$, prove that $a_n = b_n$ for every n.

161. Algebraic Operations with Power Series

The operations of algebra may be applied to power series in the same manner that they are applied to polynomials provided that the given series satisfy certain conditions of convergence. These conditions are contained in the following theorems, which are stated without proof in order that we may devote our attention to a study of their application.

Theorem I. Addition. *Two power series may be added together for all values of the variable for which both series converge. Symbolically, if*

$$f(x) = a_0 + a_1x + a_2x^2 + \cdots, \qquad g(x) = b_0 + b_1x + b_2x^2 + \cdots, \tag{1}$$

then

$$f(x) + g(x) = (a_0 + b_0) + (a_1 + b_1)x + (a_2 + b_2)x^2 + \cdots.$$

Theorem 2. Multiplication. *Two power series may be multiplied together for all values of the variable for which one series is convergent and the other is absolutely convergent. Symbolically,*

$$f(x)\cdot g(x) = a_0b_0 + (a_1b_0 + a_0b_1)x + (a_2b_0 + a_1b_1 + a_0b_2)x^2 + \cdots.$$

Illustration. Using the Maclaurin's series given in Problems 1 and 2, Exercise **86**, we have

$$\begin{aligned} e^x \cos x &= \left(1 + x + \frac{x^2}{2!} + \cdots\right)\left(1 - \frac{x^2}{2!} + \frac{x^4}{4!} - \cdots\right) \\ &= 1 + x - \frac{1}{3}x^3 - \frac{1}{6}x^4 + \cdots. \end{aligned}$$

Theorem 3. Division. *If r is the smallest root (in absolute value) of $g(x) = 0$ and if the series (1) converge respectively for $|x| < F$ and $|x| < G$, then the quotient series corresponding to $f(x)/g(x)$ converges in the interval $|x| < Q$ where Q is the smallest of the numbers r, F, and G.*

Note: When $r = 0$, the above theorem implies that division is not permissible. However, if $b_0 = b_1 = \cdots = b_k = 0$, division is valid provided that $a_0 = a_1 = \cdots = a_k = 0$. For example,

$$\begin{aligned} \frac{x}{\sin x} &= \frac{x}{x - \frac{1}{6}x^3 + \cdots} = \frac{1}{1 - \frac{1}{6}x^2 + \cdots} \\ &= 1 + \frac{1}{6}x^2 + \frac{7}{360}x^4 + \cdots, \quad (x \neq 0). \end{aligned}$$

In accordance with Theorem 3, this series converges in the interval $-\pi < x < \pi$.

Theorem 4. Substitution. *The power series obtained by substituting the second series of (1) in the first converges to $f[g(x)]$ for those values of x for which $|x| < G$ and $|u| < F$ where $u = g(x)$.*

Example. Find the power series in x for $e^{\cos x}$.

Solution: Letting $\cos x = 1 - z$, where

$$z = \frac{x^2}{2!} - \frac{x^4}{4!} + \frac{x^6}{6!} - \cdots, \tag{2}$$

we have

$$e^{\cos x} = e^{1-z} = e\cdot e^{-z} = e\left[1 - z + \frac{z^2}{2!} - \frac{z^3}{3!} + \cdots\right]. \tag{3}$$

Substituting (2) in (3), we obtain

$$e^{\cos x} = e\left[1 - \frac{x^2}{2} + \frac{x^4}{6} - \frac{31x^6}{720} + \cdots\right],$$

which converges for all values of x.

It should be noted that the required result is difficult to obtain by writing

$$e^{\cos x} = 1 + \cos x + \frac{\cos^2 x}{2!} + \cdots,$$

and then substituting the series expansion for $\cos x$.

EXERCISE 87

Find the power-series expansions of the following functions, using the theorems of Article **161**. Determine the interval of convergence.

1. $\frac{1}{2}(e^x + e^{-x})$. *Ans.* $1 + \frac{x^2}{2!} + \frac{x^4}{4!} + \frac{x^6}{6!} + \cdots,$ all values.
2. $\cos x - \sin x$.
3. $\cos^2 x = \frac{1}{2}(1 + \cos 2x)$. $1 - x^2 + \frac{1}{3}x^4 - \frac{2}{45}x^6 + \cdots,$ all values.
4. $\cos^3 x = \frac{1}{4}(\cos 3x + 3 \cos x)$.
5. $\ln \frac{1 + x}{1 - x}$. $2\left[x + \frac{x^3}{3} + \frac{x^5}{5} + \frac{x^7}{7} + \cdots\right],$ $|x| < 1$.
6. $e^x \sin x$.
7. $e^{-x} \cos 2x$. $1 - x - \frac{3}{2}x^2 + \frac{11}{6}x^3 + \cdots,$ all values.
8. $\ln^2 (1 - x)$.
9. $(1 + x^2) \operatorname{Sin}^{-1} x$. $x + \frac{7}{6}x^3 + \frac{29}{120}x^5 + \cdots,$ $|x| \leqq 1$.
10. $\frac{e^x}{1 - x}$.
11. $\frac{\cos x}{1 - \sin x}$. $1 + x + \frac{1}{2}x^2 + \frac{1}{3}x^3 + \cdots,$ $|x| < \frac{1}{2}\pi$.
12. $\frac{1}{2 - e^x}$.
13. $\frac{6 - 3x^2}{6 - 5x + x^2}$. $1 + \frac{5}{6}x + \frac{1}{36}x^2 + \cdots,$ $|x| < 2$.
14. $\frac{\ln (1 + x)}{1 - x^2}$.
15. $\frac{x^2}{1 - \cos x}$. $2 + \frac{1}{6}x^2 + \frac{1}{120}x^4 + \cdots,$ $|x| < 2\pi$.
16. $e^{\sin x}$.
17. $e^{\operatorname{Sin}^{-1} x}$. $1 + x + \frac{1}{2}x^2 + \frac{1}{3}x^3 + \cdots,$ $|x| < 1$.
18. $\ln (1 - x + x^2)$.
19. $\ln (1 + \sin x)$. $x - \frac{1}{2}x^2 + \frac{1}{6}x^3 - \frac{1}{12}x^4 + \cdots,$ $|x| < \frac{1}{2}\pi$.
20. $\sqrt{3 + \cos x}$.

Using power series, evaluate the following limits.

21. $\lim_{x\to 0} \frac{\sin x - x}{x^3}$. *Ans.* $-\frac{1}{6}$.
22. $\lim_{x\to 0} \frac{\tan^2 x - x^2}{x^4}$.
23. $\lim_{x\to 0} \frac{\ln^2 (1 + x)}{x \csc x - 1}$. 6.
24. $\lim_{x\to 0} \frac{\tan^2 x - \sin^2 x}{x^3(e^x - e^{-x})}$.

25. What is the coefficient of x^{3n} in the Maclaurin's expansion of $(1 + x + x^2)^{-1}$? *Ans.* 1.
26. Prove Theorem 1, Article **161.**

162. Differentiation and Integration of Power Series

Power series may be differentiated and integrated in accordance with the following theorems.

Theorem 1. *A power series that represents the function $f(x)$ may be differentiated term by term for all values of x within its interval of convergence, $|x| < r$, and the power series thus obtained represents the function $f'(x)$.*

Proof: If x and x_0 are two different values of the variable within the interval of convergence of the power series $\sum_{n=0}^{\infty} a_n x^n$ that represents the function $f(x)$, then, in accordance with Theorem 1 of the preceding article, we have

$$\frac{f(x) - f(x_0)}{x - x_0} = \sum_{n=0}^{\infty} a_n \left[\frac{x^n - x_0^n}{x - x_0}\right]$$

$$= \sum_{n=0}^{\infty} a_n[x^{n-1} + x^{n-2}x_0 + \cdots + x_0^{n-1}].$$

By taking the limit as $x \to x_0$, we find

$$f'(x_0) = \lim_{x \to x_0} \frac{f(x) - f(x_0)}{x - x_0} = \sum_{n=0}^{\infty} n a_n x_0^{n-1}. \tag{1}$$

The radius of convergence for the series in (1) is at least as large as r, since x_0 can be any value in the interval $|x| < r$.

By use of differentiation, we can prove the following theorem.

Theorem 2. *A power series can be integrated term by term between any limits lying in its interval of convergence.*

Proof: Let $f(x) = \sum_{n=0}^{\infty} a_n x^n$, $|x| < r$, and consider the series

$$F(x) = \sum_{n=0}^{\infty} \frac{a_n}{n+1} x^{n+1}, \quad |x| < r'. \tag{2}$$

By differentiating (2), we obtain

$$F'(x) = \sum_{n=0}^{\infty} a_n x^n. \tag{3}$$

Thus $F'(x) = f(x)$, and we have

$$F(x) = \int_0^x f(x)\,dx \qquad \text{or} \qquad F(x) - F(x_0) = \int_{x_0}^x f(x)\,dx.$$

By a comparison test with the series for $f(x)$, we see that (2) converges for all x in the interval $|x| < r$. Hence its radius of convergence is at least as large as r, that is, $r' \geqq r$. In accordance with Theorem 1, however, the radius of convergence of (3) is at least as large as that of (2), that is, $r \geqq r'$. Hence it follows that $r' = r$, meaning that the radius of convergence is unaltered when a series is either differentiated or integrated.

Illustration 1. Differentiating the series

$$\sin x = x - \frac{x^3}{3!} + \frac{x^5}{5!} - \cdots, \tag{4}$$

we obtain

$$\cos x = 1 - \frac{x^2}{2!} + \frac{x^4}{4!} - \cdots.$$

Both series converge for all values of x.

Illustration 2. Integrating the series

$$\frac{1}{1+x} = 1 - x + x^2 - \cdots, \quad |x| < 1,$$

from 0 to x, we obtain

$$\ln(1+x) = x - \tfrac{1}{2}x^2 + \tfrac{1}{3}x^3 - \cdots, \quad |x| < 1.$$

Example 1. Find the power series for $\mathrm{Sin}^{-1}\, x$ by integration.

Solution: By the binomial theorem, we have

$$\frac{1}{\sqrt{1-x^2}} = (1-x^2)^{-1/2} = 1 + \frac{1}{2}x^2 + \frac{1\cdot 3}{2\cdot 4}x^4 + \frac{1\cdot 3\cdot 5}{2\cdot 4\cdot 6}x^6 + \cdots.$$

Integrating from 0 to x, we obtain

$$\mathrm{Sin}^{-1}\, x = \int_0^x \frac{dx}{\sqrt{1-x^2}} = x + \frac{1}{2}\frac{x^3}{3} + \frac{1\cdot 3}{2\cdot 4}\frac{x^5}{5} + \cdots. \tag{5}$$

Both series converge for $|x| < 1$.

Note: Observe that the value of π may be computed from (5) by setting $x = \frac{1}{2}$. Thus

$$\frac{\pi}{6} = \frac{1}{2} + \frac{1}{2}\cdot\frac{1}{3}\left(\frac{1}{2}\right)^3 + \frac{1\cdot 3}{2\cdot 4}\cdot\frac{1}{5}\left(\frac{1}{2}\right)^5 + \cdots,$$

whence $\pi = 3.1415\cdots$.

Example 2. Find approximately the value of $\displaystyle\int_0^1 \frac{\sin x}{x}\,dx$.

Solution: Using the first three terms of (4), we obtain the approximation

$$\int_0^1 \frac{\sin x}{x}\,dx = \int_0^1 \left(1 - \frac{x^2}{3!} + \frac{x^4}{5!}\right) dx$$
$$= \left[x - \frac{x^3}{18} + \frac{x^5}{600}\right]_0^1 = 0.9461.$$

EXERCISE 88

Find the power series for the first of the following functions by differentiating the power series corresponding to the second function.

1. $\sin x$; $\cos x$. *Ans.* $x - \frac{x^3}{3!} + \frac{x^5}{5!} - \cdots$, all values.
2. $(1 - x)^{-2}$; $(1 - x)^{-1}$.
3. $\sec^2 x$; $\tan x$. $1 + x^2 + \frac{2}{3}x^4 + \cdots$, $|x| < \frac{1}{2}\pi$.
4. $\sin x + x \cos x$; $x \sin x$.
5. $\dfrac{(2 - x)e^x}{(1 - x)^2}$; $\dfrac{e^x}{1 - x}$. $2 + 5x + 8x^2 + \cdots$, $|x| < 1$.
6. $\cos x/(1 + \sin x)$; $\ln (1 + \sin x)$.

Find the power series for the first of the following functions by integrating the power series corresponding to the second function.

7. $\mathrm{Tan}^{-1} x$; $1/(1 + x^2)$. *Ans.* $x - \frac{1}{3}x^3 + \frac{1}{5}x^5 - \cdots$, $|x| < 1$.
8. $\ln (1 - x)$; $1/(1 - x)$.
9. $\ln \cos x$; $\tan x$. $-\frac{1}{2}x^2 - \frac{1}{12}x^4 - \frac{1}{45}x^6 - \cdots$, $|x| < \frac{1}{2}\pi$.
10. $\ln \dfrac{1 + x}{1 - x}$; $\dfrac{1}{1 - x^2}$.
11. $\ln (x + \sqrt{1 + x^2})$; $1/\sqrt{1 + x^2}$. $x - \frac{1}{6}x^3 + \frac{3}{40}x^5 - \cdots$, $|x| < 1$.
12. $\ln (\sec x + \tan x)$; $\sec x$.

Find approximately the values of the following integrals.

13. $\int_0^1 \sin x^2\,dx$. *Ans.* 0.3103.
14. $\int_0^1 e^{-x^2}\,dx$.
15. $\int_0^{2/3} \sqrt{1 - x^3}\,dx$. 0.6408.
16. $\int_0^{1/2} e^x \cos \sqrt{x}\,dx$.
17. $\int_0^{1/3} \dfrac{e^{-x^2}}{\sqrt{1 - x^2}}\,dx$. 0.3275.
18. $\int_0^{1/2} \dfrac{\cos x}{1 - x}\,dx$.
19. $\int_0^{1/4} e^x \ln (1 + x)\,dx$. 0.0342.
20. $\int_0^1 \sqrt{\cos x}\,dx$.
21. If $f(x) = (1 + x)^p$, then $(1 + x)^{-p}f(x) = 1$, and by differentiation we obtain

$$(1 + x)f'(x) - pf(x) = 0.$$

Show that the binomial series given in Example 2, Article **160**, satisfies this differential equation.

22. Determine a function $f(x)$ such that

$$\int_0^1 f(x)\,dx = 1 - \frac{1}{2^2} + \frac{1}{3^2} - \frac{1}{4^2} + \cdots.$$

Hint: Differentiate $\int_0^x f(x)\,dx = x - \frac{x^2}{2^2} + \frac{x^3}{3^2} - \frac{x^4}{4^2} + \cdots.$

163. Approximation Formulas Derived from Power Series

If the variable is sufficiently small, we may use the first few terms of a power series as an approximation formula for the function which it represents.

Illustration 1.

	First approximation	*Second approximation*
$(1+x)^n$	$\approx 1 + nx$	$\approx 1 + nx + \frac{1}{2}n(n-1)x^2,$
e^{-x}	$\approx 1 - x$	$\approx 1 - x + \frac{1}{2}x^2.$

In accordance with the corollary of Article **156,** if x assumes values such that the terms of an alternating series decrease, then the error introduced by the approximation is less than the magnitude of the first term omitted.

Illustration 2.

	Approximation	*Maximum error*
$\sin x$	$\approx x,$	$\lvert\frac{1}{6}x^3\rvert,$
$\sin x$	$\approx x - \frac{1}{6}x^3,$	$\lvert\frac{1}{120}x^5\rvert.$

Thus $\sin 0.3 = 0.3$, with an error not greater than $\frac{1}{6}(0.3)^3 = 0.0045$. Hence $0.2955 < \sin 0.3 < 0.3$.

Example. For what values of x will the approximation formula $\sin x = x$ give results correct to three decimal places?

Solution: Since the maximum error is given by $|\frac{1}{6}x^3|$, we must have

$$|\tfrac{1}{6}x^3| < 0.0005, \qquad \text{or} \qquad |x| < \sqrt[3]{0.003} = 0.1442 \cdots \text{rad.}$$

Thus the formula $\sin x = x$ is valid to three decimal places for values of x between -0.144 and 0.144, or in degrees, between $-8.2°$ and $8.2°$.

Note: Observe that the above discussion of errors applies only to alternating series. Errors, in general, will be considered in Article **165.**

EXERCISE 89

How accurate is each of the following approximation formulas for the values of x indicated?

1. $\sin x = x - \frac{1}{6}x^3$; (*a*) 30°, (*b*) 90°.

Ans. (*a*) Error < 0.00033, (*b*) error < 0.08.

2. $\cos x = 1 - \frac{1}{2}x^2$; (*a*) 30°, (*b*) 90°.

3. $e^{-x} = 1 - x$; (a) 0.1, (b) 0.5.

Ans. (a) Error < 0.005, (b) error < 0.125.

4. $(1 + x)^{1/2} = 1 + \frac{1}{2}x$; (a) 0.01, (b) 0.1.
5. $\text{Tan}^{-1} x = x - \frac{1}{3}x^3$; (a) 0.5, (b) 1.

Ans. (a) Error < 0.00625, (b) error < 0.2.

6. $\ln(1 + x) = x - \frac{1}{2}x^2$; (a) 0.1, (b) 0.4.

For the indicated value of x, how many terms of the Maclaurin's series of the following functions must be taken to obtain the value of the function correct to four decimal places?

7. $\sin x$; $x = 45°$. *Ans.* 3.
8. $\cos x$; $x = 30°$.
9. $(1 + x)^{1/2}$; $x = 0.2$. 5.
10. e^{-x}; $x = 1$.
11. $\text{Tan}^{-1} x$; $x = \frac{1}{2}$. 5.
12. $\ln(1 + x)$; $x = 0.2$.

For what range of values of x will the following approximation formulas be correct to four decimal places?

13. $\sin x = x - \frac{1}{6}x^3 + \frac{1}{120}x^5$. *Ans.* $|x| < 0.8212$.
14. $\cos x = 1 - \frac{1}{2}x^2 + \frac{1}{24}x^4$.
15. $(1 + x)^{-1} = 1 - x + x^2$. $|x| < 0.03684$.
16. $\ln(1 + x) = x - \frac{1}{2}x^2 + \frac{1}{3}x^3$.
17. $e^{-x} = 1 - x + \frac{1}{2}x^2$. $|x| < 0.06694$.
18. $\text{Tan}^{-1} x = x - \frac{1}{3}x^3 + \frac{1}{5}x^5$.
19. If h is small, show that $\dfrac{1}{(A - h)^2} - \dfrac{1}{(A + h)^2} \approx \dfrac{4h}{A^3}$.
20. If h is small, show that $\sin(A + h) - \sin(A - h) \approx 2h \cos A$.

164. Taylor's Series

We have seen that certain functions, such as $\ln x$, cannot be represented by a Maclaurin's series. However, by substituting $x - 1$ for z in the expansion

$$\ln(1 + z) = z - \tfrac{1}{2}z^2 + \tfrac{1}{3}z^3 - \cdots, \quad -1 < z \leqq 1,$$

it is apparent that $\ln x$ can be represented by the series

$$\ln x = (x - 1) - \tfrac{1}{2}(x - 1)^2 + \tfrac{1}{3}(x - 1)^3 - \cdots, \quad 0 < x \leqq 2.$$

In general let us assume that a function $f(x)$ can be represented within a certain interval of convergence by a series of the form

$$f(x) = c_0 + c_1(x - a) + c_2(x - a)^2 + \cdots + c_n(x - a)^n + \cdots, \qquad (1)$$

where a is an arbitrary constant and the c's are constants to be determined.

Setting $x = a$ in (1) and the successive derivatives of (1), we find, as in Article **160,** that

$$c_0 = f(a), \quad c_1 = f'(a), \quad c_2 = \frac{f''(a)}{2!}, \quad \cdots, \quad c_n = \frac{f^{(n)}(a)}{n!}, \quad \cdots.$$

Thus if $f(x)$ can be represented by a series of the type (1) that series must have the form

$$f(x) = f(a) + f'(a)(x - a) + \frac{f''(a)}{2!}(x - a)^2 + \cdots + \frac{f^{(n)}(a)}{n!}(x - a)^n + \cdots. \quad (2)$$

This series, which includes Maclaurin's series as a special case ($a = 0$), is called **Taylor's series.** It is named for the English mathematician Brook Taylor (1685–1731).

Another form of Taylor's series is obtained by placing $x = a + h$ in (2); thus

$$f(a + h) = f(a) + f'(a)\,h + \frac{f''(a)}{2!}h^2 + \cdots + \frac{f^{(n)}(a)}{n!}h^n + \cdots. \quad (3)$$

Example. Expand $\sin x$ in powers of $x - \frac{1}{4}\pi$.

Solution: Differentiating $f(x) = \sin x$, we have $f'(x) = \cos x$, $f''(x) = -\sin x$, $f'''(x) = -\cos x$, $f^{(4)}(x) = \sin x$, $\cdots$. Thus, when $x = \frac{1}{4}\pi$, we find $f(\frac{1}{4}\pi) = \sin \frac{1}{4}\pi = \frac{1}{2}\sqrt{2}$, $f'(\frac{1}{4}\pi) = \frac{1}{2}\sqrt{2}$, $f''(\frac{1}{4}\pi) = -\frac{1}{2}\sqrt{2}$, $f'''(\frac{1}{4}\pi) = -\frac{1}{2}\sqrt{2}$, $f^{(4)}(\frac{1}{4}\pi) = \frac{1}{2}\sqrt{2}$, $\cdots$. Hence, by substitution in (2), we obtain the result

$$\sin x = \frac{1}{2}\sqrt{2}\left[1 + (x - \tfrac{1}{4}\pi) - \frac{(x - \frac{1}{4}\pi)^2}{2!} - \frac{(x - \frac{1}{4}\pi)^3}{3!} + + \cdots\right]. \quad (4)$$

Using the ratio test, we can show this series to be convergent for all values of x.

The series (4) is especially useful in computing the sines of angles which are near to 45°. Thus, taking $x = 46° = \frac{46}{180}\pi$ radians, we have

$$x - \tfrac{1}{4}\pi = 1° = \tfrac{1}{180}\pi = 0.01745,$$
$$(x - \tfrac{1}{4}\pi)^2 = 0.00030,$$
$$(x - \tfrac{1}{4}\pi)^3 = 0.00001.$$

Substituting in (4), we obtain

$$\sin 46° = 0.70711[1 + 0.01745 - 0.00015 - \cdots] = 0.7193.$$

EXERCISE 90

Verify the following expansions and determine the interval of convergence.

1. $\cos x = \frac{1}{2}\sqrt{2}\left[1 - (x - \frac{1}{4}\pi) - \frac{(x - \frac{1}{4}\pi)^2}{2!} + + \cdots\right]$, all values.
2. $e^x = \frac{1}{e}\left[1 + (x + 1) + \frac{(x + 1)^2}{2!} + \cdots\right]$, all values.
3. $\sin x = \frac{1}{2} + \frac{\sqrt{3}}{2}\left(x - \frac{\pi}{6}\right) - \frac{1}{2}\cdot\frac{1}{2!}\left(x - \frac{\pi}{6}\right)^2 - \cdots$, all values.
4. $\ln x - \ln 2 = \frac{x - 2}{2} - \frac{(x - 2)^2}{2^2 \cdot 2} + \frac{(x - 2)^3}{2^3 \cdot 3} - \cdots$, $0 < x \leqq 4$.
5. $\sqrt{x} = 1 + \frac{1}{2}(x - 1) - \frac{1}{8}(x - 1)^2 + \cdots$, $0 < x < 2$.
6. $\cos(a + x) = \cos a - x \sin a - \frac{x^2}{2!}\cos a + \cdots$, all values.
7. $\ln(a + x) = \ln a + \frac{x}{a} - \frac{x^2}{2a^2} + \frac{x^3}{3a^3} - \cdots$, $-a < x \leqq a$.
8. $\tan x = 1 + 2(x - \frac{1}{4}\pi) + 2(x - \frac{1}{4}\pi)^2 + \cdots$, $0 < x < \frac{1}{2}\pi$.
9. $\sin(\frac{1}{2}\pi + x) = 1 - \frac{x^2}{2!} + \frac{x^4}{4!} - \cdots$, all values.
10. $\sin 2x = 1 - \frac{2^2}{2!}\left(x - \frac{\pi}{4}\right)^2 + \frac{2^4}{4!}\left(x - \frac{\pi}{4}\right)^4 - \cdots$, all values.
11. Square the series of Problem 1 to find the expansion of $\cos^2 x$ in powers of $x - \frac{1}{4}\pi$. *Ans.* $\frac{1}{2}[1 - 2(x - \frac{1}{4}\pi) + \frac{4}{3}(x - \frac{1}{4}\pi)^3 + \cdots]$.
12. Differentiate the series of Problem 3 to find the expansion of $\cos x$ in powers of $x - \frac{1}{6}\pi$.
13. Integrate the series of Problem 8 to find the expansion of $\ln \cos x$ in powers of $x - \frac{1}{4}\pi$. *Ans.* $\frac{1}{2}\ln\frac{1}{2} - (x - \frac{1}{4}\pi) - (x - \frac{1}{4}\pi)^2 - \cdots$.
14. Divide the series of Problem 10 by that of Problem 1 to find the expansion of $\sin x$ in powers of $x - \frac{1}{4}\pi$.
15. Differentiate the series of Problem 4 to find the expansion of $1/x$ in powers of $x - 2$. *Ans.* $\frac{1}{2} - \frac{1}{4}(x - 2) + \frac{1}{8}(x - 2)^2 - \cdots$.
16. Differentiate the series of Problem 8 to find the expansion of $\sec^2 x$ in powers of $x - \frac{1}{4}\pi$.

Approximate the following numbers to five decimal places by the use of series.

17. $\sin 47°$. *Ans.* 0.73135.
18. $\cos 44°$.
19. $\sin 87°$. 0.99863.
20. $\sin 35°$.
21. $\tan 46°$. 1.03553.
22. $e^{-0.3}$.
23. $\sqrt{4.02}$. 2.00499.
24. $e^{1.2}$ ($e = 2.718282$).
25. $\ln 1.04$. 0.03922.
26. $\ln 2.01$ ($\ln 2 = 0.693147$).
27. Find the area between the x axis and the curve $y = (x - \sin x)/x^3$ from $x = 0$ to $x = 1$, correct to four decimal places. *Ans.* 0.1639.

28. Find the area between the x axis and the curve $y = \sqrt{1 - x^4}$ from $x = 0$ to $x = \frac{1}{2}$, correct to four decimal places.

29. Evaluate $\int_3^{3.1} (x^4 - 8x^3 + 6x^2 + 8x + 7)\,dx$ by writing the integrand as a power series in $x - 3$. *Ans.* -5.323898.

30. Evaluate $\int_1^{1.2} \sqrt{x^3 - 3x^2 + 3x}\,dx$ to five decimal places. *Hint:* Substitute $z + 1$ for x.

165. Taylor's Theorem

In order to determine the conditions under which a Taylor's series will represent a given function, we shall establish the following theorem.

Taylor's Theorem. *If* $\boldsymbol{f(x)}$ *and its first n derivatives are continuous and single-valued in the interval* $\boldsymbol{a \leqq x \leqq b}$*, then*

$$\boldsymbol{f(b) = f(a) + (b - a)f'(a) + \frac{(b - a)^2}{2!} f''(a) + \cdots}$$
$$\boldsymbol{+ \frac{(b - a)^{n-1}}{(n - 1)!} f^{(n-1)}(a) + \frac{(b - a)^n}{n!} f^{(n)}(x_1),} \quad (1)$$

where $\boldsymbol{a < x_1 < b}$.

The relation (1) is known as **Taylor's formula.***

Proof: Let R_n represent the remainder defined by the relation

$$f(b) = f(a) + (b - a)f'(a) + \cdots + \frac{(b - a)^{n-1}}{(n - 1)!} f^{(n-1)}(a) + R_n. \quad (2)$$

In order to determine the value of R_n, let us define the function $P(a,b)$ by the relation

$$R_n = \frac{(b - a)^n}{n!} P,$$

and write down the auxiliary function

$$F(x) = f(b) - f(x) - (b - x)f'(x) - \cdots$$
$$- \frac{(b - x)^{n-1}}{(n - 1)!} f^{(n-1)}(x) - \frac{(b - x)^n}{n!} P, \quad (3)$$

which is formed from (2) by changing a to x in all terms except P.

It follows from (2) that $F(a) = 0$ and from (3) that $F(b) = 0$.

---

* Observe that for $n = 1$ Taylor's formula becomes the law of the mean (Article **114**). For this reason (1) is often called the *extended law of the mean.*

Hence, in accordance with Rolle's theorem (Article **113**), $F'(x)$ must be zero for some value x_1 between a and b.

Differentiating (3) with respect to x, we observe that all terms cancel, except the last two, and we have

$$F'(x) = -\frac{(b-x)^{n-1}}{(n-1)!}f^{(n)}(x) + \frac{(b-x)^{n-1}}{(n-1)!}P. \tag{4}$$

Substituting in (4) the value $x = x_1$, for which $F'(x_1) = 0$, we obtain $f^{(n)}(x_1) = P$; hence

$$R_n = \frac{(b-a)^n}{n!}f^{(n)}(x_1), \quad a < x_1 < b, \tag{5}$$

which proves the theorem.

It follows from (1) that *the Taylor's series represents $f(x)$ for those values, and only those values, for which the remainder R_n approaches zero as n increases without limit.**

Observe that the remainder term in (1) is merely the next term in the series with $f^{(n)}(a)$ replaced by $f^{(n)}(x_1)$. Since nothing is known concerning x_1, except that it lies between a and b, we cannot evaluate R_n exactly. We may, however, find a maximum bound for the remainder by choosing for x_1 that value between a and b which makes R_n as large as possible.

The relation (5), named for the French mathematician Joseph Louis Lagrange (1736–1813), is called *Lagrange's form of the remainder.* Another remainder formula, attributed to Cauchy, can be obtained in the following manner.

Take $F(x)$ as defined in (3), and consider the function

$$G(x) = F(x) + \frac{(b-x)^n}{n!}P. \tag{6}$$

Since $F(b) = 0$ and $F(a) = 0$, we have from (6)

$$G(b) = 0 \qquad \text{and} \qquad G(a) = \frac{(b-a)^n}{n!}P = R_n. \tag{7}$$

By the law of the mean, we have

$$G(b) - G(a) = G'(x_1)(b-a), \quad a < x_1 < b.$$

* It is possible for Taylor's series to converge for values of x for which the limit of the remainder is not zero. In most elementary cases, however, the interval of convergence is the same as that for which the remainder approaches zero.

Hence from (7), (6), and (4) we find

$$0 - R_n = (b - a)\left[F'(x_1) - \frac{(b - x_1)^{n-1}}{(n - 1)!} P\right]$$

$$= (b - a)\left[-\frac{(b - x_1)^{n-1}}{(n - 1)!} f^{(n)}(x_1) + \frac{(b - x_1)^{n-1}}{(n - 1)!} P - \frac{(b - x_1)^{n-1}}{(n - 1)!} P\right].$$

Solving for R_n, we obtain *Cauchy's form of the remaïnder*

$$R_n = \frac{(b - a)(b - x_1)^{n-1}}{(n - 1)!} f^{(n)}(x_1), \quad a < x_1 < b.$$

Example. Evaluate $\sqrt{e}$, using six terms of Maclaurin's series and estimate the accuracy of the result.

Solution: Taking six terms in Maclaurin's expansion of e^x and putting $x = \frac{1}{2}$, we have

$$e^{1/2} = 1 + \frac{1}{2} + \frac{(\frac{1}{2})^2}{2!} + \frac{(\frac{1}{2})^3}{3!} + \frac{(\frac{1}{2})^4}{4!} + \frac{(\frac{1}{2})^5}{5!} + R_6$$

$$= 1.648698 + R_6.$$

Since $(b - a) = \frac{1}{2}$ and $f^{(6)}(x) = e^x$, we have

$$R_6 = \frac{(\frac{1}{2})^6}{6!} e^{x_1},$$

where $0 < x_1 < \frac{1}{2}$.

The number e^{x_1} must be less than $e^{1/2}$, and since $e^{1/2} < 4^{1/2} = 2$, it follows that

$$R_6 < \frac{(\frac{1}{2})^6}{6!} \cdot 2 = 0.00004.$$

Hence the value of $\sqrt{e}$, correct to four decimals, is 1.6487.

EXERCISE 91

Evaluate each of the following numbers as directed and estimate the accuracy of the result.

1. $\sqrt[3]{e}$, using five terms of Maclaurin's series for e^x.
   Ans. 1.3956, $R_5 < 0.00005$.
2. ln 0.98, using three terms of Maclaurin's series for $\ln(1 - x)$.
3. $\sqrt{0.98}$, using three terms of Maclaurin's series for $\sqrt{1 - x}$. *Hint:* Substitute 0.81 for 0.98 in R_3. *Ans.* 0.98995, $R_3 < 0.000001$.

4. $\sqrt[3]{0.95}$, using two terms of Maclaurin's series for $\sqrt[3]{1 - x}$.
5. $\text{Sin}^{-1}(\frac{1}{3})$, using one term of Maclaurin's series for $\text{Sin}^{-1} x$.

Ans. $\frac{1}{3}$, $R_3 < 0.0102$.

6. sin 29°, using three terms of Taylor's expansion of sin x about $x = \frac{1}{6}\pi$.
7. cos 47°, using two terms of Taylor's expansion of cos x about $x = \frac{1}{4}\pi$.

Ans. 0.682, $R_2 < 0.0005$.

8. $\text{Tan}^{-1}(\frac{1}{2})$, using two terms of Maclaurin's series for $\text{Tan}^{-1} x$. Note that the series is alternating.
9. How many terms of Maclaurin's series for e^x must be used to evaluate e correct to four decimal places? *Ans.* 9 are sufficient.
10. How many terms of Maclaurin's series for ln $(1 - x)$ must be used to evaluate ln 0.95 correct to four decimal places?
11. How many terms of Taylor's expansion of sin x about $x = \frac{1}{6}\pi$ must be taken to give sin 28° correct to five decimal places? *Ans.* 3.
12. How many terms of Maclaurin's series for $\sqrt{1 - x}$ must be taken to give $\sqrt{0.97}$ correct to four decimal places?
13. For Maclaurin's expansion of e^x, show that

$$R_n < \frac{x^n e^x}{n!}, \quad \text{when } 0 < x,$$

and

$$|R_n| < \frac{|x|^n}{n!}, \quad \text{when } x < 0.$$

14. For what interval of the variable x will the first three terms of Maclaurin's series for e^x give an error less than 0.005? (See Problem 13.)
15. For Maclaurin's expansion of ln $(1 - x)$, show that

$$|R_n| < \frac{x^{n+1}}{(n + 1)(1 - x)^{n+1}}, \quad \text{when } 0 < x < 1,$$

and

$$|R_n| < \frac{|x|^{n+1}}{n + 1}, \quad \text{when } -1 \leqq x < 0.$$

16. For what interval of the variable x will the first two terms of Maclaurin's series for ln $(1 - x)$ give an error less than 0.0005? (See Problem 15.)
17. Show by long division that

$$\frac{1}{1 - t} = 1 + t + t^2 + \cdots + t^{n-1} + \frac{t^n}{1 - t}.$$

By integrating from 0 to x, where $0 < x < 1$, show that

$$\ln(1 - x) = -x - \frac{x^2}{2} - \frac{x^3}{3} - \cdots - \frac{x^n}{n} - R_n,$$

where

$$R_n = \int_0^x \frac{t^n\,dt}{1-t}; \quad \text{hence } |R_n| < \frac{1}{1-x}\int_0^x t^n\,dt = \frac{x^{n+1}}{(n+1)(1-x)}.$$

Compare this result with that obtained in Problem 15.

18. If $f'(a) = \cdots = f^{(n-1)}(a) = 0$ and $f^{(n)}(a) \neq 0$, use Taylor's theorem to show that when n is even $f(x)$ has a relative minimum or a relative maximum at $x = a$ according as $f^{(n)}(a)$ is positive or negative, respectively. When n is odd, prove that $f(x)$ has neither a maximum nor a minimum at $x = a$.

CHAPTER 19

Hyperbolic Functions

166. Definitions of the Hyperbolic Functions

We shall now consider six exponential functions which have properties very much like those of the trigonometric functions. Because of their relation to the equilateral hyperbola (Article **173**), they are called the **hyperbolic functions**, and individually are known as the *hyperbolic sine, hyperbolic cosine,* etc. They are defined as follows.

$$\sinh x = \frac{e^x - e^{-x}}{2}, \qquad \coth x = \frac{\cosh x}{\sinh x} = \frac{1}{\tanh x},$$

$$\cosh x = \frac{e^x + e^{-x}}{2}, \qquad \operatorname{sech} x = \frac{1}{\cosh x},$$

$$\tanh x = \frac{e^x - e^{-x}}{e^x + e^{-x}}, \qquad \operatorname{csch} x = \frac{1}{\sinh x}.$$

These are read "hyperbolic sine of x," etc.*

By substituting $-x$ for x in the definitions, we find

$$\sinh(-x) = -\sinh x,$$
$$\cosh(-x) = \cosh x,$$
$$\tanh(-x) = -\tanh x.$$

With these relations and the values given in Table III, page 574, we can plot the graphs shown in Figure 187.

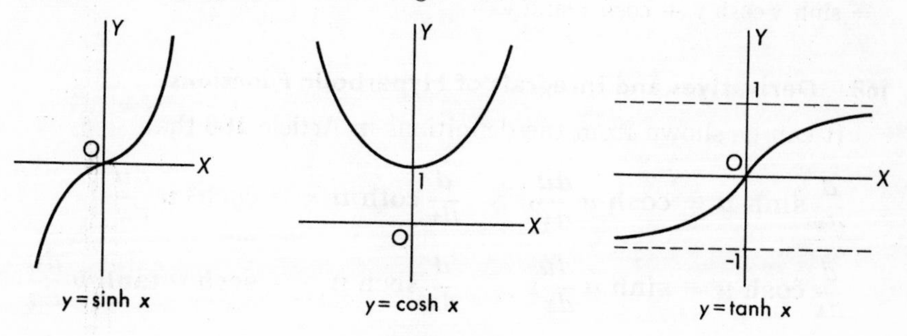

Figure 187

* The abbreviations are sometimes read as "sine h of x," etc.

167. Identities Involving Hyperbolic Functions

Using the definitions given in the preceding article, we obtain the identities

$$\cosh^2 x - \sinh^2 x = 1,$$

$$\tanh^2 x + \operatorname{sech}^2 x = 1,$$

$$\coth^2 x - \operatorname{csch}^2 x = 1.$$

For example, to establish the first relation, we have

$$\cosh^2 x - \sinh^2 x = \left(\frac{e^x + e^{-x}}{2}\right)^2 - \left(\frac{e^x - e^{-x}}{2}\right)^2$$

$$= \frac{e^{2x} + 2 + e^{-2x}}{4} - \frac{e^{2x} - 2 + e^{-2x}}{4} = \frac{4}{4} = 1.$$

Illustration 1. If $\tanh x = \frac{3}{5}$, then $\operatorname{sech} x = \sqrt{1 - (\frac{3}{5})^2} = \frac{4}{5}$. Hence $\cosh x = 1/\operatorname{sech} x = \frac{5}{4}$, and $\sinh x = \cosh x \tanh x = \frac{3}{4}$.

By addition and subtraction, it also follows from the definitions that

$$\cosh x + \sinh x = e^x,$$

$$\cosh x - \sinh x = e^{-x}.$$

These relations are useful in establishing many other formulas.

Illustration 2.

$$\sinh (x + y)$$

$$= \frac{e^{x+y} - e^{-x-y}}{2} = \frac{e^x e^y - e^{-x}e^{-y}}{2}$$

$$= \frac{(\cosh x + \sinh x)(\cosh y + \sinh y) - (\cosh x - \sinh x)(\cosh y - \sinh y)}{2}$$

$$= \sinh x \cosh y + \cosh x \sinh y.$$

168. Derivatives and Integrals of Hyperbolic Functions

It can be shown from the definitions in Article **166** that

$$\frac{d}{dx}\sinh u = \cosh u \frac{du}{dx}, \qquad \frac{d}{dx}\coth u = -\operatorname{csch}^2 u \frac{du}{dx},$$

$$\frac{d}{dx}\cosh u = \sinh u \frac{du}{dx}, \qquad \frac{d}{dx}\operatorname{sech} u = -\operatorname{sech} u \tanh u \frac{du}{dx},$$

$$\frac{d}{dx}\tanh u = \operatorname{sech}^2 u \frac{du}{dx}, \qquad \frac{d}{dx}\operatorname{csch} u = -\operatorname{csch} u \coth u \frac{du}{dx},$$

where u is a differentiable function of x. Thus, for example,

$$\frac{d}{dx}\sinh u = \frac{d}{dx}\left(\frac{e^u + e^{-u}}{2}\right) = \left(\frac{e^u - e^{-u}}{2}\right)\frac{du}{dx} = \cosh u\,\frac{du}{dx}.$$

For each of the above differentiation formulas there is a corresponding integral formula, the first two of which are

$$\int \sinh u\,du = \cosh u + C,$$

$$\int \cosh u\,du = \sinh u + C.$$

In addition to these, we can establish the following formulas.

$$\int \tanh u\,du = \int \frac{\sinh u}{\cosh u}\,du = \ln\cosh u + C,$$

$$\int \coth u\,du = \int \frac{\cosh u}{\sinh u}\,du = \ln\sinh u + C,$$

$$\int \operatorname{sech} u\,du = \int \frac{\cosh u}{\cosh^2 u}\,du = \operatorname{Tan}^{-1}(\sinh u) + C,$$

$$\int \operatorname{csch} u\,du = \ln(\coth u - \operatorname{csch} u) + C.$$

The last of the above formulas is derived as follows.

$$\begin{aligned}\int \operatorname{csch} u\,du &= \int \frac{\coth u \operatorname{csch} u - \operatorname{csch}^2 u}{\coth u - \operatorname{csch} u}\,du \\ &= \int \frac{d(\coth u - \operatorname{csch} u)}{\coth u - \operatorname{csch} u} \\ &= \ln(\coth u - \operatorname{csch} u) + C.\end{aligned}$$

Illustration.

$$\begin{aligned}\int x\operatorname{sech}^2 x\,dx &= \int x\,d(\tanh x) \\ &= x\tanh x - \int \tanh x\,dx = x\tanh x - \ln\cosh x + C.\end{aligned}$$

EXERCISE 92

1. Using Table III, evaluate (*a*) $\sinh 2$, (*b*) $\tanh 0.87$.
   Ans. (*a*) 3.6269, (*b*) 0.7006.
2. Using Table III, find x when (*a*) $\sinh x = 0.709$, (*b*) $\cosh x = 1.5$.
3. Without tables, find $\cosh x$ when $\sinh x = \frac{5}{12}$. *Ans.* $\frac{13}{12}$.
4. Without tables, find $\tanh x$ when $\cosh x = \frac{5}{3}$.

5. Using the exponential definitions, prove that $\tanh^2 x + \operatorname{sech}^2 x = 1$, and $\coth^2 x - \operatorname{csch}^2 x = 1$.

6. Prove the addition formulas

$$\sinh (x \pm y) = \sinh x \cosh y \pm \cosh x \sinh y,$$
$$\cosh (x \pm y) = \cosh x \cosh y \pm \sinh x \sinh y,$$
$$\tanh (x \pm y) = \frac{\tanh x \pm \tanh y}{1 \pm \tanh x \tanh y}.$$

7. Replacing y by x in the formulas of Problem 6, show that

$$\sinh 2x = 2 \sinh x \cosh x,$$
$$\cosh 2x = \cosh^2 x + \sinh^2 x,$$
$$\tanh 2x = \frac{2 \tanh x}{1 + \tanh^2 x}.$$

8. Using the formula for $\cosh 2x$ and replacing x by $\frac{1}{2}x$, prove that

$$\sinh \frac{x}{2} = \pm \sqrt{\frac{\cosh x - 1}{2}},$$
$$\cosh \frac{x}{2} = \sqrt{\frac{\cosh x + 1}{2}},$$
$$\tanh \frac{x}{2} = \pm \sqrt{\frac{\cosh x - 1}{\cosh x + 1}}.$$

9. Using the exponential definitions, prove that

$$(\cosh x \pm \sinh x)^n = \cosh nx \pm \sinh nx.$$

Using the relations given in Article **167** and the preceding problems, prove the following identities.

10. $\operatorname{sech} x + \sinh x \tanh x = \cosh x$.
11. $\coth x - \tanh x = \operatorname{sech} x \operatorname{csch} x$.
12. $\sinh x + \operatorname{csch} x = \cosh x \coth x$.
13. $\dfrac{1 + \cosh x}{\sinh x} - \dfrac{\sinh x}{1 + \cosh x} = 2 \operatorname{csch} x$.
14. $\sinh^2 x - \sinh^2 y = \sinh (x + y) \sinh (x - y)$.
15. $\sinh 3x = 4 \sinh^3 x + 3 \sinh x$.
16. $\cosh 3x = 4 \cosh^3 x - 3 \cosh x$.

Draw a sketch of each of the following equations.

17. $y = \coth x$.
18. $y = \operatorname{sech} x$.
19. $y = \operatorname{csch} x$.
20. $y = \sinh \sqrt{1 - x^2}$.

Differentiate each of the following functions with respect to x.

21. $\sinh^2 x$. *Ans.* $\sinh 2x$.
22. $\cosh (1/x)$.
23. $\ln \cosh 2x$. $2 \tanh 2x$.
24. $\coth (1 - x^2)$.

25. $e^x \sinh x$. *Ans.* e^{2x}.
26. $\sinh(\sin x)$.
27. $\sinh(\ln x^2)$. $x + x^{-3}$.
28. $\operatorname{sech}^3(1 - x^2)$.

Evaluate the following limits.

29. $\lim_{x\to 0} \frac{\sinh x}{x}$. *Ans.* 1.
30. $\lim_{x\to 0} \frac{\cosh x - 1}{x^2}$.
31. $\lim_{x\to 0} \frac{\tanh 2x}{x}$. 2.
32. $\lim_{x\to 0} \frac{\sinh x}{\sin x}$.
33. $\lim_{x\to 0} \frac{1 - \operatorname{sech} x}{x}$. 0.
34. $\lim_{x\to 0} \frac{\ln \cosh x}{x}$.

Evaluate the following integrals.

35. $\int \cosh 4x\, dx$. *Ans.* $\frac{1}{4}\sinh 4x + C$.
36. $\int \operatorname{sech} \frac{1}{2}x \tanh \frac{1}{2}x\, dx$.
37. $\int x \operatorname{sech}^2 x^2\, dx$. $\frac{1}{2}\tanh x^2 + C$.
38. $\int \operatorname{csch}^4 2x\, dx$.
39. $\int x^2 \operatorname{sech} \frac{1}{3}x^3\, dx$. $\operatorname{Tan}^{-1}(\sinh \frac{1}{3}x^3) + C$.
40. $\int \sin x \sinh x\, dx$.
41. $\int_0^1 \tanh x\, dx$. 0.4338.
42. $\int_{-1}^1 \sinh^2 x\, dx$.
43. From the definitions show that for all x

$$\sinh x = x + \frac{x^3}{3!} + \frac{x^5}{5!} + \cdots, \qquad \cosh x = 1 + \frac{x^2}{2!} + \frac{x^4}{4!} + \cdots.$$

44. By dividing the series expansions of Problem 43, show that

$$\tanh x = x - \tfrac{1}{3}x^3 + \tfrac{2}{15}x^5 - \tfrac{17}{315}x^7 + \cdots.$$

This expansion is valid when $|x| < \frac{1}{2}\pi$.

45. Find the area between the curve $y = \cosh x$ and the x axis from $x = 0$ to $x = 1$. *Ans.* 1.1752.
46. Find the centroid of the area described in Problem 45.
47. Find the volume generated if the area of Problem 45 is revolved about the x axis. *Ans.* $\frac{1}{4}\pi(2 + \sinh 2) = 4.4194$.
48. Show that $y = \tanh(\frac{1}{2}\ln x)$ is the equation of a hyperbola and sketch its graph.

169. The Inverse Hyperbolic Functions

As for the trigonometric functions, we write $y = \sinh^{-1} x$ to represent the equation $x = \sinh y$, and we call the function $\sinh^{-1} x$ the **inverse hyperbolic sine of x.** In like manner we define five other inverse hyperbolic functions: $\cosh^{-1} x$, $\tanh^{-1} x$, etc.

Since the hyperbolic functions were defined in terms of exponential functions, the inverse hyperbolic functions can be expressed in terms of logarithmic functions. These relations are

$$\sinh^{-1} x = \ln (x + \sqrt{x^2 + 1}), \qquad \text{(all } x),$$

$$\cosh^{-1} x = \ln (x \pm \sqrt{x^2 - 1}), \qquad (x \geqq 1),$$

$$\tanh^{-1} x = \frac{1}{2} \ln \frac{1 + x}{1 - x}, \qquad (-1 < x < 1),$$

$$\coth^{-1} x = \frac{1}{2} \ln \frac{x + 1}{x - 1}, \qquad (x^2 > 1),$$

$$\operatorname{sech}^{-1} x = \ln \left(\frac{1}{x} \pm \sqrt{\frac{1}{x^2} - 1}\right), \qquad (0 < x \leqq 1),$$

$$\operatorname{csch}^{-1} x = \ln \left(\frac{1}{x} + \sqrt{\frac{1}{x^2} + 1}\right), \qquad (x^2 > 0).$$

For example, to establish the first of these relations, we observe that the equation $y = \sinh^{-1} x$ is equivalent to

$$x = \sinh y = \frac{e^y - e^{-y}}{2}.$$

Multiplying by $2e^y$, we obtain

$$(e^y)^2 - 2x(e^y) - 1 = 0.$$

Solving this equation by means of the quadratic formula, we find

$$e^y = x + \sqrt{1 + x^2}.$$

The negative solution, $x - \sqrt{1 + x^2}$, is discarded since e^y is positive for all real values of y. Finally, by taking logarithms, we have

$$y = \sinh^{-1} x = \ln (x + \sqrt{1 + x^2}), \quad \text{for all values of } x.$$

The other formulas can be derived in a similar manner.

Note: Observe that the function $\cosh^{-1} x$ is double-valued. In subsequent work $\operatorname{Cosh}^{-1} x$ will denote the positive branch $\ln (x + \sqrt{x^2 - 1})$.

170. Derivatives of the Inverse Hyperbolic Functions

Writing the formulas of the preceding article in terms of u, where u is a differentiable function of x, we obtain the following derivatives.

$$\frac{d}{dx} \sinh^{-1} u = \frac{1}{\sqrt{u^2 + 1}} \frac{du}{dx}, \qquad \text{(all } u),$$

$$\frac{d}{dx} \operatorname{Cosh}^{-1} u = \frac{1}{\sqrt{u^2 - 1}} \frac{du}{dx}, \qquad (u > 1),$$

$$\frac{d}{dx}\tanh^{-1} u = \frac{1}{1-u^2}\frac{du}{dx}, \qquad (-1 < u < 1),$$

$$\frac{d}{dx}\coth^{-1} u = \frac{-1}{u^2-1}\frac{du}{dx}, \qquad (u^2 > 1),$$

$$\frac{d}{dx}\text{Sech}^{-1} u = \frac{-1}{u\sqrt{1-u^2}}\frac{du}{dx}, \qquad (0 < u < 1),$$

$$\frac{d}{dx}\text{csch}^{-1} u = \frac{-1}{\sqrt{u^2(1+u^2)}}\frac{du}{dx}, \qquad (u^2 > 0).$$

Illustration. If $y = \tanh^{-1}(\sin x)$, then

$$y' = \frac{1}{1-\sin^2 x}\frac{d}{dx}(\sin x) = \frac{\cos x}{\cos^2 x} = \sec x.$$

171. Integrals Leading to Inverse Hyperbolic Functions

Because of the relations given in Article **169,** we see that the integral formulas I_{21} and I_{22} may be written in the alternate form

$$I_{21} \qquad \int \frac{du}{\sqrt{u^2+a^2}} = \sinh^{-1}\frac{u}{a} + C, \qquad (\text{all } u).$$

$$I'_{21} \qquad \int \frac{du}{\sqrt{u^2-a^2}} = \text{Cosh}^{-1}\frac{u}{a} + C, \qquad (u > a > 0).$$

$$I_{22} \qquad \int \frac{du}{a^2-u^2} = \frac{1}{a}\tanh^{-1}\frac{u}{a} + C, \qquad (u^2 < a^2).$$

$$I'_{22} \qquad \int \frac{du}{u^2-a^2} = -\frac{1}{a}\coth^{-1}\frac{u}{a} + C, \qquad (u^2 > a^2).$$

These formulas can also be verified by differentiation in accordance with Article **170.**

EXERCISE 93

1. Using Table III, evaluate (*a*) $\sinh^{-1} 0.4$, (*b*) $\cosh^{-1} 2$.
   Ans. (*a*) 0.39, (*b*) ± 1.32.
2. Using Table III, find x when (*a*) $\sinh^{-1} x = 1.6$, (*b*) $\tanh^{-1} x = 2.5$.
3. Derive the logarithmic expression for $\cosh^{-1} x$.
4. Derive the logarithmic expression for $\tanh^{-1} x$.
5. Derive the formula for $\frac{d}{dx}\sinh^{-1} x$.
6. Derive the formula for $\frac{d}{dx}\tanh^{-1} x$.
7. Show that $\sinh(\sinh^{-1} x) = x$ and $\cosh(\sinh^{-1} x) = \sqrt{1+x^2}$.
8. Show that the two values for $\cosh^{-1} x$ differ only in sign.

Draw a sketch of each of the following equations.

9. $y = \sinh^{-1} x$.
10. $y = \cosh^{-1} x$.
11. $y = \tanh^{-1} x$.
12. $y = \text{sech}^{-1} x$.

Differentiate each of the following functions with respect to x.

13. $\sinh^{-1} 3x$. *Ans.* $3/\sqrt{9x^2 + 1}$.
14. $\text{Cosh}^{-1} \frac{1}{2}x$.
15. $\text{Cosh}^{-1} (\sec x)$. $\sec x$.
16. $\tanh^{-1} (1 - x^2)$.
17. $\text{csch}^{-1} (\tan x)$. $-|\csc x|$.
18. $\cosh (\sinh^{-1} x)$.
19. $\tanh^{-1} e^x$. $-\frac{1}{2} \text{csch}\, x$.
20. $e^{\coth^{-1} x}$.

Evaluate the following limits.

21. $\displaystyle\lim_{x\to 0} \frac{\sinh^{-1} x}{x}$. *Ans.* 1.
22. $\displaystyle\lim_{x\to 1} \frac{\text{Cosh}^{-1} x}{\sqrt{x - 1}}$.
23. $\displaystyle\lim_{x\to\infty} x \coth^{-1} x$. 1.
24. $\displaystyle\lim_{x\to\infty} x\, \text{csch}^{-1} x$.
25. $\displaystyle\lim_{x\to\infty} [\sinh^{-1} x - \ln x]$. $\ln 2$.
26. $\displaystyle\lim_{x\to 1} [\tanh^{-1} x + \tfrac{1}{2} \ln (1 - x)]$.

Evaluate the following integrals using the formulas of Article **171**.

27. $\displaystyle\int \frac{dx}{\sqrt{x^2 + 4}}$. *Ans.* $\sinh^{-1} \dfrac{x}{2} + C$.
28. $\displaystyle\int \frac{dx}{\sqrt{4x^2 - 9}}$.
29. $\displaystyle\int \frac{x\, dx}{16 - x^4}$. $\dfrac{1}{8} \tanh^{-1} \dfrac{x^2}{4} + C$.
30. $\displaystyle\int \frac{dx}{9x^2 - 25}$.
31. $\displaystyle\int \frac{dx}{\sqrt{x^2 - 2x}}$. $\text{Cosh}^{-1} (x - 1) + C$.
32. $\displaystyle\int \frac{dx}{x^2 - 4x + 3}$.
33. $\displaystyle\int_0^1 \frac{dx}{\sqrt{x^2 + 2x + 2}}$. *Ans.* 0.56.
34. $\displaystyle\int_{-1}^1 \frac{dx}{4 - x^2}$.
35. $\displaystyle\int_5^8 \frac{dx}{x^2 - 4x}$. $\frac{1}{4} \ln \frac{5}{2}$.
36. $\displaystyle\int_0^{\pi/2} \frac{\cos\theta\, d\theta}{\sqrt{1 + \sin^2\theta}}$.
37. Show that $\sinh^{-1} x = x - \dfrac{1}{2}\dfrac{x^3}{3} + \dfrac{1\cdot 3}{2\cdot 4}\dfrac{x^5}{5} - \cdots$, for $x^2 < 1$.
38. Show that $\tanh^{-1} x = x + \dfrac{x^3}{3} + \dfrac{x^5}{5} + \cdots$, for $x^2 < 1$.
39. Find the area between the curve $y = \sinh^{-1} x$ and the x axis from $x = 0$ to $x = 2$. *Ans.* 1.65.
40. Find the area between the curve $y = \cosh^{-1} x$ and the line $x = 4$.

172. Relations Between Trigonometric and Hyperbolic Functions

By the methods of the preceding chapter, we know that for all real z we have

$$e^z = 1 + z + \frac{z^2}{2!} + \frac{z^3}{3!} + \cdots,$$

$$\sin z = z - \frac{z^3}{3!} + \frac{z^5}{5!} - \frac{z^7}{7!} + \cdots,$$

$$\cos z = 1 - \frac{z^2}{2!} + \frac{z^4}{4!} - \frac{z^6}{6!} + \cdots,$$

$$\sinh z = z + \frac{z^3}{3!} + \frac{z^5}{5!} + \frac{z^7}{7!} + \cdots,$$

$$\cosh z = 1 + \frac{z^2}{2!} + \frac{z^4}{4!} + \frac{z^6}{6!} + \cdots.$$

In more advanced works it is shown that the above series are also convergent when z is any complex number $a + ib$, where $i = \sqrt{-1}$, and a and b are real. For this reason, when z is a complex number, the series is taken as a *definition* of the function.

Illustration. $\cos i$ means $1 - \frac{i^2}{2!} + \frac{i^4}{4!} - \cdots$, and since $i^2 = -1$, $i^4 = 1$, and so on, we have

$$\cos i = 1 + \frac{1}{2!} + \frac{1}{4!} + \cdots = \cosh 1 = 1.5431.$$

Note: Using the above series as definitions of the functions, it can be shown that the usual formulas and identities satisfied by the functions are valid when the variable is complex. As an example, by use of the formula for the sine of the sum of two angles, we may write

$$\sin (a + ib) = \sin a \cos ib + \cos a \sin ib. \tag{1}$$

Placing $z = ix$ in the above series and using the identities $i^2 = -1$, $i^3 = -i$, $i^4 = 1$, etc., we obtain the relations

$$e^{ix} = \left(1 - \frac{x^2}{2!} + \cdots\right) + i\left(x - \frac{x^3}{3!} + \cdots\right) = \cos x + i \sin x,$$

$$\sin ix = i\left(x + \frac{x^3}{3!} + \cdots\right) = i \sinh x,$$

$$\cos ix = 1 + \frac{x^2}{2!} + \cdots = \cosh x,$$

$$\sinh ix = i\left(x - \frac{x^3}{3!} + \cdots\right) = i \sin x,$$

$$\cosh ix = 1 - \frac{x^2}{2!} + \cdots = \cos x.$$

The first of the above relations is attributed to the Swiss mathematician Leonard Euler (1707–1783) and is known as **Euler's formula.** Observe also that by using the above relations, (1) can be written in the form

$$\sin (a + ib) = \sin a \cosh b + i \cos a \sinh b.$$

Example. If $\ln(x + iy) = u + iv$ is defined by the relation $e^{u+iv} = x + iy$, show that

$$\ln(x + iy) = \ln\sqrt{x^2 + y^2} + i\tan^{-1}\frac{y}{x}.$$

Solution: Using Euler's formula we have

$$x + iy = e^{u+iv} = e^u e^{iv} = e^u(\cos v + i\sin v).$$

Equating real and imaginary parts, we find

$$x = e^u \cos v, \qquad y = e^u \sin v. \tag{2}$$

Squaring the equations (2) and adding, we obtain

$$x^2 + y^2 = e^{2u}\cos^2 v + e^{2u}\sin^2 v = e^{2u};$$

hence

$$u = \tfrac{1}{2}\ln(x^2 + y^2) = \ln\sqrt{x^2 + y^2}.$$

Dividing the equations (2), we obtain

$$\frac{y}{x} = \frac{e^u \sin v}{e^u \cos v} = \tan v;$$

hence

$$v = \tan^{-1}\frac{y}{x}.$$

Observe that the function $\ln(x + iy)$ is multiple-valued, since the inverse tangent function is multiple-valued. Note, however, that the various values of the function, as used here, differ by *even* multiples of π and not by multiples of π.

173. Geometric Interpretation of Hyperbolic Functions

Consider the circle $x^2 + y^2 = 1$ and the equilateral hyperbola $x^2 - y^2 = 1$, whose equations may be written parametrically as indicated in Figures 188 and 189.

For the circle, the parameter θ is a measure of the central angle AOP in radians. Hence the area of the sector AOP is given by $\frac{1}{2}\theta$.

For the hyperbola, we find a similar result as follows.

$$\begin{aligned}
\text{Area } AOP &= \text{Area } BOP - \text{Area } BAP \\
&= \tfrac{1}{2}xy - \int_1^x \sqrt{x^2 - 1}\,dx \\
&= \tfrac{1}{2}x\sqrt{x^2 - 1} - \tfrac{1}{2}\Big[x\sqrt{x^2 - 1} - \ln(x + \sqrt{x^2 - 1})\Big]_1^x \\
&= \tfrac{1}{2}\operatorname{Cosh}^{-1} x = \tfrac{1}{2}u.
\end{aligned}$$

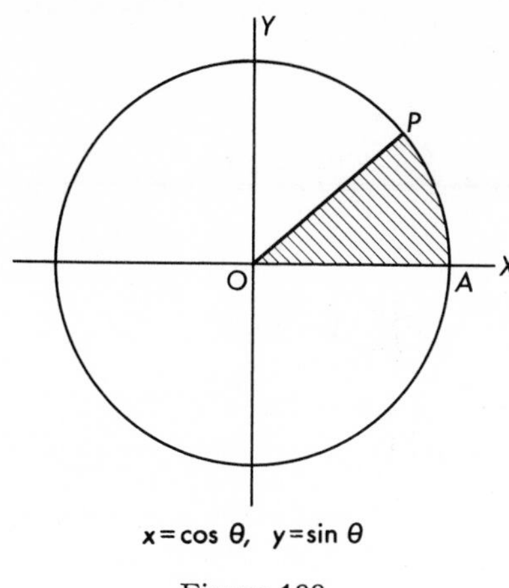

Figure 188

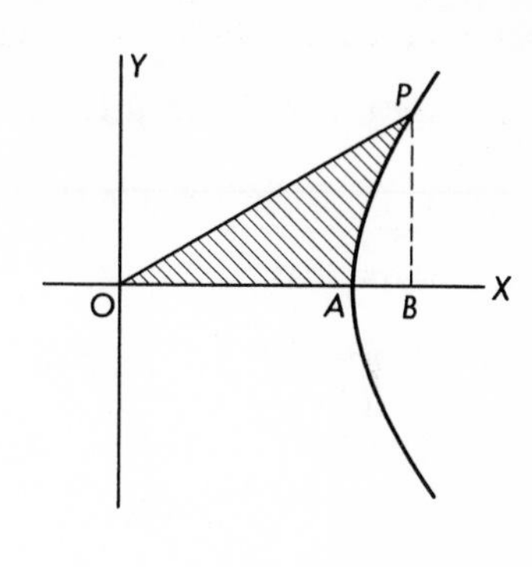

Figure 189

Thus for the circle we have

$$x = \cos\theta, \qquad y = \sin\theta, \qquad \tfrac{1}{2}\theta = \text{Area } AOP,$$

and for the hyperbola

$$x = \cosh u, \qquad y = \sinh u, \qquad \tfrac{1}{2}u = \text{Area } AOP.$$

In this respect we see that the hyperbolic functions have the same relationship to the equilateral hyperbola as the trigonometric functions have with respect to the circle.

EXERCISE 94

Using the addition formulas and the relations in Article **172,** prove each of the following.

1. $\sin(x \pm iy) = \sin x \cosh y \pm i \cos x \sinh y.$
2. $\cos(x \pm iy) = \cos x \cosh y \mp i \sin x \sinh y.$
3. $\sinh(x \pm iy) = \sinh x \cos y \pm i \cosh x \sin y.$
4. $\cosh(x \pm iy) = \cosh x \cos y \pm i \sinh x \sin y.$

Use the relations in Problems 1–4 and Article **172** to express the following complex numbers in the form $u + iv$.

5. $\sin i.$ *Ans.* $1.175i.$
6. $\cos 2i.$
7. $\cosh 4i.$ $-0.654.$
8. $\sinh \tfrac{3}{2}i.$
9. $\sin(1 + i).$ $1.30 + 0.64i.$
10. $\cos(2 - i).$
11. $\sinh(\tfrac{1}{2} - i).$ $0.28 - 0.95i.$
12. $\cosh(2i - 3).$
13. $e^{i\pi}.$ $-1.$
14. $e^{2\pi i}.$
15. $\ln i.$ $i(2n + \tfrac{1}{2})\pi.$
16. $\ln(1 + i).$
17. $\ln(-1).$ $i(2n + 1)\pi.$
18. $\ln(3 - 4i).$
19. $2^i = e^{i \ln 2}.$ $0.77 + 0.64i.$
20. $i^i = e^{i \ln i}.$

21. Prove that $\ln \dfrac{1 + ix}{1 - ix} = i2 \tan^{-1} x$.

22. By use of the identity

$$e^{ix} + e^{2ix} + \cdots + e^{nix} = \frac{e^{(n+1)ix} - e^{ix}}{e^{ix} - 1},$$

show that

$$\sum_{k=1}^{n} \sin kx = \frac{\sin \frac{1}{2}nx \sin \frac{1}{2}(n + 1)x}{\sin \frac{1}{2}x},$$

$$\sum_{k=1}^{n} \cos kx = \frac{\sin \frac{1}{2}nx \cos \frac{1}{2}(n + 1)x}{\sin \frac{1}{2}x}.$$

CHAPTER 20

Solid Analytic Geometry

174. Rectangular Coordinates

The position of a point in space can be determined by giving its directed distances from three mutually perpendicular planes. These distances are called the **rectangular coordinates** of the point. The three planes are called **coordinate planes,** their three lines of intersection the **coordinate axes,** and their point of intersection the **origin.**

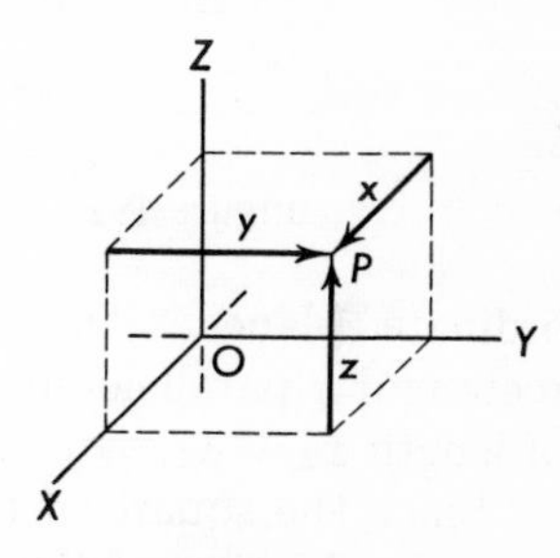

Figure 190

The three axes, called the ***x* axis, *y* axis,** and ***z* axis,** are marked in equal units, positive on one side of the origin and negative on the other. The positive sides of the axes are ordered with respect to one another, so as to form what is called a right-handed system of coordinates. That is, if the index finger of the right hand points in the direction of positive x and the middle finger toward positive y, the thumb points toward positive z.

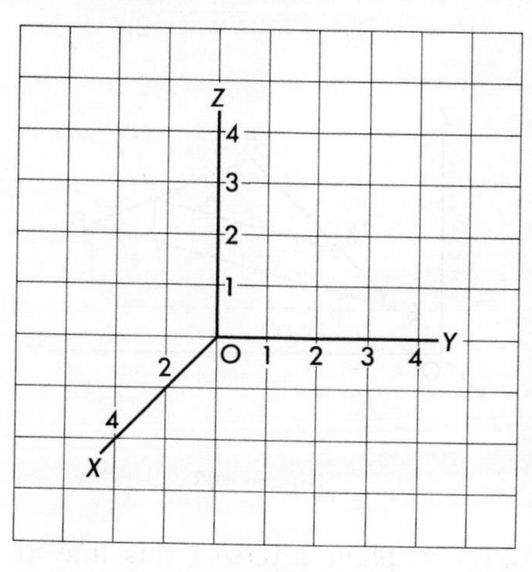

Figure 191

A point is denoted by (x,y,z), where the coordinates represent the distances of the point from the yz plane, the zx plane, and the xy plane, respectively, as shown in Figure 190.

The coordinate planes divide the space into eight parts called **octants.** The region in which all coordinates are positive is called the *first octant*; we will have no occasion to refer to the others by number.

In order to represent a figure in space on a plane, we shall use what is known as parallel projections. Draw the axes OY and OZ at right angles on a sheet of ruled paper, as shown in Figure 191, and then draw OX through O, making an angle of 135° with each of them. If the unit of length on the y and z axes is taken as the side of one of the small squares, the diagonal length of a square along the x axis is denoted by 2. In this type of drawing parallel lines will represent parallel lines, and any plane figure parallel to the yz plane will appear in its true form.

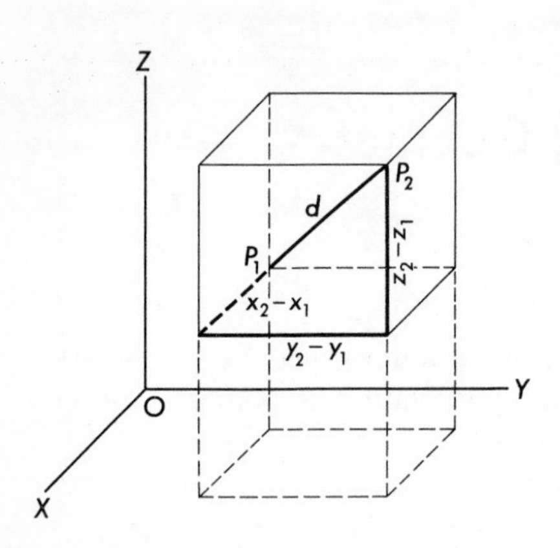

Figure 192

175. Distance Between Two Points

To find the distance d between two points $P_1(x_1,y_1,z_1)$ and $P_2(x_2,y_2,z_2)$, we pass planes through each point parallel to the coordinate planes. These planes form, as shown in Figure 192, a rectangular parallelepiped, or box, with P_1P_2 as a diagonal, and edges of length $x_2 - x_1$, $y_2 - y_1$, and $z_2 - z_1$.

Since the square of the diagonal of a rectangular parallelepiped is equal to the sum of the squares of its sides, we have

$$\boldsymbol{d = \sqrt{(x_2 - x_1)^2 + (y_2 - y_1)^2 + (z_2 - z_1)^2}}.$$

Illustration. The distance between the points $(2,-2,1)$ and $(3,0,-1)$ is

$$d = \sqrt{(3 - 2)^2 + (0 + 2)^2 + (-1 - 1)^2} = \sqrt{(1)^2 + (2)^2 + (-2)^2} = 3.$$

176. Point on the Line Joining Two Points

Let $P(x,y,z)$ be any point lying on the line joining $P_1(x_1,y_1,z_1)$ and $P_2(x_2,y_2,z_2)$, and so located that the segment P_1P is a given fraction k of the entire segment P_1P_2; thus

$$P_1P = k \cdot P_1P_2.$$

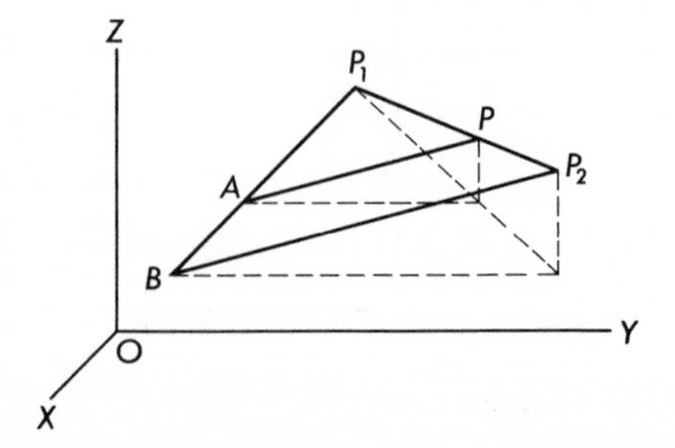

Figure 193

Draw a line through P_1 parallel to the x axis, and let planes through P and P_2 parallel to the yz plane intersect this line at A and B, respectively. Then, as shown in Figure 193, P_1AP and

P_1BP_2 are similar right triangles; hence

$$\frac{P_1A}{P_1B} = \frac{P_1P}{P_1P_2} = k \qquad \text{or} \qquad P_1A = kP_1B.$$

However, $P_1B = x_2 - x_1$ and $P_1A = x - x_1$; thus we have

$$x - x_1 = k(x_2 - x_1).$$

A similar result for y and z is readily derived. Hence the coordinates of P are

$$\mathbf{x = x_1 + k(x_2 - x_1),\ y = y_1 + k(y_2 - y_1),\ z = z_1 + k(z_2 - z_1).} \quad (1)$$

In particular, if P is the mid-point of P_1P_2, we have

$$\mathbf{x = \tfrac{1}{2}(x_1 + x_2), \qquad y = \tfrac{1}{2}(y_1 + y_2), \qquad z = \tfrac{1}{2}(z_1 + z_2).}$$

Example. If the point $(a,b,2)$ is on the line joining the points $(4,-2,3)$ and $(-5,4,0)$, find a and b.

Solution: Substituting in (1), we have

$$a = 4 + k(-5 - 4), \qquad b = -2 + k(4 + 2), \qquad 2 = 3 + k(0 - 3).$$

From the last equation $k = \frac{1}{3}$; hence we have

$$a = 4 - 9(\tfrac{1}{3}) = 1 \quad \text{and} \quad b = -2 + 6(\tfrac{1}{3}) = 0.$$

EXERCISE 95

1. Plot the points $(4,5,6)$, $(3,-2,1)$, $(-2,0,4)$, and $(0,-4,0)$.
2. Plot the points $(2,3,-2)$, $(-4,5,0)$, $(-2,-3,-1)$, and $(-1,2,-4)$.
3. From the point $(4,5,6)$ draw line segments perpendicular to each of the coordinate planes.
4. From the point $(2,5,3)$ draw line segments perpendicular to each of the coordinate axes.
5. Draw a rectangular parallelepiped, or box, with its edges parallel to the coordinate axes and having points $(2,2,4)$ and $(5,6,3)$ as vertices of a diagonal.
6. In the xy plane draw a circle with radius 5 and center at the origin.
7. Where is a point located if (a) $x = 0$, (b) $x = y = 0$, (c) $x = y = z = 0$?
   Ans. (a) yz plane, (b) z axis, (c) origin.
8. Where is a point located if (a) $x = y$, (b) $x = y = z$?
9. Find the coordinates of the foot of the perpendicular drawn from the point $(3,4,5)$ to (a) the x axis, (b) the xy plane.
   Ans. (a) $(3,0,0)$, (b) $(3,4,0)$.
10. Find the coordinates of the foot of the perpendicular drawn from the point $(4,3,-2)$ to (a) the z axis, (b) the zx plane.

Find the distances and mid-points between the following points.

11. $(3,4,2)$, $(1,6,3)$. *Ans.* 3, $(2,5,\frac{5}{2})$.
12. $(1,-2,3)$, $(4,0,-3)$.
13. $(2,-4,1)$, $(\frac{1}{2},2,3)$. $\frac{13}{2}$, $(\frac{5}{4},-1,2)$.
14. $(3,0,-2)$, $(5,-4,2)$.
15. $(4,-3,2)$, $(-2,3,-5)$. 11, $(1,0,-\frac{3}{2})$.
16. $(-2,-\frac{1}{2},5)$, $(5,1,-4)$.
17. Find the points that trisect the segment joining the points $(3,-1,5)$ and $(0,5,-4)$. *Ans.* $(2,1,2)$, $(1,3,-1)$.
18. If a line is extended from $A(-1,0,2)$ through $B(1,3,-1)$ to a point C so that $BC = AB$, find the coordinates of C.
19. Find the coordinates of the point where the segment joining the points $(2,-2,1)$ and $(5,1,-2)$ crosses the xy plane. *Ans.* $(3,-1,0)$.
20. Find the coordinates of the point where the segment joining the points $(2,-1,2)$ and $(-6,3,4)$ crosses the yz plane.
21. Show that the points $(1,-1,3)$, $(2,1,7)$, and $(4,2,6)$ are the vertices of a right triangle, and find its area. *Ans.* $\frac{3}{2}\sqrt{14}$.
22. Show that the points $(2,-2,1)$, $(3,1,2)$, and $(1,2,1)$ are the vertices of a right triangle, and find its area.
23. Show that the points $(1,2,-1)$, $(3,-2,3)$, and $(4,2,2)$ are the vertices of an isosceles triangle, and find its area. *Ans.* 9.
24. Show that the points $(-1,0,2)$, $(3,2,0)$, and $(2,-3,-1)$ are the vertices of an isosceles triangle, and find its area.
25. Prove that the points $(1,2,-1)$, $(2,5,-2)$, $(4,4,-3)$, and $(3,1,-2)$ are the vertices of a rectangle, and find its area. *Ans.* $\sqrt{66}$.
26. Find the points on the x axis that are 7 units distant from the point $(2,6,3)$.
27. Determine a and b so that the points $(1,-1,-3)$, $(2,0,-1)$, and $(a,b,3)$ lie on a straight line. *Ans.* $a = 4$, $b = 2$.
28. If the mid-point of a segment is $(6,4,2)$ and one end point is $(2,5,-1)$, what are the coordinates of the other end?
29. Determine the vertices of a triangle whose sides have the mid-points $(3,2,3)$, $(-1,1,5)$, and $(0,3,4)$. *Ans.* $(4,4,2)$, $(2,0,4)$, $(-4,2,6)$.
30. Two vertices of a triangle are $(3,5,-2)$ and $(5,-1,4)$, and the medians intersect at $(2,-1,1)$. Find the third vertex of the triangle.

177. Direction of a Line

When a line in space is taken in a definite sense from one extreme to the other, the line is said to be **directed.** If two lines intersect, their angle of intersection is taken as the angle between their positive directions. If the lines do not intersect, the angle between them is *defined* to be the angle between two intersecting lines whose directions are the same as those of the given lines. Thus, as far as directions are concerned, any line can be substituted for another line having the same direction.

For a directed line L passing through the origin the angles α, β, and γ formed by L with the x, y, and z axes, respectively, are called the **direction angles** of L, and the cosines of these angles are the **direction cosines** of L.

If the positive sense of L is reversed, the direction angles are replaced by their supplements, and hence the signs of the direction cosines are reversed. Thus in order to have a unique set of direction cosines, L must be a directed line.

Consider now any point $P(x,y,z)$ on L, as shown in Figure 194. Denoting the length of OP by r, we have

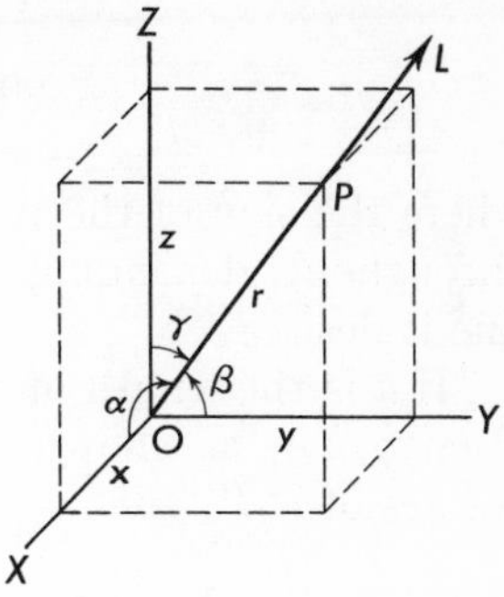

$$\cos \alpha = \frac{x}{r}, \qquad \cos \beta = \frac{y}{r}, \qquad \cos \gamma = \frac{z}{r}, \qquad (1)$$

Figure 194

where

$$r = \sqrt{x^2 + y^2 + z^2}.$$

Illustration 1. The direction cosines of the line from the origin to the point $(6,-2,3)$ are $\cos \alpha = \frac{6}{7}$, $\cos \beta = -\frac{2}{7}$, $\cos \gamma = \frac{3}{7}$, since

$$r = \sqrt{(6)^2 + (-2)^2 + (3)^2} = 7.$$

If we square relations (1) and add, we obtain

$$\cos^2 \alpha + \cos^2 \beta + \cos^2 \gamma = \frac{x^2}{r^2} + \frac{y^2}{r^2} + \frac{z^2}{r^2} = \frac{r^2}{r^2}.$$

Hence the direction cosines of any line satisfy the relation

$$\mathbf{\cos^2 \alpha + \cos^2 \beta + \cos^2 \gamma = 1.} \qquad (2)$$

Illustration 2. If $\alpha = 45°$ and $\beta = 60°$, it follows from (2) that

$$\cos^2 \gamma = 1 - \cos^2 45° - \cos^2 60° = 1 - \tfrac{1}{2} - \tfrac{1}{4} = \tfrac{1}{4}.$$

Hence $\cos \gamma = \pm\frac{1}{2}$, and $\gamma = 60°$ or $120°$.

Any set of numbers a, b, c that are proportional to the direction cosines of a line are called **direction numbers** of the line, and written in the form $[a,b,c]$ will be referred to as the **direction** of the line. To find the direction cosines of a line when its direction $[a,b,c]$ is known, we set

$$a = k \cos \alpha, \qquad b = k \cos \beta, \qquad c = k \cos \gamma, \qquad (3)$$

where k is a constant of proportionality. Squaring and adding these equations, we obtain

$$a^2 + b^2 + c^2 = k^2(\cos^2 \alpha + \cos^2 \beta + \cos^2 \gamma) = k^2.$$

Hence $k = \pm\sqrt{a^2 + b^2 + c^2}$; substituting this value in (3), we have

$$\cos\alpha = \frac{a}{\pm\sqrt{a^2 + b^2 + c^2}}, \qquad \cos\beta = \frac{b}{\pm\sqrt{a^2 + b^2 + c^2}},$$

$$\cos\gamma = \frac{c}{\pm\sqrt{a^2 + b^2 + c^2}},$$

where the sign of the radical is either positive throughout or negative throughout, depending on which of the two possible directions of the line is desired.

If d is the length of the line segment from the point $P_1(x_1,y_1,z_1)$ to $P_2(x_2,y_2,z_2)$, as shown in Figure 192, it is clear that the direction cosines of P_1P_2 are

$$\cos\alpha = \frac{x_2 - x_1}{d}, \qquad \cos\beta = \frac{y_2 - y_1}{d}, \qquad \cos\gamma = \frac{z_2 - z_1}{d}.$$

Hence the direction of a line segment from the point $P_1(x_1,y_1,z_1)$ to the point $P_2(x_2,y_2,z_2)$ can be expressed as $[x_2 - x_1, y_2 - y_1, z_2 - z_1]$.

Illustration 3. Direction numbers for the line through the points $(-1,0,-3)$ and $(0,4,5)$ are $[0 - (-1), 4 - 0, 5 - (-3)]$ or $[1,4,8]$. Since $1^2 + 4^2 + 8^2 = 81 = 9^2$, the direction cosines are $[\frac{1}{9},\frac{4}{9},\frac{8}{9}]$ or $[-\frac{1}{9},-\frac{4}{9},-\frac{8}{9}]$.

As a special instance of the above result, it follows that direction numbers for a radius vector drawn to the point $P(x,y,z)$ are $[x,y,z]$.

178. Angle Between Two Lines

Let L_1 and L_2 be two lines with directions $[a_1,b_1,c_1]$ and $[a_2,b_2,c_2]$, respectively. In order to find the angle ϕ between L_1 and L_2, consider the radius vectors drawn from the origin to the points $P_1(a_1,b_1,c_1)$ and $P_2(a_2,b_2,c_2)$ as shown in Figure 195. These vectors have the same directions as L_1 and L_2, and hence the angle P_1OP_2 is ϕ. Letting $OP_1 = r_1$, $OP_2 = r_2$, and $P_1P_2 = d$, we have by trigonometry

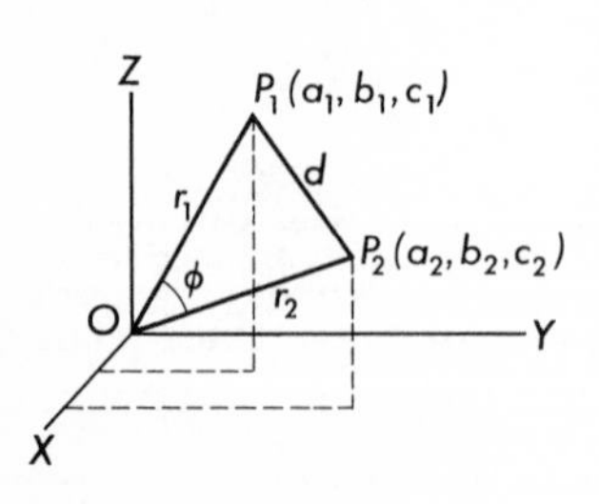

Figure 195

$$\cos\phi = \frac{r_1^2 + r_2^2 - d^2}{2r_1r_2}. \tag{1}$$

However, by the distance formula, we have

$$r_1^2 = a_1^2 + b_1^2 + c_1^2, \qquad r_2^2 = a_2^2 + b_2^2 + c_2^2,$$
$$d^2 = (a_2 - a_1)^2 + (b_2 - b_1)^2 + (c_2 - c_1)^2.$$

On substituting these relations in (1) and simplifying, we obtain the following result.

Theorem. *The angle* $\boldsymbol{\phi}$ *between two lines having the directions* $[\boldsymbol{a}_1,\boldsymbol{b}_1,\boldsymbol{c}_1]$ *and* $[\boldsymbol{a}_2,\boldsymbol{b}_2,\boldsymbol{c}_2]$, *respectively, is determined by the relation*

$$\cos \boldsymbol{\phi} = \frac{\boldsymbol{a}_1\boldsymbol{a}_2 + \boldsymbol{b}_1\boldsymbol{b}_2 + \boldsymbol{c}_1\boldsymbol{c}_2}{\sqrt{\boldsymbol{a}_1^2 + \boldsymbol{b}_1^2 + \boldsymbol{c}_1^2}\sqrt{\boldsymbol{a}_2^2 + \boldsymbol{b}_2^2 + \boldsymbol{c}_2^2}}. \tag{2}$$

Illustration. If $[1,2,2]$ and $[3,4,-12]$ are the directions of two lines, we have

$$\cos \phi = \frac{(1)(3) + (2)(4) + (2)(-12)}{(3)(13)} = -\frac{1}{3},$$

Hence the angle between the lines is 109.5°.

Since two lines are perpendicular when, and only when, $\cos \phi = 0$, we have the following result.

Corollary. *Two lines having the directions* $[\boldsymbol{a}_1,\boldsymbol{b}_1,\boldsymbol{c}_1]$ *and* $[\boldsymbol{a}_2,\boldsymbol{b}_2,\boldsymbol{c}_2]$, *respectively, are perpendicular when, and only when,*

$$\boldsymbol{a}_1\boldsymbol{a}_2 + \boldsymbol{b}_1\boldsymbol{b}_2 + \boldsymbol{c}_1\boldsymbol{c}_2 = \mathbf{0}. \tag{3}$$

Note: Since the direction cosines of OP_1 and OP_2 in Figure 195 are

$$\cos \alpha_1 = \frac{a_1}{r_1}, \qquad \cos \beta_1 = \frac{b_1}{r_1}, \qquad \cos \gamma_1 = \frac{c_1}{r_1},$$

and

$$\cos \alpha_2 = \frac{a_2}{r_2}, \qquad \cos \beta_2 = \frac{b_2}{r_2}, \qquad \cos \gamma_2 = \frac{c_2}{r_2},$$

respectively, we find on substituting in (2) that the angle between two lines can be expressed in terms of their direction cosines as

$$\cos \phi = \cos \alpha_1 \cos \alpha_2 + \cos \beta_1 \cos \beta_2 + \cos \gamma_1 \cos \gamma_2.$$

Example. Find the direction of a line that is perpendicular to each of two lines whose directions are $[3,2,-1]$ and $[1,-3,4]$, respectively.

Solution: Denoting the direction of the required line by $[a,b,c]$, we have from (3)

$$3a + 2b - c = 0 \qquad \text{and} \qquad a - 3b + 4c = 0.$$

If we solve these equations for a and c in terms of b, we obtain $a = -\frac{5}{13}b$ and $c = \frac{11}{13}b$. Since only the ratios of a, b, and c are significant, on taking $b = 13$ we obtain the direction $[-5,13,11]$ for the required line.

EXERCISE 96

1. If a line makes an angle of 45° with OX and 60° with OZ, what angle does it make with OY? *Ans.* 60° or 120°.
2. If a line makes an angle of 45° with the x and y axes, what angle does it make with the z axis?
3. Draw radius vectors so that $\cos\alpha = \frac{2}{3}$ and $\cos\beta = -\frac{2}{3}$.
4. Where must a point lie if its radius vector has (*a*) $\cos\alpha = 0$, (*b*) $\cos\alpha = \frac{1}{2}$, (*c*) $\cos\alpha = 1$?
5. What are the direction cosines of the x axis? *Ans.* [1,0,0].
6. What are the direction cosines of a line that makes equal angles with the axes?

Find direction cosines for the lines that have the following direction numbers.

7. [2,−2,1]. *Ans.* $[\frac{2}{3},-\frac{2}{3},\frac{1}{3}]$.
8. [3,−2,−6].
9. $[3,3,-3\frac{1}{2}]$. $[\frac{6}{11},\frac{6}{11},-\frac{7}{11}]$.
10. $[-\frac{1}{4},\frac{1}{3},1]$.

Find direction numbers for the line that joins the following points.

11. (2,0,−1), (4,−2,3). *Ans.* [1,−1,2].
12. (5,1,−3), (2,7,3).
13. (1,3,4), (−2,3,7). [1,0,−1].
14. (−3,−2,4), (−3,5,4).

Find the acute angle between two lines that have the following direction numbers.

15. [1,1,0], [2,1,2]. *Ans.* 45°.
16. [1,−1,0], [−1,0,−1].
17. [3,4,5], [1,3,0]. 47.9°.
18. [1,2,3], [3,2,1].

Using direction numbers, prove the following.

19. The points (1,0,−2), (3,−1,1), and (7,−3,7) lie in a straight line.
20. The points (−2,1,−5), (−1,0,−2), and (2,−3,7) lie in a straight line.
21. The points (−1,1,3), (1,−2,4), and (4,−1,1) are the vertices of a right triangle.
22. The points (2,−1,2), (3,1,3), and (5,0,3) are the vertices of a right triangle.
23. The points (1,0,2), (3,−1,3), (2,2,2), and (0,3,1) are the vertices of a parallelogram.
24. The points (3,1,−2), (3,0,1), (5,3,2), and (5,4,−1) are the vertices of a rectangle.
25. Find direction numbers for a line that is perpendicular to each of two lines whose directions are [2,−1,2] and [3,0,1]. *Ans.* [1,−4,−3].
26. Find direction numbers for a line that is perpendicular to each of two lines whose directions are [−1,2,4] and [2,3,−2].
27. Find direction numbers for a line that is perpendicular to the triangle formed by the points (2,3,1), (6,−3,2), and (4,0,3). *Ans.* [3,2,0].

28. Using the formula, Area $= \frac{1}{2}ab \sin C$, find the area of the triangle whose vertices are $A(3,0,1)$, $B(-1,4,1)$, and $C(0,-1,2)$.
29. Find the angles of the triangle given in the preceding problem.
Ans. $A = 64.8°$, $B = 35.3°$, $C = 80.0°$.
30. Show that three edges of a tetrahedron whose vertices are $(1,3,-1)$, $(-1,2,-1)$, $(2,1,0)$, and $(0,5,4)$ are mutually perpendicular, and find its volume.

179. Locus of a Point in Space

The locus of a point moving in space in accordance with some single condition is usually a surface. Thus the surface of a sphere is the locus of a point that moves at a constant distance from a fixed point.

For a locus to be of value analytically, however, it is important that we be able to express the given condition in terms of the coordinates of a point on the locus. If this is done, the result is called the **equation of the locus.**

Illustration. The locus of points equidistant from the points (0,0,0) and (2,2,2) has the equation $\sqrt{x^2 + y^2 + z^2} = \sqrt{(x-2)^2 + (y-2)^2 + (z-2)^2}$. Squaring and simplifying, the equation of the locus becomes $x + y + z = 3$.

Conversely, we can state the following.

The locus of an equation in one or more of the variables x, y, and z is usually a surface, and this surface contains those points, and only those, whose coordinates satisfy the equation.

Note: In exceptional instances an equation may have a locus other than a surface. For example, the locus of $x^2 + y^2 = 0$ is the z axis, and the locus of $x^2 + y^2 + z^2 = 0$ is the origin. An equation such as $z^2 = -4$ has no locus, since no real points will satisfy the equation.

180. Equation of a Plane

Let $[A,B,C]$ be the direction of a line L that is perpendicular to a plane RS at the point P_1, as shown in Figure 196. Since the plane can be considered as the locus of a point P which moves so that P_1P is always perpendicular to L, the equation of the plane can be obtained by applying this condition. Thus, since $[x - x_1, y - y_1, z - z_1]$ is the direction of P_1P, we have

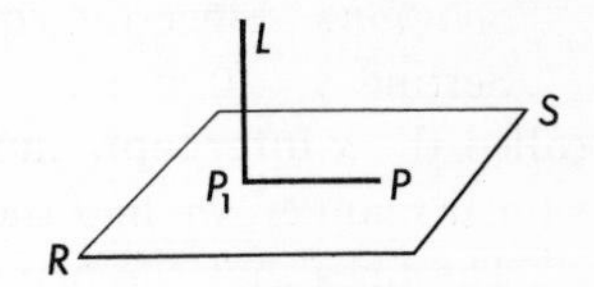

Figure 196

$$A(x - x_1) + B(y - y_1) + C(z - z_1) = 0.$$

This is called the **point-direction** form of the equation of a plane. It is to be noted particularly that the direction associated with a plane is the *normal* (or perpendicular) direction to the plane. The above equation also establishes the following theorem.

Theorem 1. *Every plane can be represented by an equation of the first degree.*

Conversely, every equation of the first degree

$$Ax + By + Cz + D = 0. \tag{1}$$

represents a plane. For if x', y', and z' are values satisfying (1), we have

$$Ax' + By' + Cz' + D = 0. \tag{2}$$

Subtracting (2) from (1), we can express (1) in the form

$$A(x - x') + B(y - y') + C(z - z') = 0.$$

This, however, is the equation of a plane through the point (x',y',z') with a normal direction $[A,B,C]$. Thus equation (1) represents a plane, and we have the following result.

Theorem 2. *The locus of an equation of the first degree is a plane.*

The linear equation

$$\mathbf{Ax + By + Cz + D = 0} \tag{3}$$

is called the **general form** of the equation of a plane. If certain of the variables in (3) are missing, as indicated below, the plane has the property stated.

$Ax + By + D = 0$, perpendicular to the xy plane,
$Ax + Cz + D = 0$, perpendicular to the zx plane,
$By + Cz + D = 0$, perpendicular to the yz plane,
$Ax + D = 0$, parallel to the yz plane,
$By + D = 0$, parallel to the zx plane,
$Cz + D = 0$, parallel to the xy plane.

Example 1. Sketch the locus of the equation $2x + 3y + 4z = 12$.

Solution: Since the equation is of first degree, it represents a plane.

Setting $y = 0$ and $z = 0$ in the equation, we get $x = 6$. This value is called the **x intercept,** and indicates where the plane cuts the x axis. In a similar manner, we find the y and z intercepts to be 4 and 3, respectively.

The lines that the plane forms with the coordinate planes are called the **traces** of the plane. The equations of the xy, yz, and zx traces for the given plane are

$$2x + 3y = 12, \qquad 3y + 4z = 12, \qquad 2x + 4z = 12,$$

respectively. The traces and intercepts are shown in Figure 197.

Example 2. Find the equation of a plane through the point $(1,2,-1)$ and parallel to the plane $2x - 3y + 4z + 6 = 0$.

Solution: A line normal to a plane has as direction numbers the coefficients of x, y, and z, respectively. Thus, for the given plane, the normal direction is $[2,-3,4]$. Since parallel planes have the same normal directions, the equation of the required plane is

$$2(x - 1) - 3(y - 2) + 4(z + 1) = 0,$$

or

$$2x - 3y + 4z + 8 = 0.$$

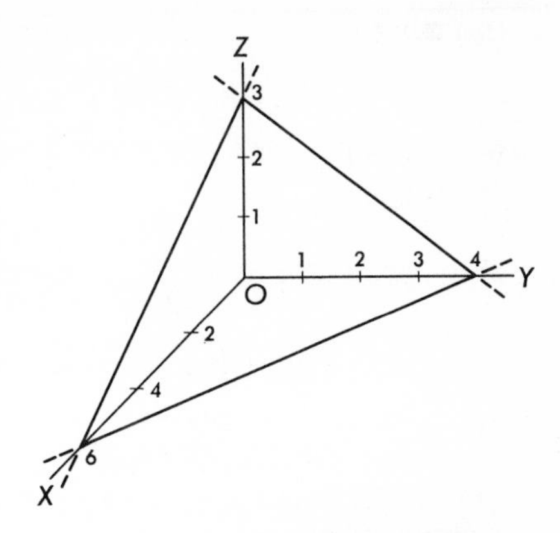

Figure 197

Example 3. Find the equation of the plane through the point $(4,3,6)$ and perpendicular to the line joining that point to the point $(2,3,1)$.

Solution: The plane is perpendicular to the line joining the given points; hence its normal direction is $[4 - 2, 3 - 3, 6 - 1]$ or $[2,0,5]$. Therefore the equation of the plane is

$$2(x - 4) + 5(z - 6) = 0,$$

or

$$2x + 5z - 38 = 0.$$

181. Normal Equation of a Plane

Let p denote the length of the radius vector drawn perpendicular to the plane

$$Ax + By + Cz + D = 0, \tag{1}$$

as shown in Figure 198. Since OP is normal to the plane (1), its direction cosines are

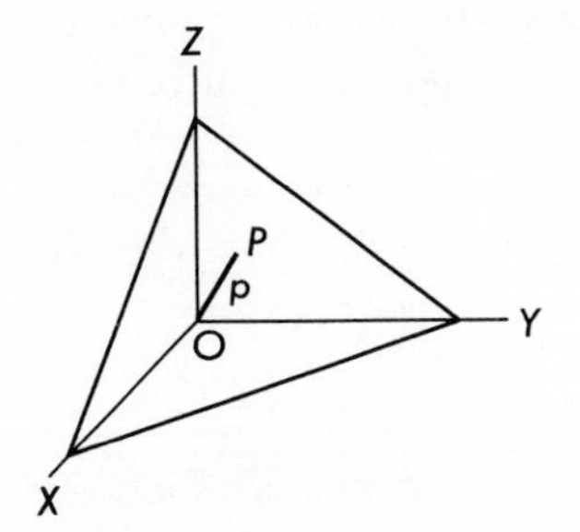

Figure 198

$$\cos \alpha = \frac{A}{\pm\sqrt{A^2 + B^2 + C^2}},$$

$$\cos \beta = \frac{B}{\pm\sqrt{A^2 + B^2 + C^2}},$$

$$\cos \gamma = \frac{C}{\pm\sqrt{A^2 + B^2 + C^2}}, \tag{2}$$

where the same sign of the radical is taken throughout. Since the coordinates of P are $(p \cos \alpha, p \cos \beta, p \cos \gamma)$, on substituting in (1) we have

$$pA \cos \alpha + pB \cos \beta + pC \cos \gamma = -D.$$

Inserting the values (2), we obtain

$$\frac{pA^2 + pB^2 + pC^2}{\pm\sqrt{A^2 + B^2 + C^2}} = -D;$$

hence

$$p = \frac{-D}{\pm\sqrt{A^2 + B^2 + C^2}}.$$

Thus if equation (1) is written in the form

$$\frac{\boldsymbol{Ax + By + Cz}}{\pm\sqrt{\boldsymbol{A^2 + B^2 + C^2}}} = \frac{\boldsymbol{-D}}{\pm\sqrt{\boldsymbol{A^2 + B^2 + C^2}}}, \tag{3}$$

where the sign of the radical is chosen to make the right member positive, the coefficients of x, y, and z are the direction cosines of the radius vector drawn perpendicular to the plane and the constant denotes its length. Equation (3) is called the **normal form** of the equation of a plane.

Illustration 1. The equation of the plane $2x - y + 2z + 6 = 0$ in normal form is

$$\frac{2x - y + 2z}{-\sqrt{(2)^2 + (-1)^2 + (2)^2}} = \frac{-6}{-\sqrt{(2)^2 + (-1)^2 + (2)^2}},$$

or

$$-\frac{2}{3}x + \frac{1}{3}y - \frac{2}{3}z = 2.$$

The distance from the point (x_1,y_1,z_1) to a plane whose equation is (1) can be found in the following manner. The equation of a plane parallel to (3) and passing through the given point can be written as

$$\frac{Ax + By + Cz}{\pm\sqrt{A^2 + B^2 + C^2}} = \frac{Ax_1 + By_1 + Cz_1}{\pm\sqrt{A^2 + B^2 + C^2}}, \tag{4}$$

where the sign of the radical in (3) and (4) is the same. In this case the right side of (4) may be positive or negative, but in either event the distance between the given point and (1) is equal to the distance between the parallel planes (3) and (4), which in turn is given by the difference in the right members of (3) and (4). Thus we have the following result.

Theorem. *The distance* $\mathbf{d}$ *from the plane* (1) *to the point* $(\mathbf{x_1,y_1,z_1})$ *is*

$$\mathbf{d} = \frac{\mathbf{Ax_1 + By_1 + Cz_1 + D}}{\pm\sqrt{\mathbf{A^2 + B^2 + C^2}}},$$

where the sign of the radical is taken opposite to that of $\mathbf{D}$.

Illustration 2. The distance from the point $(2,-3,-1)$ to the plane $2x - 3y + 6z + 7 = 0$ is $d = \frac{2(2) - 3(-3) + 6(-1) + 7}{-7} = -2$. The numerical value 2 denotes the distance, and the negative sign signifies that the given point and the origin are on the same side of the plane.

The angle between two planes is by definition either of the supplementary angles between the normals to the planes. Since the coefficients of x, y, and z are direction numbers of the respective normals, it follows from (2), Article **178**, that the angle ϕ between the planes

$$A_1x + B_1y + C_1z + D_1 = 0, \qquad A_2x + B_2y + C_2z + D_2 = 0$$

is determined by

$$\cos\phi = \pm\frac{A_1A_2 + B_1B_2 + C_1C_2}{\sqrt{A_1^2 + B_1^2 + C_1^2}\sqrt{A_2^2 + B_2^2 + C_2^2}}.$$

Illustration 3. The cosine of the acute angle between the planes $x + 2y - 2z = 5$ and $3x - 5y + 4z = 2$ is

$$\cos\phi = \left|\frac{(1)(3) + (2)(-5) + (-2)(4)}{3\cdot 5\sqrt{2}}\right| = \frac{1}{\sqrt{2}};$$

hence $\phi = 45°$.

182. Planes Determined by Three Conditions

Although four arbitrary constants appear in the equation of a plane, a division by one of them indicates that the equation contains only three essential constants. Hence three independent conditions will determine a specific plane.

Example 1. Find the equation of the plane that contains the points $(1,-2,4)$, $(4,1,7)$, and $(-1,5,1)$.

Solution: The equation of the plane passing through the first of the given points is

$$A(x - 1) + B(y + 2) + C(z - 4) = 0. \tag{1}$$

Substituting the coordinates of the other two points in (1), we obtain

$$3A + 3B + 3C = 0,$$
$$-2A + 7B - 3C = 0.$$

Solving for A and C in terms of B, we get $A = -10B$ and $C = 9B$. Substituting these values in (1), we obtain

$$-10B(x - 1) + B(y + 2) + 9B(z - 4) = 0.$$

Dividing by B and simplifying gives the required equation

$$10x - y - 9z + 24 = 0.$$

Example 2. Find the equation of the plane that contains the point $(1,-1,2)$ and is perpendicular to each of the planes $2x + 3y - 2z = 5$ and $x + 2y - 3z = 8$.

Solution: The equation of the plane containing the given point is

$$A(x - 1) + B(y + 1) + C(z - 2) = 0. \tag{2}$$

Applying the condition of perpendicularity of (2) with each of the given planes, we have

$$2A + 3B - 2C = 0,$$
$$A + 2B - 3C = 0.$$

Solving these equations, we find $A = -5C$ and $B = 4C$. Hence the required equation is

$$-5C(x - 1) + 4C(y + 1) + C(z - 2) = 0,$$

or

$$5x - 4y - z = 7.$$

Example 3. Find the equation of a plane that is 1 unit distant from the origin and has the xy trace $3x + 4y = 13$.

Solution: The general equation of a plane that has the given trace is

$$3x + 4y + kz = 13. \tag{3}$$

Writing (3) in normal form, we have

$$\frac{3x + 4y + kz}{\sqrt{3^2 + 4^2 + k^2}} = \frac{13}{\sqrt{3^2 + 4^2 + k^2}}.$$

Since the right member represents the distance to the origin, we have

$$\frac{13}{\sqrt{25 + k^2}} = 1.$$

Solving, we find $k = \pm 12$. Hence the two planes,

$$3x + 4y \pm 12z = 13,$$

satisfy the given conditions.

EXERCISE 97

Draw the traces of the following planes. Find the intercepts and the distance of the plane from the origin.

1. $2x + 3y + 6z = 12$. *Ans.* $d = \frac{12}{7}$.
2. $x - 4y + 8z = 8$.
3. $12y - 5z = 60$. $d = \frac{60}{13}$.
4. $3x + 4y = 12$.

Find the equation of the locus whose points satisfy the following condition.

5. Equidistant from the points $(1,3,-1)$ and $(-1,2,0)$. *Ans.* $2x + y - z = 3$.
6. Distance from the point $(1,-1,2)$ equals 3.
7. Equidistant from the zx plane and the point $(0,5,0)$. *Ans.* $x^2 + z^2 = 10y - 25$.
8. Sum of distances from the points $(0,0,4)$ and $(0,0,-4)$ equals 10.

Find the distance between the following planes.

9. $\begin{cases} x - 2y + 2z = 6, \\ 3x - 6y + 6z = 2. \end{cases}$ *Ans.* 16/9.
10. $\begin{cases} 5x - 3y - 4z = 40, \\ -5x + 3y + 4z = 20. \end{cases}$

Find the acute angle between the following planes.

11. $\begin{cases} x + 4y - z = 5, \\ y + z = 2. \end{cases}$ *Ans.* 60°.
12. $\begin{cases} 4x - y + 8z = 9, \\ x + 3y + z = 4. \end{cases}$

Find the distance between the given point and plane.

13. $(3,2,-1)$, $7x - 6y + 6z + 8 = 0$. *Ans.* 1.
14. $(-1,5,2)$, $4y - 3z + 6 = 0$.
15. $(-2,8,-3)$, $9x - y - 4z = 0$. $\sqrt{2}$.
16. $(4,-1,5)$, $5x + 6 = 0$.

Draw a figure of the solid that is bounded by the following planes.

17. $y + z = 3$, $x = 4$, $x = 0$, $y = 0$, and $z = 0$.
18. $x = y$, $x + 2z = 10$, $x = 0$, $y = 6$, and $z = 0$.
19. $x + 2y + 2z = 12$, $3x + 4y = 12$, $x = 0$, $y = 0$, and $z = 0$.
20. $x + y + z = 6$, $x = 0$, $y = 0$, $y = 3$, and $z = 0$.

Find the equation of a plane parallel to the plane $6x - 3y - 2z + 9 = 0$, and satisfying the following conditions.

21. Passing through the point $(-1,3,-5)$. *Ans.* $6x - 3y - 2z + 5 = 0$.
22. Passing at a distance 2 from the origin.

Find the equation of a plane perpendicular to the line joining the points $(2,-1,2)$ and $(3,2,-1)$, and satisfying the following conditions.

23. Passing through the point $(4,-2,1)$. *Ans.* $x + 3y - 3z + 5 = 0$.
24. Having an x intercept equal to 3.

Find the equation of the plane containing the following points.

25. $(3,-1,-4)$, $(-2,2,1)$, and $(0,4,-1)$. *Ans.* $x + z + 1 = 0$.
26. $(-1,2,0)$, $(3,2,-1)$, and $(5,1,1)$.

Find the equation of the plane through the point $(2,0,1)$, perpendicular to the plane $2x - 4y - z = 7$, and satisfying the following conditions.

27. Passing through the point $(-1,2,0)$. *Ans.* $6x + 5y - 8z = 4$.
28. Perpendicular to the plane $x - y + z = 1$.
29. Find the point of intersection of the planes $x + 5y - 2z = 9$, $3x - 2y + z = 3$, and $x + y + z = 2$. *Ans.* $(2,1,-1)$.
30. Do the points $(-1,3,6)$ and $(2,-3,0)$ lie on the same side of the plane $2x - 3y + 4z = 12$?
31. Two faces of a cube lie in the planes $2x - y + 2z - 3 = 0$ and $6x - 3y + 6z + 8 = 0$. Find the volume of the cube. *Ans.* 4913/729.
32. Find the area of the triangle that the coordinate planes cut from the plane $x + 4y + 8z = 16$. *Hint:* Find the volume of the tetrahedron.
33. Find k so that the plane $(k + 1)x - y + (2 - k)z = 5$ is perpendicular to the plane $2x + 6y - z + 3 = 0$. *Ans.* $k = 2$.
34. A plane parallel to the y axis passes through the points $(-2,3,1)$ and $(1,-4,2)$. Find its equation.
35. A plane through the z axis is perpendicular to the plane $3x - 5y - 2z = 7$. Find its equation. *Ans.* $5x + 3y = 0$.
36. A plane through the origin is perpendicular to the plane $2x - y - z = 5$ and parallel to the line joining the points $(1,2,3)$ and $(4,-1,2)$. Find its equation.
37. Find the equation of a plane that makes an angle of 45° with the z axis, and has x and y intercepts of 3 and 4, respectively. *Ans.* $4x + 3y \pm 5z = 12$.
38. Find the point equidistant from the four points $(0,0,0)$, $(0,3,0)$, $(0,0,5)$, and $(3,4,2)$.
39. If a plane has non-zero intercepts a, b, and c, show that its equation is $x/a + y/b + z/c = 1$. This is called the **intercept form** of the equation of a plane.
40. A plane through the points $(8,0,0)$ and $(0,8,0)$ is tangent to the sphere that has its center at the point $(2,2,2)$ and a radius of 2. Find its equation.

183. Equations of a Line

Two surfaces will generally intersect in a curve, although it is possible that parts of the surfaces may coincide, they may have isolated points in common, or they may not intersect at all. The latter instances are exceptional, and in general we can state the following.

The locus of two simultaneous equations in space is a curve containing those points and only those points whose coordinates satisfy both equations.

Since two equations of the first degree represent two planes, and since non-parallel planes intersect in a line, we have the following result.

Theorem. *The locus of two simultaneous equations of the first degree*

$$\begin{aligned} A_1x + B_1y + C_1z + D_1 &= 0, \\ A_2x + B_2y + C_2z + D_2 &= 0, \end{aligned} \tag{1}$$

is a straight line, provided $A_1:B_1:C_1 \neq A_2:B_2:C_2$.

The equations (1) are called the **general form** of the equations of a line. Since many planes can be passed through a given line, and since any two of these determine the line, it is evident that the representation (1) is not unique.

Of the many planes passing through the line (1), those that are perpendicular to the coordinate planes are of special interest. These planes are called the *projecting planes*, and their traces give the *projections* of the line on the coordinate planes.

Illustration. The equation of the xy projection of the line $x + 2y - z = 0$, $3x - y + z = 4$ is found by eliminating z between the equations. Thus, adding the equations, we have $4x + y = 4$. The projections on the other coordinate planes can be found in a similar manner.

Example. Determine the points where the line

$$\begin{aligned} 3x - 2y + 6z &= 0, \\ x + 2y - 2z &= 8 \end{aligned}$$

pierces the coordinate planes, and draw the line. Find direction numbers for the line.

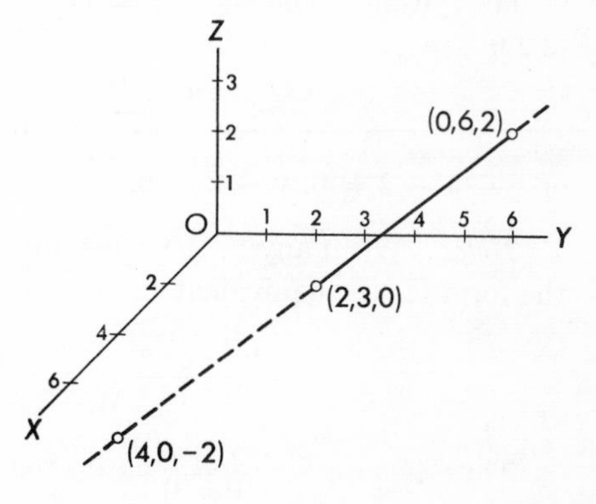

Figure 199

Solution: Substituting $x = 0$ in the given equations, we obtain

$$\begin{aligned} -2y + 6z &= 0, \\ 2y - 2z &= 8, \end{aligned}$$

which have the simultaneous solution $y = 6$ and $z = 2$. Thus the given line pierces the yz plane at the point (0,6,2). In a similar manner, we find the other piercing points as shown in Figure 199.

Since the line is now known to contain the points (0,6,2) and (2,3,0), its direction numbers are the differences in the coordinates $[2, -3, -2]$.

184. Symmetric Equations of a Line

The equations of a line through the point (x_1,y_1,z_1) and having the direction numbers $[a,b,c]$ can be found as follows. If (x,y,z) is a point on the line, it is necessary that the differences $x - x_1$, $y - y_1$, and $z - z_1$ be proportional to the direction numbers. This means that x, y, and z must satisfy the equations

$$\frac{x - x_1}{a} = \frac{y - y_1}{b} = \frac{z - z_1}{c}. \tag{1}$$

The equations (1) represent two independent linear equations, and are called the **symmetric form** of the equations of a line.

If (x_1,y_1,z_1) and (x_2,y_2,z_2) are two distinct points, the direction of the line joining them is $[x_2 - x_1, y_2 - y_1, z_2 - z_1]$. Hence the equations of the line are

$$\frac{x - x_1}{x_2 - x_1} = \frac{y - y_1}{y_2 - y_1} = \frac{z - z_1}{z_2 - z_1}. \tag{2}$$

The equations (2) are called the **two-point form** of the equations of a line.

Illustration. The equations of the line through the points $(1,2,-1)$ and $(2,2,0)$ are

$$\frac{x - 1}{1} = \frac{y - 2}{0} = \frac{z + 1}{1},$$

or $x - z - 2 = 0$, $y - 2 = 0$.

Note: When any of the constants a, b, and c are zero, we shall mean by the form (1) the equivalent equations

$$\frac{a}{x - x_1} = \frac{b}{y - y_1} = \frac{c}{z - z_1}.$$

Thus the form $\frac{x}{1} = \frac{y}{0} = \frac{z}{0}$ means the equations determined from $\frac{1}{x} = \frac{0}{y} = \frac{0}{z}$, which in this case are $y = 0$ and $z = 0$.

If the equations of a line are given in general form, an equivalent symmetric form can be found merely by finding two points on the line and then substituting in (2).

Example 1. Write the equations of the line $x - y + 2z = 2$, $2x + y - z = 1$ in symmetric form.

Solution: Setting $z = 0$ in the equations and solving, we find that $x = 1$ and $y = -1$. Letting $x = 0$ and solving, we obtain $y = 4$ and $z = 3$.

Thus, since $(1,-1,0)$ and $(0,4,3)$ are two points on the line, the equations of the line in symmetric form are

$$\frac{x-1}{-1} = \frac{y+1}{5} = \frac{z}{3}.$$

Example 2. Find the equations of a line through the point $(-1,3,4)$ and perpendicular to the plane $3x - y - z = 5$.

Solution: Since the normal (or perpendicular) direction to the given plane is $[3,-1,-1]$, the equations of the required line are

$$\frac{x+1}{3} = \frac{y-3}{-1} = \frac{z-4}{-1}.$$

Example 3. Show that the lines $x = y = z + 2$ and $\dfrac{x-1}{1} = \dfrac{y}{0} = \dfrac{z}{2}$ meet, and find their point of intersection.

Solution: Writing the equations of the lines in general form, we have $x = y$, $y = z + 2$ and $y = 0$, $z = 2x - 2$.

In order that the given lines meet, it is necessary that these four equations have a common solution. Since $x = 0$, $y = 0$, and $z = -2$ satisfy all four equations, the given lines intersect at the point $(0,0,-2)$.

Example 4. Find the equation of the plane that contains the line $\dfrac{x-2}{3} = \dfrac{y}{-1} = \dfrac{z+3}{2}$ and is parallel to the line $\dfrac{x+1}{4} = \dfrac{y-2}{2} = \dfrac{z}{3}$.

Solution: Writing the equations of the first line in general form, we have

$$x + 3y - 2 = 0, \qquad 2y + z + 3 = 0. \tag{3}$$

All values of x and y that satisfy (3) will also satisfy the relation

$$(x + 3y - 2) + k(2y + z + 3) = 0. \tag{4}$$

Hence (4) represents a family of planes passing through the line (3). Writing the equation (4) in general form, we have

$$x + (2k + 3)y + kz + (3k - 2) = 0. \tag{5}$$

In order that the second of the given lines be parallel to (5), its direction $[4,2,3]$ must be perpendicular to the normal direction of the plane (5). This means that

$$4(1) + 2(2k + 3) + 3(k) = 0.$$

Hence $k = -\frac{10}{7}$; substituting this value in (5), we obtain the equation of the required plane.

$$7x + y - 10z - 44 = 0.$$

EXERCISE 98

Find the points where the following lines pierce the coordinate planes, and draw the lines.

1. $x + y + 4z = 6,\quad 2x - 3y - 2z = 2.$ *Ans.* $(0,-2,2)$, $(2,0,1)$, $(4,2,0)$.
2. $2x + y + z = 6,\quad x + 2y - z = 0.$
3. $x - y + 2z = 2,\quad 2x - 3y + 4z = 0.$ $(0,4,3)$, $(6,4,0)$.
4. $4x - 3y - 5z = 1,\quad 15x = 12y + 20z.$

Find the equations of the line through the following points.

5. $(1,3,-2)$, $(2,2,0)$. *Ans.* $\dfrac{x-2}{1} = \dfrac{y-2}{-1} = \dfrac{z}{2}.$
6. $(2,-2,3)$, $(-1,2,5)$.
7. $(-1,3,4)$, $(4,3,9)$. $\dfrac{x+1}{1} = \dfrac{y-3}{0} = \dfrac{z-4}{1}.$
8. $(3,-1,-2)$, $(5,3,-2)$.

Write the following equations in symmetric form.

9. $x + 2y + 3z = 1,\quad x + y + 2z = 0.$ *Ans.* $\dfrac{x+1}{1} = \dfrac{y-1}{1} = \dfrac{z}{-1}.$
10. $x + 2y + 4z = 0,\quad 2x + 4y - z = 9.$
11. $3x + y - 2z = 7,\quad 6x - 5y - 4z = 7.$ $\dfrac{x-2}{2} = \dfrac{y-1}{0} = \dfrac{z}{3}.$
12. $2x + 4y + z = 4x + 2y - z = 3.$
13. Find the acute angle between the lines $\dfrac{x}{2} = \dfrac{y}{2} = \dfrac{z}{1}$ and $\dfrac{x}{5} = \dfrac{y}{4} = \dfrac{z}{-3}.$ *Ans.* $45°$.
14. Find the equations of the line parallel to the line $\dfrac{x}{1} = \dfrac{y}{-1} = \dfrac{z+1}{2}$ and passing through the point $(1,-2,0)$.
15. Find the equations of the line perpendicular to the plane $2x + 3y - 7 = 0$ at the point $(2,1,0)$. *Ans.* $\dfrac{x-2}{2} = \dfrac{y-1}{3} = \dfrac{z}{0}.$
16. Show that the points $(\frac{1}{3},\frac{3}{4},\frac{1}{2})$, $(\frac{1}{2},\frac{1}{2},\frac{1}{3})$, and $(\frac{2}{3},\frac{1}{4},\frac{1}{6})$ lie on a line and find its equations.

Find the equation of the plane containing the line $x = y = z$ and satisfying the following conditions.

17. Passing through the point $(1,2,3)$. *Ans.* $x - 2y + z = 0.$
18. Parallel to the line $\dfrac{x+1}{3} = \dfrac{y}{2} = \dfrac{z}{-1}.$
19. Passing through the line $x + 1 = y + 1 = z.$ $x - y = 0.$
20. Passing through the line $x = 2y = 3z.$

21. Show that the line $\frac{x}{3} = \frac{y}{-2} = \frac{z}{2}$ is parallel to the plane $2x + 2y - z = 6$, and find the distance between them. *Ans.* 2.

22. Find the acute angle between the line $\frac{x}{3} = \frac{y}{1} = \frac{z}{0}$ and the plane $x + 2y = 7$.

23. Find the point on the line $x = y = z$ that is equidistant from the points (3,0,5) and (1,−1,4). *Ans.* (2,2,2).

24. Find the equation of the plane through the points (1,0,1) and (1,1,0) that is parallel to the line $x = y = z - 1$.

25. Find the equations of the line through the point (4,3,2) that is perpendicular to the z axis. *Ans.* $\frac{x}{4} = \frac{y}{3} = \frac{z-2}{0}$.

26. Show that the line $\frac{x+1}{1} = \frac{y}{-1} = \frac{z-2}{2}$ is in the plane $2x + 4y + z = 0$.

27. Show that the lines $x + y - 3z = 0,\ \ 2x + 3y - 8z = 1$ and $3x - y - z = 3,\ \ x + y - 3z = 5$ are parallel.

28. Find the equation of the plane determined by the lines in Problem 27.

29. Show that the lines $\frac{x}{1} = \frac{y+3}{2} = \frac{z+1}{3}$ and $\frac{x-3}{2} = \frac{y}{1} = \frac{z-1}{-1}$ intersect by finding their point of intersection. *Ans.* (1,−1,2).

30. Find the equation of the plane determined by the lines in Problem 29.

31. Find the distance between the parallel lines $\frac{x}{6} = \frac{y}{-2} = \frac{z}{1}$ and $\frac{x-7}{6} = \frac{y}{-2} = \frac{z+1}{1}$. *Ans.* 3.

32. Find the distance from the point (2,3,4) to the line $x = y = z$.

33. Find the distance between the lines $\frac{x}{1} = \frac{y}{2} = \frac{z-6}{3}$ and $\frac{x}{3} = \frac{y}{2} = \frac{z}{1}$. *Ans.* $\sqrt{6}$.

34. Find the area of the triangle whose sides have the equations $\frac{x}{3} = \frac{y}{4} = \frac{z}{5}$, $\frac{x}{2} = \frac{y}{1} = \frac{z}{-2}$, and $\frac{x}{1} = \frac{y+5}{3} = \frac{z+16}{7}$.

35. If t is a parameter, show that $x = x_1 + at,\ \ y = y_1 + bt,\ \ z = z_1 + ct$ are parametric equations of a line that passes through the point (x_1,y_1,z_1) with direction numbers $[a,b,c]$.

36. Show that $\begin{vmatrix} B_1 & C_1 \\ B_2 & C_2 \end{vmatrix}$, $\begin{vmatrix} C_1 & A_1 \\ C_2 & A_2 \end{vmatrix}$, and $\begin{vmatrix} A_1 & B_1 \\ A_2 & B_2 \end{vmatrix}$ are direction numbers for a line whose equations are $A_1x + B_1y + C_1z + D_1 = 0,\ \ A_2x + B_2y + C_2z + D_2 = 0$.

185. Equation of a Surface

It is apparent from our previous work that an equation in the variables x, y, and z usually represents a surface. In order to depict graphically the nature of a surface, the following considerations will prove helpful.

Extent. The extent of a surface is the ranges of the variables x, y, and z which are permissible as coordinates of a point on the surface. Thus, for the equation $x^2 + 4y^2 + 9z^2 = 36$, the permissible ranges of the variables are $-6 \leqq x \leqq 6$, $-3 \leqq y \leqq 3$, and $-2 \leqq z \leqq 2$, respectively.

Intercepts. The intercepts of a surface are determined by the points where the surface cuts the coordinate axes. Thus, for the equation $x + y^2 - z^2 = 4$, the surface has an x intercept 4, y intercepts -2 and 2, and no z intercepts.

Traces. The traces of a surface are the curves of intersection of the surface with the coordinate planes. Thus, for the equation $x^2 + y^2 + z = 4$, the xy trace is the circle $x^2 + y^2 = 4$, the zx trace the parabola $x^2 + z = 4$, and the yz trace the parabola $y^2 + z = 4$.

Sections. The sections of a surface are the curves of intersection of the surface with specified planes. Thus, for the equation $z = xy$, the section in the plane $y = 4$ is the line $z = 4x$, and the section in the plane $x = y$ is a parabola whose points are determined by the equation $z = y^2$.

Symmetry with respect to a coordinate plane. A surface is symmetric with respect to the yz plane if, and only if, its equation is unaltered when x is replaced by $-x$. Similar statements hold for symmetry with respect to the other coordinate planes. Thus, for the equation $x + y^2 + z^2 = y$, the surface is symmetric with respect to the xy plane, and it is not symmetric with respect to the yz or zx planes.

Symmetry with respect to a coordinate axis. A surface is symmetric with respect to the x axis if, and only if, its equation is unaltered when y and z are replaced by $-y$ and $-z$, respectively. Similar statements hold for symmetry with respect to the other coordinate axes. Thus, for the equation $z = xy + y^2$, the surface is symmetric with respect to the z axis, and it is not symmetric with respect to the x or y axes.

Symmetry with respect to the origin. A surface is symmetric with respect to the origin if, and only if, its equation is unaltered when x, y, and z are replaced by $-x$, $-y$, and $-z$, respectively. Thus, for the equation $x^2 + z^2 + xy = 4$, the surface is symmetric with respect to the origin.

Example 1. Sketch the surface whose equation is

$$\frac{x^2}{16} + \frac{y^2}{9} + \frac{z^2}{4} = 1.$$

Solution: Setting pairs of the variables equal to zero in turn, we obtain the x, y, and z intercepts ± 4, ± 3, and ± 2, respectively.

Setting each of the variables equal to zero in turn, we find that the traces in the yz, zx, and xy planes are ellipses whose respective equations are

$$\frac{y^2}{9} + \frac{z^2}{4} = 1, \qquad \frac{x^2}{16} + \frac{z^2}{4} = 1, \qquad \frac{x^2}{16} + \frac{y^2}{9} = 1.$$

Since the surface is symmetric with respect to the origin and all the coordinate axes and planes, the first-octant sketch shown in Figure 200 is sufficient to indicate the appearance of the surface.

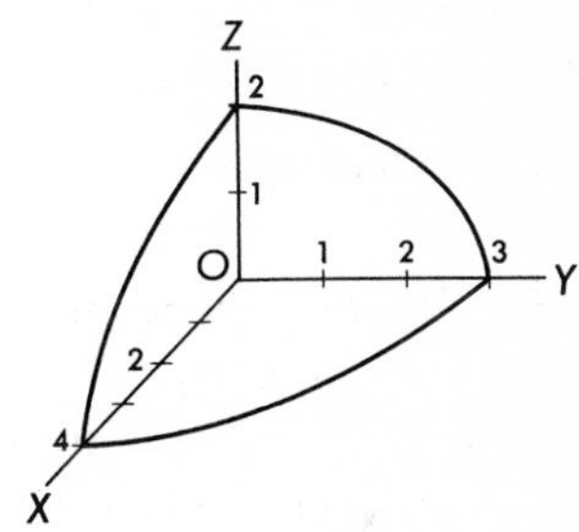

Figure 200

Example 2. Sketch the surface whose equation is $z^2 = x^2 + y^2$.

Solution: It is evident that the zero intercepts and the traces $z = \pm x$ and $z = \pm y$ are not sufficient to determine the appearance of the surface. Hence we take sections parallel to the xy plane. Thus, for $z = 2$ and $z = -2$, we obtain circular sections whose equations are $x^2 + y^2 = 4$. These sections together with the traces give the cone shown in Figure 201.

Observe, as in this example, that when a surface is of infinite extent, we sketch only the portion of it that is included between sections parallel to one (or more) of the coordinate planes.

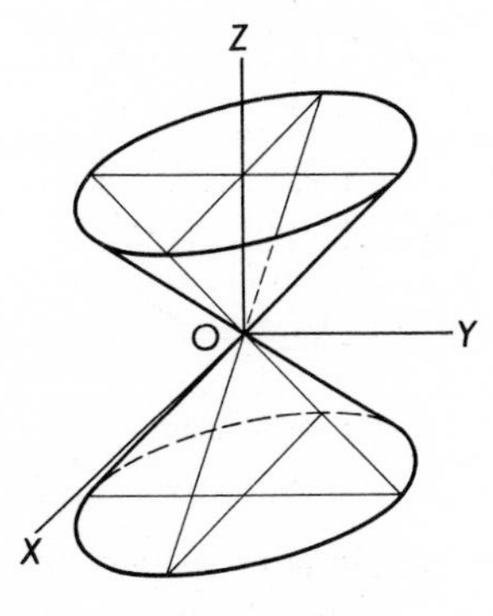

Figure 201

Any surface which is generated by a straight line that remains parallel to a fixed line and intersects a fixed curve is called a **cylinder.** The curve is called a **directing curve,** the moving line a **generator,** and a particular position of the generator is an **element** of the cylinder.

A section by a plane perpendicular to the generators is called a **right section,** and it is evident that all right sections are identical curves. If the right sections have centers, the line through these centers is called the **axis** of the cylinder.

In accordance with these definitions, we have the following result.

Theorem. *An equation in two variables represents a cylinder whose generators are perpendicular to the plane of the two variables and whose directing curve is the trace of the equation in that plane.*

For example, if x_1 and y_1 are values satisfying the equation $f(x,y) = 0$, it follows that the coordinates of all points on the line $x = x_1$, $y = y_1$ are on the surface. The surface is thus generated by these lines, all of which are perpendicular to the xy plane and pass through the xy trace.

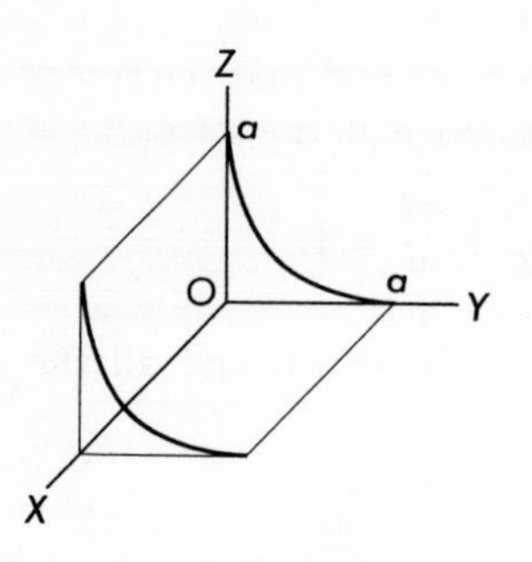

Figure 202

Example 3. Sketch the surface whose equation is $\sqrt{y} + \sqrt{z} = \sqrt{a}$.

Solution: Since the yz trace of the surface is a parabolic arc as shown in **66,** page 9, we obtain the cylindrical surface shown in Figure 202.

186. Quadric Surfaces

A surface whose equation is of the second degree in the variables x, y, and z is called a **quadric surface.** Except for degenerate cases, these surfaces can be classified into the nine types that are listed below.

Ellipsoid. The locus of the equation

$$\frac{x^2}{a^2} + \frac{y^2}{b^2} + \frac{z^2}{c^2} = 1$$

is an ellipsoid. This surface is symmetric with respect to the three coordinate planes, is bounded, and has a point of symmetry at the origin, called the **center.**

The segments of length $2a$, $2b$, and $2c$ along the coordinate axes are called the **axes** of the ellipsoid. When these axes are equal, the surface is a sphere.

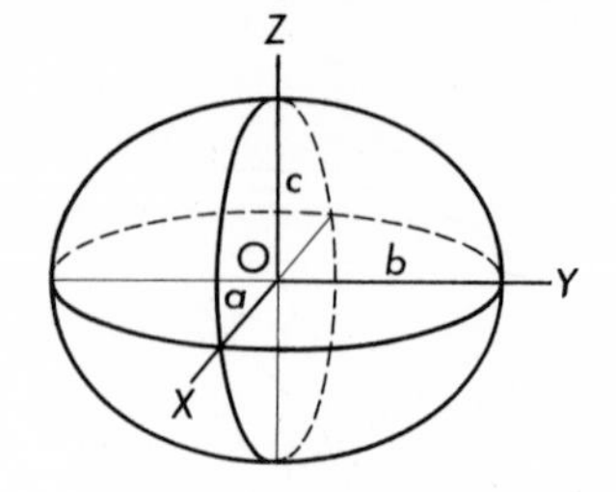

Figure 203

Hyperboloid of one sheet. The locus of the equation

$$\frac{x^2}{a^2} + \frac{y^2}{b^2} - \frac{z^2}{c^2} = 1$$

is a hyperboloid of one sheet. This surface is symmetric with respect to the z axis, called the **axis** of the surface, and has a point of symmetry at the origin, called the **center.**

Sections of this surface made by the planes $z = k$ are ellipses. The ellipse is smallest when $k = 0$, and increases in size as k increases numerically. The surface thus extends indefinitely in each of these directions.

Hyperboloid of two sheets. The locus of the equation

$$\frac{x^2}{a^2} - \frac{y^2}{b^2} - \frac{z^2}{c^2} = 1$$

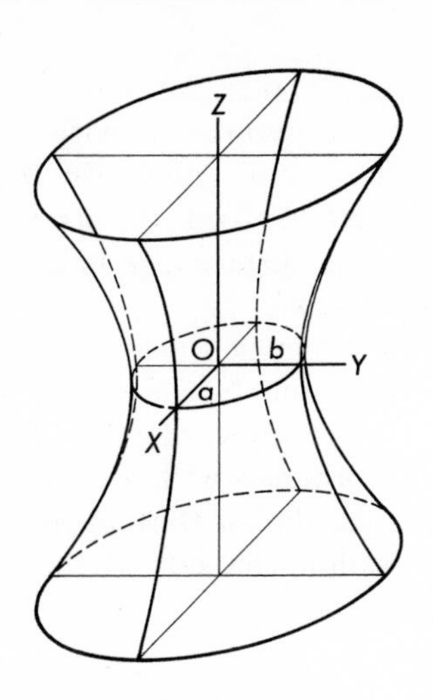

Figure 204

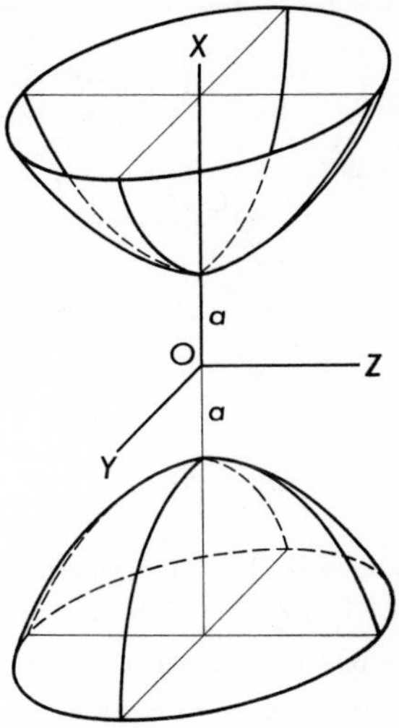

Figure 205

is a hyperboloid of two sheets. This surface is symmetric with respect to the x axis, called the **axis** of the surface, and has a point of symmetry at the origin, called the **center.**

Sections of this surface made by the planes $x = k$ are ellipses starting with a point-ellipse when $|k| = a$, and increasing in size as k increases numerically. The surface thus consists of two distinct parts that extend indefinitely in each of these directions.

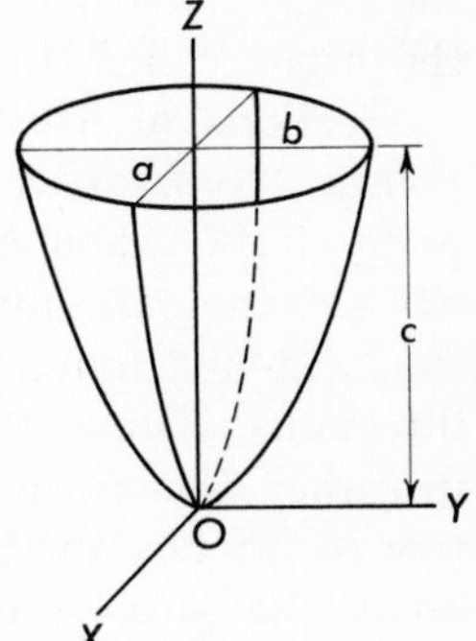

Figure 206

Elliptic paraboloid. The locus of the equation

$$\frac{x^2}{a^2} + \frac{y^2}{b^2} = \frac{z}{c}$$

is an elliptic paraboloid. This surface is symmetric with respect to the z axis, called the **axis** of the surface, and the axis intersects the surface at a point called the **vertex.**

Sections of this surface made by the planes $z = k$ are ellipses starting with a point-ellipse when $k = 0$, and increasing in size as k

increases numerically with the same sign as c. The surface thus lies on one side of the xy plane and extends indefinitely in one direction.

Hyperbolic paraboloid. The locus of the equation

$$\frac{x^2}{a^2} - \frac{y^2}{b^2} = \frac{z}{c}$$

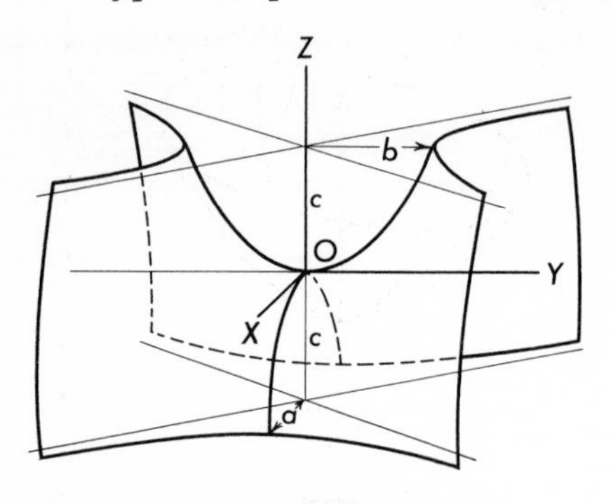

Figure 207

is a hyperbolic paraboloid. This surface is symmetric with respect to the z axis, called the **axis** of the surface, and the axis intersects the surface at a point called the **vertex.**

Sections of this surface made by the planes $x = h$ are parabolas that open upward or downward in accordance with the sign of c. Sections made by the planes $y = k$ are parabolas that open in the opposite direction. The surface thus is "saddle-shaped" at the vertex and extends indefinitely in all directions.

Elliptic cone. The locus of the equation

$$\frac{x^2}{a^2} + \frac{y^2}{b^2} = \frac{z^2}{c^2}$$

is an elliptic cone. This surface is symmetric with respect to the z axis, called the **axis** of the surface, and has a point of symmetry at the origin, called the **vertex.**

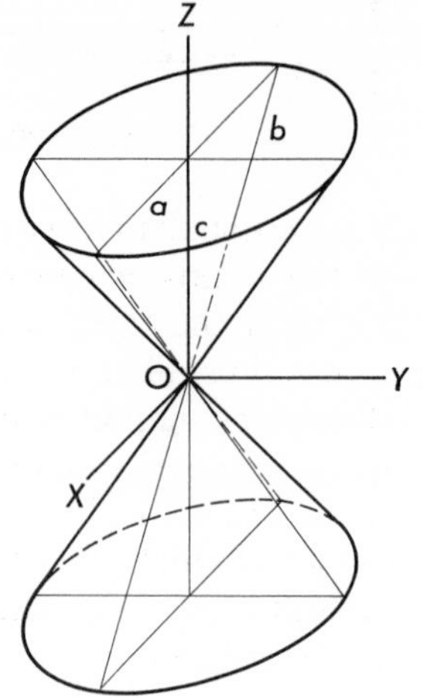

Figure 208

Sections of this surface made by the planes $z = k$ are ellipses starting with a point-ellipse when $k = 0$ and increasing in size as k increases numerically. The surface thus extends indefinitely in each of these directions. Since the trace of this surface in either the zx or yz plane consists of a pair of intersecting lines (degenerate hyperbola), the surface can be considered as a limiting surface existing between a hyperboloid of one sheet and a hyperboloid of two sheets.

Elliptic, parabolic, and hyperbolic cylinders. The loci of equations in two variables, such as

$$\frac{x^2}{a^2} + \frac{y^2}{b^2} = 1, \qquad \frac{x^2}{a^2} = \frac{y}{b}, \qquad \frac{x^2}{a^2} - \frac{y^2}{b^2} = 1,$$

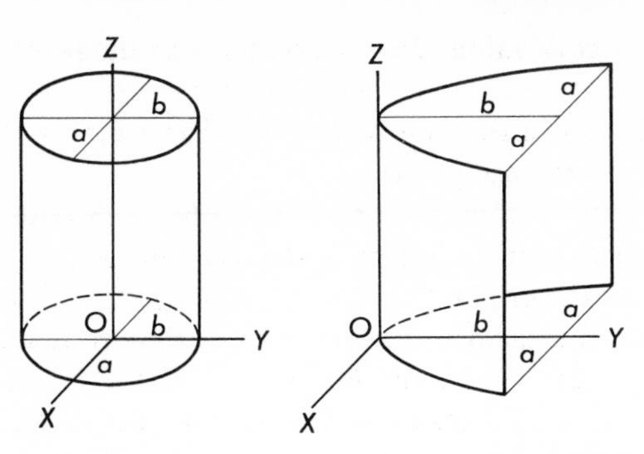

Figure 209

are called elliptic, parabolic, and hyperbolic cylinders, respectively. These surfaces have elements perpendicular to the xy plane, and are named in accordance with their trace in that plane.

EXERCISE 99

Sketch and name the locus of each of the following equations.

1. $x^2 + 4y^2 + 16z^2 = 64.$
2. $x^2 + 4y^2 + 16z^2 = 64z.$
3. $x + 4y^2 + z^2 = 0.$
4. $2z = 8 - x^2 - y^2.$
5. $x^2 - 4y^2 + 9z^2 = 36.$
6. $y^2 + z^2 = 4x^2 + 4.$
7. $x^2 - 4y^2 + 9z^2 = 0.$
8. $x^2 - 4y^2 + 9z^2 = 4x.$
9. $2x + z^2 = 4.$
10. $x^2 + y^2 = 2(x + y).$
11. $x^2 = y^2 + z^2 + 4.$
12. $4y^2 - x - 9z^2 = 36.$

Factor the following equations and describe the locus of each.

13. $z^2 - 2z - 3 = 0.$ *Ans.* Two planes.
14. $x^2 - y^2 = 0.$
15. $x^2z + y^2z = 0.$ xy plane and z axis.
16. $yz + 1 = y + z.$

Draw a figure of the solid in the first octant that is bounded by the coordinate planes and the following surfaces.

17. $x^2 + y^2 + z^2 = 25,\quad y = 4.$
18. $y^2 + z^2 = 25,\quad x^2 + z^2 = 25.$
19. $4x^2 + y^2 + 4z^2 = 64,\quad x^2 + y^2 = 16.$
20. $4x^2 + 4y^2 + z^2 = 64,\quad y + z = 4.$
21. $x^2 + y^2 = 64 - 8z,\quad x = 4,\quad y = 4.$
22. $x^2 + y^2 = z^2 + 9,\quad z = 4.$
23. $x^2 + y^2 = 16,\quad x + y + z = 8.$
24. $x^2 + y^2 + 4z = 64,\quad x^2 + y^2 = z^2.$
25. Find the center and radius of the sphere whose equation is $x^2 + y^2 + z^2 = 6x + 8z.$ *Ans.* $C(3,0,4)$, 5.

26. Find the equation of the sphere of radius 2 whose center is at the point $(1,-1,0)$.
27. Find the equation of the sphere in the first octant that has a radius 3 and is tangent to the three coordinate planes.

Ans. $x^2 + y^2 + z^2 - 6x - 6y - 6z + 18 = 0.$

28. Find the equation of the sphere that is tangent to the plane $6x + 6y + 7z = 22$ and has its center at the origin.
29. Find the equation of the central quadric $Ax^2 + By^2 + Cz^2 = K$ that passes through the points $(2,2,2)$, $(1,0,0)$, and $(0,2,3)$.

Ans. $20x^2 - 31y^2 + 16z^2 = 20.$

30. Find the equation of a cone whose yz trace is the ellipse $y^2 + 2z^2 = 1$ and whose vertex is at the point $(2,0,0)$.

CHAPTER 21

Partial Differentiation

187. Functions of Two or More Variables; Continuity

In the preceding chapters we have discussed the applications of the calculus to functions of a single variable. We shall now apply the same principles to functions of more than one independent variable.

If three variables x, y, and z are related so that, for each number pair (x,y) in a domain of real numbers, we obtain one or more real values for z, then z is said to be a **function of two variables** defined in the domain D. If the number pair (x,y) is considered as the rectangular coordinates of a point in a plane, the domain of definition may be considered as a region in the coordinate plane. Thus, for the function

$$z = \sqrt{9 - x^2 - y^2},$$

the domain consists of all coordinate number pairs corresponding to the points on or interior to the circle $x^2 + y^2 = 9$. The corresponding range of the function is $0 \leqq z \leqq 3$.

In the same manner, a correspondence in which a real number y is determined by n numbers $(x_1, x_2, \cdots, x_n)$ is called a *function of n variables*, and is written as $y = f(x_1, x_2, \cdots, x_n)$.

In the work that follows we shall be concerned primarily with functions which are continuous. The definition of continuity for a function of two variables is given below. A similar definition holds for functions of more than two variables.

A function $f(x,y)$ of two independent variables is said to be continuous for $x = a$ and $y = b$, if it is defined for these and for neighboring values, and if

$$\lim_{\substack{x \to a \\ y \to b}} f(x,y) = f(a,b),$$

no matter how x and y approach their respective limits a and b.

For instance, $f(x,y) = xy$ is continuous at any point (a,b), since

$$|f(x,y) - f(a,b)| = |xy - ab| = |xy - xb + xb - ab|$$
$$\leqq |x(y - b)| + |b(x - a)|$$

can be made arbitrarily small by making both $|x - a|$ and $|y - b|$ small.

Illustration. Observe that the function $f(x,y) = \dfrac{x^2 - y^2}{x^2 + y^2}$ is not continuous at $(0,0)$, since $f(0,0)$ is undefined, and furthermore

$$\lim_{x\to 0}\left[\lim_{y\to 0} f(x,y)\right] = 1 \quad \text{and} \quad \lim_{y\to 0}\left[\lim_{x\to 0} f(x,y)\right] = -1.$$

By writing $f(x,y)$ in polar coordinates, we obtain $f(r\cos\theta, r\sin\theta) = \cos 2\theta$, which indicates that the function can assume all values between -1 and 1 no matter how close the point (x,y) is to the origin.

Note also that the function $f(x,y) = (x^2 + y^2)\sqrt{x^2 - 1}$ is discontinuous at the origin, since $(0,0)$ is an isolated point.

Considering x, y, and z to be the rectangular coordinates of a point in space, we know from analytic geometry that a relation of the form $z = f(x,y)$ represents, in general, a surface. From a geometric point of view the definition of continuity states essentially that a *sufficiently small change in the independent variables produces an arbitrarily small change in the function.* Thus, in Figure 210, the increment Δz is small when Δx and Δy are small. Conversely, when the function is continuous, Δz approaches zero when Δx and Δy both independently approach zero.

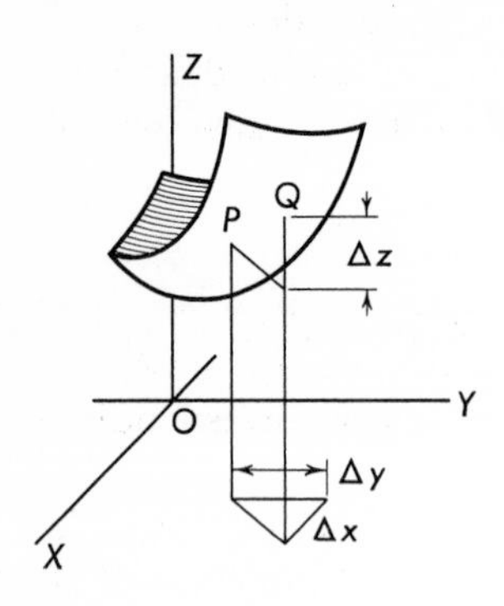

Figure 210

A function $f(x,y)$ is said to be continuous in a *region* of the xy plane when it is continuous at each point of the region. A continuous function of two or more variables has properties similar to those of a continuous function of one variable. For example, if $f(x,y)$ is continuous in a domain D, then there exist points in D where $f(x,y)$ attains its maximum value M, its minimum value m, and any intermediate value from m to M.

188. Partial Derivatives

Let us consider a function z of two independent variables

$$z = f(x,y). \tag{1}$$

If y is held constant in (1), z becomes a function of x alone. As a result, we can compute the derivative of z with respect to x. The derivative found in this manner is called the **partial derivative** of z with respect to x, and is denoted by the symbol $\partial z/\partial x$. In like manner, when x is held constant, we can find the partial derivative of z with respect to y. This derivative is denoted by $\partial z/\partial y$.

Illustration. If $z = x^2 + 3xy - 4y^2$, we obtain

$$\frac{\partial z}{\partial x} = 2x + 3y, \qquad \frac{\partial z}{\partial y} = 3x - 8y.$$

Other symbols used to represent the partial derivatives of a function of two variables are

$$\frac{\partial z}{\partial x}, \quad \frac{\partial f}{\partial x}, \quad \frac{\partial}{\partial x} f(x,y), \quad f_x(x,y), \quad f_x, \quad z_x,$$

$$\frac{\partial z}{\partial y}, \quad \frac{\partial f}{\partial y}, \quad \frac{\partial}{\partial y} f(x,y), \quad f_y(x,y), \quad f_y, \quad z_y.$$

In general, a function $u = f(x,y,z,\cdots)$ of any number of variables may have a partial derivative with respect to each of its variables. Thus, in accordance with the definition of a derivative, it follows that

$$\frac{\partial u}{\partial x} = \lim_{\Delta x \to 0} \frac{f(x + \Delta x, y, z, \cdots) - f(x,y,z,\cdots)}{\Delta x},$$

and so on for the other variables, provided the limits exist.

Example. If $z = \dfrac{x^3 - y^3}{xy}$, show that $x\dfrac{\partial z}{\partial x} + y\dfrac{\partial z}{\partial y} = z$.

Solution: Writing $z = x^2y^{-1} - x^{-1}y^2$, we have

$$z_x = 2xy^{-1} + x^{-2}y^2, \qquad z_y = -x^2y^{-2} - 2x^{-1}y.$$

Hence

$$\begin{aligned} xz_x + yz_y &= 2x^2y^{-1} + x^{-1}y^2 - x^2y^{-1} - 2x^{-1}y^2 \\ &= x^2y^{-1} - x^{-1}y^2 = z. \end{aligned}$$

189. Geometric Interpretation of Partial Derivatives

Let $z = f(x,y)$ be the equation of the surface shown in Figure 211. If a plane is passed through any point P of the surface parallel to the xz plane, we cut from the surface a curve APB. As a point moves along this curve, its coordinates z and x vary while *y remains constant*, and the slope of the tangent line at P represents the rate at which z

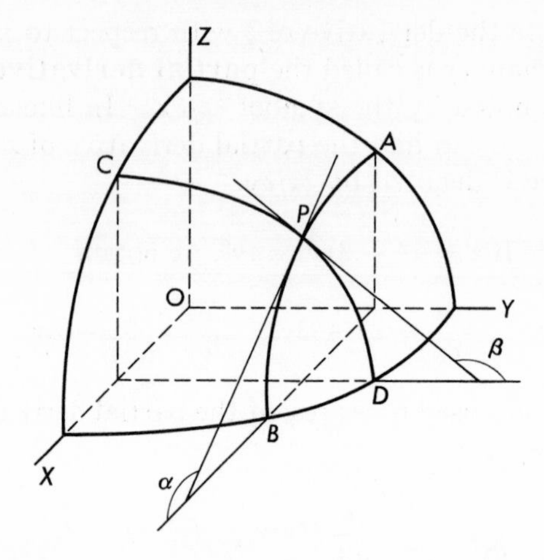

Figure 211

changes with respect to x. Thus the partial derivatives have the geometrical significance

$$\frac{\partial z}{\partial x} = \tan \alpha = \text{slope of } APB \text{ at } P,$$

$$\frac{\partial z}{\partial y} = \tan \beta = \text{slope of } CPD \text{ at } P.$$

190. Partial Derivatives of Higher Order

Since the partial derivatives of a function $z = f(x,y)$ are themselves functions of x and y, they may in turn be differentiated. Their partial derivatives, if they exist, are called the **second partial derivatives** of z, and each is denoted by one of the following symbols.

$$\frac{\partial}{\partial x}\left(\frac{\partial z}{\partial x}\right) = \frac{\partial^2 z}{\partial x^2} = z_{xx} = \frac{\partial^2 f}{\partial x^2} = f_{xx},$$

$$\frac{\partial}{\partial x}\left(\frac{\partial z}{\partial y}\right) = \frac{\partial^2 z}{\partial x\, \partial y} = z_{yx} = \frac{\partial^2 f}{\partial x\, \partial y} = f_{yx},$$

$$\frac{\partial}{\partial y}\left(\frac{\partial z}{\partial x}\right) = \frac{\partial^2 z}{\partial y\, \partial x} = z_{xy} = \frac{\partial^2 f}{\partial y\, \partial x} = f_{xy},$$

$$\frac{\partial}{\partial y}\left(\frac{\partial z}{\partial y}\right) = \frac{\partial^2 z}{\partial y^2} = z_{yy} = \frac{\partial^2 f}{\partial y^2} = f_{yy}.$$

Of the four derivatives shown above only three are usually distinct from one another. This is true since it can be shown that z_{yx} and z_{xy}

are identical for all values of x and y for which the derivatives are continuous.

Illustration 1. If $z = x^3y + 4xy^2$, we have

$$z_x = 3x^2y + 4y^2; \quad \text{hence} \quad z_{xy} = 3x^2 + 8y,$$

and

$$z_y = x^3 + 8xy; \quad \text{hence} \quad z_{yx} = 3x^2 + 8y.$$

Because of the above property, it follows that a mixed partial derivative of higher order may be obtained by differentiating with respect to the variables in any order whatsoever. As an illustration of the manner of proof, we have

$$\frac{\partial^3 z}{\partial x^2\,\partial y} = \frac{\partial}{\partial x}\left(\frac{\partial^2 z}{\partial x\,\partial y}\right) = \frac{\partial}{\partial x}\left(\frac{\partial^2 z}{\partial y\,\partial x}\right) = \frac{\partial^3 z}{\partial x\,\partial y\,\partial x},$$

and

$$\frac{\partial^3 z}{\partial x\,\partial y\,\partial x} = \frac{\partial^2}{\partial x\,\partial y}\left(\frac{\partial z}{\partial x}\right) = \frac{\partial^2}{\partial y\,\partial x}\left(\frac{\partial z}{\partial x}\right) = \frac{\partial^3 z}{\partial y\,\partial x^2}.$$

Thus we conclude that a function of two variables has only four distinct partial derivatives of the third order, namely,

$$\frac{\partial^3 z}{\partial x^3}, \quad \frac{\partial^3 z}{\partial x^2\,\partial y}, \quad \frac{\partial^3 z}{\partial x\,\partial y^2}, \quad \frac{\partial^3 z}{\partial y^3}.$$

The above discussion applies in like manner to functions of any number of variables.

Illustration 2. If $V = x^2 + y^2 + z^2$, then $V_x = 2x$, $V_y = 2y$, $V_z = 2z$, and $V_{xx} = V_{yy} = V_{zz} = 2$, $V_{xy} = V_{xz} = V_{yz} = 0$.

EXERCISE 100

1. What is the domain of $\sqrt{\dfrac{x - y}{x + y}}$ as a real function? At what points is it discontinuous? *Ans.* $x^2 > y^2$ and $x = y$; $x + y = 0$.
2. What is the domain of $xy/\ln(x^2 + y^2 - 1)$ as a real function? At what points is it discontinuous?
3. The function $f(x,y) = \dfrac{\sin(x - y)}{x - y}$, $x \neq y$, and $f(x,y) = h$, $x = y$ is continuous. What is the value of h? *Ans.* 1.
4. Is the function $f(x,y) = \dfrac{2x^2y^2}{x^2 + y^2}$, $(x,y) \neq (0,0)$, and $f(0,0) = 0$ continuous?

Find the first partial derivatives of the following functions.

5. $u = \dfrac{x - y}{x + y}$. *Ans.* $\dfrac{\partial u}{\partial x} = \dfrac{2y}{(x + y)^2}$, $\dfrac{\partial u}{\partial y} = \dfrac{-2x}{(x + y)^2}$.

6. $u = \sqrt{x^2 - y^2}$.

7. $z = x \sin(y - x)$.
Ans. $z_x = \sin(y - x) - x\cos(y - x)$, $z_y = x\cos(y - x)$.

8. $z = \ln(x + \sqrt{x^2 - y^2})$.

9. $v = \operatorname{Cot}^{-1}\dfrac{y}{x}$. *Ans.* $v_x = \dfrac{y}{x^2 + y^2}$, $v_y = \dfrac{-x}{x^2 + y^2}$.

10. $v = \operatorname{Sin}^{-1}\sqrt{1 - x^2y^2}$.

11. $u = xy + yz + zx$. $u_x = y + z$, $u_y = x + z$, $u_z = x + y$.

12. $u = \ln\sqrt{x^2 + y^2 + z^2}$.

13. If $f(x,y) = 2x^2 - xy$, find $f_x(2,3)$ and $f_y(2,3)$. $5, -2$.

14. If $f(x,y) = \dfrac{x}{x - y}$, find $f_x(1,0)$ and $f_y(1,0)$.

15. If $F(x,y) = \ln(x^2y - xy^2)$, find $F_x(3,2)$ and $F_y(3,2)$. $\frac{4}{3}, -\frac{1}{2}$.

16. If $F(x,y) = e^{-x}\tan(x + y)$, find $F_x(0,\frac{1}{4}\pi)$ and $F_y(0,\frac{1}{4}\pi)$.

17. If $z = \dfrac{x^2y^2}{x + y}$, show that $x\dfrac{\partial z}{\partial x} + y\dfrac{\partial z}{\partial y} = 3z$.

18. If $z = Ax^3 + Bx^2y + Cxy^2 + Dy^3$, show that $xz_x + yz_y = 3z$.

19. If $u = \dfrac{e^{x+y}}{e^x + e^y}$, show that $\dfrac{\partial u}{\partial x} + \dfrac{\partial u}{\partial y} = u$.

20. If $u = (Ax^2 + Bxy + Cy^2)^n$, show that $xu_x + yu_y = 2nu$.

21. If $z = e^{-y}\cos(x - y)$, show that $z_x + z_y + z = 0$.

22. If $u = x^3 + y^3 + z^3 - 3xyz$, show that $xu_x + yu_y + zu_z = 3u$.

23. If $u = e^{x/y} + e^{y/z} + e^{z/x}$, show that $xu_x + yu_y + zu_z = 0$.

24. If $u = x^2y + y^2z + z^2x$, show that $u_x + u_y + u_z = (x + y + z)^2$.

In each of the following show that $\dfrac{\partial^2 z}{\partial x\,\partial y} = \dfrac{\partial^2 z}{\partial y\,\partial x}$.

25. $z = (x^2 + y^2)^{3/2}$.

26. $z = \dfrac{x + y}{x - y}$.

27. $z = \operatorname{Sin}^{-1}\dfrac{y}{x}$.

28. $z = \ln(x + \sqrt{x^2 + y^2})$.

In each of the following show that $\dfrac{\partial^2 z}{\partial x^2} + \dfrac{\partial^2 z}{\partial y^2} = 0$.

29. $z = \ln(x^2 + y^2)$.

30. $z = e^x \sin y + e^y \sin x$.

31. $z = \operatorname{Tan}^{-1}\dfrac{y}{x}$.

32. $z = \operatorname{Tan}^{-1}\dfrac{2xy}{x^2 - y^2}$.

33. If $u = (Ax^2 + By^2)^3$, verify that $\dfrac{\partial^3 u}{\partial x^2\,\partial y} = \dfrac{\partial^3 u}{\partial y\,\partial x^2}$.

34. If $z = \ln(x - y) + \tan(x + y)$, show that $z_{xx} = z_{yy}$.

35. If $z = xy + y \ln xy$, show that $xz_{xx} + yz_{xy} = y^2 z_{yy}$.
36. As $(x,y) \to (0,0)$, prove that $x + y$ approaches a limit but that x/y does not.
37. If $f(x,y) = x^2 - y^2$, how close to the origin should the point (x,y) be taken in order that $|f(x,y) - f(0,0)| < 0.01$?

    Ans. $-0.1 < x,y < 0.1$.
38. If $f(x,y) = 2xy/(x^2 + y^2)$ for $(x,y) \neq (0,0)$ and $f(0,0) = 0$, show that $\partial f/\partial x$ and $\partial f/\partial y$ exist at (0,0) but are not continuous there.
39. A function $f(x,y,z)$ is said to be *homogeneous* of order n provided $f(tx,ty,tz) = t^n f(x,y,z)$. If its partial derivatives exist, prove that $xf_x + yf_y + zf_z = n\,f(x,y,z)$.
40. If $f(x,y)$ is a homogeneous function of order n and if its second partial derivatives exist, show that $x^2 f_{xx} + 2xyf_{xy} + y^2 f_{yy} = n(n - 1)f(x,y)$.

191. Increment and Total Differential of a Function

Let us consider a function of two independent variables $z = f(x,y)$. If x and y are assigned arbitrary increments Δx and Δy, the given function changes by an amount

$$\Delta z = f(x + \Delta x, y + \Delta y) - f(x,y), \tag{1}$$

which is called the **increment** of the function.

Illustration 1. If $z = 2x^2 + 3y^2$, we have

$$z + \Delta z = 2(x + \Delta x)^2 + 3(y + \Delta y)^2.$$

Hence

$$\Delta z = 4x\,\Delta x + 6y\,\Delta y + 2(\Delta x)^2 + 3(\Delta y)^2.$$

In general, the increment Δz may be expressed in the form indicated in the following theorem.

Theorem. *If z and its first partial derivatives are continuous in the neighborhood of the point (x,y), then*

$$\Delta z = \frac{\partial z}{\partial x}\Delta x + \frac{\partial z}{\partial y}\Delta y + \epsilon_1\,\Delta x + \epsilon_2\,\Delta y, \tag{2}$$

where ϵ_1 and ϵ_2 are quantities such that

$$\lim_{\Delta x,\Delta y \to 0} \epsilon_1 = 0 \quad \textit{and} \quad \lim_{\Delta x,\Delta y \to 0} \epsilon_2 = 0.$$

Proof: Adding and subtracting $f(x,y + \Delta y)$ in the right member of (1), we have

$$\Delta z = f(x + \Delta x,y + \Delta y) - f(x,y + \Delta y) + f(x,y + \Delta y) - f(x,y). \tag{3}$$

Applying the law of the mean, Article **114,** to each of the two differences in (3), we obtain

$$f(x + \Delta x, y + \Delta y) - f(x, y + \Delta y) = \Delta x \frac{\partial}{\partial x} f(x + \theta_1 \Delta x, y + \Delta y),$$

$$f(x, y + \Delta y) - f(x, y) = \Delta y \frac{\partial}{\partial y} f(x, y + \theta_2 \Delta y),$$

where $0 < \theta_1 < 1$ and $0 < \theta_2 < 1$. Substituting these relations in (3), we have

$$\Delta z = f_x(x + \theta_1 \Delta x, y + \Delta y)\, \Delta x + f_y(x, y + \theta_2 \Delta y)\, \Delta y. \tag{4}$$

Since by hypothesis the partial derivatives are continuous near (x,y), we may write

$$f_x(x + \theta_1 \Delta x, y + \Delta y) = f_x(x,y) + \epsilon_1,$$
$$f_y(x, y + \theta_2 \Delta y) = f_y(x,y) + \epsilon_2,$$

where ϵ_1 and ϵ_2 are quantities such that

$$\lim_{\Delta x, \Delta y \to 0} \epsilon_1 = 0, \qquad \lim_{\Delta y \to 0} \epsilon_2 = 0.$$

Substituting in (4), we obtain the result (2), and the theorem is proved.

Note: Observe in Illustration 1 that $\epsilon_1 = 2\,\Delta x$ and $\epsilon_2 = 3\,\Delta y$.

For sufficiently small values of Δx and Δy, we see that Δz is given to any desired accuracy by the sum of the first two terms in the right member of (2). This sum is called the **total differential** or **differential** of z and is denoted by the symbol dz. Thus, by definition,

$$dz = \frac{\partial z}{\partial x} \Delta x + \frac{\partial z}{\partial y} \Delta y. \tag{5}$$

When $z = x$ or $z = y$, the equation (5) gives respectively $dx = \Delta x$ or $dy = \Delta y$. For this reason, *we define the differential of each independent variable to be the same as its increment.* The relation (5) may then be written in its usual form

$$\boldsymbol{dz = \frac{\partial z}{\partial x} dx + \frac{\partial z}{\partial y} dy.} \tag{6}$$

A similar definition applies to functions of more than two independent variables. For example, if $u = f(x,y,z)$, we have

$$du = \frac{\partial u}{\partial x} dx + \frac{\partial u}{\partial y} dy + \frac{\partial u}{\partial z} dz. \tag{7}$$

Illustration 2. If $u = xy^2z^3$, then by (7) we have

$$du = y^2z^3\,dx + 2xyz^3\,dy + 3xy^2z^2\,dz.$$

The general differential operations that apply to functions of a single variable may easily be shown to apply to functions of several variables. For example, if u is a differentiable function of x and y, it follows for $z = \tan u$ that

$$\frac{\partial z}{\partial x} = \sec^2 u\,\frac{\partial u}{\partial x} \qquad \text{and} \qquad \frac{\partial z}{\partial y} = \sec^2 u\,\frac{\partial u}{\partial y}.$$

Hence

$$\frac{\partial z}{\partial x}\,dx + \frac{\partial z}{\partial y}\,dy = \sec^2 u\left\{\frac{\partial u}{\partial x}\,dx + \frac{\partial u}{\partial y}\,dy\right\},$$

which by (6) means that

$$dz = \sec^2 u\,du.$$

192. Approximations and Errors

When small changes are made in the variables of a function u, it follows from the discussion in the preceding article that the differential du may be taken as an approximation for Δu. This is also true when the variables are measurements which are subject to small experimental errors. In the latter case du is called the **approximate error** in u.

Example 1. Two sides and the included angle of a triangle change from 6, 8, and 30° to 6.2, 8.1, and 29°, respectively. Find, approximately, the change in the area.

Solution: Using the relation $A = \frac{1}{2}xy\sin\theta$, we obtain the differential of area

$$dA = \tfrac{1}{2}y\sin\theta\,dx + \tfrac{1}{2}x\sin\theta\,dy + \tfrac{1}{2}xy\cos\theta\,d\theta. \tag{1}$$

From the given data we have $x = 6$, $y = 8$, $\theta = 30°$ and $dx = 0.2$, $dy = 0.1$, $d\theta = -1° = -\pi/180$. Hence, by substitution in (1), we find

$$dA = \frac{1}{2}(8)\left(\frac{1}{2}\right)(0.2) + \frac{1}{2}(6)\left(\frac{1}{2}\right)(0.1) + \frac{1}{2}(6)(8)\left(\frac{\sqrt{3}}{2}\right)\left(-\frac{\pi}{180}\right)$$
$$= 0.4 + 0.15 - 0.363 = 0.187.$$

The actual increase is $\Delta A = 0.174$.

As in Article **36,** if du is the error in u, the ratio du/u is called the **relative error** in u, and $100(du/u)$ the **percentage error.** The following example illustrates how logarithmic differentiation may be used to determine a relative error.

Example 2. The diameter and height of a right circular cylinder are measured to be 5 and 8 inches, respectively. If each of these dimensions may be in error by ± 0.1 inch, find the greatest possible percentage error in the volume of the cylinder.

Solution: The volume V of a right circular cylinder with diameter x and height y is $V = \frac{1}{4}\pi x^2 y$. Taking logarithms, we have

$$\ln V = \ln \tfrac{1}{4}\pi + 2 \ln x + \ln y;$$

hence, by differentiation,

$$\frac{dV}{V} = \frac{2\,dx}{x} + \frac{dy}{y}.$$

It is apparent that dV/V will be greatest when dx and dy are positive. Thus, taking $x = 5$, $y = 8$, $dx = 0.1$, and $dy = 0.1$, we obtain a maximum relative error of

$$\frac{dV}{V} = \frac{2(0.1)}{5} + \frac{0.1}{8} = 0.0525,$$

and a maximum percentage error of $5\frac{1}{4}\%$.

EXERCISE 101

Find the total differential of each of the following functions.

1. $3x^3 + 4x^2y - 2y^3$. *Ans.* $(9x^2 + 8xy)\,dx + (4x^2 - 6y^2)\,dy$.
2. $\sqrt{x^2 + y^2}$.
3. $(x^2 - y^2)^3$. $6(x^2 - y^2)^2(x\,dx - y\,dy)$.
4. $\operatorname{Sin}^{-1}(y/x)$.
5. $xy + z^2$. $y\,dx + x\,dy + 2z\,dz$.
6. If the partial derivatives of the function $u(x,y,z)$ exist, prove that $d(\sin u) = \cos u\,du$.

Find the increment and differential of each of the following functions for the given values of the variables and their increments.

7. $x^2 - 2xy + 3y^2$; $x = 2$, $y = 1$, $\Delta x = 0.3$, $\Delta y = -0.1$. *Ans.* 0.58, 0.4.
8. $x \ln y + y \ln x$; $x = y = 1$, $\Delta x = 0.01$, $\Delta y = 0.02$.
9. $x\sqrt{x - y}$; $x = 6$, $y = 2$, $\Delta x = \Delta y = \frac{1}{4}$. $\frac{1}{2}$, $\frac{1}{2}$.
10. $y \operatorname{Tan}^{-1} xy$; $x = 2$, $y = 0.5$, $\Delta x = -0.05$, $\Delta y = 0.01$.
11. x^2yz^3; $x = y = 1$, $z = 2$, $\Delta x = \Delta z = 0.1$, $\Delta y = -0.2$. *Ans.* 0.964648, 1.2.
12. $e^x \sin(y - z)$; $x = y = z = 0$, $\Delta x = -0.1$, $\Delta y = 0.2$, $\Delta z = 0.05$.

13. Find the approximate change in the length of the hypotenuse of a right triangle when its legs change from 6 feet and 8 feet to 6.1 feet and 7.9 feet, respectively. *Ans.* -0.02 ft.
14. Find an approximate value of $\sqrt{(4.99)^3 - (2.02)^2}$. *Hint:* Use $z = \sqrt{x^3 - y^2}$ and find $z + dz$.
15. Find by use of differentials the approximate area of a right triangle if the length of the long leg and hypotenuse are 14.9 inches and 17.1 inches, respectively. *Ans.* 62.6 sq. in.
16. Find, approximately, the amount of metal in a closed tin can 3 inches in diameter and 5 inches high, if the metal is $\frac{1}{32}$ inch thick. *Hint:* Use $V = \frac{1}{4}\pi D^2 H$ and find dV.
17. Find by use of differentials the approximate total area of a right circular cone whose base radius and height are 5.03 inches and 11.89 inches, respectively. *Ans.* 90.24π sq. in.
18. Using differentials, find an approximate value for $\mu = \sin i/\sin r$ when $i = 29°30'$ and $r = 46°$.
19. Two sides and the included angle of a triangle are found by measurement to be 40 feet, 33 feet, and 60°, respectively. If there is a possible error of 0.5 foot in measuring each side and 0.5° in measuring the angle, what is approximately the greatest possible error in the computed value of the third side? *Ans.* 0.76 ft.
20. A chord of a circle and the central angle which it subtends are measured to be 6 inches and 60°. If there are possible errors in these measurements of 0.1 inch and 1°, respectively, find the greatest possible relative error in the computed value of the radius.
21. The specific gravity of a body is given by the formula $s = A/(A - W)$, where A is the weight in air and W the weight in water. If, for a certain body, $A = 16$ pounds, $W = 8$ pounds, and each of these values may be in error by 0.01 pound, what is approximately the greatest possible error in the computed value of s? *Ans.* 0.00375.
22. If each of the dimensions of a rectangular box is measured with an error not exceeding 1%, what is approximately the greatest possible percentage error in the computed value of the volume?
23. The bases and side of an isosceles trapezoid are found by measurement to be 4 feet, 10 feet, and 5 feet, respectively. If each of these measurements may be in error by 2%, find approximately the greatest possible percentage error in the computed value of the area. *Ans.* 4.9%.
24. When two electrical resistances r_1 and r_2 are connected in series or in parallel, the circuit resistance R is given by $R = r_1 + r_2$ or $1/R = 1/r_1 + 1/r_2$, respectively. If the values r_1 and r_2 are subject to the same percentage error e, show in both cases that e is approximately the greatest percentage error in R.

193. Total Derivatives

Let us now consider the function

$$z = f(x,y), \tag{1}$$

where x and y are both continuous functions of a third variable t; that is,

$$x = \phi(t), \qquad y = \psi(t). \tag{2}$$

If the values (2) are substituted in (1), z becomes a function of the single variable t, and its derivative may be found in the usual manner. Thus, as given in (2), Article **191,** we divide Δz by Δt to obtain

$$\frac{\Delta z}{\Delta t} = \frac{\partial z}{\partial x}\frac{\Delta x}{\Delta t} + \frac{\partial z}{\partial y}\frac{\Delta y}{\Delta t} + \epsilon_1 \frac{\Delta x}{\Delta t} + \epsilon_2 \frac{\Delta y}{\Delta t}, \tag{3}$$

and then let Δt approach zero. However, as Δt approaches zero, it follows from $\Delta x = \phi(t + \Delta t) - \phi(t)$ and $\Delta y = \psi(t + \Delta t) - \psi(t)$ that Δx and Δy also approach zero. Hence

$$\lim_{\Delta t \to 0} \epsilon_1 = 0, \qquad \lim_{\Delta t \to 0} \epsilon_2 = 0,$$

and in the limit (3) becomes

$$\frac{dz}{dt} = \frac{\partial z}{\partial x}\frac{dx}{dt} + \frac{\partial z}{\partial y}\frac{dy}{dt}, \tag{4}$$

provided the indicated derivatives exist.

Multiplying both members of (4) by dt, we see that formula (6) of Article **191** *is also valid when x and y are related variables.*

Illustration 1. If $z = x \ln y$, $x = t^2$, $y = e^t$, then $\frac{\partial z}{\partial x} = \ln y$, $\frac{\partial z}{\partial y} = \frac{x}{y}$, $\frac{dx}{dt} = 2t$, $\frac{dy}{dt} = e^t$, and by (4)

$$\frac{dz}{dt} = (\ln e^t)\, 2t + \left(\frac{t^2}{e^t}\right) e^t = 3t^2.$$

The above result could be obtained more easily by first writing $z = t^2 \ln e^t = t^3$, and then differentiating. This method of substitution is usually more difficult, however, and is often impossible when the relations (2) are given implicitly.

Following a similar procedure, we have the following result.

Theorem. *If $\mathbf{u}$ is a function of n variables $\mathbf{x}, \mathbf{y}, \mathbf{z}, \cdots$, and each of these variables is a function of $\mathbf{t}$, then*

$$\frac{du}{dt} = \frac{\partial u}{\partial x}\frac{dx}{dt} + \frac{\partial u}{\partial y}\frac{dy}{dt} + \frac{\partial u}{\partial z}\frac{dz}{dt} + \cdots. \tag{5}$$

Taking $t = x$, we can write the above result in the following form.

Corollary. *If* u *is a function of* n *variables* $x, y, z, \cdots$, *and each of the* $(n - 1)$ *variables* $y, z, \cdots$ *is a function of* x, *then*

$$\frac{du}{dx} = \frac{\partial u}{\partial x} + \frac{\partial u}{\partial y}\frac{dy}{dx} + \frac{\partial u}{\partial z}\frac{dz}{dx} + \cdots. \tag{6}$$

Illustration 2. If $z = x/y$ and $x^2 + y^2 = a^2$, then $z_x = 1/y$, $z_y = -x/y^2$, $x + yy' = 0$, and by (6)

$$\frac{dz}{dx} = \frac{1}{y} + \left(-\frac{x}{y^2}\right)\left(-\frac{x}{y}\right) = \frac{y^2 + x^2}{y^3} = \frac{a^2}{y^3}.$$

Observe in the above illustration the difference in meaning between dz/dx and $\partial z/\partial x$. The partial derivative $\partial z/\partial x$ is obtained from $z = f(x,y)$ on the supposition that y is constant, whereas y is actually a function of x and hence must vary as x varies. On the other hand, we have

$$\frac{dz}{dx} = \lim_{\Delta x \to 0}\left(\frac{\Delta z}{\Delta x}\right),$$

where Δz is the *total increment of* z caused by the increment Δx and the related increment Δy. In order to emphasize its meaning, dz/dx is called the **total derivative** of z with respect to x.

The above formulas are useful in many applications where several time-rates are involved.

Example. The height of a right circular cylinder is 50 inches and decreases at the rate of 4 inches per second, while the radius of the base is 20 inches and increases at the rate of 1 inch per second. At what rate is the volume changing?

Solution: Using the formula $V = \pi r^2 h$ and applying (4), we obtain

$$\frac{dV}{dt} = 2\pi rh\frac{dr}{dt} + \pi r^2\frac{dh}{dt}.$$

Since $h = 50$, $r = 20$, $\dfrac{dh}{dt} = -4$, and $\dfrac{dr}{dt} = 1$, we find

$$\frac{dV}{dt} = 2\pi(20)(50)(1) + \pi(20)^2(-4) = 400\pi.$$

Thus the volume is increasing 1257 cubic inches per second.

194. Chain Rule for Partial Derivatives

A functional dependency such as that discussed in the preceding article is often indicated by writing

$$u \to (x, y, z, \cdots) \to t. \tag{1}$$

This is called a *chain relation* and is used to indicate that the function u is defined in terms of intermediate variables x, y, z, $\cdots$, each of which in turn is expressed in terms of the variable t. The relation (1) means essentially that u is a function of one independent variable and as such could be written as $u = f(t)$.

In a similar manner u can be expressed as a function of two variables s and t in a chain relation

$$u \to (x, y, z, \cdots) \to (s, t). \tag{2}$$

In this case each of the intermediate variables is a function of both s and t. If the variable s is held constant, the relation (2) becomes a relation like (1) and so, by the theorem in the preceding article, we have

$$\frac{\partial u}{\partial t} = \frac{\partial u}{\partial x}\frac{\partial x}{\partial t} + \frac{\partial u}{\partial y}\frac{\partial y}{\partial t} + \frac{\partial u}{\partial z}\frac{\partial z}{\partial t} + \cdots, \tag{3}$$

where the partial derivatives with respect to t imply that s is being held constant. Similarly, if t is held constant we obtain

$$\frac{\partial u}{\partial s} = \frac{\partial u}{\partial x}\frac{\partial x}{\partial s} + \frac{\partial u}{\partial y}\frac{\partial y}{\partial s} + \frac{\partial u}{\partial z}\frac{\partial z}{\partial s} + \cdots. \tag{4}$$

The relations (3) and (4) indicate in general how the chain rule operates. It is immaterial how many intermediate and independent variables are involved in the chain. Observe, however, that a partial derivative such as (3) involves *all* of the intermediate variables and only *one* independent variable.

Illustration. If $w = u^2 + v^2$, and $u = xyz$, $v = x^2 + z^2$, the partial derivative of w with respect to y is

$$\begin{aligned}\frac{\partial w}{\partial y} &= \frac{\partial w}{\partial u}\frac{\partial u}{\partial y} + \frac{\partial w}{\partial v}\frac{\partial v}{\partial y}\\ &= (2u)(xz) + (2v)(0) = 2x^2yz^2.\end{aligned}$$

Note: A function is sometimes expressed in a form such as $u = f(x^2 - y^2, xy)$; this signifies a chain relation $u = f(s,t)$, $s = x^2 - y^2$, $t = xy$. Thus, for example, we find $\partial u/\partial x = (\partial f/\partial s)2x + (\partial f/\partial t)y$. However, since s and t were not involved in the given function, it is customary to write f_1 and

f_2 to indicate the partial derivatives with respect to their positions in the function; thus for the given relation we would write

$$\frac{\partial u}{\partial x} = f_1 \cdot 2x + f_2 \cdot y.$$

195. Differentiation of Implicit Functions

If $z = f(x,y)$ and y is a function of x, it follows from Article **193** that

$$\frac{dz}{dx} = \frac{\partial f}{\partial x} + \frac{\partial f}{\partial y}\frac{dy}{dx}.$$

For $z = 0$ identically, we have $dz/dx = 0$; hence

$$\frac{\partial f}{\partial x} + \frac{\partial f}{\partial y}\frac{dy}{dx} = 0.$$

Solving for dy/dx, we obtain the following result.

Theorem 1. *If* $\mathbf{y}$ *is defined as an implicit function of* $\boldsymbol{x}$ *by the equation* $\boldsymbol{f(x,y)} = \mathbf{0}$, *then*

$$\frac{\boldsymbol{dy}}{\boldsymbol{dx}} = -\frac{\dfrac{\boldsymbol{\partial f}}{\boldsymbol{\partial x}}}{\dfrac{\boldsymbol{\partial f}}{\boldsymbol{\partial y}}}, \quad \frac{\boldsymbol{\partial f}}{\boldsymbol{\partial y}} \neq \mathbf{0}. \tag{1}$$

Illustration 1. If $f(x,y) \equiv x \sin y + y \cos x = 0$, we have

$$\frac{\partial f}{\partial x} = \sin y - y \sin x, \qquad \frac{\partial f}{\partial y} = x \cos y + \cos x,$$

and by (1)

$$\frac{dy}{dx} = -\frac{\sin y - y \sin x}{x \cos y + \cos x}. \tag{2}$$

The method of implicit differentiation discussed in Article **59** always gives the same result as (1). For example, differentiating the function of Illustration 1, we obtain

$$\left(\sin y + x \cos y \frac{dy}{dx}\right) + \left(\cos x \frac{dy}{dx} - y \sin x\right) = 0,$$

which leads to (2).

Now let z be defined as a function of x and y by the equation

$F(x,y,z) = 0$. If y is held constant, $F(x,y,z)$ reduces to a function of x and z alone, and by use of (1) we obtain

$$\frac{\partial z}{\partial x} = -\frac{\dfrac{\partial F}{\partial x}}{\dfrac{\partial F}{\partial z}}, \quad \frac{\partial F}{\partial z} \neq 0,$$

where the left member is a partial derivative since y is held constant.

In a similar manner, by holding x constant we find $\partial z/\partial y$.

Theorem 2. *If* $\mathbf{z}$ *is defined as an implicit function of* $\mathbf{x}$ *and* $\mathbf{y}$ *by the equation* $\mathbf{F(x,y,z) = 0}$, *then*

$$\frac{\partial \mathbf{z}}{\partial \mathbf{x}} = -\frac{\mathbf{F_x}}{\mathbf{F_z}}, \quad \frac{\partial \mathbf{z}}{\partial \mathbf{y}} = -\frac{\mathbf{F_y}}{\mathbf{F_z}}, \quad \mathbf{F_z \neq 0}. \tag{3}$$

Illustration 2. If $F \equiv x^3 + y^3 + z^3 + 3xyz = 0$, we have

$$F_x = 3x^2 + 3yz, \quad F_y = 3y^2 + 3xz, \quad F_z = 3z^2 + 3xy,$$

and by (3)

$$\frac{\partial z}{\partial x} = -\frac{x^2 + yz}{z^2 + xy}, \quad \frac{\partial z}{\partial y} = -\frac{y^2 + xz}{z^2 + xy}.$$

EXERCISE 102

Find du/dt in each of the following.

1. $u = x^2 - 2xy + y^2, \quad x = (t + 1)^2, \quad y = (t - 1)^2.$ *Ans.* $32t$.
2. $u = \text{Tan}^{-1}(xy), \quad x = \sin t, \quad y = \sec t.$
3. $u = x \sin y, \quad x = 1/t, \quad y = \text{Tan}^{-1} t.$ $-t/(1 + t^2)^{3/2}$.
4. $u = \ln \sqrt{\dfrac{x - y}{x + y}}, \quad x = \sec t, \quad y = \tan t.$

Find du/dx in each of the following.

5. $u = (x - y)/(1 - y), \quad y = x^{-2}.$ *Ans.* $1 - (x + 1)^{-2}$.
6. $u = \text{Sin}^{-1}(x/y), \quad y = \sqrt{1 + x^2}.$
7. $u = \ln(x^2 + y^2 + z^2), \quad y = x \sin x, \quad z = x \cos x.$ $2/x$.
8. $u = (x + y)/(x + z), \quad y = \ln x, \quad z = \ln(1/x).$

Find dy/dx in each of the following.

9. $2x^3 + 3x^2y - y^3 = 1.$ *Ans.* $2x/(y - x)$.
10. $\ln(x^2 + y^2) = 2\,\text{Tan}^{-1}(y/x).$
11. $2x^2 - 3xy + y^2 = 0.$ 1 or 2.
12. $x^y y^x = 1.$ *Hint:* Take logarithms.

Find $\partial z/\partial x$ and $\partial z/\partial y$ in each of the following.

13. $x^2 + y^2 + z^2 = 9$. *Ans.* $-x/z$, $-y/z$.
14. $xy + yz + zx = 4xyz$.
15. $e^x + e^y + e^z = e^{x+y+z}$. $-(e^y + e^z)/(e^x + e^y)$, $-(e^x + e^z)/(e^x + e^y)$.
16. $z = y \operatorname{Tan}^{-1}(zx)$.

Find $\partial u/\partial x$ and $\partial u/\partial y$ in each of the following.

17. $u = r^2 + s^2$, $r = x + y$, $s = x - y$. *Ans.* $4x$, $4y$.
18. $u = p + qr$, $p = x^2$, $q = xy$, $r = y^2$.
19. $u = r^2 \sin 2\theta$, $r = \sqrt{x^2 + y^2}$, $\theta = \operatorname{Tan}^{-1}(y/x)$. $|2y|$, $|2x|$.
20. $u = (m - n)/(m + n)$, $m = \sin(x + y)$, $n = \sin(x - y)$.
21. Angle A of triangle ABC is decreasing at the rate of 2° per second, while the sides AB and AC are increasing at the rates 2 and 3 feet per second, respectively. If at a certain instant $A = 60°$, $AB = 8$ feet, $AC = 5$ feet, how fast is the area of the triangle changing? *Ans.* 14.4 sq. ft./sec.
22. In Problem 21, how fast is the side BC changing?
23. A particle P is moving with a constant speed of 13 feet per second clockwise around the circle $x^2 + y^2 = 25$, where x and y are expressed in feet. When P passes through the point (3,4), how fast is it moving away from the point $A(0,2)$? *Ans.* $\frac{6}{5}\sqrt{13}$ ft./sec.
24. In Problem 23, find the angular velocity of the line AP.
25. If $f(x,y) = 0$, show that $\dfrac{d^2y}{dx^2} = -(f_y^2 f_{xx} - 2f_x f_y f_{xy} + f_x^2 f_{yy})/f_y^3$.
26. Use the transformation $y - ax = u$, $y + ax = v$ to find the partial differential equation in V, u, and v that corresponds to $\dfrac{\partial V}{\partial x} - a\dfrac{\partial V}{\partial y} = 0$.
27. If $u = f(x + iy) + g(x - iy)$, where $i = \sqrt{-1}$, show that $\dfrac{\partial^2 u}{\partial x^2} + \dfrac{\partial^2 u}{\partial y^2} = 0$.
28. By use of the relations $x = r\cos\theta$, $y = r\sin\theta$, express Laplace's equation $\dfrac{\partial^2 u}{\partial x^2} + \dfrac{\partial^2 u}{\partial y^2} = 0$ in polar coordinates.
29. If $f(x,y) = 0$ and $g(x,z) = 0$, and z is taken for the independent variable, show that $\dfrac{\partial g}{\partial x}\dfrac{\partial f}{\partial y}\dfrac{dy}{dz} = \dfrac{\partial f}{\partial x}\dfrac{\partial g}{\partial z}$.
30. When y is eliminated from the two equations $z = F(x,y)$ and $G(x,y) = 0$, the result can be written as $z = H(x)$. Express the derivative $H'(x)$ in terms of F_x, F_y, G_x, and G_y.
31. If $F(p,v,t) = 0$, show that $\dfrac{\partial p}{\partial t}\dfrac{\partial t}{\partial v}\dfrac{\partial v}{\partial p} = -1$. Explain.

32. If $E = f(V,T)$ and $PV = k$, where k is a constant, find $\left(\frac{\partial E}{\partial P}\right)_T$ and $\left(\frac{\partial E}{\partial T}\right)_P$. *Note:* The notation $(\partial E/\partial P)_T$ signifies that P and T are to be considered the independent variables.

33. If $w = F(xz,yz)$, show that $x\frac{\partial w}{\partial x} + y\frac{\partial w}{\partial y} = z\frac{\partial w}{\partial z}$.

196. Tangent Line and Normal Plane to a Curve

Let the equation of the curve shown in Figure 212 be

$$x = f(t), \qquad y = g(t), \qquad z = h(t), \tag{1}$$

and let $P(x_1,y_1,z_1)$ and $Q(x_1 + \Delta x, y_1 + \Delta y, z_1 + \Delta z)$ be two points on the curve corresponding to the values t_1 and $t_1 + \Delta t$ of the parameter. The direction cosines of PQ, in accordance with **44,** page 6, are proportional to the numbers $[\Delta x, \Delta y, \Delta z]$, and hence to

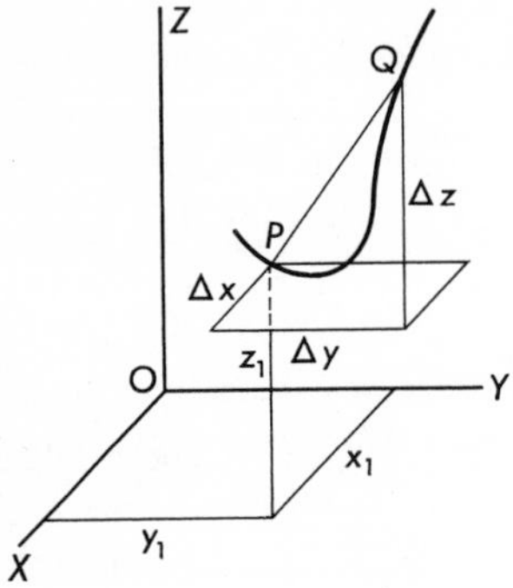

$$\left[\frac{\Delta x}{\Delta t}, \frac{\Delta y}{\Delta t}, \frac{\Delta z}{\Delta t}\right]. \tag{2}$$

Figure 212

As Δt approaches zero, Q approaches P along the curve, and if the line PQ approaches a limit, this limiting line is called the tangent line at P. Hence the direction numbers of the tangent at P are the limits of (2), that is,

$$\left[\left(\frac{dx}{dt}\right)_1, \left(\frac{dy}{dt}\right)_1, \left(\frac{dz}{dt}\right)_1\right], \tag{3}$$

where the subscript indicates the value for $t = t_1$.

Thus, in accordance with **47,** page 6, the equations of the line tangent to the curve (1) at $P(x_1,y_1,z_1)$ are

$$\frac{x - x_1}{\left(\frac{dx}{dt}\right)_1} = \frac{y - y_1}{\left(\frac{dy}{dt}\right)_1} = \frac{z - z_1}{\left(\frac{dz}{dt}\right)_1}. \tag{4}$$

Also, in accordance with **46,** page 6, the equation of the plane normal to the curve (1) at $P(x_1,y_1,z_1)$ is

$$\left(\frac{dx}{dt}\right)_1(x - x_1) + \left(\frac{dy}{dt}\right)_1(y - y_1) + \left(\frac{dz}{dt}\right)_1(z - z_1) = 0. \tag{5}$$

Illustration 1. For the curve $x = t$, $y = t^2$, $z = t^3$ at the point where $t_1 = 2$, we have $x_1 = 2$, $y_1 = 4$, $z_1 = 8$ and $(dx/dt)_1 = 1$, $(dy/dt)_1 = 4$, $(dz/dt)_1 = 12$. Substituting these values in (4) and (5), we obtain the tangent line

$$\frac{x-2}{1} = \frac{y-4}{4} = \frac{z-8}{12},$$

and the normal plane

$$(x-2) + 4(y-4) + 12(z-8) = 0.$$

Now let us consider the curve defined in rectangular coordinates by the intersection of the two surfaces

$$F(x,y,z) = 0, \qquad G(x,y,z) = 0, \tag{6}$$

whose total differentials are

$$\begin{aligned} F_x\,dx + F_y\,dy + F_z\,dz &= 0, \\ G_x\,dx + G_y\,dy + G_z\,dz &= 0. \end{aligned}$$

Solving the above equations for dy and dz in terms of dx, it can be shown that

$$dx:dy:dz = \begin{vmatrix} F_y & F_z \\ G_y & G_z \end{vmatrix} : \begin{vmatrix} F_z & F_x \\ G_z & G_x \end{vmatrix} : \begin{vmatrix} F_x & F_y \\ G_x & G_y \end{vmatrix}. \tag{7}$$

Thus, in accordance with (3), these determinants evaluated at a point $P(x_1,y_1,z_1)$ of the curve give the direction of the tangent line at that point. The equations of the tangent line and normal plane may then be found from (4) and (5) by using the values (7) in place of (3).

Illustration 2. Consider the circle which is defined by the equations

$$\begin{aligned} F(x,y,z) &\equiv x^2 + y^2 + z^2 - 14 = 0, \\ G(x,y,z) &\equiv x^2 + y^2 - 5 = 0, \end{aligned}$$

and which passes through the point $P(1,2,3)$. For the above equations, we have $F_x = 2x$, $F_y = 2y$, $F_z = 2z$, and $G_x = 2x$, $G_y = 2y$, $G_z = 0$. Hence, in accordance with (7), at P we find

$$dx:dy:dz = \begin{vmatrix} 4 & 6 \\ 4 & 0 \end{vmatrix} : \begin{vmatrix} 6 & 2 \\ 0 & 2 \end{vmatrix} : \begin{vmatrix} 2 & 4 \\ 2 & 4 \end{vmatrix} = -24:12:0 = 2:-1:0.$$

Thus by (4) the equations of the tangent line are

$$\frac{x-1}{2} = \frac{y-2}{-1} = \frac{z-3}{0}, \qquad \text{or} \qquad \begin{cases} z = 3, \\ x + 2y = 5, \end{cases}$$

and by (5) the equation of the normal plane is

$$2(x-1) - (y-2) = 0 \qquad \text{or} \qquad 2x - y = 0.$$

Note: At points where all the numbers in (3) are zero, the tangent line and normal plane are not determined. Such points are called *singular points* of the curve.

197. Normal Line and Tangent Plane to a Surface

Let us consider a surface whose equation is

$$S(x,y,z) = 0, \tag{1}$$

and let the equations

$$x = f(t), \qquad y = g(t), \qquad z = h(t) \tag{2}$$

define a curve which lies on (1) and passes through the point $P(x_1,y_1,z_1)$. Since the values (2) satisfy (1) for all values of t, it follows from the theorem, Article **194,** that

$$\left(\frac{\partial S}{\partial x}\right)_1 \left(\frac{dx}{dt}\right)_1 + \left(\frac{\partial S}{\partial y}\right)_1 \left(\frac{dy}{dt}\right)_1 + \left(\frac{\partial S}{\partial z}\right)_1 \left(\frac{dz}{dt}\right)_1 = 0. \tag{3}$$

This relation expresses the fact that the lines having the direction numbers

$$\left[\left(\frac{\partial S}{\partial x}\right)_1, \left(\frac{\partial S}{\partial y}\right)_1, \left(\frac{\partial S}{\partial z}\right)_1\right] \tag{4}$$

and

$$\left[\left(\frac{dx}{dt}\right)_1, \left(\frac{dy}{dt}\right)_1, \left(\frac{dz}{dt}\right)_1\right] \tag{5}$$

are mutually perpendicular. For a given point on the surface it is clear that the numbers (4) represent a fixed direction. Since this direction is perpendicular to (5), which are the direction numbers at P of any curve on the surface, we call (4) *the direction numbers of the normal to the surface at the point P.*

Thus the equations of the normal line to the surface (1) at $P(x_1,y_1,z_1)$ are

$$\frac{x - x_1}{\left(\frac{\partial S}{\partial x}\right)_1} = \frac{y - y_1}{\left(\frac{\partial S}{\partial y}\right)_1} = \frac{z - z_1}{\left(\frac{\partial S}{\partial z}\right)_1}, \tag{6}$$

and the equation of the tangent plane to the surface is

$$\left(\frac{\partial S}{\partial x}\right)_1 (x - x_1) + \left(\frac{\partial S}{\partial y}\right)_1 (y - y_1) + \left(\frac{\partial S}{\partial z}\right)_1 (z - z_1) = 0. \tag{7}$$

Illustration. At the point $(1,2,-2)$ of the ellipsoid $S(x,y,z) \equiv 9x^2 + 4y^2 + z^2 - 29 = 0$, we have

$$\left(\frac{\partial S}{\partial x}\right)_1 = (18x)_1 = 18,$$

$$\left(\frac{\partial S}{\partial y}\right)_1 = (8y)_1 = 16,$$

$$\left(\frac{\partial S}{\partial z}\right)_1 = (2z)_1 = -4.$$

Hence by (6) the equations of the normal line are

$$\frac{x-1}{9} = \frac{y-2}{8} = \frac{z+2}{-2},$$

and by (7) the equation of the tangent plane is

$$9(x-1) + 8(y-2) - 2(z+2) = 0.$$

EXERCISE 103

Find the equations of the tangent line and the normal plane to each of the following curves at the point indicated.

1. $x = t^2 + 1, \quad y = t - 1, \quad z = t^3; \quad t = 1.$
   Ans. $\frac{1}{2}(x-2) = y = \frac{1}{3}(z-1)$; $2x + y + 3z = 7$.
2. $x = 2t^4, \quad y = t^2, \quad z = 1 - t^3; \quad t = 1.$
3. $x = 2t - 1, \quad y = 6 - t^2, \quad z = 4/t; \quad t = 2.$
   Ans. $\frac{1}{2}(x-3) = -\frac{1}{4}(y-2) = -(z-2)$; $2x - 4y - z + 4 = 0$.
4. $x = t^2 + 3t - 4, \quad y = t^3 - 2t^2 + 1, \quad z = t^2 - t^4; \quad t = 1.$
5. $x = \cos t, \quad y = \sin t, \quad z = t; \quad t = \frac{1}{2}\pi.$
   Ans. $x + z = \frac{1}{2}\pi$, $y = 1$; $z - x = \frac{1}{2}\pi$.
6. $x = e^t, \quad y = e^{-t}, \quad z = t; \quad t = 0.$
7. $x^2 + y^2 + z^2 = 9, \quad z = xy; \quad (1,2,2).$
   Ans. $\frac{1}{4}(x-1) = -\frac{1}{5}(y-2) = \frac{1}{3}(z-2)$; $4x - 5y + 3z = 0$.
8. $x^2 - y^2 + z^2 = 2, \quad 3x^2 + 2y^2 - z^2 = 2; \quad (1,0,-1).$
9. $x^2 + y^2 = 25, \quad 2x + y - z^2 = 6; \quad (3,4,2).$
   Ans. $\frac{1}{16}(x-3) = -\frac{1}{12}(y-4) = \frac{1}{5}(z-2)$; $16x - 12y + 5z = 10$.
10. $x + xy = z, \quad z + zx = y; \quad (\frac{1}{2},3,2).$
11. $z = 2x^2 - xy, \quad xy + yz + zx = 3; \quad (1,1,1).$
    Ans. $x = 1$, $y + z = 2$; $y = z$.
12. $x + \ln y = z, \quad y + \ln z = x; \quad (1,1,1).$

Find the equations of the normal line and the tangent plane to each of the following surfaces at the point indicated.

13. $x^2 + y^2 + z^2 = 49; \quad (2,3,6).$
    Ans. $\frac{1}{2}(x-2) = \frac{1}{3}(y-3) = \frac{1}{6}(z-6)$; $2x + 3y + 6z = 49$.
14. $z^2 = x^2 + y^2; \quad (3,4,5).$

15. $xy + yz + zx = 11$; $(1,2,3)$.
Ans. $\frac{1}{5}(x-1) = \frac{1}{4}(y-2) = \frac{1}{3}(z-3)$; $5x + 4y + 3z = 22$.

16. $z^2 = x + y + 2$; $(3,-1,2)$.

17. $4x^2 + 3y^2 + z^2 = 8$; $(\frac{1}{2},1,2)$.
Ans. $\frac{1}{2}(x-\frac{1}{2}) = \frac{1}{3}(y-1) = \frac{1}{2}(z-2)$; $2x + 3y + 2z = 8$.

18. $(x+y)^2 + z^2 = 25$; $(1,2,4)$.

19. $xyz = x + y + z$; $(\frac{1}{2},\frac{1}{3},-1)$.
Ans. $\frac{1}{8}(x-\frac{1}{2}) = \frac{1}{9}(y-\frac{1}{3}) = \frac{1}{5}(z+1)$; $8x + 9y + 5z = 2$.

20. $\sqrt{x} + \sqrt{y} + \sqrt{z} = 6$; $(1,4,9)$.

21. Find the equation of the tangent plane to the paraboloid $z = ax^2 + by^2$ at the point (x_1,y_1,z_1). *Ans.* $\frac{1}{2}(z + z_1) = ax_1x + by_1y$.

22. Find the equation of the tangent plane to the ellipsoid $ax^2 + by^2 + cz^2 = d$ at the point (x_1,y_1,z_1).

23. Show that the surfaces $4x^2 + y^2 + 9z^2 = 108$ and $xyz = 36$ are tangent at the point $(3,6,2)$.

24. Using (7), Article **196,** find direction numbers for the straight line

$$\begin{cases} A_1x + B_1y + C_1z + D_1 = 0, \\ A_2x + B_2y + C_2z + D_2 = 0. \end{cases}$$

25. The surface $z = x^2 + 2y^2$ is cut by the curve $x = t - 1$, $y = -2/t$, $z = t^2 - 1$ at the point $(1,-1,3)$. What is their angle of intersection? *Hint:* Using **45,** page 6, first find the angle between the curve and the normal to the surface. *Ans.* $90° - \text{Cos}^{-1}\dfrac{8}{3\sqrt{161}} = 12.1°$.

26. Show that the curves $x = t^2$, $y = 1 - t$, $z = 2/t$ and $x = 2t$, $y = t^2 - \frac{1}{4}$, $z = 1/t$ intersect at the point $(1,0,2)$, and find their angle of intersection.

27. Show that the curve $x = \frac{2}{3}(t^3 + 2)$, $y = 2t^2$, $z = 3t - 2$ is perpendicular to the surface $x^2 + 2y^2 + 3z^2 = 15$ at the point $(2,2,1)$.

28. Find the angle at which the line $x = y = z$ pierces the ellipsoid $x^2 + y^2 + 5z^2 = 7$.

29. Prove that the tetrahedron formed by the coordinate planes and any tangent plane to the surface $xyz = a^3$ has a constant volume equal to $\frac{9}{2}a^3$.

30. Find the intercepts on the coordinate axes made by any tangent plane of the surface $x^{2/3} + y^{2/3} + z^{2/3} = a^{2/3}$, and show that the sum of their squares is constant.

198. Maxima and Minima

A function $f(x,y)$ of two independent variables is said to have a relative **maximum value** (or **minimum value**) for $x = a$, $y = b$, if $f(a,b)$ is greater (or less) than $f(x,y)$ for all values of x and y in the neighborhood of a and b.

If $f(x,y)$ has a maximum (or minimum) value at $x = a$, $y = b$, it follows that the function $f(x,b)$ of the single variable x has a maximum (or minimum) at $x = a$. By Article **31,** this means that

$$\left(\frac{\partial f(x,b)}{\partial x}\right)_{x=a} = 0.$$

Since a similar result holds for the function $f(a,y)$ we conclude that *if a function $f(x,y)$ of two independent variables is to have a relative maximum or minimum value $f(a,b)$, it is necessary that*

$$\frac{\partial}{\partial x} f(x,y) = 0, \qquad \frac{\partial}{\partial y} f(x,y) = 0, \tag{1}$$

for $x = a$, $y = b$.

Note: As for functions of a single variable, a relative maximum or minimum may occur where the partial derivatives (1) do not exist. For example, the function $\sqrt{x^2 + y^2}$ has an obvious minimum at (0,0), but neither partial derivative exists there. In the remaining discussion we shall omit further reference to this type of critical point.

Illustration. To find the minimum value attained by the function $f(x,y) = x^2 + y^2 + 2x - 4y$, we apply (1) to obtain

$$\frac{\partial f}{\partial x} = 2x + 2 = 0, \qquad \frac{\partial f}{\partial y} = 2y - 4 = 0.$$

Solving, we find $x = -1$, $y = 2$, and hence $f(-1,2) = -5$. Writing the given function in the form $f(x,y) = (x + 1)^2 + (y - 2)^2 - 5$, we see that -5 is a minimum value.

By reasoning as above, we obtain the following general result.

Theorem. *If a function of n independent variables $f(x,y,z,\cdots)$ and its first partial derivatives exist in a region containing $(a,b,c,\cdots)$ as an interior point, then in order that $f(a,b,c,\cdots)$ be a relative maximum or minimum of $f(x,y,z,\cdots)$, it is necessary that*

$$\frac{\partial f}{\partial x} = 0, \qquad \frac{\partial f}{\partial y} = 0, \qquad \frac{\partial f}{\partial z} = 0, \qquad \cdots, \tag{2}$$

for $x = a$, $y = b$, $z = c$, $\cdots$.

Example 1. Find the shortest distance from the point (1,2,3) to the plane $2x + 2y + z = 5$.

Solution: The distance L from the given point to a general point (x,y,z) of the plane is

$$L = \sqrt{(x - 1)^2 + (y - 2)^2 + (z - 3)^2}. \tag{3}$$

Taking x and y to be the independent variables, we substitute $5 - 2x - 2y$ for z, and on squaring, (3) becomes

$$L^2 = (x - 1)^2 + (y - 2)^2 + (2 - 2x - 2y)^2. \tag{4}$$

Clearly, L is a minimum when L^2 is a minimum; hence, applying (2) to (4), we find

$$\frac{\partial(L^2)}{\partial x} = 2(x - 1) - 4(2 - 2x - 2y) = 0,$$

$$\frac{\partial(L^2)}{\partial y} = 2(y - 2) - 4(2 - 2x - 2y) = 0.$$

Solving these equations simultaneously, we have

$$\begin{cases} 5x + 4y = 5, \\ 4x + 5y = 6; \end{cases} \qquad \text{hence} \quad x = \tfrac{1}{9}, \quad y = \tfrac{10}{9}.$$

Thus $z = 5 - 2(\frac{1}{9}) - 2(\frac{10}{9}) = \frac{23}{9}$, and substitution in (3) gives

$$L = \sqrt{(-\tfrac{8}{9})^2 + (-\tfrac{8}{9})^2 + (-\tfrac{4}{9})^2} = \tfrac{4}{3}.$$

Observe that **48,** page 6, gives the same result.

When a function is defined in a bounded domain, it is possible that the function may attain its absolute maximum or minimum at some point on the boundary without satisfying the relations (2).

Example 2. The temperature in degrees centigrade at each point (x,y) in the region $x^2 + y^2 \leqq 1$ is given by $T = 16x^2 + 24x + 40y^2$. Find the temperature at the hottest and coldest point in the region.

Solution: By applying (2), we find

$$\frac{\partial T}{\partial x} = 32x + 24 = 0 \qquad \text{and} \qquad \frac{\partial T}{\partial y} = 80y = 0.$$

Hence, at the critical point $(-3/4,0)$, we find the minimum temperature $T = -9°\text{C}$.

Since the maximum temperature must necessarily be on the boundary, we get the boundary temperatures by substituting $1 - x^2$ for y^2 in the formula for T; thus

$$T = -24x^2 + 24x + 40, \quad -1 \leqq x \leqq 1. \tag{5}$$

From $dT/dx = -48x + 24 = 0$, we find that T has a maximum value of 46 when $x = \frac{1}{2}$. For the given region this means that the temperature attains its maximum value of 46°C at the two points $(\frac{1}{2}, \pm\frac{1}{2}\sqrt{3})$. Observe in (5) that the minimum boundary temperature is $-8°\text{C}$.

EXERCISE 104

Find the maximum or minimum values of the following functions.

1. $x^2 + 2xy + 2y^2 - 6y$. *Ans.* -9, min.
2. $4x - x^2 - y^2$.
3. $4x + 6y - x^2 - y^2$. 13, max.
4. $2x - 2x^2 + 2xy - y^2$.
5. $3xy - x^3 - y^3$. 1, max.
6. $x + y - \ln xy$.
7. $xy + \frac{1}{x} + \frac{1}{y}$. 3, min.
8. $xy\, e^{-(x^2+y^2)}$.
9. $2x^2 + y^2 + 2z^2 + 2xy - 2y - 6z$. $-6\frac{1}{2}$, min.
10. $16xyz - 4x^2yz - 2xy^2z - xyz^2$.
11. Find the maximum value of the function $xye^{-(2x+y/2)}$ in the first quadrant. Find its maximum value if, in addition, $x + y = 1$. *Ans.* $1/e^2$, $2/9e$.
12. Find two positive numbers whose sum exceeds the sum of their cubes by the greatest amount.
13. Using calculus, find the shortest distance from the origin to the plane $2x + 3y + 6z = 21$. *Ans.* 3.
14. Find the volume of the largest rectangular parallelepiped that has three faces in the coordinate planes and one vertex in the plane $x + 2y + 3z = 4$.
15. Determine the constants m and k so that the sum of the squares of the *vertical* distances from the points (0,3), (1,5), and (2,4) to the line $y = mx + k$ shall be a minimum. *Ans.* $m = \frac{1}{2}$, $k = \frac{7}{2}$.
16. An open tank in the form of a rectangular parallelepiped is to be built to hold 500 cubic feet of acid. What dimensions will make the cost of lining the tank as small as possible?
17. Find the shortest distance from the origin to the surface $xyz^2 = 2$. *Ans.* 2.
18. Find the shortest distance between the lines $2x = y = z$ and $x = y = 26 - z$. *Hint:* Minimize the distance between the points $(p,2p,2p)$ and $(q,q,26 - q)$.
19. A long strip of tin 12 inches wide is made into a trough by bending up equal amounts along the sides so as to form a trapezoidal cross section with equal base angles. Find the width across the bottom and the base angles when the carrying capacity of the trough is a maximum. *Ans.* 4 in., 120°.
20. Find the point (x,y) such that the sum of the squares of its distances from the points (x_1,y_1), (x_2,y_2), and (x_3,y_3) is a minimum.

21. Find the volume of the largest rectangular parallelepiped that can be inscribed in the ellipsoid $x^2 + 3y^2 + 9z^2 = 9$. *Ans.* 8.
22. Find four positive numbers whose sum is 12 and whose product is a maximum.
23. What is the shortest distance from the point $(2,\frac{5}{9},0)$ to the ellipsoid $9x^2 + 16y^2 + 36z^2 = 144$? *Ans.* $\frac{14}{9}$.
24. For what point in space is the sum of the squares of its distances from the points (0,0,0), (1,0,0), (0,1,0), and (0,0,1) a minimum?
25. Show that a triangle with constant perimeter has maximum area when its sides are equal. *Hint:* Maximize $A = \sqrt{s(s-x)(s-y)(s-z)}$ where $z = 2s - x - y$ and s is constant.
26. The temperature in degrees centigrade at each point (x,y) in the region bounded by the lines $x = 0$, $y = 0$, and $x + y = 3$ is given by $T = 8x^2 - 4xy + 5y^2 - 4x - 8y$. Find the temperature at the hottest and coldest point in the region.
27. The electric potential at each point (x,y) in the region $0 \leqq x,y \leqq 1$ is given by $V = 48xy - 32x^3 - 24y^2$. Locate and find the maximum and the minimum potential in this square region. *Ans.* 2 at $(\frac{1}{2},\frac{1}{2})$, -32 at $(1,0)$.
28. Find the minimum volume bounded by the coordinate planes and a plane that is tangent to the ellipsoid $x^2/a^2 + y^2/b^2 + z^2/c^2 = 1$ at a point in the first octant.
29. If (x,y,z) is a point on the sphere $x^2 + y^2 + z^2 = r^2$, show that the maximum value of $ax + by + cz$ is $r\sqrt{a^2 + b^2 + c^2}$. What can be said of the plane $ax + by + cz = r\sqrt{a^2 + b^2 + c^2}$?
30. In a triangle ABC, show that $\sin \frac{1}{2}A \sin \frac{1}{2}B \sin \frac{1}{2}C \leqq \frac{1}{8}$.

199. Differentiation of a Definite Integral

Consider the integral

$$F = \int_a^b f(x,\alpha)\,dx, \quad \alpha_0 \leqq \alpha \leqq \alpha_1,$$

where α is a parameter independent of x, and a and b are finite constants. If α is given an increment $\Delta\alpha$, F is changed by an amount ΔF where

$$\Delta F = \int_a^b f(x,\alpha + \Delta\alpha)\,dx - \int_a^b f(x,\alpha)\,dx$$

$$= \int_a^b [f(x,\alpha + \Delta\alpha) - f(x,\alpha)]\,dx,$$

whence

$$\frac{\Delta F}{\Delta\alpha} = \int_a^b \frac{f(x,\alpha + \Delta\alpha) - f(x,\alpha)}{\Delta\alpha}\,dx. \tag{1}$$

When $f(x,\alpha)$ is continuous and $\partial f/\partial\alpha$ exists, the law of the mean assures the existence of an α' such that the integrand in (1) equals $f_\alpha(x,\alpha')$, $\alpha \leqq \alpha' \leqq \alpha + \Delta\alpha$. When $\partial f/\partial\alpha$ is also continuous, we have $f_\alpha(x,\alpha') = f_\alpha(x,\alpha) + \epsilon(x)$, where $\epsilon(x) \to 0$ when $\Delta\alpha \to 0$ for any x in $a \leqq x \leqq b$. Thus (1) becomes

$$\frac{\Delta F}{\Delta\alpha} = \int_a^b \frac{\partial}{\partial\alpha} f(x,\alpha)\, dx + \int_a^b \epsilon(x)\, dx. \tag{2}$$

The last integral in (2) is less in absolute value tnan $M_\epsilon(b - a)$, where M_ϵ is the largest value of $\epsilon(x)$ in the interval $a \leqq x \leqq b$. It is clear that M_ϵ can be made as small as we please by taking $\epsilon(x)$ sufficiently small. Hence, by taking the limit in (2) as $\Delta\alpha \to 0$, we obtain*

$$\frac{dF}{d\alpha} = \int_a^b \frac{\partial f}{\partial\alpha}\, dx. \tag{3}$$

Illustration. For the integral

$$F = \int_0^1 3(x + \alpha)^2\, dx = \Big[(x + \alpha)^3\Big]_0^1 = 3\alpha^2 + 3\alpha + 1,$$

we find $dF/d\alpha = 6\alpha + 3$. On the other hand, by differentiating the integral, we get

$$\frac{dF}{d\alpha} = \int_0^1 6(x + \alpha)\, dx = \Big[3(x + \alpha)^2\Big]_0^1 = 6\alpha + 3.$$

A more general result occurs when one or both of the limits of integration also depend on α. Since the integral F is a function of the upper limit b, we know by the Funaamental Theorem that

$$\frac{\partial F}{\partial b} = f(b,\alpha). \tag{4}$$

Similarly, since $\int_a^b f(x,\alpha)\, dx = -\int_b^a f(x,\alpha)\, dx$, we have

$$\frac{\partial F}{\partial a} = -f(a,\alpha). \tag{5}$$

Thus, if the limits a and b are functions of the parameter α, then from

$$\frac{dF}{d\alpha} = \frac{\partial F}{\partial\alpha} + \frac{\partial F}{\partial b}\frac{db}{d\alpha} + \frac{\partial F}{\partial a}\frac{da}{d\alpha}$$

and the relations (3), (4), and (5), we have the following result.

* It can be shown that this result is valid for infinite limits, provided the given integral is uniformly convergent.

Theorem. *If* $F(\alpha) = \int_{a(\alpha)}^{b(\alpha)} f(x,\alpha)\,dx$, *where* $f(x,\alpha)$ *and* $f_\alpha(x,\alpha)$ *are continuous functions, and* $b'(\alpha)$ *and* $a'(\alpha)$ *exist, then*

$$\frac{dF}{d\alpha} = \int_{a(\alpha)}^{b(\alpha)} \frac{\partial f(x,\alpha)}{\partial \alpha}\,dx + f(b,\alpha)\frac{db}{d\alpha} - f(a,\alpha)\frac{da}{d\alpha}. \tag{6}$$

A definite integral whose value is difficult to obtain by elementary means can sometimes be determined by using this rule of differentiation.

Example. Evaluate $\int_0^1 \frac{x^\alpha - 1}{\ln x}\,dx, \quad \alpha > -1.$

Solution: Let

$$F(\alpha) = \int_0^1 \frac{x^\alpha - 1}{\ln x}\,dx. \tag{7}$$

Differentiating with respect to α, we obtain

$$F'(\alpha) = \int_0^1 \frac{x^\alpha \ln x}{\ln x}\,dx = \left[\frac{x^{\alpha+1}}{\alpha+1}\right]_0^1 = \frac{1}{1+\alpha}.$$

Hence $F(\alpha) = \ln(1+\alpha) + C$, and, since in (7) it is evident that $F(0) = 0$, we find $C = 0$; therefore

$$\int_0^1 \frac{x^\alpha - 1}{\ln x}\,dx = \ln(1+\alpha), \quad \alpha > -1.$$

EXERCISE 105

Find the derivatives with respect to α of the following integrals without first integrating. Check your result by evaluating the integral and then differentiating.

1. $\int_{-1}^{1} (2\alpha x + \alpha^2)\,dx.$ *Ans.* 4α.
2. $\int_0^{\pi} \cos(x+\alpha)\,dx.$
3. $\int_0^{\alpha} \frac{x-\alpha}{x+\alpha}\,dx.$ $1 - \ln 4$.
4. $\int_1^{1/\alpha} \ln \alpha x\,dx, \quad 0 < \alpha < 1.$

Use differentiation, when necessary, to evaluate the following integrals.

5. $\int_0^{\pi} \frac{dx}{\alpha - \cos x}, \quad \alpha > 1.$ See page 309. *Ans.* $\frac{\pi}{\sqrt{\alpha^2 - 1}}$.
6. $\int_0^{\pi} \ln(1 + \alpha \cos x)\,dx, \quad 0 \leqq \alpha \leqq 1.$
7. $\int_0^{\infty} \frac{e^{-\alpha x} \sin x}{x}\,dx, \quad \alpha > 0.$ $\mathrm{Cot}^{-1}\,\alpha$.
8. $\int_0^{\infty} \frac{e^{-x} - e^{-\alpha x}}{x \sec x}\,dx, \quad \alpha > 0.$

9. $\displaystyle\int_0^{\pi} \frac{\ln(1+\sin\alpha\cos x)}{\cos x}\,dx, \quad 0 \leqq \alpha \leqq \tfrac{1}{2}\pi.$ *Ans.* $\pi\alpha$.

10. $\displaystyle\int_0^{\infty} \frac{\text{Tan}^{-1}\alpha x - \text{Tan}^{-1}\beta x}{x}\,dx, \quad \alpha > 0, \ \beta > 0.$

11. $\displaystyle\int_0^{\infty} \frac{e^{-x} - e^{-\alpha x}}{x}\,dx, \quad \alpha > 0.$ $\ln\alpha$.

12. $\displaystyle\int_0^{\infty} e^{-x^2}\cos\alpha x\,dx.$

13. $\displaystyle\int_0^{\pi} \ln(1 - 2\alpha\cos x + \alpha^2)\,dx.$ $\begin{cases} 0, & \text{if } \alpha^2 \leqq 1, \\ \pi\ln\alpha^2, & \text{if } \alpha^2 > 1. \end{cases}$

14. $\displaystyle\int_0^{\pi} \frac{\sin x\,dx}{\sqrt{1 - 2\alpha\cos x + \alpha^2}}.$

15. Show in two ways that the integral $\displaystyle\int_{\pi/6\alpha}^{\pi/2\alpha} \frac{\sin\alpha x}{x}\,dx$ has a constant value independent of α.

16. From $\displaystyle\int_0^{\infty} e^{-\alpha x}\,dx = \frac{1}{\alpha}$, $\alpha > 0$, by differentiation show that

$$\int_0^{\infty} x^n e^{-\alpha x}\,dx = \frac{n!}{\alpha^{n+1}}.$$

17. From $\displaystyle\int_0^{\infty} \frac{dx}{x^2+\alpha} = \frac{\pi}{2\sqrt{\alpha}}$, $\alpha > 0$, by differentiation show that

$$\int_0^{\infty} \frac{dx}{(x^2+\alpha)^{n+1}} = \frac{\pi}{2}\cdot\frac{1\cdot 3\cdots(2n-1)}{2\cdot 4\ \cdots\ (2n)}\cdot\frac{1}{\alpha^{n+1/2}}.$$

18. From $\displaystyle\int_0^{\infty} e^{-\alpha x^2}\,dx = \tfrac{1}{2}\sqrt{\frac{\pi}{\alpha}}$, $\alpha > 0$, by differentiation show that

$$\int_0^{\infty} x^{2n} e^{-\alpha x^2}\,dx = \frac{\sqrt{\pi}}{2}\cdot\frac{1\cdot 3\cdots(2n-1)}{2^n\alpha^{n+1/2}}.$$

19. Verify that $y = \dfrac{1}{\pi}\displaystyle\int_0^{\pi} \cos(x\cos\phi)\,d\phi$ is a solution of the differential equation $x\dfrac{d^2y}{dx^2} + \dfrac{dy}{dx} + xy = 0$.

20. Verify that $y = \dfrac{1}{k}\displaystyle\int_0^{x} f(t)\sin k(x-t)\,dt$ is a solution of the differential equation $\dfrac{d^2y}{dx^2} + k^2y = f(x)$, where k is a constant.

21. Prove that $F(1) = \pi(\ln 2)/8$ by differentiating

$$F(\alpha) = \int_0^{\alpha} \frac{\ln(1+\alpha x)}{1+x^2}\,dx, \quad \alpha > 0$$

and evaluating the resulting integral.

22. If the function $f(x,\alpha)$ and its first two partial derivatives with respect to α exist and are continuous, we know by Taylor's formula for $n = 2$ that

$$f(x,\alpha + \Delta\alpha) = f(x,\alpha) + \Delta\alpha f_\alpha(x,\alpha) + \frac{(\Delta\alpha)^2}{2} f_{\alpha\alpha}(x,\alpha'), \quad \alpha < \alpha' < \alpha + \Delta\alpha.$$

Use this fact to prove the relation (3) in the preceding article.

200. Taylor's Series for Functions of Two Variables

If $f(x,y)$ and all its partial derivatives are continuous in the neighborhood of $x = a$ and $y = b$, we may expand $f(x,y)$ in a power series by using the method of expansion which applies to functions of a single variable. This is done by letting $x = a + ht$ and $y = b + kt$, where h and k are constants. Then

$$F(t) = f(x,y) = f(a + ht, b + kt) \tag{1}$$

is a function of the single variable t, and by Maclaurin's formula

$$F(t) = F(0) + F'(0)\,t + \frac{F''(0)}{2!}\,t^2 + \cdots. \tag{2}$$

Differentiating (1) with respect to t, we have

$$\begin{aligned} F'(t) &= f_x(x,y)\,\frac{dx}{dt} + f_y(x,y)\,\frac{dy}{dt} \\ &= f_x(x,y)\,h + f_y(x,y)\,k. \end{aligned} \tag{3}$$

Differentiating $F'(t)$ in the same manner, we find

$$F''(t) = f_{xx}(x,y)\,h^2 + 2f_{xy}(x,y)\,hk + f_{yy}(x,y)\,k^2,$$

and so on for the higher derivatives. A study of the method by which these derivatives are found indicates that they may be written symbolically in the form

$$F'(t) = \left(h\frac{\partial}{\partial x} + k\frac{\partial}{\partial y}\right) f(x,y),$$

$$F''(t) = \left(h\frac{\partial}{\partial x} + k\frac{\partial}{\partial y}\right)^2 f(x,y),$$

$$F'''(t) = \left(h\frac{\partial}{\partial x} + k\frac{\partial}{\partial y}\right)^3 f(x,y),$$

$$\cdots\cdots\cdots\cdots\cdots\cdots\cdots\cdots$$

where $\left(h\frac{\partial}{\partial x}\right)^n\left(k\frac{\partial}{\partial y}\right)^m f(x,y)$ means $h^n k^m \frac{\partial^{n+m}}{\partial x^n \partial y^m} f(x,y)$.

When $t = 0$, we have $x = a$ and $y = b$; hence

$$F(0) = f(a,b), \qquad F'(0) = h f_x(a,b) + k f_y(a,b), \qquad \ldots.$$

If these values are substituted in (2), and t is taken equal to 1, we obtain

$$f(a + h, b + k) = f(a,b) + \{h f_x(a,b) + k f_y(a,b)\} + \frac{1}{2!}\left\{h^2 f_{xx}(a,b) + 2hk f_{xy}(a,b) + k^2 f_{yy}(a,b)\right\} + \cdots,$$

where h and k may now be considered as variables.

Replacing h by $(x - a)$ and k by $(y - b)$, we obtain **Taylor's series** for a function of two variables

$$\boldsymbol{f(x,y) = f(a,b) + \{(x - a)f_x(a,b) + (y - b)f_y(a,b)\} + \frac{1}{2!}\left\{(x - a)^2 f_{xx}(a,b) + 2(x - a)(y - b)f_{xy}(a,b) + (y - b)^2 f_{yy}(a,b)\right\} + \cdots.} \tag{4}$$

Taking $a = 0$ and $b = 0$ in (4), we obtain an expansion corresponding to Maclaurin's series

$$f(x,y) = f(0,0) + \{x f_x(0,0) + y f_y(0,0)\} + \frac{1}{2!}\left\{x^2 f_{xx}(0,0) + 2xy f_{xy}(0,0) + y^2 f_{yy}(0,0)\right\} + \cdots. \tag{5}$$

Illustration. To obtain the expansion of $x \ln (x - y)$ about $(2,1)$ we compute

$$\begin{aligned}
f(x,y) &= x \ln (x - y), & f(2,1) &= 0,\\
f_x(x,y) &= \ln (x - y) + x/(x - y), & f_x(2,1) &= 2,\\
f_y(x,y) &= -x/(x - y), & f_y(2,1) &= -2,\\
f_{xx}(x,y) &= (x - 2y)/(x - y)^2, & f_{xx}(2,1) &= 0,\\
f_{xy}(x,y) &= y/(x - y)^2, & f_{xy}(2,1) &= 1,\\
f_{yy}(x,y) &= -x/(x - y)^2, & f_{yy}(2,1) &= -2.
\end{aligned}$$

Substituting in (4), we obtain the required result

$$x \ln (x - y) = 2(x - 2) - 2(y - 1) + (x - 2)(y - 1) - (y - 1)^2 + \cdots.$$

Note: Many expansions in two or more variables may be found by proper use of the expansions for a single variable. For example, the Maclaurin's series for e^{xy} is

$$e^{xy} = 1 + (xy) + \frac{(xy)^2}{2!} + \frac{(xy)^3}{3!} + \cdots.$$

When the law of the mean (Article **114**) is applied to $F(t)$ for $t = 0$ to $t = 1$, we obtain

$$F(1) = F(0) + F'(t), \quad 0 < t < 1.$$

By use of the relations (1) and (3), this can be written as

$$f(a + h,b + k) = F(a,b) + h\,f_x(a + th,b + tk) + k\,f_y(a + th,b + tk), \qquad 0 < t < 1.$$

If we now set $a + h = x$, $a + th = x'$, $b + k = y$, and $b + tk = y'$, it follows that $a < x' < x$ and $b < y' < y$, and the preceding relation becomes

$$f(x,y) = f(a,b) + \left\{(x - a)f_x(x',y') + (y - b)f_y(x',y')\right\}, \quad \begin{cases} a < x' < x, \\ b < y' < y. \end{cases}$$

This is the analogue of the law of the mean for a function of two variables.

201. Sufficient Condition for a Maximum or Minimum

In order that $f(a,b)$ be a relative maximum or minimum value of the function $f(x,y)$, it was shown in Article **198** that the following conditions must be satisfied.

$$f_x(a,b) = 0, \qquad f_y(a,b) = 0. \tag{1}$$

The question as to whether the conditions (1) actually give a maximum, a minimum, or neither, can in part be determined by observing that $x = a$, $y = b$ will be a critical value of $f(x,y)$ when $t = 0$ is a critical value of the function $F(t) = f(a + ht, b + kt)$.

We know from Article **33** that a function $F(t)$ has a maximum or minimum value at $t = 0$, according as $F'(0) = 0$ and $F''(0) < 0$ or $F''(0) > 0$, respectively. The condition $F'(0) = 0$ leads to (1), whereas the conditions $F''(0) \lessgtr 0$ give

$$h^2 f_{xx} + 2hk\,f_{xy} + k^2 f_{yy} \lessgtr 0 \tag{2}$$

for $x = a$, $y = b$, and any values of h and k. If we multiply and divide the left side of (2) by f_{xx}, and then complete the square on the first two terms of the numerator, we obtain*

$$\frac{(h\,f_{xx} + k\,f_{xy})^2 + k^2(f_{xx}f_{yy} - f_{xy}^2)}{f_{xx}}, \quad f_{xx} \neq 0. \tag{3}$$

---

* If $f_{xx} = 0$, use f_{yy} and continue in a similar manner. If $f_{xx} = 0$ and $f_{yy} = 0$, the left side of (2) reduces to $2hkf_{xy}$, which may be positive or negative according to the choice of h and k. This means that $f(a,b)$ is neither a maximum nor minimum value of the function $f(x,y)$.

If $\Delta \equiv (f_{xx}f_{yy} - f_{xy}^2) > 0$, we see that the numerator of (3) is positive for all values of h and k. Hence (3) will be positive or negative according as f_{xx} (or f_{yy}, which by $\Delta > 0$ must have the same sign) is positive or negative. Thus if $\Delta > 0$, $f(a,b)$ is a maximum or minimum when $f_{xx}(a,b)$ is negative or positive, respectively.

If $\Delta < 0$, it can be shown that (3) is positive for some values of h and k, and negative for others. Thus in this case $f(a,b)$ is neither a maximum nor minimum.

If $\Delta = 0$, further tests are needed to determine whether $f(a,b)$ is a maximum, a minimum, or neither. For example, when $f_{xx} = f_{xy} = f_{yy} = 1$, we have $\Delta = 0$, and by (2) $f(a,b)$ is a minimum. On the other hand, when $f_{xx} = f_{xy} = f_{yy} = -1$, we have $\Delta = 0$, and by (2) $f(a,b)$ is a maximum.

Theorem. *If $x = a$, $y = b$ is a solution of the equations*

$$\frac{\partial f}{\partial x} = 0, \qquad \frac{\partial f}{\partial y} = 0, \tag{4}$$

and if for these values

$$\Delta = \frac{\partial^2 f}{\partial x^2}\frac{\partial^2 f}{\partial y^2} - \left(\frac{\partial^2 f}{\partial x\, \partial y}\right)^2 > 0, \tag{5}$$

the function $f(x,y)$ will have a relative maximum or minimum value $f(a,b)$ according as $\partial^2 f/\partial x^2$ (or $\partial^2 f/\partial y^2$) is negative or positive for $x = a$, $y = b$.

If (4) holds and $\Delta < 0$, $f(a,b)$ is neither a maximum nor minimum. If $\Delta = 0$, the test fails.

Example. Examine the function $xy(x + y - 3)$ for maximum and minimum values.

Solution: Let $f(x,y) = xy(x + y - 3)$; then

$$f_x = y(2x + y - 3), \qquad f_y = x(x + 2y - 3),$$
$$f_{xx} = 2y, \qquad f_{xy} = 2x + 2y - 3, \qquad f_{yy} = 2x. \tag{6}$$

Solving $f_x = 0$ and $f_y = 0$ simultaneously, we obtain the solutions (0,0), (0,3), (3,0), and (1,1). For each of these pairs of values we find the values (6), and by substitution in (5), we obtain $\Delta = -9, -9, -9$, and 3, respectively. Hence $f(x,y)$ is neither a maximum nor minimum for the first three sets of values, but when $x = 1$, $y = 1$, it follows from $f_{xx} = 2 > 0$ that the given function is a minimum.

EXERCISE 106

Verify the following expansions.

1. $\cos x \cos y = 1 - \dfrac{x^2 + y^2}{2!} + \dfrac{x^4 + 6x^2y^2 + y^4}{4!} - \cdots.$

2. $1/(1 + xy) = 1 - xy + x^2y^2 - x^3y^3 + \cdots.$
3. $e^x \cos y = 1 + x + \frac{1}{2}(x^2 - y^2) + \frac{1}{6}x(x^2 - 3y^2) + \cdots.$
4. $\ln (1 + x)(1 + y) = (x + y) - \frac{1}{2}(x^2 + y^2) + \frac{1}{3}(x^3 + y^3) - \cdots.$
5. $\sqrt{x + y} = 1 + \frac{1}{2}x + \frac{1}{2}(y - 1) - \frac{1}{8}x^2 - \frac{1}{4}x(y - 1) - \frac{1}{8}(y - 1)^2 + \cdots.$
6. $\text{Tan}^{-1} (y/x) = \frac{1}{4}\pi - \frac{1}{2}(x - 1) + \frac{1}{2}(y - 1)$
$$+ \tfrac{1}{4}(x - 1)^2 - \tfrac{1}{4}(y - 1)^2 + \cdots.$$
7. Expand $x^2 + xy$ about (2,3).
Ans. $10 + 7(x - 2) + 2(y - 3) + (x - 2)^2 + (x - 2)(y - 3).$
8. Expand $x^3 + 2xy^2$ about (1,1).

Verify the following approximation formulas for small values of x and y.

9. $e^x \sin y = y + xy.$
10. $e^{-x} \ln (1 + y) = y(1 - x - \frac{1}{2}y).$
11. $\sqrt{\dfrac{1 + x}{1 + y}} = 1 + \dfrac{1}{2} (x - y).$
12. $\dfrac{\sin (x + y)}{x + y} = 1 - \dfrac{1}{6} (x + y)^2.$

Examine the following functions for maximum and minimum values.

13. $x^2 + xy + y^2 - 3x + 2.$ *Ans.* $(2, -1)$, min.
14. $ax + by - x^2 - y^2.$
15. $4xy - x^4 - y^4.$ $(1,1)$, max., $(-1,-1)$, max.
16. $y^4 + 6x^2y^2 + x^2 - 4x + 4.$
17. $xy - \ln (x^2 + y^2).$ None.
18. $x^2 + y^2 - \sqrt{\frac{1}{2}(x + y)}.$
19. $x^2 + 1 + 2x \sin y.$ $(-1, \frac{1}{2}\pi)$, min., $(1, \frac{3}{2}\pi)$, min.
20. $\sin x + \sin y + \sin x \cos y.$
21. Derive a theorem for a function of two variables that is analogous to Taylor's theorem, Article **165.**

CHAPTER 22

Multiple Integrals

202. Double Integrals

The limit approached by sums of the form

$$f(x_1') \Delta x_1 + f(x_2') \Delta x_2 + \cdots + f(x_n') \Delta x_n,$$

as every $\Delta x_k \to 0$ and $n \to \infty$, is defined to be the definite integral

$$\int_a^b f(x)\, dx \tag{1}$$

of a function of one variable on the interval from a to b. The generalization of this definition to two dimensions is called a *double integral* and is defined in the following way. Let R be a closed finite region in the xy plane that is bounded by one or more curves. Let the function $f(x,y)$ of two independent variables x and y be single-valued in R. Now suppose that the region R is divided in any manner into n parts, each a part of area ΔA_1, ΔA_2, $\cdots$, ΔA_n. If (x_k',y_k') is any point belonging to the subregion ΔA_k, we form the sum

$$f(x_1',y_1') \Delta A_1 + f(x_2',y_2') \Delta A_2 + \cdots + f(x_n',y_n') \Delta A_n. \tag{2}$$

If this sum has a limit as the maximum diameter of every subregion ΔA_k approaches zero and $n \to \infty$, we denote the limit by the symbol

$$\iint_R f(x,y)\, dA, \tag{3}$$

and call it the **double integral** of $f(x,y)$ over the region R.

In much the same manner as the definite integral (1) can be interpreted as an area in a plane, the double integral (3) can be interpreted as a volume of a solid. For example, if the function $f(x,y)$ is positive, the equation $z = f(x,y)$ represents a surface above the region R as shown in Figure 213. If ΔA_k is small, the term $f(x_k',y_k') \Delta A_k$ represents a reasonable approximation to the volume of that portion of the solid which is above ΔA_k and below the surface. The sum (2) then gives an approximation to the total volume of the solid, and the exact volume is defined to be

$$V = \iint_R f(x,y)\, dA. \tag{4}$$

If the function $f(x,y)$ is negative in parts of R, it should be noted that the formula (4) gives the algebraic sum of the volume, a volume below the xy plane being treated as negative.

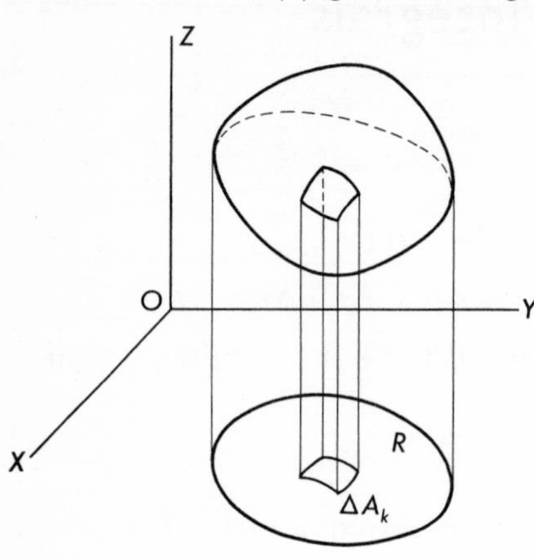

Figure 213

Another important interpretation of the double integral (3) can be made by considering the region R to be a thin sheet of matter whose variable mass per unit area at each point (x,y) is given by the function $f(x,y)$. With exactly the same reasoning, we obtain in this case the total mass

$$M = \iint_R f(x,y)\, dA. \tag{5}$$

If, in particular, we take $f(x,y) = 1$, we observe that the value obtained from either (4) or (5) is numerically equal to the area of the region R; thus

$$A = \iint_R dA.$$

Although double integrals are helpful in formulating many physical principles, such as those illustrated, their usefulness would be limited if it were necessary to evaluate a limit of sums in every instance. Fortunately, this is not necessary since we can show that a double integral can be evaluated in a simpler fashion by what is called an *iterated integral.*

203. Iterated Integrals

In a manner analogous to partial differentiation, a function of two independent variables may be integrated with respect to one variable while holding the other variable constant. For example, if x is regarded as a constant, we have

$$\int_0^{4x} xy\, dy = \left[\tfrac{1}{2}xy^2\right]_0^{4x} = 8x^3.$$

This process is called *partial integration* with respect to y. When the limits are functions of x as indicated in the above example, the integral is a function of x; hence the result may be integrated with respect to x. For example,

$$\int_1^2 \left[\int_0^{4x} xy\,dy\right] dx = \int_1^2 8x^3\,dx = \Big[2x^4\Big]_1^2 = 30.$$

In general, an expression of the form

$$\int_a^b \int_{y_1(x)}^{y_2(x)} f(x,y)\,dy\,dx, \qquad \text{or} \qquad \int_a^b \left[\int_{y_1(x)}^{y_2(x)} f(x,y)\,dy\right] dx, \tag{1}$$

where a and b are constants, is called an **iterated integral.** To find the value of (1) we first integrate $f(x,y)$ partially with respect to y and insert the limits for y. This gives a function of x, say $F(x)$. We then evaluate the definite integral $\int_a^b F(x)\,dx$.

In a similar manner, the double integral

$$\int_c^d \int_{x_1(y)}^{x_2(y)} f(x,y)\,dx\,dy, \qquad \text{or} \qquad \int_c^d \left[\int_{x_1(y)}^{x_2(y)} f(x,y)\,dx\right] dy$$

has a value which is found by integrating partially with respect to x between the limits $x_1(y)$ and $x_2(y)$, and then integrating the result with respect to y between the limits c and d.

Illustration 1. Integrating first with respect to x, we have

$$\begin{aligned}\int_0^a \int_0^{y^2/a} e^{x/y}\,dx\,dy &= \int_0^a \Big[ye^{x/y}\Big]_0^{y^2/a} dy \\ &= \int_0^a (ye^{y/a} - y)\,dy \\ &= \Big[aye^{y/a} - a^2e^{y/a} - \tfrac{1}{2}y^2\Big]_0^a = \tfrac{1}{2}a^2.\end{aligned}$$

Note: The integral (1) is often written in the form

$$\int_a^b dx \int_{y_1(x)}^{y_2(x)} f(x,y)\,dy.$$

This symbolism indicates more clearly the required order of integration.

In Article **148** it was shown that the volume of a solid is given by the integral

$$V = \int_a^b A(x)\,dx, \tag{2}$$

where $A(x)$ represents the area of a section of the solid made by a plane that is perpendicular to the x axis. This result can be used in the following way to determine the value of double integrals such as those discussed in the preceding article.

Let a plane $x = x'$ be passed through the cylindrical solid that stands on a region R, as shown in Figure 214. Since the area of the section that this plane makes with the solid is the same as the area under the curve of intersection of the plane $x = x'$ with the upper surface $z = f(x,y)$, the sectional area can be represented as an integral of the form

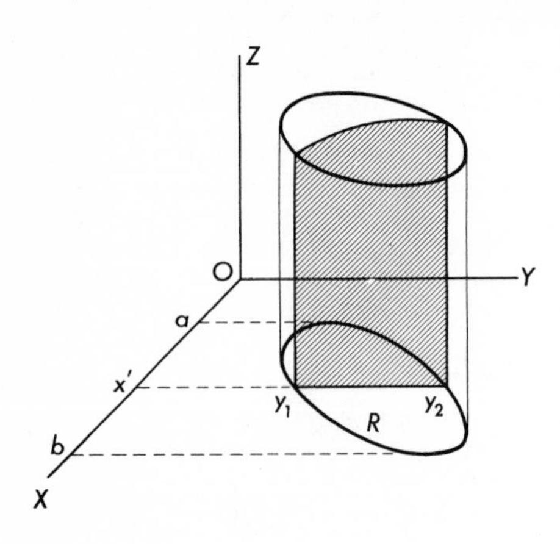

Figure 214

$$A(x') = \int_{y_1}^{y_2} f(x',y)\, dy,$$

where the limits of integration are determined by the intersection of the plane $x = x'$ with the curve that bounds the region R.

If R is a region in the xy plane of such a kind that the line $x = x'$ cuts the boundary of R just twice, and if a and b are the smallest and largest values that x can have in R, then by (2) we obtain the volume expressed as an iterated integral in the form

$$V = \int_a^b A(x)\, dx = \int_a^b \left[\int_{y_1}^{y_2} f(x,y)\, dy\right] dx,$$

where the unnecessary prime on the letter x has been dropped.

By following a similar procedure, we could cut the volume by a plane perpendicular to the y axis, and arrive at the result

$$V = \int_c^d dy \int_{x_1}^{x_2} f(x,y)\, dx,$$

where the limits x_1 and x_2 are functions of y determined by the boundary of R, and c and d are the smallest and largest values of y in R.

When the function $f(x,y)$ is continuous, it can be shown that the preceding integrals exist. Hence, in eliminating the geometrical concept of volume, we obtain the following important conclusion.

Theorem. *The value of the double integral* $\iint_R f(x,y)\,dA$ *of a continuous function over a region R is given by either of the iterated integrals*

$$\int_a^b dx \int_{y_1}^{y_2} f(x,y)\,dy, \qquad \int_c^d dy \int_{x_1}^{x_2} f(x,y)\,dx,$$

where the limits of integration are appropriately determined by the boundary of R.

Illustration 2. If the region R is the triangle bounded by the lines $x = 1$, $y = 0$, and $y = 2x$, the value of the double integral $\iint_R f(x,y)\,dA$ is given by either of the iterated integrals

$$\int_0^1 dx \int_0^{2x} f(x,y)\,dy \qquad \text{or} \qquad \int_0^2 dy \int_{y/2}^1 f(x,y)\,dx.$$

EXERCISE 107

Evaluate the following iterated integrals.

1.	$\int_0^1 \int_0^4 x^3\,dy\,dx.$	*Ans.* 1.	2.	$\int_0^2 \int_0^x y\,dy\,dx.$
3.	$\int_1^2 \int_0^{2y} x^3y\,dx\,dy.$	42.	4.	$\int_0^4 \int_0^{1-y} y^2\,dx\,dy.$
5.	$\int_0^3 \int_{-x}^x xy\,dy\,dx.$	0.	6.	$\int_1^3 \int_0^y (x + y)\,dx\,dy.$
7.	$\int_0^{\pi/2} \int_0^{\sin y} \frac{x\,dx\,dy}{\sqrt{1 - x^2}}.$	$\frac{1}{2}\pi - 1.$	8.	$\int_0^2 \int_{2y}^{3y} \frac{dx\,dy}{x - y}.$
9.	$\int_{-1}^1 \frac{dy}{y} \int_1^{e^y} \frac{dx}{x}.$	2.	10.	$\int_0^1 dx \int_1^{\tan x} \frac{dy}{1 + y^2}.$
11.	$\int_0^1 \int_0^x e^{x+y}\,dy\,dx.$	$\frac{1}{2}(e - 1)^2.$	12.	$\int_0^\pi \int_0^{a \cos \theta} r \sin \theta\,dr\,d\theta.$
13.	$\int_0^a dy \int_0^{\sqrt{a^2-y^2}} x\,dx.$	$\frac{1}{3}a^3.$	14.	$\int_0^\pi \int_0^{y^2} \sin (x/y)\,dx\,dy.$
15.	$\int_0^1 \int_0^{3v} \sqrt{u + v}\,du\,dv.$	$\frac{28}{15}.$	16.	$\int_0^1 \int_0^{\operatorname{Cos}^{-1} r} r \cos \theta\,d\theta\,dr.$
17.	$\int_0^1 \int_{x^2}^x \sqrt{\frac{x}{y}}\,dy\,dx.$	$\frac{1}{5}.$	18.	$\int_0^1 dy \int_{y^2}^y \sqrt{\frac{x}{y}}\,dx.$
19.	$\int_0^1 \int_0^1 \lvert x - y\rvert\,dy\,dx.$	$\frac{1}{3}.$	20.	$\int_0^{\pi/3} \tan \phi\,d\phi \int_\phi^{\pi/3} \sin \theta\,d\theta.$

For the functions and regions indicated, give and evaluate the two equivalent iterated forms of $\iint_R f(x,y)\,dA$.

21. $f(x,y) = 4xy - y^2$, R the rectangle bounded by $x = 1$, $x = 2$, $y = 0$, $y = 3$. *Ans.* 18.
22. $f(x,y) = 8y - x$, R the triangle bounded by $x = 1$, $y = 0$, $y = x$.
23. $f(x,y) = 2xy$, R the triangle with vertices at (0,0), (2,0), and (0,4). *Ans.* 16/3.
24. $f(x,y) = x$, R the first-quadrant region inside the circle $x^2 + y^2 = 4$.
25. $f(x,y) = x^2 + y^2$, R the region bounded by $y = x$ and $y^2 = 4x$. *Ans.* 768/35.
26. Describe the region of integration R used in determining the iterated integrals of Problems 6, 11, and 18.
27. Show that the double integral of $\dfrac{\partial^2 f(x,y)}{\partial x\,\partial y}$ over the rectangle $x_0 \leqq x \leqq x_1$, $y_0 \leqq y \leqq y_1$ is $f(x_1,y_1) - f(x_1,y_0) - f(x_0,y_1) + f(x_0,y_0)$.
28. Evaluate $\int_0^1 \int_0^1 f(x,y)\,dx\,dy$, when $f(x,y) = \begin{cases} x, & \text{for } x \geqq y, \\ y, & \text{for } x < y. \end{cases}$

204. Iterated Integrals in Rectangular Coordinates

Let $f(x,y)$ be a continuous function defined in a region R for which the variable domains are $a \leqq x \leqq b$ and $c \leqq y \leqq d$. In conformity with the definition of a double integral as a limit of a sum, let us divide R into subregions by a rectangular network of lines parallel to the x and y axes, as shown in Figure 215. The subregions ΔA_{ik} of R thus formed are of two kinds: complete rectangles and parts of rectangles cut off by the boundary of R. The total area of the boundary subregions can be made as small as we desire by increasing the number of lines in the network and thereby reducing the size of all subregions. If M is the maximum value of $|f(x,y)|$ in R, and if the total area of the boundary regions is made less than ϵ/M, the contribution made by these sums in the definition of a double integral will be less than ϵ, since

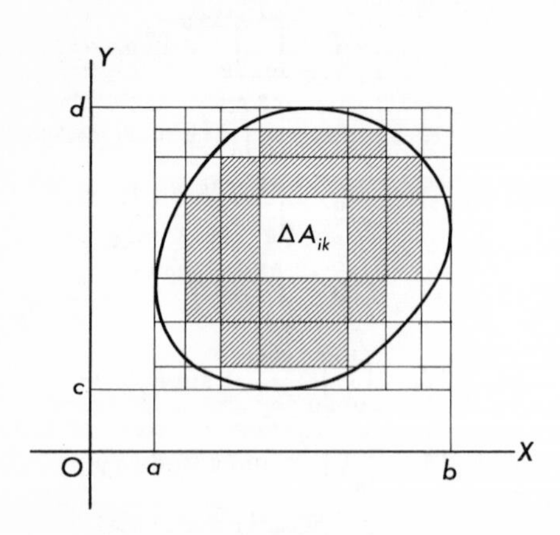

Figure 215

$|f(x_i,y_k)\,\Delta A_{ik}| \leqq M\,\Delta A_{ik}$, where (x_i,y_k) is any point in ΔA_{ik}. For this reason it follows that the definition

$$\iint_R f(x,y)\,dA = \lim_{n,m\to\infty} \sum_{i=1}^{n} \sum_{k=1}^{m} f(x_i,y_k)\,\Delta A_{ik} \tag{1}$$

may be taken such that all ΔA_{ik} are complete rectangles with dimensions Δx_i, Δy_k, and it is immaterial whether or not the ΔA_{ik} include or exclude those rectangles that contain part of the boundary of R.

If the limit indicated in (1) is to exist, the order of evaluation of the limits on n and m must necessarily be of no consequence; therefore it follows that

$$\begin{aligned}\iint_R f(x,y)\,dA &= \lim_{n\to\infty} \sum_{i=1}^{n} \left\{ \lim_{m\to\infty} \sum_{k=1}^{m} f(x_i,y_k)\,\Delta y_k \right\} \Delta x_i \\ &= \lim_{m\to\infty} \sum_{k=1}^{m} \left\{ \lim_{n\to\infty} \sum_{i=1}^{n} f(x_i,y_k)\,\Delta x_i \right\} \Delta y_k.\end{aligned}$$

These limits taken in turn give us the iterated integrals set forth in the theorem of the preceding article.

205. Plane Areas by Double Integration

A plane area $BCDE$ (Figure 216), which is bounded by the curves $y = y_1(x)$ and $y = y_2(x)$ and the vertical lines $x = a$ and $x = b$, may be represented by a double integral in the following manner.

With little loss of generality, we may draw a set of vertical lines at equal intervals Δx and a set of horizontal lines at equal intervals Δy. We thus divide the plane into a network of elementary rectangles each having the area $\Delta A = \Delta y\,\Delta x$. The sum of the areas of all the small rectangles which lie within and on the boundary $BCDE$ gives an approximation to its area. The limit of this sum as Δx and Δy approach zero is equal to the area. That is,

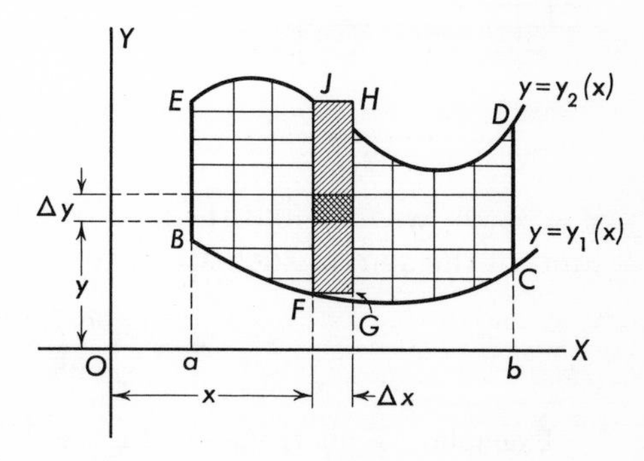

Figure 216

$$A = \lim_{\Delta y,\Delta x\to 0} \sum \Delta y\,\Delta x. \tag{1}$$

In accordance with the conclusions in the preceding article and the Fundamental Theorem (Article **45**), the limit (1) may be evaluated by first combining the rectangles in one vertical strip as indicated in Figure 216. Thus

$$\text{Area } FGHJ = \left[\lim_{\Delta y \to 0} \sum \Delta y\right] \Delta x = \left[\int_{y_1(x)}^{y_2(x)} dy\right] \Delta x.$$

Then adding the areas of the vertical strips as Δx approches zero, we obtain the required result

$$\mathbf{A} = \int_a^b \left[\int_{y_1(x)}^{y_2(x)} \mathbf{dy}\right] \mathbf{dx} = \int_a^b \int_{y_1(x)}^{y_2(x)} \mathbf{dy\ dx}. \tag{2}$$

In like manner for the area $BCDE$ (Figure 217), which is bounded by the horizontal lines $y = c$ and $y = d$ and the curves $x = x_1(y)$ and

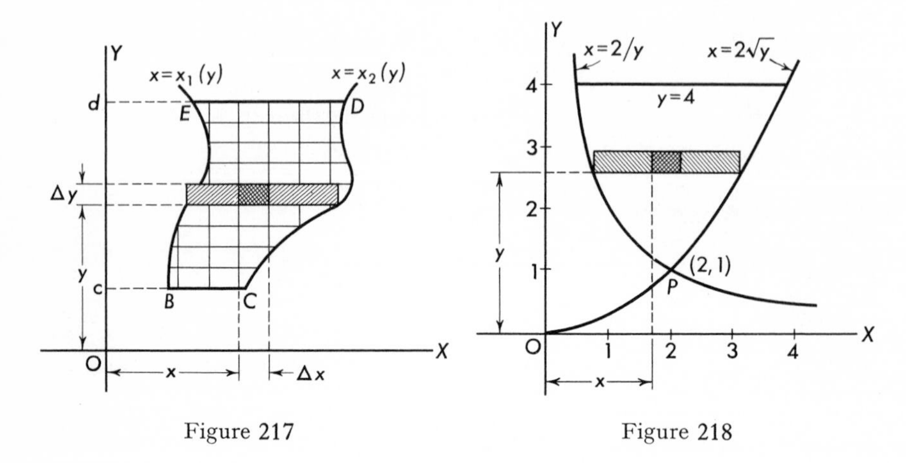

Figure 217

Figure 218

$x = x_2(y)$, we first find the area of a horizontal strip and then take the limit of the sum of such strips to obtain the formula

$$\mathbf{A} = \int_c^d \int_{x_1(y)}^{x_2(y)} \mathbf{dx\ dy}. \tag{3}$$

Example. Find the area (Figure 218) bounded by the curves $xy = 2$, $4y = x^2$, and the line $y = 4$.

Solution: The point P at which the given curves intersect is found to be (2,1). Hence, by substitution in (3), the required area is

$$A = \int_1^4 \int_{2/y}^{2\sqrt{y}} dx\, dy = \int_1^4 \left(2\sqrt{y} - \frac{2}{y}\right) dy = \frac{28}{3} - 2 \ln 4.$$

Note: Observe that nothing is gained by finding an area by double integration, since the first integration always reduces the integral to the form

$\int y\,dx$ or $\int x\,dy$. However, in computing other quantities associated with the area, there is usually an advantage in using double integrals. This will become evident in subsequent work.

206. Centroid and Moment of Inertia of a Plane Area

In Articles **49** and **52** a single integration was used to find either the first or second moment of a plane area with respect to an axis. Different procedures were necessary, however, depending on whether the elementary strip was taken parallel or perpendicular to the axis. In this article we shall see that the latter complication is avoided when the moments are expressed as double integrals.

Consider the plane area A (Figure 219), bounded by the curves $y = y_1(x)$ and $y = y_2(x)$ and the lines $x = a$ and $x = b$. Selecting a rectangular element of area $\Delta A = \Delta y\,\Delta x$ with one vertex at the point (x,y), we observe that the increments $y\,\Delta y\,\Delta x$ and $x\,\Delta y\,\Delta x$ are approximate moments of ΔA with respect to the x axis and y axis, respectively.

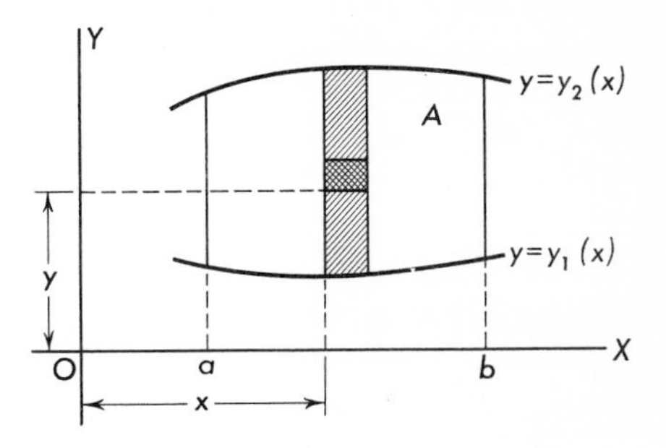

Figure 219

Following the procedure indicated in the preceding article, the moments for a vertical strip with respect to the x axis and y axis, are respectively

$$\left[\int_{y_1(x)}^{y_2(x)} y\,dy\right]\Delta x \qquad \text{and} \qquad \left[\int_{y_1(x)}^{y_2(x)} x\,dy\right]\Delta x.$$

Hence the moments for the entire area A are

$$M_x = \int_a^b \int_{y_1(x)}^{y_2(x)} y\,dy\,dx, \qquad M_y = \int_a^b \int_{y_1(x)}^{y_2(x)} x\,dy\,dx. \tag{1}$$

It follows from (1) that the coordinates of the centroid $(\bar{x},\bar{y})$ of the area A may be found from

$$\boldsymbol{A\bar{x} = \int_a^b \int_{y_1(x)}^{y_2(x)} x\,dy\,dx, \qquad A\bar{y} = \int_a^b \int_{y_1(x)}^{y_2(x)} y\,dy\,dx.} \tag{2}$$

Since the moments of inertia I_x and I_y of the element of area ΔA are given approximately by $y^2\,\Delta y\,\Delta x$ and $x^2\,\Delta y\,\Delta x$, respectively, we conclude by reasoning as above that

$$\boldsymbol{I_x = \int_a^b \int_{y_1(x)}^{y_2(x)} y^2\,dy\,dx, \qquad I_y = \int_a^b \int_{y_1(x)}^{y_2(x)} x^2\,dy\,dx.} \tag{3}$$

For an area of the type shown in Figure 217, the first integration is taken with respect to x and the limits of the integrals in (2) and (3) are the same as those of the integral (3) in the preceding article.

Example 1. Find the centroid of the area (Figure 220) bounded by the parabola $y = x^2$ and the line $y = x + 2$.

Solution: Solving the given equations simultaneously, we find the points of intersection $(-1,1)$ and $(2,4)$.

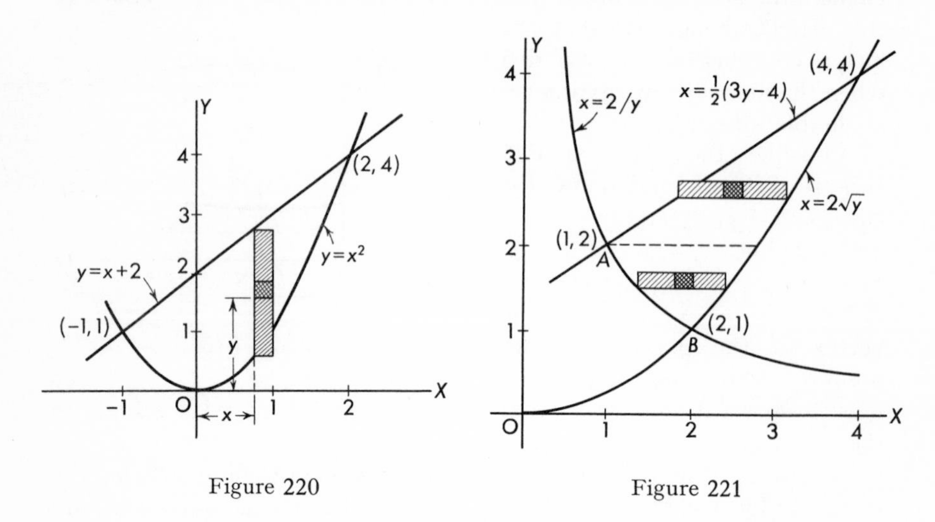

Figure 220

Figure 221

Using (2), Article **205,** the area is

$$A = \int_{-1}^{2}\int_{x^2}^{x+2} dy\,dx = \int_{-1}^{2} (x + 2 - x^2)\,dx = \tfrac{9}{2}.$$

By (2) we have

$$\tfrac{9}{2}\bar{x} = \int_{-1}^{2}\int_{x^2}^{x+2} x\,dy\,dx = \int_{-1}^{2} x(x + 2 - x^2)\,dx = \tfrac{9}{4},$$

$$\tfrac{9}{2}\bar{y} = \int_{-1}^{2}\int_{x^2}^{x+2} y\,dy\,dx = \tfrac{1}{2}\int_{-1}^{2} [(x + 2)^2 - (x^2)^2]\,dx = \tfrac{36}{5}.$$

Hence the centroid of the area is $(\frac{1}{2},\frac{8}{5})$.

Example 2. Find the moment of inertia of the first-quadrant area (Figure 221) bounded by the curves $xy = 2$, $4y = x^2$, and $3y = 2x + 4$ with respect to the x axis.

Solution: Solving the given equations simultaneously in pairs, we find the points of intersection (1,2), (2,1), and (4,4).

Divide the given area into two parts by a horizontal line through A. Integrating first with respect to x in each part, we obtain in accordance with (3)

$$\begin{aligned} I_x &= \int_1^2 \int_{2/y}^{2\sqrt{y}} y^2\,dx\,dy + \int_2^4 \int_{(3y-4)/2}^{2\sqrt{y}} y^2\,dx\,dy \\ &= \int_1^2 (2y^{5/2} - 2y)\,dy + \int_2^4 (2y^{5/2} - \tfrac{3}{2}y^3 + 2y^2)\,dy \\ &= (\tfrac{32}{7}\sqrt{2} - \tfrac{25}{7}) + (\tfrac{430}{21} - \tfrac{32}{7}\sqrt{2}) = \tfrac{355}{21}. \end{aligned}$$

This result could also be obtained by drawing a vertical line through B and integrating first with respect to y in each of the areas thus formed.

EXERCISE 108

Using double integration in each of the following, find the area bounded by the given curves.

1. $y = 3x - x^2, \quad y = x.$ *Ans.* $\frac{4}{3}$.
2. $y = x^3, \quad y = 2x^2.$
3. $3x = 4 - y^2, \quad x = y^2.$ $\frac{16}{9}$.
4. $y^2 = x^3, \quad x^2 = y^3.$
5. $y = x\,e^{-x}, \quad y = x, \quad x = 2.$ $1 + 3\,e^{-2}$.
6. $y = \sin 2x, \quad y = \sin x.$ (Smallest area.)
7. $(x^2 + 4)y = 8, \quad 2y = 3x + 4, \quad 2y = x.$ $\pi + 1$.
8. $y = e^x, \quad y = e^{-x},$ line from $(1,e)$ to $(2,e^{-2})$.

Using double integration in each of the following, find the centroid of the area bounded by the given curves.

9. $y = x^2, \quad y = 4x - x^2.$ *Ans.* $(1,2)$.
10. $y = \sqrt{25 - x^2}, \quad xy = 12.$
11. $2y = x^3, \quad y^2 = 8x.$ $(\frac{24}{25}, \frac{12}{7})$.
12. $y^2 = 1 + x^2, \quad x = 2y - 2.$
13. $y = \ln x, \quad y = 1, \quad y = 0, \quad x = 0.$ $\left(\dfrac{e+1}{4}, \dfrac{1}{e-1}\right)$.
14. $y = \sin x, \quad y = x, \quad x = \frac{1}{2}\pi.$
15. $y = x^2, \quad 2x - y = 1, \quad 4x + y + 4 = 0.$ $(-\frac{1}{2}, -\frac{1}{5})$.
16. $y^2 = x^3, \quad x + y = 2, \quad x = 4.$

Using double integration in each of the following, find I_x and I_y for the area bounded by the given curves.

17. $4y = x^3, \quad y = |x|.$ *Ans.* $\frac{4}{5}, \frac{4}{3}$.
18. $y = 2x^2, \quad y^2 = 32x.$
19. $xy = 4, \quad 2x + y = 6.$ $2, \frac{1}{2}$.
20. $xy = y - x, \quad y = 4x.$

21. $y = e^x, \quad y = e, \quad x = 0.$ *Ans.* $\frac{1}{9}(1 + 2e^3), \frac{2}{3}(3 - e).$
22. $y = \cos x, \quad y = 0, \quad x = 0.$ (First quadrant.)
23. $x^2 + y^2 = a^2, \quad x = a, \quad y = a.$ *Ans.* $I_x = I_y = a^4(16 - 3\pi)/48.$
24. $4y = x^2, \quad x + y = 8, \quad x = 0.$ (First quadrant.)

207. Iterated Integrals in Polar Coordinates

If a function $f(x,y)$ is expressed in polar coordinates as

$$f(r \cos \theta, r \sin \theta) = F(r,\theta),$$

the double integral of $f(x,y)$ over a region R may be written either as

$$\iint_R f(x,y)\, dA$$

or

$$\iint_R F(r,\theta)\, dA. \tag{1}$$

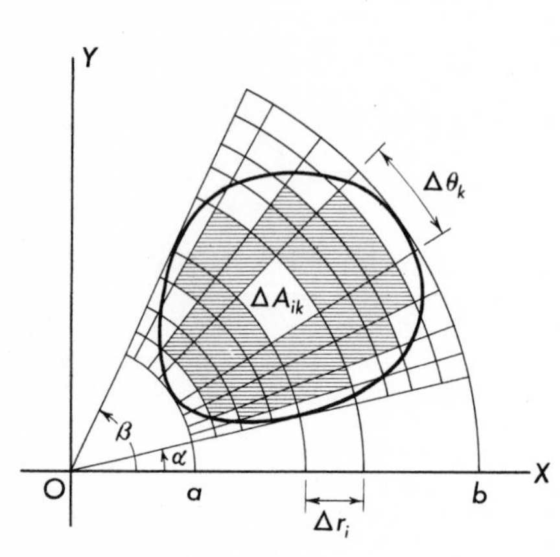

Figure 222

The limit defining the latter double integral can be written as

$$\lim_{n,m\to\infty} \sum_{i=1}^{n} \sum_{k=1}^{m} F(r'_i,\theta'_k)\, \Delta A_{ik}, \tag{2}$$

where (r'_i,θ'_k) is any point in the subregion ΔA_{ik}. In order to evaluate (1) in polar coordinates, we first divide the region R into a network of subregions corresponding to $r =$ constant and $\theta =$ constant; that is, by a set of concentric circles about the origin, and a set of radial lines emanating from the origin, as shown in Figure 222.

Since, as in Article **204,** the total area of the boundary subregions can be made as small as we desire, it is immaterial whether or not they are included in the sum (2). The area of each subregion is the difference in area between two sectors, as shown in Figure 223. Hence, in accordance with **5,** page 1, the area is

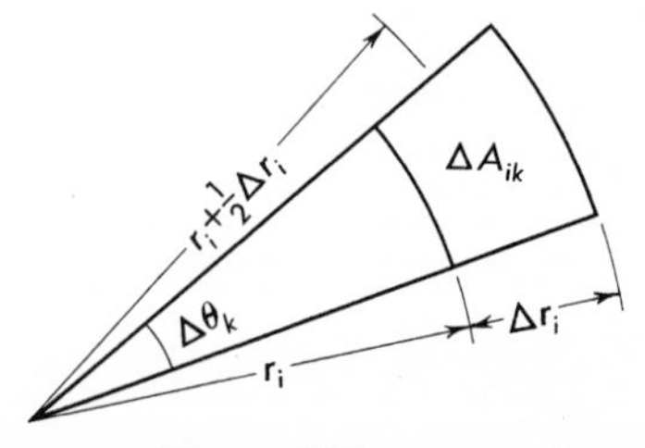

Figure 223

$$\Delta A_{ik} = \tfrac{1}{2}[(r_i + \Delta r_i)^2 - r_i^2]\, \Delta\theta_k$$
$$= (r_i + \tfrac{1}{2}\, \Delta r_i)\, \Delta r_i\, \Delta\theta_k.$$

By selecting r'_i in (2) to be $r_i + \frac{1}{2}\Delta r_i$, the area of a subregion can be written as

$$\Delta A_{ik} = r'_i \, \Delta r_i \, \Delta\theta_k,$$

and the limit (2) becomes

$$\lim_{n,m\to\infty} \sum_{i=1}^{n} \sum_{k=1}^{m} F(r'_i,\theta'_k) r'_i \, \Delta r_i \, \Delta\theta_k, \tag{3}$$

where it is understood that the summations extend over those i and k that correspond to subregions within and on the boundary of R.

If the limit (3) is to exist, it follows, as in Article **204,** that

$$\iint_R F(r,\theta)\, dA = \int_a^b r\, dr \int_{\theta_1(r)}^{\theta_2(r)} F(r,\theta)\, d\theta$$

$$= \int_\alpha^\beta d\theta \int_{r_1(\theta)}^{r_2(\theta)} r\, F(r,\theta)\, dr.$$

208. Plane Areas in Polar Coordinates

With little loss in generality, the development of the preceding article could be as follows for a plane area $BCDE$ (Figure 224) which is

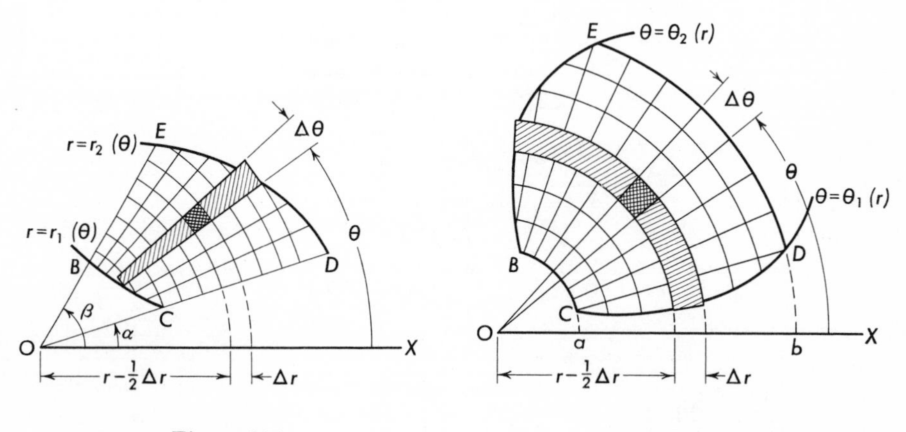

Figure 224

Figure 225

bounded by the polar curves $r = r_1(\theta)$ and $r = r_2(\theta)$ and the radial lines $\theta = \alpha$ and $\theta = \beta$.

Draw radial lines from O at equal angular intervals $\Delta\theta$ from $\theta = \alpha$ to $\theta = \beta$, and draw arcs of circles with centers at the origin and successive radii differing by Δr. In this way we divide the plane into a network of elementary areas ΔA, where each represents the difference in area between two circular sectors. If r denotes the distance from O to the center of one of these elements of area, then by **5**, page 1,

$$\Delta A = \tfrac{1}{2}(r + \tfrac{1}{2}\Delta r)^2\,\Delta\theta - \tfrac{1}{2}(r - \tfrac{1}{2}\Delta r)^2\,\Delta\theta = r\,\Delta r\,\Delta\theta.$$

Adding the elements of area contained within and on the boundary of $BCDE$, we obtain an approximation to the area. Taking the limit of this sum as Δr and $\Delta\theta$ approach zero, and reasoning as in Article **205**, we find

$$\mathbf{A} = \int_\alpha^\beta \int_{r_1(\theta)}^{r_2(\theta)} \mathbf{r\,dr\,d\theta}. \tag{1}$$

In like manner for an area (Figure 225) which is bounded by the polar curves $\theta = \theta_1(r)$ and $\theta = \theta_2(r)$, and the circles $r = a$ and $r = b$, we obtain

$$\mathbf{A} = \int_a^b \int_{\theta_1(r)}^{\theta_2(r)} \mathbf{r\,d\theta\,dr}. \tag{2}$$

Example 1. Find the area inside the circle $r = 2a \cos\theta$ and outside the circle $r = a$.

Solution: Solving the given equations simultaneously, we find the points of intersection as indicated in Figure 226.

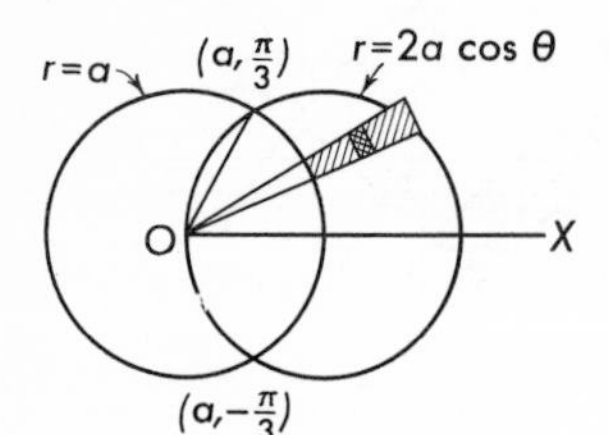

Figure 226

Using (1) and taking symmetry into account, we have

$$A = 2\int_0^{\pi/3} \int_a^{2a\cos\theta} r\,dr\,d\theta$$

$$= \int_0^{\pi/3} (4a^2\cos^2\theta - a^2)\,d\theta = \left(\frac{\pi}{3} + \frac{\sqrt{3}}{2}\right)a^2.$$

Since in polar coordinates, $x = r\cos\theta$, $y = r\sin\theta$, and $dA = r\,dr\,d\theta$, it follows from Article **206** that

$$\mathbf{M_x} = \iint \mathbf{r^2 \sin\theta\,dr\,d\theta}, \qquad \mathbf{M_y} = \iint \mathbf{r^2\cos\theta\,dr\,d\theta}, \tag{3}$$

$$\mathbf{I_x} = \iint \mathbf{r^3\sin^2\theta\,dr\,d\theta}, \qquad \mathbf{I_y} = \iint \mathbf{r^3\cos^2\theta\,dr\,d\theta}, \tag{4}$$

where the order of integration is arbitrary.

Thus, to find the centroid of the area shown in Figure 226, we have $\bar{y} = 0$ and

$$M_y = 2\int_0^{\pi/3}\int_a^{2a\cos\theta} r^2\cos\theta\, dr\, d\theta$$

$$= \frac{2}{3}\int_0^{\pi/3}\cos\theta\,(8a^3\cos^3\theta - a^3)\,d\theta = \left(\frac{2\pi}{3} + \frac{\sqrt{3}}{4}\right)a^3.$$

Hence

$$\bar{x} = \frac{M_y}{A} = \frac{\left(\frac{2\pi}{3} + \frac{\sqrt{3}}{4}\right)a^3}{\left(\frac{\pi}{3} + \frac{\sqrt{3}}{2}\right)a^2} = 1.32a.$$

The integral

$$\iint r^2 \cdot r\, dr\, d\theta \tag{5}$$

evaluated on a plane area such as that shown in Figure 224 or 225 is called the **polar moment of inertia** of the area with respect to the origin. Denoting (5) by I_0, we see from (4) that

$$I_0 = I_x + I_y. \tag{6}$$

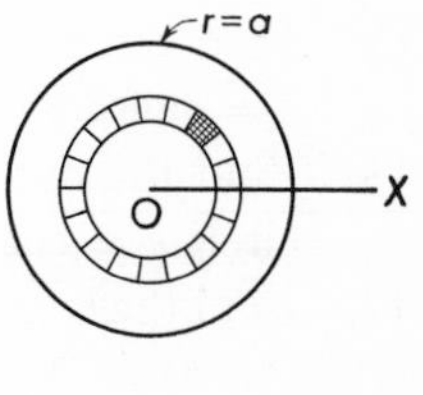

Example 2. Find the polar moment of inertia of a circle with respect to its center.

Solution: For the circle $r = a$ we have, by (5),

$$I_0 = \int_0^a\int_0^{2\pi} r^3\, d\theta\, dr = \tfrac{1}{2}\pi a^4.$$

r=a
O
X

Figure 227

Also, since $I_x = I_y$ by symmetry, it follows from (6) that $I_x = \frac{1}{2}I_0 = \frac{1}{4}\pi a^4 = \frac{1}{4}Aa^2$. That is, the moment of inertia of a circle with respect to a diameter is one-fourth the area of the circle times the square of the radius.

EXERCISE 109

Use double integration to solve the following problems.

1. Find the area inside the circle $r = 2\sqrt{3}\sin\theta$ which is outside the circle $r = 3$. *Ans.* $\frac{1}{2}(3\sqrt{3} - \pi)$.
2. Find the area inside the circle $r = 1$ which is outside the cardioid $r = 1 - \cos\theta$.
3. Find the area inside the circle $r = 6$ which lies to the right of the parabola $r = 3\sec^2\frac{1}{2}\theta$. *Ans.* $18\pi - 24$.
4. Find the area common to the circles $r = 2\cos\theta$ and $r = \sin\theta + \cos\theta$.

5. Find the first-quadrant area bounded by the curve $r = 2 \tan \theta$ and the lines $r = \sqrt{2} \sec \theta$ and $\theta = 0$. *Ans.* $\frac{1}{2}\pi - 1$.
6. Find the smaller area bounded by the cardioid $r = 1 - \cos \theta$ and the tangent line $4r = \sec \theta$.
7. Find the area enclosed by the cardioid $r = a(1 + \cos \theta)$. *Ans.* $\frac{3}{2}\pi a^2$.
8. Find the area inside the cardioid $r = a(1 + \cos \theta)$ which lies to the right of the parabola $r(1 + \cos \theta) = a$. *Hint:* Use the identity $1 + \cos \theta \equiv 2 \cos^2 \frac{1}{2}\theta$.
9. Find the area enclosed by the lemniscate $r^2 = a^2 \cos 2\theta$. *Ans.* a^2.
10. Find the total area enclosed by the eight-leaved rose $r^2 = a^2 \cos 4\theta$.
11. Find the area inside the limaçon $r = 3 - 2 \cos \theta$ which lies between the circles $r = 2$ and $r = 3$. *Ans.* $\frac{11}{3}\pi + \frac{11}{2}\sqrt{3} - 12$.
12. Find the first-quadrant area bounded by the curves $r = \sin \theta$, $r = 1$, $r = \frac{1}{2}\sqrt{2}$, and $\theta = 0$. *Hint:* Draw the line $\theta = \frac{1}{4}\pi$, and find separately the areas of the two parts.
13. Find the centroid of the area that is inside the circle $r = 2 \cos \theta$ and outside the circle $r = \sqrt{2}$. *Ans.* $\bar{x} = \frac{1}{2}\pi$.
14. Find the centroid of the smaller area bounded by the circle $r = 2$ and the line $r = \sec \theta$.
15. Find the centroid of the area enclosed in the upper loop of the curve $r = \sin^2 \theta$. *Ans.* $\bar{y} = 512/315\pi$.
16. Find the centroid of the first-quadrant area which is bounded by the circle $r = \cos \theta$ and the lines $r = \sec \theta$ and $\theta = \frac{1}{4}\pi$.
17. Find the centroid of the area enclosed by the cardioid $r = a(1 + \cos \theta)$. *Ans.* $\bar{x} = \frac{5}{6}a$.
18. Find the centroid of the first-quadrant area enclosed by the four-leaved rose $r = a \sin 2\theta$.
19. Find I_0 for the area enclosed by the limaçon $r = 3 - 2 \cos \theta$. *Ans.* $\frac{195}{2}\pi$.
20. Find I_x for the area enclosed by the circle $r = \sin \theta$.
21. Find I_0 for the area enclosed in the loop of the curve $r = \tan \frac{1}{2}\theta$. *Ans.* $\frac{1}{4}\pi - \frac{2}{3}$.
22. Find I_x for the area common to the circles $r = 4 \sin \theta$ and $r = 4 \cos \theta$. *Hint:* Observe that $I_x = I_y = \frac{1}{2}I_0$.
23. Find I_0 for the area of the four-leaved rose $r = a \cos 2\theta$. *Ans.* $\frac{3}{16}\pi a^4$.
24. Find I_0 for the area enclosed by the loop of the strophoid $r = a(\sec \theta - \tan \theta)$. *Hint:* Show that $r = a \tan \frac{1}{4}(\pi - 2\theta)$.
25. Prove that $\int_0^\infty e^{-x^2}\,dx = \frac{1}{2}\sqrt{\pi}$. *Hint:* Evaluate $\int_0^\infty e^{-x^2}\,dx \int_0^\infty e^{-y^2}\,dy$ in polar coordinates.

209. Volumes by Double Integration

Let R represent the region in the xy plane which is bounded by the curves $y = y_1(x)$ and $y = y_2(x)$ and the lines $x = a$ and $x = b$, and let S denote the surface defined by the equation $z = f(x,y)$. The volume V of the space which lies under S and directly above R may be represented by a double integral in the following manner.

Divide the region R into a rectangular network of elements of dimensions Δx and Δy, and on each element construct a rectangular parallelepiped which has one of its upper vertices on the surface S. The volume of a typical column is $z\,\Delta y\,\Delta x$, and the sum of all such columns taken over R gives an approximation to the required volume. The limit of this sum as Δx and Δy approach zero is equal to the volume, that is,

$$V = \lim_{\Delta y,\Delta x \to 0} \sum z\,\Delta y\,\Delta x = \iint_R z\,dy\,dx. \tag{1}$$

As in Article **205**, the limit (1) may be evaluated by first combining the vertical columns in one laminar section such as PQ in Figure 228. Then adding all such sections, we obtain

$$\boldsymbol{V = \int_a^b \int_{y_1(x)}^{y_2(x)} f(x,y)\,dy\,dx.} \tag{2}$$

For a region R of the type shown in Figure 217, the volume of the space above R and below S is

$$\boldsymbol{V = \int_c^d \int_{x_1(y)}^{x_2(y)} f(x,y)\,dx\,dy.} \tag{3}$$

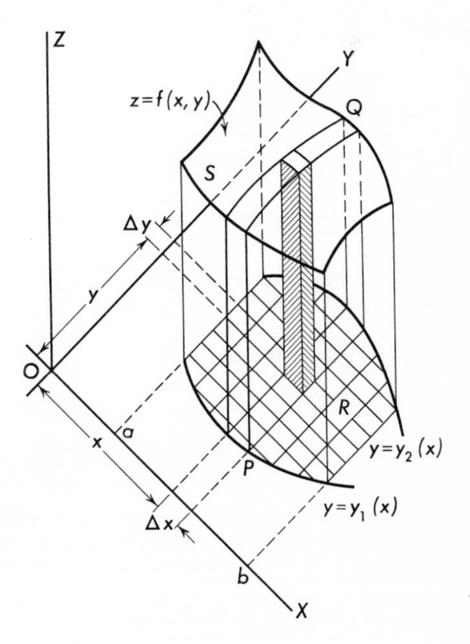

Figure 228

Illustration 1. The volume (Figure 229) above the square $x = 0$, $x = 1$, $y = 0$, $y = 1$, and below the paraboloid $z = 4 - x^2 - y^2$ is by (2)

$$V = \int_0^1 \int_0^1 (4 - x^2 - y^2)\,dy\,dx$$

$$= \int_0^1 \left(\tfrac{11}{3} - x^2\right) dx = \tfrac{10}{3}.$$

It is important that the region R be clearly defined since it alone determines the limits of the integrals (2) and (3).

Illustration 2. To find the volume bounded by the paraboloid $z = 4 - x^2 - y^2$ and the xy plane, we first take $z = 0$ to determine the xy trace. (Figure 229.) Thus R in this case is the interior of the circle $x^2 + y^2 = 4$. Taking symmetry into account, we find the volume

$$V = 4 \int_0^2 \int_0^{\sqrt{4-x^2}} (4 - x^2 - y^2)\, dy\, dx = 8\pi.$$

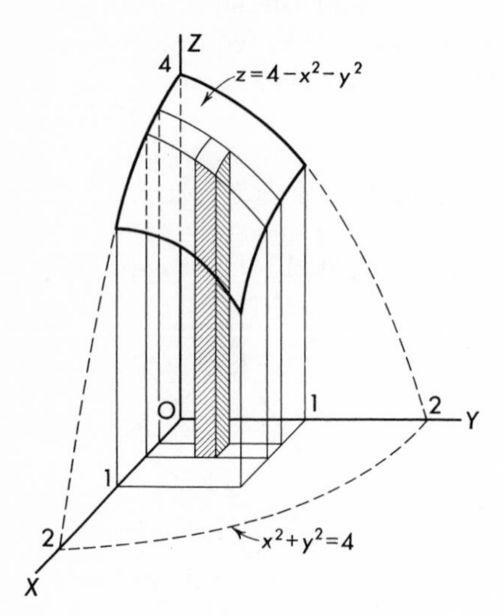

Figure 229

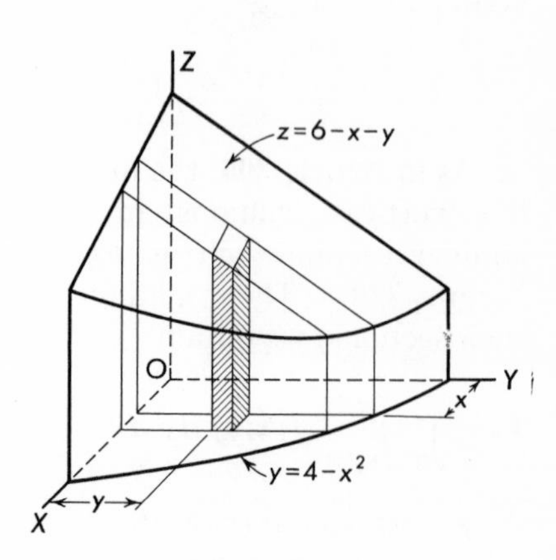

Figure 230

Example. Find the volume (Figure 230) in the first octant under the plane $x + y + z = 6$ and inside the cylinder $y = 4 - x^2$.

Solution: Substituting in (2), we have

$$\begin{aligned} V &= \int_0^2 \int_0^{4-x^2} (6 - x - y)\, dy\, dx \\ &= \int_0^2 \left[6y - xy - \tfrac{1}{2}y^2\right]_0^{4-x^2} dx \\ &= \tfrac{292}{15}. \end{aligned}$$

Integrating first with respect to x gives the same result

$$V = \int_0^4 \int_0^{\sqrt{4-y}} (6 - x - y)\, dx\, dy = \tfrac{292}{15}.$$

EXERCISE 110

If R denotes the square bounded by $x = 0$, $x = 1$, $y = 0$, $y = 1$ in the xy plane, find the volume of the space above R and below the following surfaces.

1. $x + 2y + 4z = 8$. *Ans.* $\frac{13}{8}$.
2. $z = 1 - xy$.
3. $z = \sqrt{x} + \sqrt{y}$. $\frac{4}{3}$.
4. $z = \sqrt{4 - x^2}$.

If R denotes the triangle bounded by $x + y = 1$, $x = 0$, $y = 0$ in the xy plane, find the volume of the space above R and below the following surfaces.

5. $2x + y + 3z = 6$. *Ans.* $\frac{5}{6}$.
6. $z = 1 - y^2$.
7. $z = \sqrt{x + y}$. $\frac{2}{5}$.
8. $z = e^x$.

Find the volumes of the following solids by double integration.

9. The solid bounded by the cylinder $x^2 + y^2 = 4$ and the planes $z + y = 2$ and $z = 0$. *Ans.* 8π.
10. The solid in the first octant bounded by the cylinder $x^2 + z = 1$, the plane $x + y = 1$, and the coordinate planes.
11. The tetrahedron bounded by the plane $x + 2y + 3z = 6$ and the coordinate planes. *Ans.* 6.
12. The solid bounded by the paraboloid $z = 4 - x^2 - 4y^2$ and the plane $z = 0$.
13. The solid in the first octant bounded by the surface $z = xy$, the cylinder $y^2 = 4ax$, and the planes $y = a$ and $z = 0$. *Ans.* $a^4/192$.
14. The solid in the first octant lying within the cylinders $x^2 + z^2 = a^2$ and $y^2 + z^2 = a^2$.
15. The solid bounded by the paraboloid $z = x^2 + y$ and the planes $y = x$, $x = 1$, $y = 0$, and $z = 0$. *Ans.* $\frac{5}{12}$.
16. The solid bounded by the cylinder $x^2 + y^2 = 2x$ and the planes $z = x + 2y + 1$ and $z = 0$.
17. The solid in the first octant bounded by the five surfaces $z = e^{x+y}$, $y = \ln x$, $x = 2$, $y = 0$, and $z = 0$. *Ans.* e.
18. The solid in the first octant bounded by the planes $2x + y + z = 2$ and $x = 0$, and inside the cylinder $y^2 + z^2 = 1$. *Hint:* Evaluate $\int\int x\, dz\, dy$ over the circle $y^2 + z^2 = 1$, $x = 0$.
19. The solid bounded by the surface $x^{1/2} + y^{1/2} + z^{1/2} = a^{1/2}$ and the coordinate planes. *Ans.* $a^3/90$.
20. The solid formed by the closed surface $x^{2/3} + y^{2/3} + z^{2/3} = a^{2/3}$. *Hint:* Use the trigonometric substitution $y = (a^{2/3} - x^{2/3})^{3/2} \sin^3 \theta$ to evaluate the first integral.
21. Evaluate $\int_0^1 dy \int_y^1 \sin x^2\, dx$. *Ans.* $\frac{1}{2}(1 - \cos 1)$.

22. The volume V under the hyperboloid $z = xy$ and above a region R in the xy plane is given by

$$V = \int_0^1 dy \int_0^y xy\, dx + \int_1^2 dy \int_0^{2-y} xy\, dx.$$

Sketch the region in the xy plane and express V as a double integral in which the order of integration is reversed.

23. If $b > a > 0$, prove that $\int_0^\infty \frac{e^{-ax} - e^{-bx}}{x}\, dx = \ln \frac{b}{a}\cdot$ *Hint:* Use $\int_a^b e^{-xy}\, dy = \frac{e^{-ax} - e^{-bx}}{x}$ to form a double integral, and evaluate by changing the order of integration.

210. Volumes in Cylindrical Coordinates

In many problems the computations that are involved may be simplified by using some coordinate system other than rectangular coordinates. One such system, called **cylindrical coordinates,** consists of the usual polar coordinates r and θ in the xy plane, and the rectangular coordinate z. Thus, for the point $P(r,\theta,z)$ or $P(x,y,z)$ in Figure 231, we see that

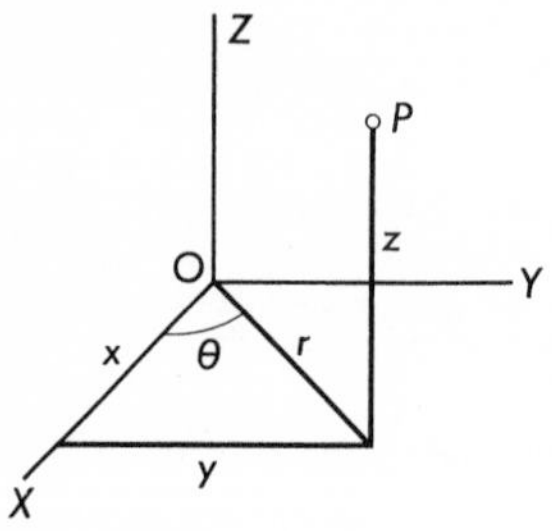

Figure 231

$$x = r\cos\theta, \qquad y = r\sin\theta, \qquad z = z;$$

$$r^2 = x^2 + y^2, \qquad \theta = \tan^{-1}(y/x).$$

The equation of a surface expressed in rectangular coordinates may be changed to cylindrical coordinates by using the above relations. For example, the equation of the plane $z = x + y$ becomes $z = r(\cos\theta + \sin\theta)$. Cylindrical coordinates are particularly useful when the surfaces involved are surfaces of revolution. In this case the equation of the surface contains only two variables. For example, in cylindrical coordinates the circular cone $z^2 = x^2 + y^2$ has the equation $z = r$.

Let us suppose now that a region R in the xy plane is divided into a network of elementary polar subregions as shown in Figure 232. By methods similar to those already discussed, it is clear that the volume of the space under the surface $z = F(r,\theta)$ and above R is defined by

$$V = \lim_{\Delta r, \Delta\theta \to 0} \sum zr\, \Delta r\, \Delta\theta = \iint_R zr\, dr\, d\theta.$$

Depending on the bounds of the region R the value of the above limit is given by

$$V = \int_{\alpha}^{\beta} \int_{r_1(\theta)}^{r_2(\theta)} F(r,\theta)\, r\, dr\, d\theta,$$

or

$$V = \int_{a}^{b} \int_{\theta_1(r)}^{\theta_2(r)} F(r,\theta)\, r\, d\theta\, dr. \quad (1)$$

Illustration. The volume bounded by the paraboloid $z = 4 - x^2 - y^2$ and the xy plane was found in Illustration 2 of the preceding article. In cylindrical coordinates the equation of the surface is $z = 4 - r^2$ and the xy trace is $r = 2$. Hence by (1) the volume is

$$V = \int_0^{2\pi} \int_0^2 (4 - r^2) r\, dr\, d\theta$$

$$= \int_0^{2\pi} \left[2r^2 - \tfrac{1}{4}r^4\right]_0^2 d\theta = 8\pi.$$

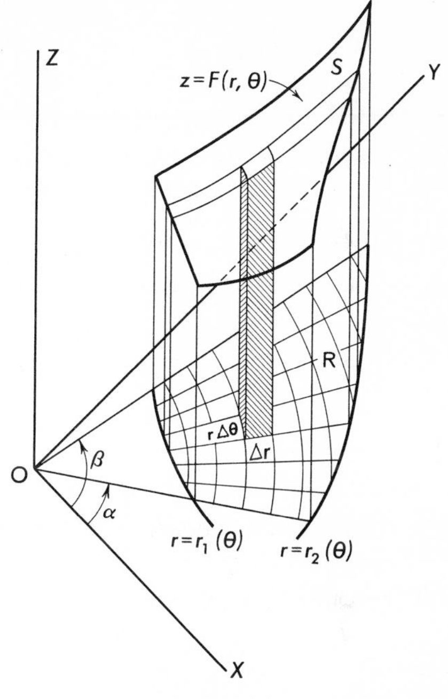

Figure 232

Example. Find the volume of the solid which is bounded by the sphere $x^2 + y^2 + z^2 = a^2$ and enclosed in the cylinder $x^2 + y^2 = ay$.

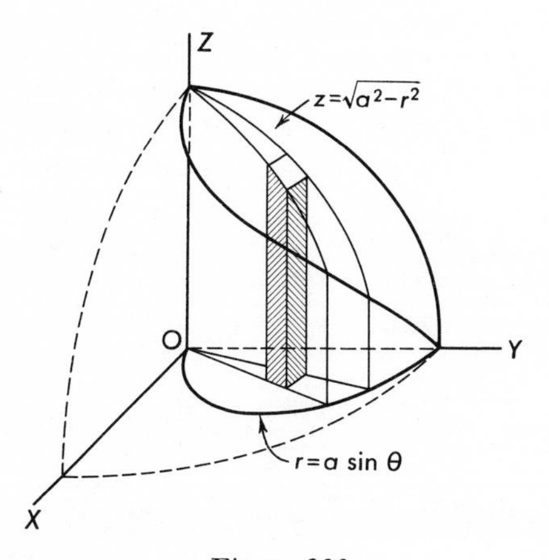

Figure 233

Solution: One fourth of the designated solid is shown in Figure 233 with the equations expressed in cylindrical coordinates.

Substituting in (1) and taking symmetry into account, we find

$$V = 4 \int_0^{\pi/2} \int_0^{a \sin \theta} \sqrt{a^2 - r^2}\, r\, dr\, d\theta$$

$$= \frac{4}{3} \int_0^{\pi/2} \left[-(a^2 - r^2)^{3/2}\right]_0^{a \sin \theta} d\theta$$

$$= \frac{4a^3}{3} \int_0^{\pi/2} (1 - \cos^3 \theta)\, d\theta.$$

Using the Wallis formula, page 567, we obtain the result $V = \frac{2}{9}(3\pi - 4)a^3$.

EXERCISE 111

If R denotes the first-quadrant quarter-circle bounded by $r = 1$ in the xy plane, find the volume of the space above R and below the following surfaces.

1. $z = 1 - r^2$. *Ans.* $\frac{1}{8}\pi$.
2. $z = \sin\theta$.
3. $z = r^2 \sin 2\theta$. $\frac{1}{4}$.
4. $z = r^2 \cos^2\theta$.

If R denotes the first-quadrant semicircle bounded by $r = \cos\theta$ in the xy plane, find the volume of the space above R and below the following surfaces.

5. $z = 2 - 2r^2$. *Ans.* $\frac{5}{32}\pi$.
6. $z = \sin 2\theta$.
7. $z = r^2 \sin^2\theta$. $\pi/128$.
8. $z = r(\sin\theta + \cos\theta)$.

Using cylindrical coordinates, find the volumes of the following solids by double integration.

9. The solid bounded by the sphere $r^2 + z^2 = 4$ and enclosed in the cylinder $r = 1$. *Ans.* $\frac{4}{3}\pi(8 - 3\sqrt{3})$.
10. The solid in the first octant bounded by the cone $z = r$, the cylinder $r = 2\sin\theta$, and the plane $\theta = \frac{1}{2}\pi$.
11. The solid in the first octant bounded by the paraboloid $4z = r^2$ and the planes $r = 2\sec\theta$, $\theta = 0$, $\theta = \frac{1}{4}\pi$, and $z = 0$. *Ans.* $\frac{4}{3}$.
12. The solid in the first octant enclosed in the cylinder $r = \sin 2\theta$ and bounded by the planes $z = r\sin\theta$ and $z = 0$.
13. The solid enclosed by the sphere $x^2 + y^2 + z^2 = a^2$. *Ans.* $\frac{4}{3}\pi a^3$.
14. The solid bounded by the sphere $x^2 + y^2 + (z + 1)^2 = 4$ and above the plane $z = 0$.
15. The solid in the first octant bounded by the surface $z = r^2 \sin 2\theta$, the cylinder $r = \tan\theta$, and the planes $\theta = \frac{1}{4}\pi$ and $z = 0$. *Ans.* $\frac{3}{8} - \frac{1}{2}\ln 2$.
16. The solid bounded by the hyperboloid $z^2 - x^2 - y^2 = 9$ and the plane $z = 5$.
17. The solid enclosed by the torus $(x^2 + y^2 + z^2)^2 = x^2 + y^2$. *Ans.* $\frac{1}{4}\pi^2$.
18. The solid enclosed by the surface $b^4(x^2 + y^2) + a^2z^4 = a^2b^4$.

211. Areas of Curved Surfaces

Consider a surface defined by the equation $z = f(x,y)$, and let S represent the area bounded by a closed curve C on the surface. If the projection of S on the xy plane is denoted by A (Figure 234), and A is divided into rectangular elements $\Delta x\, \Delta y$, a typical element projected vertically will cut an element of area ΔS from the surface. This vertical column also cuts an element of area $\Delta S'$ from a plane which is tangent to the surface at one vertex P of ΔS.

If γ is the acute angle between this tangent plane and the xy plane, then

$$\Delta A = \Delta S' \cos \gamma. \tag{1}$$

We observe, however, that γ is also the acute angle between the z axis and the normal to the surface at P. Since, by Article **197,** the direction

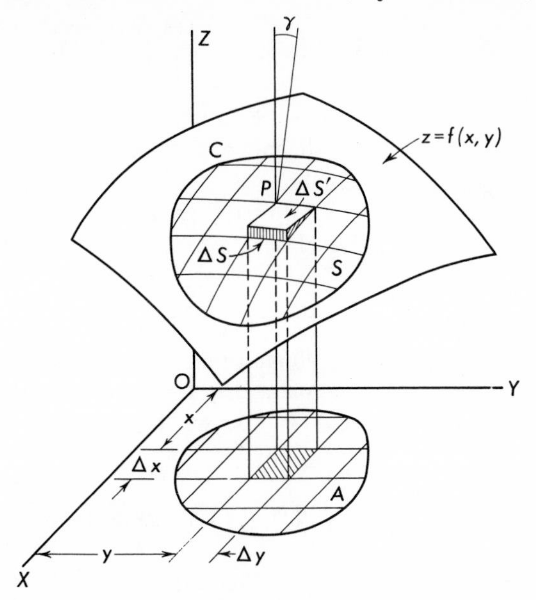

Figure 234

cosines of the normal are proportional to $\partial z/\partial x$, $\partial z/\partial y$, -1, it follows from **45,** page 6, that

$$\cos \gamma = \frac{1}{\sqrt{1 + \left(\frac{\partial z}{\partial x}\right)^2 + \left(\frac{\partial z}{\partial y}\right)^2}},$$

and hence (1) becomes

$$\Delta S' = \sqrt{1 + \left(\frac{\partial z}{\partial x}\right)^2 + \left(\frac{\partial z}{\partial y}\right)^2}\, \Delta x\, \Delta y. \tag{2}$$

When Δx and Δy are sufficiently small, the area $\Delta S'$ on the tangent plane is approximately equal to the element of area ΔS on the surface, that is, $\Delta S'/\Delta S$ approaches 1 as Δx and Δy approach 0. For this reason, we define the area S of the surface by the limit

$$\boldsymbol{S = \iint_{(A)} \sqrt{1 + \left(\frac{\partial z}{\partial x}\right)^2 + \left(\frac{\partial z}{\partial y}\right)^2}\, dx\, dy.} \tag{3}$$

Similarly, by projecting S on the other coordinate planes, the required area may be found by use of one of the formulas

$$S = \iint_{(A')} \sqrt{1 + \left(\frac{\partial x}{\partial y}\right)^2 + \left(\frac{\partial x}{\partial z}\right)^2}\, dy\, dz, \tag{4}$$

$$S = \iint_{(A'')} \sqrt{1 + \left(\frac{\partial y}{\partial x}\right)^2 + \left(\frac{\partial y}{\partial z}\right)^2}\, dz\, dx, \tag{5}$$

where A' and A'' are the projections of S on the yz plane and zx plane, respectively.

To evaluate the integrals (3), (4), or (5) we choose appropriate limits which depend solely on the shape of the projected plane areas A, A', or A'', respectively.

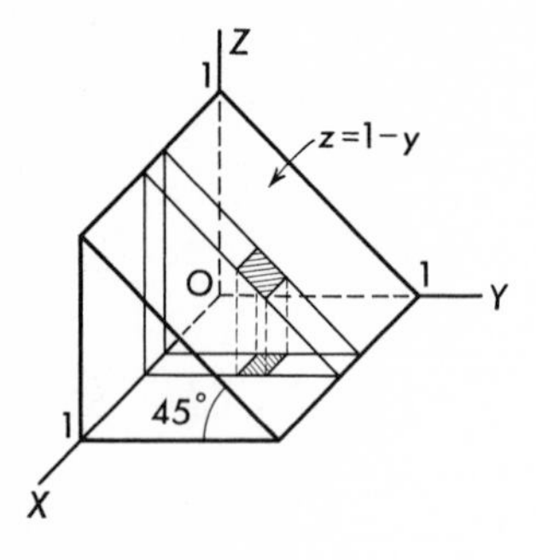

Figure 235

Illustration. For the first-octant area of the plane $z = 1 - y$ between the planes $x = 0$ and $x = 1$, we have $z_x = 0$ and $z_y = -1$. Hence by (3)

$$S = \int_0^1 \int_0^1 \sqrt{1 + (0)^2 + (-1)^2}\, dx\, dy = \sqrt{2}.$$

Observe that the area S in Figure 235 and its projection A satisfy the relation (1); that is, $A = S \cos \gamma = \sqrt{2} \cos 45° = 1$.

Example 1. Find the area in the first octant cut from the cylindrical surface $x^2 + y^2 = a^2$ by the plane $z = x$.

Solution: Projecting the required area S on the zx plane, we obtain the triangle BOC (Figure 236) with the boundaries $z = 0$, $z = x$, and $x = a$.

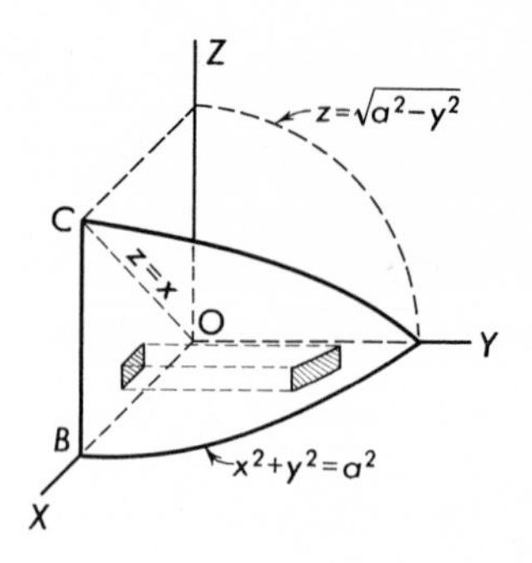

Figure 236

Since for the cylinder $y = \sqrt{a^2 - x^2}$ we have $\partial y/\partial x = -x/\sqrt{a^2 - x^2}$ and $\partial y/\partial z = 0$, it follows from (5) that

$$S = \int_0^a \int_0^x \frac{a}{\sqrt{a^2 - x^2}}\, dz\, dx = a \int_0^a \frac{x\, dx}{\sqrt{a^2 - x^2}} = a^2.$$

This result is also given by

$$S = \int_0^a \int_z^a \frac{a}{\sqrt{a^2 - x^2}}\, dx\, dz,$$

in which the order of integration over BOC is interchanged. Observe, however, that the latter integral is much more difficult to evaluate. This illustrates the advantage to be gained in carefully selecting the order of integration.

Observe also that if the area S is projected on the zy plane, we find by (4)

$$S = \int_0^a \int_0^{\sqrt{a^2-y^2}} \frac{a}{\sqrt{a^2 - y^2}}\, dz\, dy = a \int_0^a dy = a^2.$$

Thus we see that the choice of projection also affects the work involved. There is no set rule to indicate which integral is going to be the simplest to solve. Hence in some cases several of the integrals should be considered.

Example 2. By double integration, find the area of the surface of the sphere

$$x^2 + y^2 + z^2 = a^2.$$

Solution: For the given equation, we have

$$\frac{\partial z}{\partial x} = -\frac{x}{z}, \qquad \frac{\partial z}{\partial y} = -\frac{y}{z};$$

hence

$$1 + \left(\frac{\partial z}{\partial x}\right)^2 + \left(\frac{\partial z}{\partial y}\right)^2 = 1 + \frac{x^2}{z^2} + \frac{y^2}{z^2} = \frac{a^2}{z^2}. \tag{6}$$

Since BCD (Figure 237) represents one-eighth of the total surface, we have by (3) and (6)

$$S = 8 \iint_{(A)} \frac{a}{\sqrt{a^2 - x^2 - y^2}}\, dx\, dy, \tag{7}$$

where A denotes the quarter circle BOC.

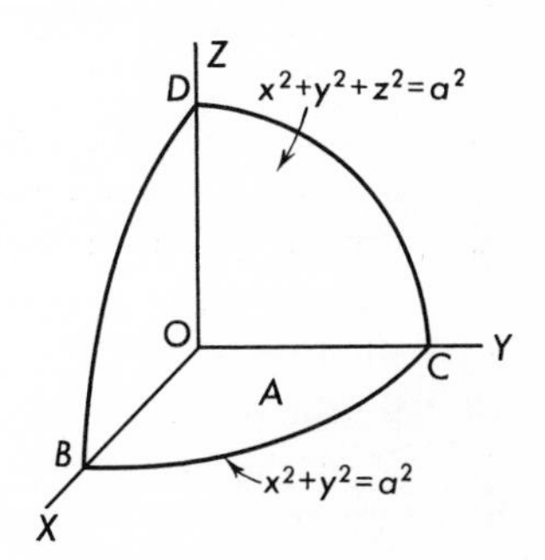

Figure 237

Although the integral (7) may be evaluated using rectangular coordinates, it is simpler to change to polar coordinates. That is, in (7) we substitute $r \cos \theta$ for x, $r \sin \theta$ for y, and $r\, dr\, d\theta$ for $dx\, dy$. Making this substitution and providing limits, (7) becomes

$$S = 8 \int_0^{\pi/2} \int_0^a \frac{a}{\sqrt{a^2 - r^2}}\, r\, dr\, d\theta$$

$$= 8a \int_0^{\pi/2} \left[-\sqrt{a^2 - r^2}\right]_0^a d\theta = 4\pi a^2.$$

EXERCISE 112

Find the area of that portion of the following surfaces which is bounded by the planes $x = 0$, $x = 1$, $y = 0$, and $y = 1$.

1. $x + 2y + z = 4$. *Ans.* $\sqrt{6}$.
2. $z = 1 - y^2$.
3. $z = x^{3/2} + \sqrt{3}y$. $\frac{61}{27}$.
4. $3z = 2x^{3/2} + 2y^{3/2}$.

Find the area of that portion of the following surfaces which is bounded by the planes $x = 1$, $y = 0$, and $y = x$.

5. $2x + 2y + z = 4$. *Ans.* $\frac{3}{2}$.
6. $z = x^2$.
7. $z = \frac{2}{3}(1 + y^2)^{3/2}$. $\frac{2}{3}$.
8. $z = x^3 + \sqrt{15}y$.
9. Find the area of the surface in the first octant cut from the cylinder $x^2 + z^2 = a^2$ by the plane $y = 2z$. *Ans.* $2a^2$.
10. Find the area of the surface of the cylinder $x^2 + z^2 = a^2$ intercepted by the cylinder $x^2 + y^2 = a^2$.
11. Find the area of the surface in the first octant cut from the cone $z^2 = x^2 + y^2$ by the plane $x + y = a$. *Ans.* $\frac{1}{2}\sqrt{2}a^2$.
12. Find the total area of the solid enclosed by the cylinders $x^{2/3} + z^{2/3} = a^{2/3}$ and $y^{2/3} + z^{2/3} = a^{2/3}$.
13. Find the area of the surface in the first octant cut from the cylinder $x^2 = 4y$ by the plane $2x + 2z = 3$. *Ans.* $\frac{13}{96} + \frac{3}{2}\ln 2$.
14. Find the area of the surface $z = \frac{2}{3}(1 + x^2 + y^2)^{3/2}$ intercepted by the planes $x = 0$, $x = 1$, $y = 0$, and $y = 1$.
15. Find the area of that part of the upper half of the sphere $x^2 + y^2 + z^2 = a^2$ whose projection on the xy plane is bounded by one loop of the rose $r = a \cos 2\theta$. *Ans.* $\frac{1}{2}(\pi - 2)a^2$.
16. Find the surface area of that part of the paraboloid $z = 4 - x^2 - y^2$ which lies above the xy plane.
17. Find the area of the surface of the sphere $x^2 + y^2 + z^2 = 4a^2$ intercepted by the cylinder $x^2 + y^2 = a^2$. *Ans.* $8(2 - \sqrt{3})\pi a^2$.
18. Find the area of that part of the paraboloid $2z = x^2 + y^2$ whose projection on the xy plane is bounded by the lemniscate $r^2 = \cos 2\theta$.
19. Find the first-octant area of the surface $az = xy$ intercepted by the cylinder $x^2 + y^2 = a^2$. *Ans.* $\frac{1}{6}(2\sqrt{2} - 1)\pi a^2$.
20. Find the area of the surface of the sphere $x^2 + y^2 + z^2 = a^2$ intercepted by the cylinder $y^2 + z^2 = ay$. *Hint:* Project the surface on the yz plane; let $y = r\cos\theta$, $z = r\sin\theta$, and substitute $r\,dr\,d\theta$ for $dy\,dz$.

212. Triple Integrals

Let V be a closed finite region of three-dimensional space, and let $f(x,y,z)$ be a function that is single-valued at each point (x,y,z) of V. Suppose that the region V is divided in some manner into n parts, each part of volume $\Delta V_1, \Delta V_2, \cdots, \Delta V_n$. Let (x'_k,y'_k,z'_k) denote any point within or on the boundary of the subregion ΔV_k, and consider the sum

$$\sum_{k=1}^{n} f(x'_k,y'_k,z'_k)\, \Delta V_k. \tag{1}$$

If, as $n \to \infty$ and the maximum diameter of every subregion approaches zero, the sum (1) has a limit that is independent of the type of subdivision used and the choice of the points (x'_k,y'_k,z'_k), we denote the limit by the symbol

$$\iiint_V f(x,y,z)\, dV,$$

and call it the **triple integral** of $f(x,y,z)$ over the spatial region V. As in the case of the double integral, it can be shown that the preceding limit exists for every function $f(x,y,z)$ that is continuous in V.

In a three-dimensional space, triple integrals can be used to express many physical quantities such as mass, center of gravity, and moment of inertia. Thus the mass of a solid that occupies a volume V and has a continuous density $\rho(x,y,z)$ is

$$M = \iiint_V \rho(x,y,z)\, dV.$$

For the center of gravity $(\bar{x},\bar{y},\bar{z})$ of the solid, we have

$$M\bar{x} = \iiint_V x\rho(x,y,z)\, dV,$$

with similar expressions for $\bar{y}$ and $\bar{z}$. The moment of inertia of the solid is

$$I = \iiint_V r^2\rho(x,y,z)\, dV,$$

where r is the distance from the point (x,y,z) of the solid to the axis about which the moment is taken.

Note: The manner in which we have generalized the dimensionality of an integral makes it apparent that we could in the same way just as easily define an n-fold integral

$$\int \cdots \int_{V_n} f(x_1,x_2, \cdots, x_n)\, dV_n$$

over an n-dimensional region in an n-dimensional space. Integrals of this more general type are used and have practical significance in many problems pertaining to statistics, mechanics, and other areas.

213. Iterated Integrals

As for double integrals the expression

$$\int_a^b \int_{y_1(x)}^{y_2(x)} \int_{z_1(x,y)}^{z_2(x,y)} f(x,y,z)\,dz\,dy\,dx \tag{1}$$

is called an **iterated integral.** It indicates that three successive integrations are to be performed in the following order: first with respect to z, then with respect to y, and finally with respect to x.

Five other integrals similar to (1) may be obtained by interchanging the order of integration. In all these it is important to observe that when an integration is performed with respect to a variable, that variable is eliminated completely from the remaining integral.

Illustration 1. Evaluating $\int_0^1 dy \int_0^y dx \int_0^{xy} z\,dz$, we have

$$\tfrac{1}{2}\int_0^1 dy \int_0^y x^2y^2\,dx = \tfrac{1}{6}\int_0^1 y^5\,dy = \tfrac{1}{36}.$$

Illustration 2. Evaluating $\int_0^{\pi/2} \int_0^{\cos\theta} \int_{r^2}^{r\cos\theta} r\,dz\,dr\,d\theta$, we have

$$\int_0^{\pi/2} \int_0^{\cos\theta} (r^2\cos\theta - r^3)\,dr\,d\theta = \tfrac{1}{12}\int_0^{\pi/2} \cos^4\theta\,d\theta = \tfrac{1}{64}\pi.$$

EXERCISE 113

Evaluate the following iterated integrals.

1. $\int_0^1 \int_0^x \int_0^{x+y} (x + y + z)\,dz\,dy\,dx.$ *Ans.* $\frac{7}{8}$.
2. $\int_0^2 \int_1^z \int_0^{yz} xyz\,dx\,dy\,dz.$
3. $\int_1^2 y\,dy \int_y^{y^2} dx \int_0^{\ln x} e^z\,dz.$ $\frac{47}{24}$.
4. $\int_0^a \int_0^{\sqrt{a^2-x^2}} \int_0^{a-x} y\,dz\,dy\,dx.$
5. $\int_0^{\pi/2} \int_x^{\pi/2} \int_0^{xy} \cos\frac{z}{x}\,dz\,dy\,dx.$ $\frac{1}{2}\pi - 1.$
6. $\int_3^5 \int_{-x}^x \int_0^{\sqrt{x^2+y^2}} \frac{y\,dz\,dy\,dx}{x^2 + y^2 + z^2}.$
7. $\int_{\pi/6}^{\pi/2} \int_0^{\cos y} \int_y^{\pi-y} \sin(y + z)\,dz\,dx\,dy.$ $\frac{5}{12}$.
8. $\int_0^{\pi/4} \int_0^{2\sin\theta} \int_0^{r\cos\theta} r\,dz\,dr\,d\theta.$

9. $\int_0^{\pi/2} d\theta \int_0^a r\,dr \int_{1-\cos\theta}^{1+\cos\theta} z\,dz.$ *Ans.* a^2.

10. $\int_0^{\pi/4} \int_{2\sin\theta}^{2\cos\theta} \int_0^{r\sin\theta} r^2 \cos\theta\,dz\,dr\,d\theta.$

11. $\int_0^{2\pi} \int_0^{\pi} \int_0^a r^2 \sin\theta\,dr\,d\theta\,d\phi.$ $\frac{4}{3}\pi a^3$.

12. $\int_{\pi/4}^{\pi/2} \sin\phi\,d\phi \int_{\pi/4}^{\phi} \sin^2\theta\,d\theta \int_0^{a\csc\theta} r^3\,dr.$

214. Iterated Triple Integrals in Rectangular Coordinates

The value of a triple integral can be determined by extending the concept of an iterated integral to three dimensions. The methods used are analogous to those employed in evaluating double integrals, and no further justification of the methods will be considered here.

To obtain an iterated triple integral in rectangular coordinates, we divide the three-dimensional space into small rectangular parallelepipeds by sets of planes parallel to the coordinate planes. Those parallelepipeds that contain points within and on the boundary of a region V are denoted by $\Delta V_1, \Delta V_2, \cdots, \Delta V_n$, the dimensions of ΔV_k being $\Delta x_k, \Delta y_k, \Delta z_k$. If (x_k,y_k,z_k) is a point of ΔV_k, we have

$$\lim_{n\to\infty} \sum_{k=1}^{n} f(x_k,y_k,z_k)\,\Delta x_k\,\Delta y_k\,\Delta z_k = \iiint_V f(x,y,z)\,dV, \tag{1}$$

the limit being taken as the dimensions of all parallelepipeds approach zero.

If R (Figure 238) denotes the region in the xy plane that is determined by the projection of the points of V on that plane, we observe that a rectangular column erected on an element ΔA_k of R will contain those parallelepipeds that lie between a lower surface $z = z_1(x,y)$ and an upper surface $z = z_2(x,y)$ that bounds V. This observation indicates that the value of the triple integral can be represented as a double integral having the form

$$\iint_R \left[\int_{z_1(x,y)}^{z_2(x,y)} f(x,y,z)\,dz\right] dA. \tag{2}$$

Evaluation of the double integral (2) gives the result

$$\iiint_V f(x,y,z)\,dV = \int_a^b dx \int_{y_1(x)}^{y_2(x)} dy \int_{z_1(x,y)}^{z_2(x,y)} f(x,y,z)\,dz, \tag{3}$$

where the limits y_1, y_2, a, and b are determined by the boundary of R.

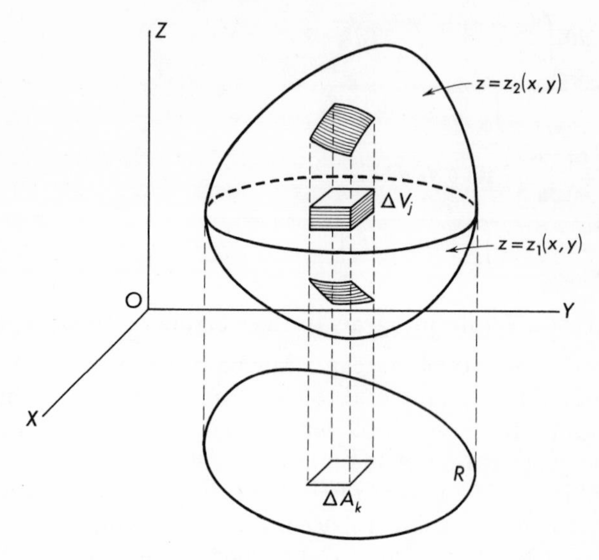

Figure 238

It is apparent that five other formulas like (3) could be obtained, one for each of the possible orders of integration of x, y, and z.

215. Volumes by Triple Integration

A volume V (Figure 239), which is bounded by the surfaces $z = z_1(x,y)$ and $z = z_2(x,y)$, the cylinders $y = y_1(x)$ and $y = y_2(x)$, and the planes $x = a$ and $x = b$, may, with little loss of generality, be represented by an iterated integral in the following manner.

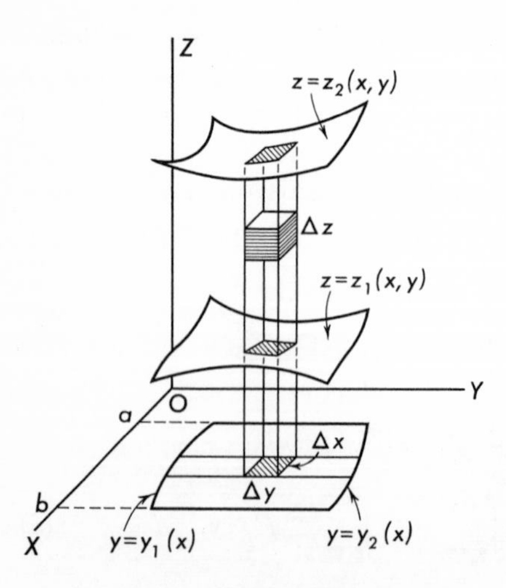

Figure 239

Construct three sets of planes parallel to the coordinate planes and spaced at intervals Δx, Δy, and Δz, respectively. The space is thus divided into cells consisting of rectangular parallelepipeds, each having the volume $\Delta V = \Delta z\, \Delta y\, \Delta x$. The sum of the volumes of all the elements that lie within and on the boundary of V gives an approximation to its volume. The limit of this sum, as Δx, Δy, and Δz approach zero, gives the required volume, that is,

$$V = \lim_{\Delta z, \Delta y, \Delta x \to 0} \sum \Delta z \, \Delta y \, \Delta x = \iiint_V dz \, dy \, dx. \tag{1}$$

The limit (1) may be evaluated by first combining the elements of volume in one vertical column as Δz approaches zero; thus

$$\text{Volume of column} = \left[\int_{z_1(x,y)}^{z_2(x,y)} dz \right] \Delta y \, \Delta x.$$

Then continuing as in Article **211,** we obtain the required result

$$V = \int_a^b \int_{y_1(x)}^{y_2(x)} \int_{z_1(x,y)}^{z_2(x,y)} dz \, dy \, dx, \tag{2}$$

which corresponds to (3) in the preceding article for $f(x,y,z) = 1$.

Again it is clear that the order of integration in (2) is immaterial provided the limits are chosen to include all the given volume.

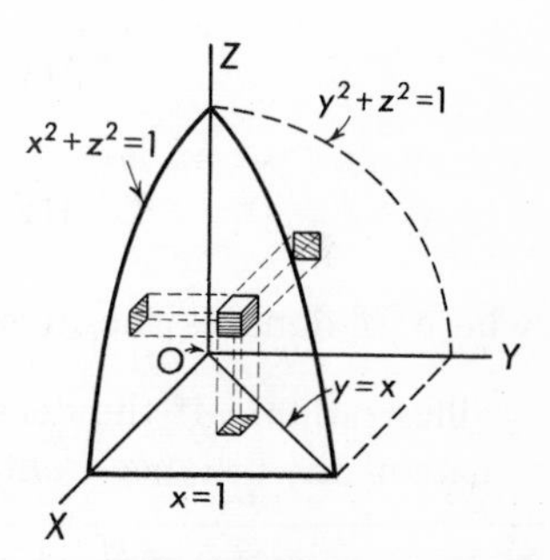

Figure 240

Illustration. The volume of the first-octant solid (Figure 240), which is bounded by the cylinder $x^2 + z^2 = 1$, and the planes $y = x$, $y = 0$, and $z = 0$, is given by any one of the following six iterated integrals.

$$\int_0^1 \int_0^x \int_0^{\sqrt{1-x^2}} dz \, dy \, dx, \qquad \int_0^1 \int_y^1 \int_0^{\sqrt{1-x^2}} dz \, dx \, dy,$$

$$\int_0^1 \int_0^{\sqrt{1-x^2}} \int_0^x dy \, dz \, dx, \qquad \int_0^1 \int_0^{\sqrt{1-z^2}} \int_0^x dy \, dx \, dz,$$

$$\int_0^1 \int_0^{\sqrt{1-y^2}} \int_y^{\sqrt{1-z^2}} dx \, dz \, dy, \qquad \int_0^1 \int_0^{\sqrt{1-z^2}} \int_y^{\sqrt{1-z^2}} dx \, dy \, dz.$$

Note: Remember that the work involved in evaluating a multiple integral is often made easier by changing the order of integration. Thus, for example,

$$\int_0^1 \int_0^{\sqrt{1-y^2}} \frac{y \, dx \, dy}{\sqrt{x^2 + y^2}} = \int_0^1 y \ln \left(\frac{1 + \sqrt{1 - y^2}}{y} \right) dy,$$

whereas

$$\int_0^1 \int_0^{\sqrt{1-x^2}} \frac{y \, dy \, dx}{\sqrt{x^2 + y^2}} = \int_0^1 (1 - x) \, dx.$$

216. Center of Gravity and Moment of Inertia of a Solid

If the density ρ of a solid is constant or a function of the coordinates x, y, z, it follows by the reasoning of the preceding articles that the mass of the solid is given by

$$M = \iiint_V \rho\, dz\, dy\, dx, \tag{1}$$

where the integral is computed throughout the volume occupied by the solid.

By similar reasoning it is clear that the coordinates $(\bar{x},\bar{y},\bar{z})$ of the center of gravity of the solid may be found by use of the formulas

$$M\bar{x} = \iiint_V \rho x\, dz\, dy\, dx, \tag{2}$$

$$M\bar{y} = \iiint_V \rho y\, dz\, dy\, dx, \tag{3}$$

$$M\bar{z} = \iiint_V \rho z\, dz\, dy\, dx, \tag{4}$$

where M denotes the mass (1).

Illustration. If the density in a unit cube $0 \leqq x, y, z \leqq 1$ varies as the square of the distance from one vertex, say $(0,0,0)$, we have from (1)

$$M = \int_0^1 \int_0^1 \int_0^1 k(x^2 + y^2 + z^2)\, dz\, dy\, dx = k.$$

By symmetry we thus obtain from (2)

$$\bar{x} = \bar{y} = \bar{z} = \int_0^1 \int_0^1 \int_0^1 x(x^2 + y^2 + z^2)\, dz\, dy\, dx = \tfrac{7}{12}.$$

When a mass is concentrated at a point, its moment of inertia with respect to an axis is defined to be the magnitude of the mass multiplied by the square of its distance from the axis. Thus if a differential element of mass $dM = \rho\, dz\, dy\, dx$ is considered to be concentrated at the point (x,y,z), the moments of inertia of the solid with respect to the coordinate axes are

$$I_x = \iiint_V \rho(y^2 + z^2)\, dz\, dy\, dx, \tag{5}$$

$$I_y = \iiint_V \rho(z^2 + x^2)\, dz\, dy\, dx, \tag{6}$$

$$I_z = \iiint_V \rho(x^2 + y^2)\, dz\, dy\, dx. \tag{7}$$

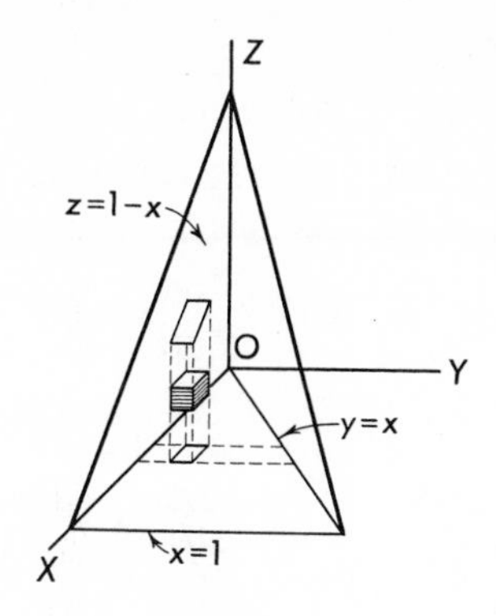

Figure 241

Example. A solid (Figure 241) of constant density ρ is bounded by the four planes $x + z = 1$, $y = x$, $y = 0$, and $z = 0$. Find its moment of inertia with respect to the z axis.

Solution: In accordance with (7), we have

$$I_z = \int_0^1 dx \int_0^x dy \int_0^{1-x} \rho(x^2 + y^2)\, dz$$

$$= \rho \int_0^1 (1 - x)\, dx \int_0^x (x^2 + y^2)\, dy$$

$$= \tfrac{4}{3}\rho \int_0^1 (1 - x)x^3\, dx = \tfrac{1}{15}\,\rho.$$

EXERCISE 114

By triple integration in each of the following, find the volume of the solid bounded by the given surfaces.

1. $x + y + 2z = 2,\quad x = 0,\quad y = 0,\quad z = 0.$ *Ans.* $\frac{2}{3}$.
2. $z^2 = 4y,\quad x^2 = 4y,\quad y = 4.$ (First octant.)
3. $z = x^2 + y^2,\quad x = y,\quad x = 2,\quad y = 0,\quad z = 0.$ $\frac{16}{3}$.
4. $x + y + z = 4,\quad y = 3z,\quad x = 0,\quad y = 0.$
5. $x^2 + 4y^2 = z,\quad x^2 + 4y^2 = 12 - 2z.$ 6π.
6. $z = 8/(x^2 + 4),\quad y = x,\quad x = 0,\quad y = 2,\quad z = 0.$

If the density varies as indicated, find the mass of the solid bounded by the given surfaces.

7. $x = 0,\quad x = 1,\quad y = 0,\quad y = 1,\quad z = 0,\quad z = 1;\quad \rho = kx.$ *Ans.* $\frac{1}{2}k$.
8. $x^2 + z^2 = 4,\quad y = x,\quad y = 0,\quad z = 0,$ (First octant.); $\rho = kz.$
9. $zy = 4,\quad x = 0,\quad x = 2,\quad y = 1,\quad y = 4,\quad z = 0;\quad \rho = ky^2.$ *Ans.* $60k$.
10. $x + y + z = 1,\quad x = 0,\quad y = 0,\quad z = 0;\quad \rho = kxy.$
11. $z = xy,\quad x = 1,\quad y = 1,\quad z = 0;\quad \rho = k\sqrt{x^2 + y^2}.$ *Ans.* $\frac{2}{15}k(2\sqrt{2} - 1)$.
12. $z = e^{-x-y},\quad x + y = 1,\quad x = 0,\quad y = 0,\quad z = 0;\quad \rho = k(x + y).$

If the density varies as indicated, find the center of gravity of the solid bounded by the given surfaces.

13. $x + y = 1,\quad x = 0,\quad y = 0,\quad z = 0,\quad z = 1;\quad \rho = kxy.$ *Ans.* $(\frac{2}{5}, \frac{2}{5}, \frac{1}{2})$.
14. $x + y + z = 4,\quad x = 0,\quad y = 0,\quad z = 0;\quad \rho = k.$
15. $z = x^2 + y^2,\quad x = 0,\quad x = 1,\quad y = 0,\quad y = 1;\quad \rho = k.$ *Ans.* $(\frac{5}{8}, \frac{5}{8}, \frac{7}{15})$.
16. $z^2 = 4x,\quad y = 2x,\quad x = 4,\quad y = 0,\quad z = 0,$ (First octant.); $\rho = k.$

17. $x + z = 1,\ \ y = x,\ \ y = 0,\ \ z = 0;\ \ \rho = ky.$ *Ans.* $(\frac{3}{5}, \frac{2}{5}, \frac{1}{5})$.
18. $z = xy,\ \ x^2 + y^2 = 1,\ \ z = 0,$ (First octant.); $\rho = k.$

If the density varies as indicated, find the designated moment of inertia for the solid bounded by the given surfaces.

19. I_x: $x = 0,\ \ x = 1,\ \ y = 0,\ \ y = 1,\ \ z = 0,\ \ z = 1;\ \ \rho = kz.$ *Ans.* $\frac{5}{12}k$.
20. I_z: $x + z = 1,\ \ y + z = 1,\ \ x = 0,\ \ y = 0,\ \ z = 0;\ \ \rho = k.$
21. I_y: $x^2 + z^2 = 1,\ \ y = x,\ \ y = 0,\ \ z = 0,$ (First octant.); $\rho = kz.$ *Ans.* $\frac{1}{12}k$.
22. I_z: $z^2 = xy,\ \ x^2 + y^2 = 1,\ \ z = 0,$ (First octant.); $\rho = kz.$
23. I_z: $x + y + 2z = 4,\ \ x = 0,\ \ y = 0,\ \ z = 0;\ \ \rho = k.$ *Ans.* $\frac{256}{15}k$.
24. I_z: $x^2 + z^2 = a^2,\ \ y^2 + z^2 = a^2;\ \ \rho = k.$
25. By changing the order of integration, show that

$$\int_0^x du \int_0^u f(t)\,dt = \int_0^x (x - t) f(t)\,dt$$

and

$$\int_0^x dv \int_0^v du \int_0^u f(t)\,dt = \frac{1}{2!}\int_0^x (x - t)^2 f(t)\,dt.$$

Generalize by mathematical induction.

217. Triple Integrals in Cylindrical Coordinates

The volume of a solid or a quantity associated with the volume of a solid may often be found more readily by dividing the space as a whole into elements of volume differing in shape from the parallelepipeds used in connection with the rectangular coordinates x, y, and z.

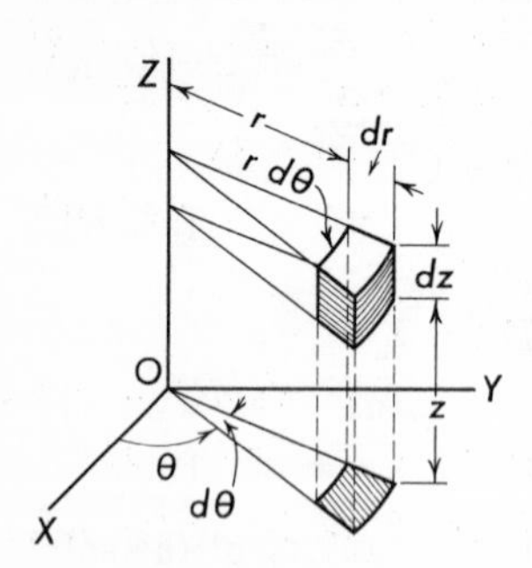

Figure 242

Thus for cylindrical coordinates the space is divided into elements of volume by (*a*) planes through the z axis at angular intervals $d\theta$, (*b*) circular cylinders with axes on the z axis and at radial intervals dr, and (*c*) planes perpendicular to the z axis at intervals dz. Since for each element of volume (Figure 242), the cross-sectional area is $r\,dr\,d\theta$ and the height is dz, it follows that the differential of volume is,

$$dV = r\,dz\,dr\,d\theta. \tag{1}$$

Example 1. Find the volume of the solid bounded by the paraboloid $z = 1 - (x^2 + y^2)$ and the plane $z = 0$.

Solution: In accordance with (1), the volume is given by

$$V = \iiint_V r\,dz\,dr\,d\theta.$$

The limits for the above integral are found as follows. The first integration keeps r and θ fixed (Figure 243) and adds the elements of volume along a vertical column from the plane $z = 0$ to the paraboloid $z = 1 - r^2$. The next integration keeps θ fixed and adds the columns from the z axis to the circle $r = 1$. This gives the volume of a wedge. Then the wedges are added from $\theta = 0$ to $\theta = 2\pi$. Hence

$$V = \int_0^{2\pi} \int_0^1 \int_0^{1-r^2} r\,dz\,dr\,d\theta = \tfrac{1}{2}\pi.$$

Example 2. Find the mass of a right circular cone of altitude a and

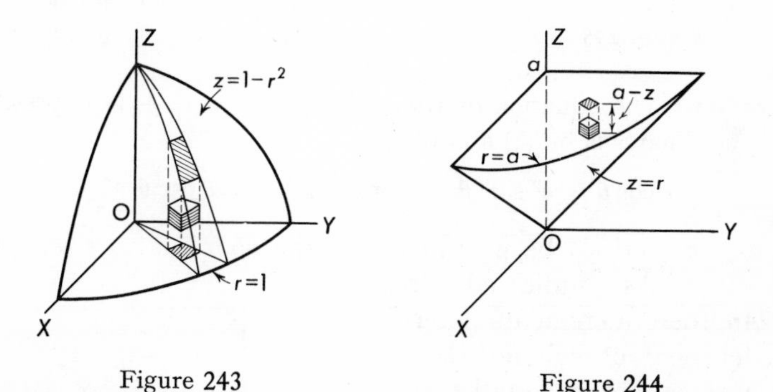

Figure 243

Figure 244

radius of base a if the density at any point is proportional to the distance from the base.

Solution: Placing the cone as shown in Figure 244, we have

$$\begin{aligned} M &= \iiint_V k(a - z)\cdot r\,dz\,dr\,d\theta \\ &= k\int_0^{2\pi} \int_0^a \int_r^a (ar - zr)\,dz\,dr\,d\theta \\ &= \tfrac{1}{12}k\pi a^4. \end{aligned}$$

218. Triple Integrals in Spherical Coordinates

In addition to rectangular and cylindrical coordinates, the position of a point P in space can be determined by three numbers (r,θ,ϕ) which are called its **spherical coordinates.** In this case r denotes the distance OP (Figure 245), θ the angle POZ, and ϕ the angle between the planes POZ and XOZ. Without loss of generality, the coordinates θ and ϕ are restricted to the ranges $0 \leqq \theta \leqq \pi$ and $0 \leqq \phi \leqq 2\pi$. If P is regarded as a point on the surface of a sphere, the angle θ is the *colatitude* of P, and ϕ is its *longitude*.

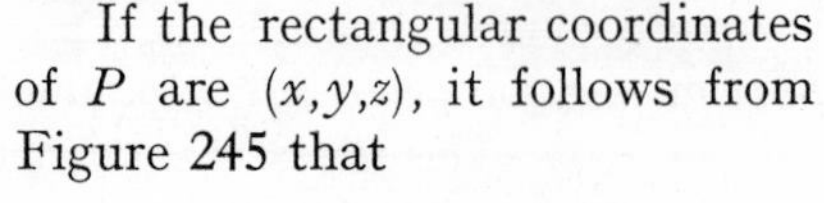

Figure 245

If the rectangular coordinates of P are (x,y,z), it follows from Figure 245 that

$$x = r \sin\theta \cos\phi,$$
$$y = r \sin\theta \sin\phi,$$
$$z = r \cos\theta, \tag{1}$$

whence

$$x^2 + y^2 = r^2 \sin^2\theta,$$
$$x^2 + y^2 + z^2 = r^2. \tag{2}$$

Illustration. The equation of the paraboloid $z = x^2 + y^2$ expressed in spherical coordinates is by (1) and (2)

$$r \cos\theta = r^2 \sin^2\theta, \qquad \text{or} \qquad r = \cot\theta \csc\theta.$$

Let dr, $d\theta$, and $d\phi$ be increments of the coordinates r, θ, and ϕ, respectively. As indicated in Figure 246, these increments determine an element of volume, three of whose edges are of lengths dr, $r\,d\theta$, and $r \sin\theta\, d\phi$. When the increments are sufficiently small, it can be shown that the volume of this element does not differ appreciably from that of a rectangular parallelepiped having these three lengths for edges. We assume this fact here and conclude that in spherical coordinates the differential of volume is

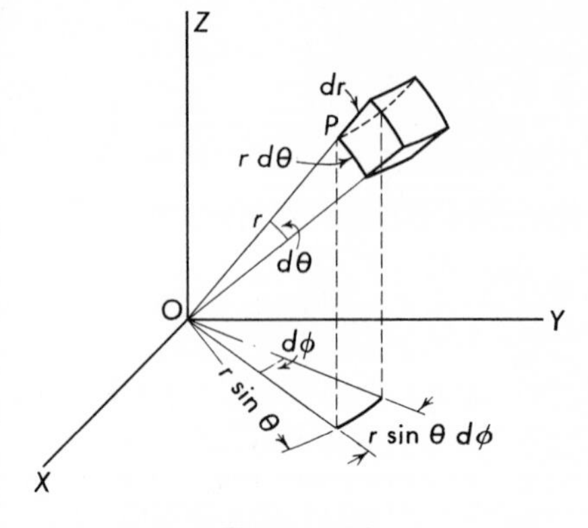

Figure 246

$$\boldsymbol{dV = r^2 \sin\theta\, dr\, d\theta\, d\phi.} \tag{3}$$

Example. Find the mass of a sphere of radius a when the density at any point is proportional to the distance from the center.

Solution: If the center of the sphere is placed at the origin, its equation

in spherical coordinates is $r = a$. Since the density at any point is $\rho = kr$, we have in accordance with (3)

$$M = \iiint_V kr \cdot r^2 \sin\theta \, dr \, d\theta \, d\phi.$$

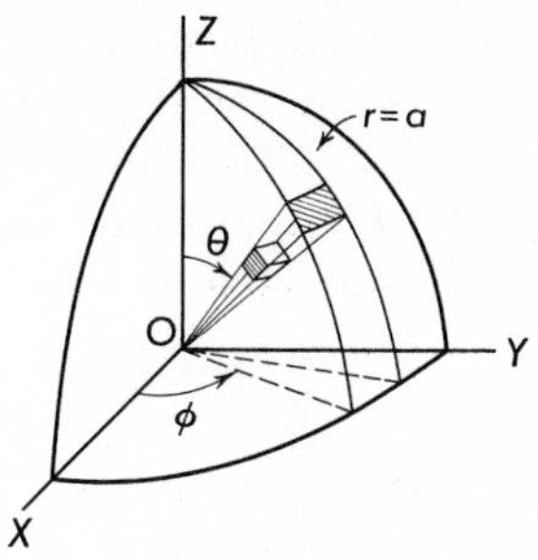

Figure 247

The limits for the above integral are determined as follows. For the first integration with θ and ϕ constant, we add elements along a radius vector (Figure 247) from $r = 0$ to $r = a$. This gives the mass of a tapering column. Then, with ϕ constant, we add all such columns from $\theta = 0$ to $\theta = \pi$. This gives the mass of a slice similar in form to a section of an orange. Finally, all slices are added from $\phi = 0$ to $\phi = 2\pi$. Thus

$$M = k \int_0^{2\pi} \int_0^{\pi} \int_0^{a} r^3 \sin\theta \, dr \, d\theta \, d\phi = k\pi a^4.$$

EXERCISE 115

Solve each of the following using cylindrical coordinates.

1. Find the volume in the first octant bounded by the cylinder $x^2 + y^2 = 1$ and the plane $z = y$. *Ans.* $\frac{1}{3}$.
2. Find the mass of the solid bounded by the paraboloid $z = 4 - x^2 - y^2$ and the plane $z = 0$, if the density at any point is proportional to the distance from the xy plane.
3. Find the center of gravity of a right circular cone of altitude a and radius of base a, if the density at any point is proportional to the distance from the base. *Ans.* $\frac{2}{5}a$ from base.
4. Find the moment of inertia of a right circular cylinder of altitude h and radius a with respect to its axis, if the density at any point is proportional to the distance from the axis.
5. If the density at any point is proportional to the distance from the xy plane, find the mass in the first octant which is bounded by the cone $z = r$, the cylinder $r = 4\sin\theta$, and the plane $\theta = \frac{1}{2}\pi$. *Ans.* $6k\pi$.
6. Find the centroid of the homogeneous solid which is bounded by the hyperboloid $z^2 = x^2 + y^2 + 9$ and the plane $z = 5$.

Solve each of the following using spherical coordinates.

7. Find the volume in the first octant bounded by the sphere $x^2 + y^2 + z^2 = a^2$, and inside the cone $z^2 = x^2 + y^2$ $(\theta = \frac{1}{4}\pi)$. *Ans.* $\frac{1}{12}\pi a^3(2 - \sqrt{2})$.
8. Find the centroid of the volume in the first octant bounded by the sphere $r = a$.

9. Find the mass of a sphere of radius a if the density at any point is proportional to the distance from a fixed diameter. *Ans.* $\frac{1}{4}k\pi^2a^4$.
10. Find the moment of inertia with respect to a diameter of a solid sphere if the density at any point is proportional to the square of the distance from the center.
11. Find the center of gravity of a hemisphere of radius a if the density at any point is proportional to the distance from the base.
Ans. $\frac{8}{15}a$ from base.
12. Find the volume bounded by the closed surface $(x^2 + y^2 + z^2)^2 = az^3$.

Determine the region of integration for each of the following integrals and evaluate the integral by changing to cylindrical coordinates.

13. $\displaystyle\int_0^3 \int_0^{\sqrt{9-x^2}} \int_0^2 \frac{dz\,dy\,dx}{\sqrt{x^2+y^2}}$. *Ans.* 3π.

14. $\displaystyle\int_0^1 \int_0^{\sqrt{1-x^2}} \int_0^{\sqrt{1-x^2-y^2}} \frac{z\,dz\,dy\,dx}{\sqrt{x^2+y^2}}$.

Determine the region of integration for each of the following integrals and evaluate the integral by changing to spherical coordinates.

15. $\displaystyle\int_0^a \int_0^{\sqrt{a^2-x^2}} \int_0^{\sqrt{a^2-x^2-y^2}} \frac{dz\,dy\,dx}{x^2+y^2+z^2}$. *Ans.* $\frac{1}{2}\pi a$.

16. $\displaystyle\int_0^2 \int_0^{\sqrt{4-x^2}} \int_0^{\sqrt{4-x^2-y^2}} \frac{dz\,dy\,dx}{\sqrt{x^2+y^2}}$.

CHAPTER 23

Differential Equations

219. Definitions

An equation which contains derivatives or differentials is called a **differential equation.** Thus

$$\frac{d^2y}{dx^2} + m^2y = 0, \tag{1}$$

$$\left(x\frac{dy}{dx} - y\right)^2 = x^4, \tag{2}$$

$$(x + y)\,dx + x^2y^3\,dy = 0, \tag{3}$$

$$Ry'' = [1 + y'^2]^{3/2} \tag{4}$$

are examples of differential equations.

The **order** of a differential equation is defined as the same as the order of the highest derivative involved in the equation. Thus equations (2) and (3) are of first order, whereas (1) and (4) are of second order.

The **degree** of a differential equation is defined as the same as the degree or power of the highest ordered derivative, after the equation has been rationalized and cleared of fractions with respect to all the derivatives. Thus equations (1) and (3) are of first degree, whereas (2) and (4) are of second degree.

220. Solutions of Differential Equations

A relation among the variables which reduces a differential equation to an algebraic identity is called a **solution** of the equation.

Illustration. The equation

$$\frac{d^2y}{dx^2} - y = 0$$

has

$$y = c_1e^x + c_2e^{-x}$$

as a solution, since

$$y' = c_1e^x - c_2e^{-x}, \qquad y'' = c_1e^x + c_2e^{-x},$$

and by substitution

$$y'' - y = 0.$$

The arbitrary constants c_1 and c_2 appearing in the above illustration are called *constants of integration*. A solution which contains a number of independent* arbitrary constants equal to the order of the equation is called the *complete* or *general solution*. A solution which can be obtained from the general solution by giving specific values to one or more of the constants is called a *particular solution*.

Example 1. Show that

$$y = c_1x^5 + c_2x^{-1} - \ln x \tag{1}$$

is a solution of the differential equation

$$x^2\frac{d^2y}{dx^2} - 3x\frac{dy}{dx} - 5y = 4 + 5\ln x, \tag{2}$$

and obtain the particular solution for which $y = 5$ and $y' = 0$, when $x = 1$.

Solution: Differentiating (1), we obtain

$$y' = 5c_1x^4 - c_2x^{-2} - x^{-1}, \tag{3}$$

$$y'' = 20c_1x^3 + 2c_2x^{-3} + x^{-2}. \tag{4}$$

Substituting (1), (3), and (4) in (2), we obtain an identity. This proves that (1) is a solution of (2) for all values of c_1 and c_2.

Now substituting $x = 1$, $y = 5$ in (1), and $x = 1$, $y' = 0$ in (3), we obtain

$$5 = c_1 + c_2 \qquad \text{and} \qquad 1 = 5c_1 - c_2.$$

Solving, we find $c_1 = 1$ and $c_2 = 4$. Hence the required particular solution is

$$y = x^5 + 4x^{-1} - \ln x.$$

The general solution for a differential equation of the form

$$\frac{d^ny}{dx^n} = f(x)$$

may be found by repeated integrations; thus

$$\frac{d^{n-1}y}{dx^{n-1}} = \int\frac{d^ny}{dx^n}\,dx = \int f(x)\,dx + c_1.$$

* The relation $y = x + c_1 + c_2$ involves only one constant since $(c_1 + c_2)$ is no more general than a single constant. Similarly, $c_1e^{x+c_2} = c_1e^{c_2}e^x$ is no more general than c_1e^x.

It is evident that each successive integration will introduce another constant of integration.

Example 2. Solve $\frac{d^2y}{dx^2} = x \sin x$.

Solution: Integrating with respect to x, we find

$$\frac{dy}{dx} = \int x \sin x \, dx = \sin x - x \cos x + c_1.$$

Integrating again, we obtain the general solution

$$y = \int \sin x \, dx - \int x \cos x \, dx + \int c_1 \, dx$$

$$= -2 \cos x - x \sin x + c_1 x + c_2.$$

EXERCISE 116

State the order and degree of each of the following differential equations and verify the corresponding solutions.

1. $\frac{d^2y}{dx^2} + \frac{dy}{dx} - 2y = 0, \quad y = c_1 e^x + c_2 e^{-2x}.$ *Ans.* 2, 1.
2. $\frac{d^2y}{dx^2} - \frac{1}{x}\frac{dy}{dx} - 3x = 0, \quad y = x^3 + c_1 x^2 + c_2.$
3. $\left(\frac{dy}{dx}\right)^2 + 8x^3 \frac{dy}{dx} = 16x^2 y, \quad y = 2cx^2 + c^2.$ 1, 2.
4. $\frac{d^2y}{dx^2} + 9y = 0, \quad y = c_1 \sin (3x + c_2).$
5. $y = 2x \frac{dy}{dx} + y^2 \left(\frac{dy}{dx}\right)^3, \quad y^2 = cx + \frac{1}{8}c^3.$ 1, 3.
6. $y \frac{d^2y}{dx^2} + \left(\frac{dy}{dx}\right)^2 + 1 = 0, \quad (x - c_1)^2 + y^2 = c_2.$
7. $x^2 y \frac{d^2y}{dx^2} + \left(x \frac{dy}{dx} - y\right)^2 = 0, \quad y^2 = c_1 x^2 + c_2 x.$ 2, 1.
8. $\left(\frac{1}{y}\frac{dy}{dx}\right)^2 - \frac{1}{y}\frac{d^2y}{dx^2} = x^2 - \ln y, \quad \ln y = c_1 e^x + c_2 e^{-x} + x^2 + 2.$
9. $\left(\frac{d^2y}{dx^2}\right)^2 + \left(\frac{dy}{dx}\right)^2 = 1, \quad y = c_1 - \cos (x + c_2).$ 2, 2.
10. $4x^2 \frac{d^3y}{dx^3} + 8x \frac{d^2y}{dx^2} + \frac{dy}{dx} = 0, \quad y = (c_1 + c_2 \ln x) \sqrt{x} + c_3.$
11. $y \frac{d^2y}{dx^2} - \left(\frac{dy}{dx}\right)^2 - y^2 \frac{dy}{dx} = 0, \quad c_1 y = (y + c_2) e^{c_2 x}.$ 2, 1.
12. $\frac{d^2y}{dx^2} + 2 \cot x \frac{dy}{dx} + 2 \tan y \left(\frac{dy}{dx}\right)^2 = 0, \quad \tan y = c_1 \cot x + c_2.$

For the problem indicated find a particular solution that satisfies the given conditions.

13. Problem 1. $y = y' = 1$ when $x = 0$. *Ans.* $y = e^x$.
14. Problem 2. $y = 1$ when $x = 1$, and $y = 5$ when $x = 2$.
15. Problem 3. $y = -1$ when $x = 1$. *Ans.* $y = 1 - 2x^2$.
16. Problem 4. $y = 1$ when $x = 0$, and $y = 0$ when $x = \frac{1}{2}\pi$.
17. Problem 5. $y' = 1$ when $x = 0$. *Ans.* $y^2 = 2x + 1$.
18. Problem 6. $y = 3$, $y' = -\frac{4}{3}$ when $x = 5$.
19. Problem 7. $y = 2$, $y' = 1$ when $x = 1$. $y^2 = 4x$.
20. Problem 9. $y = 1$ when $x = \frac{1}{4}\pi$, and $y = 0$ when $x = -\frac{1}{4}\pi$.

Find the general solution for each of the following differential equations.

21. $\dfrac{d^2y}{dx^2} = \dfrac{1}{x}$. *Ans.* $y = x \ln x + c_1x + c_2$.

22. $\dfrac{d^3y}{dx^3} = x^2$.

23. $\dfrac{d^2y}{dx^2} = 4 \cos 2x$. $y = -\cos 2x + c_1x + c_2$.

24. $\dfrac{d^2y}{dx^2} = xe^x$.

25. $\dfrac{d^3y}{dx^3} = e^{-x}$. $y = -e^{-x} + c_1x^2 + c_2x + c_3$.

26. $\dfrac{d^4y}{dx^4} = x + \sin x$.

27. $\dfrac{d^2y}{dx^2} = 2 \sec^2 x \tan x$. $y = \tan x + c_1x + c_2$.

28. $\dfrac{d^2y}{dx^2} = \dfrac{ax + b}{cx + d}$.

221. Differential Equations of First Order and First Degree

A differential equation of first order and first degree may be written in the differential form

$$\boldsymbol{M(x,y)\,dx + N(x,y)\,dy = 0,} \tag{1}$$

where M and N are functions of x and y. We shall now consider two methods for solving certain equations of the form (1).

A. *Variables separable.* If by algebraic processes (1) may be written in the form

$$M_1(x)\,dx + N_1(y)\,dy = 0, \tag{2}$$

where M_1 and N_1 are functions of one variable as indicated, we say that the *variables have been separated.* In this case, by integration, we obtain the general solution

$$\int M_1(x)\,dx + \int N_1(y)\,dy = C,$$

where C is an arbitrary constant.

Example 1. Solve the equation $(1 + x^2)\dfrac{dy}{dx} + xy = 0.$

Solution: Writing the given equation in differential form, we have

$$xy\,dx + (1 + x^2)\,dy = 0.$$

To separate the variables we divide by $y(1 + x^2)$; thus

$$\frac{x\,dx}{1 + x^2} + \frac{dy}{y} = 0.$$

By integration, we obtain

$$\tfrac{1}{2}\ln(1 + x^2) + \ln y = C, \quad \text{or} \quad \ln y\sqrt{1 + x^2} = C.$$

Hence

$$y\sqrt{1 + x^2} = c,$$

where $c = e^C$.

B. *Homogeneous equations.* The differential equation (1) is said to be *homogeneous* when M and N are homogeneous functions of the same degree in x and y.* In this case we can write (1) in the form

$$\frac{dy}{dx} = -\frac{M}{N} = f\left(\frac{y}{x}\right). \tag{3}$$

This follows from the fact that M/N is a homogeneous function of degree zero in x and y.

Changing the dependent variable by the substitution $y = vx$, (3) may be written as

$$x\frac{dv}{dx} + v = f(v); \quad \text{hence} \quad \frac{dv}{f(v) - v} = \frac{dx}{x}, \tag{4}$$

in which the variables are separated. Integrating in (4) and replacing v by y/x gives the required solution.

Example 2. Solve the equation $(y^2 - xy)\,dx + x^2\,dy = 0.$

---

* $F(x,y)$ is a homogeneous function of degree n in x and y provided $F(kx,ky) \equiv k^nF(x,y)$. For example, $x^2 + y^2$ and $x^2 \sin(y/x)$ are homogeneous functions of degree 2 in x and y.

Solution: Setting $y = vx$, and $dy = v\,dx + x\,dv$, we have

$$(v^2x^2 - vx^2)\,dx + x^2(v\,dx + x\,dv) = 0,$$
$$x^2v^2\,dx + x^3\,dv = 0.$$

Dividing by x^3v^2, we obtain

$$\frac{dx}{x} + \frac{dv}{v^2} = 0; \quad \text{hence} \quad \ln x - \frac{1}{v} = c.$$

Putting $v = y/x$ and simplifying gives

$$\ln x = \frac{x}{y} + c, \qquad \text{or} \qquad y = \frac{x}{\ln x - c}.$$

EXERCISE 117

Find the general solution of the following differential equations.

1. $(y + 2)\,dx + (x - 2)\,dy = 0.$ *Ans.* $xy + 2x - 2y = c.$
2. $xy^2\,dx + (x^2 + 1)\,dy = 0.$
3. $(x + y)\,dx - x\,dy = 0.$ $y = x\ln x - cx.$
4. $(y^2 - xy)\,dx + x^2\,dy = 0.$
5. $\tan y\,dx + (x + 1)\,dy = 0.$ $(x + 1)\sin y = c.$
6. $dx + 3x^2y^2\,dy = 0.$
7. $y^2\,dx - (1 - x)\,dy = 0.$ $y\ln c(x - 1) = 1.$
8. $(x + 2y)\,dx - (2x + y)\,dy = 0.$
9. $(1 + y^2)\,dx - (1 + x^2)\,dy = 0.$ $y(1 - cx) = x + c.$
10. $y(1 - x)\,dx + x^2\,dy = 0.$
11. $(x^2 + y^2)\,dx - xy\,dy = 0.$ $y^2 = 2x^2\ln cx.$
12. $(y^2 - xy)\,dx + (x^2 - xy)\,dy = 0.$
13. $\tan y\,dx + \tan x\,dy = 0.$ $\sin x\sin y = c.$
14. $\sqrt{1 + y^2}\,dx + x\,dy = 0.$
15. $\dfrac{dy}{dx} = \dfrac{y}{x} + \tan\dfrac{y}{x}.$ $\sin\dfrac{y}{x} = cx.$
16. $xy' = y + xe^{y/x}.$
17. $y^3\,dx - x^3\,dy = 0.$ $x^2 - y^2 = cx^2y^2.$
18. $(1 - x)\,dy - y^2\,dx = 0.$
19. $(x + y)\,dx + (x - y)\,dy = 0.$ $x^2 + 2xy - y^2 = c.$
20. $2x^2y + y^3 - x^3y' = 0.$
21. $\sin x\cos^2 y\,dx + \cos^2 x\,dy = 0.$ $\sec x + \tan y = c.$
22. $dx - dy = y^2\,dx + x^2\,dy.$
23. $x\,dx + (y\,dx - x\,dy)\cos\dfrac{y}{x} = 0.$ $\ln x - \sin\dfrac{y}{x} = c.$
24. $2x^2y + 3y^3 - (x^3 + 2xy^2)y' = 0.$

25. $x^2\,dy + y^2\,dx = xy(x\,dy - y\,dx).$ *Ans.* $\dfrac{1}{x} + \dfrac{1}{y} + \ln\dfrac{y}{x} = c.$

26. $ye^{2x}\,dx = (1 + e^{2x})\,dy.$

27. $(3y - 2x)\,dx - (2y - x)\,dy = 0.$ $x/2(y - x) - \ln(y - x) = c.$

28. $(3x^2 - 2xy + y^2) - (x - y)^2y' = 0.$

29. $\sec x\,dy - 4\sin x\sec y\,dx = 0.$ $\sin y + \cos 2x = c.$

30. $e^{x+y}\,dx + e^{x-y}\,dy = 0.$

For the following differential equations find the particular solution which satisfies the given condition.

31. $x\,dx - 4y\,dy = 0;\quad y = 2$ when $x = 5.$ *Ans.* $x^2 - 4y^2 = 9.$

32. $(y - 2)\,dx + \cot x\,dy = 0;\quad y = 6$ when $x = 0.$

33. $(y + 3x)\,dx + x\,dy = 0;\quad y = 3$ when $x = 1.$ $3x^2 + 2xy = 9.$

34. $(3x + y)\,dx - (x + 3y)\,dy = 0;\quad y = 2$ when $x = 4.$

35. $4\sqrt{1 - y^2}\,dx - x^{-3}\,dy = 0;\quad y = 0$ when $x = 0.$
Ans. $y = \sin x^4,\quad x^4 \leqq \tfrac{1}{2}\pi.$

36. $x(y + 1)\,dx + y(x + 1)\,dy = 0;\quad y = 1$ when $x = 0.$

37. Find the equation of the curve whose slope at any point is equal to $y/(y - x)$ and which passes through the point $(-1,2)$.
Ans. $y^2 - 2xy = 8.$

38. Find the equation of the curve whose slope at any point is equal to $-(y + 1)/(x + 1)$ and which passes through the point $(0,0)$.

Changing variables as indicated, find the general solution of the following differential equations.

39. $(2x + 3y^3)\,dx + 9xy^2\,dy = 0.$ Let $y^3 = z.$ *Ans.* $x^2 + 3xy^3 = c.$

40. $\dfrac{dy}{dx} = \dfrac{2x + y - 1}{2x + y + 1}.$ Let $y = z - 2x.$

41. $x^2\,dy - 2xy\,dx - y^3\,dx = 0.$ Let $y = x^2/z.$ $3x^4 + 2x^3y^2 = cy^2.$

42. $(4x + 5y + 5)\,dx + (5x - 6y + 8)\,dy = 0.$ Let $4x + 5y + 5 = u$ and $5x - 6y + 8 = v.$

222. Exact Differential Equations

Even though the variables are not separable in a given differential equation, certain *integrable combinations* may occur that make it possible to solve the equation readily.

Illustration 1. The equation $(2x + y)\,dx + x\,dy = 0$ can be written in the form $2x\,dx + (y\,dx + x\,dy) = 0$, whence $d(x^2) + d(xy) = 0$. Thus, by integration, we obtain the solution $x^2 + xy = c$.

A few of the simpler integrable combinations are as follows:

$$\text{I.}\qquad x\,dy + y\,dx = d(xy),$$

$$\text{II.}\qquad (x\,dy - y\,dx)/x^2 = d(y/x),$$

$$\text{III.}\qquad (x\,dy - y\,dx)/y^2 = d(-x/y),$$

$$\text{IV.}\qquad (x\,dy - y\,dx)/(x^2 + y^2) = d(\text{Tan}^{-1}\, y/x),$$

$$\text{V.}\qquad (x\,dy - y\,dx)/(x^2 - y^2) = d[\tfrac{1}{2}\ln (x + y)/(x - y)].$$

Illustration 2. The equation $(2xy^2 + y)\,dx - x\,dy = 0$ contains the combination $y\,dx - x\,dy$. Because y^2 is available in the remaining term, we write the equation in the form $2x\,dx + \dfrac{y\,dx - x\,dy}{y^2} = 0$; whence $x^2 + \dfrac{x}{y} = c$, or $y = x/(c - x^2)$.

When a differential equation,

$$M(x,y)\,dx + N(x,y)\,dy = 0, \tag{1}$$

is such that the left side is the exact differential of some function $u(x,y)$, that is, $M\,dx + N\,dy \equiv du$, we say that (1) is an **exact differential equation,** and its solution is $u(x,y) = c$. Recalling that the total differential of a function $u(x,y)$ is defined by

$$du = \frac{\partial u}{\partial x}\,dx + \frac{\partial u}{\partial y}\,dy, \tag{2}$$

we observe for an exact equation that

$$\frac{\partial u}{\partial x} = M, \qquad \frac{\partial u}{\partial y} = N. \tag{3}$$

Since, however, $\dfrac{\partial^2 u}{\partial y\,\partial x} = \dfrac{\partial^2 u}{\partial x\,\partial y}$, it follows from (3) that

$$\frac{\partial M}{\partial y} = \frac{\partial N}{\partial x} \tag{4}$$

is a *necessary* requirement in order that (1) be an exact differential equation.

We can also show that the condition (4) is *sufficient* in order to ensure the existence of a function $u(x,y)$ that satisfies (2) and (3). For example, let G denote the integral $\int M\,dx$, where y is held constant during the integration. Thus $\partial G/\partial x = M$, and by the condition (4) we have

$$\frac{\partial^2 G}{\partial y\,\partial x} = \frac{\partial M}{\partial y} = \frac{\partial N}{\partial x}.$$

Hence

$$\frac{\partial N}{\partial x} = \frac{\partial^2 G}{\partial y\, \partial x} = \frac{\partial^2 G}{\partial x\, \partial y} = \frac{\partial}{\partial x}\left(\frac{\partial G}{\partial y}\right),$$

and by integration with respect to x, we obtain

$$N = \frac{\partial G}{\partial y} + f(y),$$

where the constant involved in the integration may depend on the variable y. Thus it follows that

$$M\, dx + N\, dy = \frac{\partial G}{\partial x}\, dx + \frac{\partial G}{\partial y}\, dy + f(y)\, dy = d[G + F(y)],$$

where $F(y)$ is such that $F'(y) = f(y)$.

Theorem. *A necessary and sufficient condition that* (1) *be an exact differential equation is that* $\dfrac{\partial M}{\partial y} = \dfrac{\partial N}{\partial x}$, *and the solution of* (1) *is* $u(x,y) = c$, *where* $u_x = M$ *and* $u_y = N$.

Example. Solve $(2x + y - 3)\, dx + (x - 4y + 1)\, dy = 0$.

Solution: Since

$$\frac{\partial}{\partial y}(2x + y - 3) = 1 = \frac{\partial}{\partial x}(x - 4y + 1),$$

we see that the given equation is exact; hence

$$\frac{\partial u}{\partial x} = 2x + y - 3.$$

By integration, we find

$$u = x^2 + xy - 3x + f(y), \tag{5}$$

and since $u_y = x - 4y + 1$, we must have

$$x + f'(y) = x - 4y + 1.$$

Again by integration, we obtain $f(y) = -2y^2 + y$, and the substitution of this value in (5) gives the solution

$$x^2 + xy - 3x - 2y^2 + y = c.$$

Occasionally an equation which is not exact can be made exact by multiplying the equation by some function of the variables. Any multiplicative factor that has this property is called an **integrating factor.** Thus an integrating factor for the equation given in Illustration 2 is $1/y^2$. Observe also that integrating factors are not unique. For, if $I(x,y)$ is an integrating factor that reduces (1) to $du(x,y) = 0$, then $F(u)\, I(x,y)$ is also an integrating factor, the function $F(u)$ being arbitrary.

EXERCISE 118

Use the integrable combinations listed in the preceding article to find the general solution of the following differential equations.

1. $(3x^2 + 2y)\,dx + 2x\,dy = 0.$ *Ans.* $x^3 + 2xy = c.$
2. $(x + y + 1)\,dx + (x - y - 1)\,dy = 0.$
3. $(2xy^2 + y)\,dx + (y - x)\,dy = 0.$ $x^2 + \dfrac{x}{y} + \ln y = c.$
4. $y\,dx + (x^2 + y^2 - x)\,dy = 0.$
5. $2x^2y\,dx + y\,dx + x\,dy = 0.$ $xy = ce^{-x^2}.$
6. $y\,dx - (x^2 - y^2 + x)\,dy = 0.$
7. $(3x - 2y^2)\,dx - 2xy\,dy = 0.$ $x^3 - x^2y^2 = c.$
8. $y(x\,dy - y\,dx) + (x^2 - y^2)\,dy = 0.$

Determine which of the following differential equations are exact, and solve each equation that is exact.

9. $(2x + 3y)\,dx + (3x - 4y)\,dy = 0.$ *Ans.* $x^2 + 3xy - 2y^2 = c.$
10. $(2xy^2 + 1)\,dx + 2x^2y\,dy = 0.$
11. $(3x^2y^2 + 2y^3)\,dx + (2x^3y + 6xy^2)\,dy = 0.$ $x^3y^2 + 2xy^3 = c.$
12. $2x\left(1 + \dfrac{1}{y}\right)dx + \dfrac{y - x^2}{y^2}\,dy = 0.$
13. $ye^x\,dx + e^x\,dy = 0.$ $y = ce^{-x}.$
14. $(x^3 + y^3)\,dx + (3xy^2 + ay^3)\,dy = 0.$
15. $\sin x \sin y\,dx - \cos x \cos y\,dy = 0.$ $\cos x \sin y = c.$
16. $(x^2 - 4xy + 4y^2)\,dx + (2y^2 + 8xy + 2x^2)\,dy = 0.$
17. Prove that an equation is exact if its variables have been separated.
18. Find an integrating factor for $(2x + y)\,dx - (x - 2y)\,dy = 0$, and solve.
19. Find an integrating factor for $(xy - y)\,dx + (x^2 - 2x + 3y)\,dy = 0$, and solve. *Ans.* $x^2y^2 - 2xy^2 + 2y^3 = c.$
20. Find an integrating factor for $(xy^2 - y)\,dx + (x^2y - 3x)\,dy = 0$, and solve.
21. If $M \equiv y\,f(xy)$ and $N \equiv x\,g(xy)$, show that $1/(xM - yN)$ is an integrating factor provided $xM - yN \neq 0$. If $xM - yN = 0$, show that the equation $M\,dx + N\,dy = 0$ is exact.
22. If M and N are homogeneous functions of the nth degree, show that $1/(xM + yN)$ is an integrating factor provided $xM + yN \neq 0$. *Hint:* Use the fact that $xF_x + yF_y = nF$ for a homogeneous function of degree n.
23. If $\left(\dfrac{\partial M}{\partial y} - \dfrac{\partial N}{\partial x}\right)\Big/ N = f(x)$, show that $e^{\int f(x)\,dx}$ is an integrating factor.
24. If $\left(\dfrac{\partial N}{\partial x} - \dfrac{\partial M}{\partial y}\right)\Big/ M = g(y)$, show that $e^{\int g(y)\,dy}$ is an integrating factor.

223. Linear Equations of the First Order

A differential equation (of any order) which is of the first degree in the dependent variable and in each of its derivatives is called a **linear differential equation.** Thus

$$\frac{dy}{dx} + P(x)\,y = Q(x) \tag{1}$$

is a *linear differential equation of the first order.*

An equation of the form (1) may be solved in the following manner. Multiplying both sides of (1) by the expression $e^{\int P(x)dx}$, we have

$$\frac{dy}{dx}\,e^{\int P(x)dx} + y\,P(x)\,e^{\int P(x)dx} = Q(x)\,e^{\int P(x)dx},$$

which can be written in the form

$$\frac{d}{dx}\left(y\,e^{\int P(x)dx}\right) = Q(x)\,e^{\int P(x)dx}.$$

Hence, by integration, we obtain the general solution

$$y\,e^{\int P(x)dx} = \int Q(x)\,e^{\int P(x)dx}\,dx + C.$$

Note: The preceding integrating factor is determined as follows. In order that $I(x)$ be an integrating factor of (1), it is necessary that

$$I(x)\frac{dy}{dx} + I(x)P(x)y = \frac{d}{dx}(Iy).$$

This means that $I(x)P(x)y = I'(x)y$; hence $I'(x)/I(x) = P(x)$. By integration, we obtain $\ln I(x) = \int P(x)\,dx$, which gives $I(x) = e^{\int P(x)dx}$.

Example. Solve the equation $\dfrac{dy}{dx} + y \cot x = 1$.

Solution: For the integrating factor, we have

$$e^{\int P\,dx} = e^{\int \cot x\,dx} = e^{\ln \sin x} = \sin x.$$

Multiplying both sides of the given equation by $\sin x$, we obtain

$$\sin x\frac{dy}{dx} + y\cos x = \sin x.$$

By integration,

$$y \sin x = \int \sin x\,dx = -\cos x + c.$$

Hence

$$y = -\cot x + c \csc x.$$

224. Equations Reducible to Linear Equations

Any non-linear equation that can be written in the form

$$\frac{d}{dx}\{f(y)\} + P(x)\, f(y) = Q(x)$$

is said to be *linear in* $f(y)$, and may be solved as a linear equation.

The equation, named for the Swiss mathematician Jacob Bernoulli (1654–1705),

$$\frac{dy}{dx} + P(x)\, y = Q(x)\, y^n, \qquad (n \neq 1)$$

can be solved in this manner. Thus, dividing by y^n, we have

$$y^{-n}\frac{dy}{dx} + P(x)\, y^{-n+1} = Q(x),$$

and the substitution $y^{-n+1} = z$ reduces the equation above to the linear form

$$\frac{1}{1-n}\frac{dz}{dx} + P(x)\, z = Q(x).$$

Example 1. Solve $\dfrac{dy}{dx} + \dfrac{y}{x} = \dfrac{y^2}{x^2}$. (1)

Solution: This is a Bernoulli equation with $n = 2$. Hence we set $y^{-1} = z$, and (1) reduces to

$$\frac{dz}{dx} - \frac{z}{x} = -\frac{1}{x^2}. \qquad (2)$$

For this equation $P(x) = -1/x$; hence the integrating factor is

$$e^{\int P\,dx} = e^{-\int (1/x)dx} = e^{-\ln x} = e^{\ln (1/x)} = \frac{1}{x}.$$

Multiplying both sides of (2) by $1/x$, we find

$$\frac{1}{x}\frac{dz}{dx} - \frac{z}{x^2} = -\frac{1}{x^3}; \quad \text{hence} \quad \frac{z}{x} = \frac{1}{2x^2} + C.$$

Putting $1/y$ for z, the general solution of (1) may be expressed in the form

$$y = \frac{2x}{1 + cx^2},$$

where $c = 2C$.

Note: Two general solutions of a differential equation are equivalent when one constant of integration can be expressed in terms of the other. Thus $y = x + c(x-1)$ and $y = 1 + c'(x-1)$ are equivalent since $c' =$

$c + 1$. The constant is usually chosen so as to give the final result its simplest form.

Example 2. Find the solution of $y' + xe^{-y} = -2x$ that satisfies the condition $y = 0$ when $x = 0$.

Solution: Placing $e^y = z$, the given equation reduces to the linear equation

$$z' + 2xz = -x.$$

Multiplying by e^{x^2} and integrating gives

$$ze^{x^2} = -\tfrac{1}{2}e^{x^2} + C, \qquad \text{or} \qquad e^y = Ce^{-x^2} - \tfrac{1}{2}. \tag{3}$$

Applying the condition $y = 0$ when $x = 0$ in (3), we find $C = \frac{3}{2}$. Hence the required solution is

$$y = \ln\left(\tfrac{3}{2}e^{-x^2} - \tfrac{1}{2}\right).$$

EXERCISE 119

Find the general solution of each of the following differential equations.

1. $\dfrac{dy}{dx} + \dfrac{y}{x} = 3x$. *Ans.* $y = x^2 + \dfrac{c}{x}$.
2. $\dfrac{dy}{dx} + y = e^{-x}$.
3. $x\dfrac{dy}{dx} - 2y = -x$. $y = x + cx^2$.
4. $x\dfrac{dy}{dx} + y = 2x - 1$.
5. $\dfrac{dy}{dx} - y = e^{2x}$. $y = e^{2x} + ce^{x}$.
6. $\dfrac{dy}{dx} - y\tan x + 1 = 0$.
7. $(x + 1)\dfrac{dy}{dx} - 2y = 2(x + 1)$. *Ans.* $y = c(x + 1)^2 - 2x - 2$.
8. $(x + x^3)\dfrac{dy}{dx} + 4x^2y = 2$.
9. $\dfrac{dy}{dx} + \dfrac{y}{2x} = \dfrac{1}{y}$. *Ans.* $y^2 = x + \dfrac{c}{x}$.
10. $x\dfrac{dy}{dx} + 2y = xy^2$.
11. $x\dfrac{dy}{dx} + y + x^2y^2 = 0$. $x^2y - cxy = 1$.
12. $x\dfrac{dy}{dx} - y + \dfrac{x}{2y} = 0$.
13. $\dfrac{dy}{dx} + y = 2\cos x$. *Ans.* $y = \sin x + \cos x + ce^{-x}$.
14. $\dfrac{dy}{dx} - y\cot x = 2x - x^2\cot x$.
15. $\dfrac{dy}{dx} - y + (x^2 + 2x)y^2 = 0$. $x^2y + cye^{-x} = 1$.
16. $\dfrac{dy}{dx} + y\tan x = \sec x$.
17. $\sin 2x\dfrac{dy}{dx} - 2y = -2\cos x$. $y = \sec x + c\tan x$.

18. $y\dfrac{dy}{dx} + \dfrac{1}{2}y^2 = e^x.$

19. $nx\dfrac{dy}{dx} - 2y = -kxy^{1-n}.$ *Ans.* $y^n = kx + cx^2.$

20. $x\dfrac{dy}{dx} - ny = x^{n+1}.$

For the following differential equations find the particular solution that satisfies the given condition.

21. $\dfrac{dy}{dx} - \dfrac{3y}{x} = 2;\quad y = 6$ when $x = 2.$ *Ans.* $y = x^3 - x.$

22. $x\dfrac{dy}{dx} + 2y = xy^2;\quad y = \dfrac{1}{3}$ when $x = 3.$

23. $\dfrac{dy}{dx} - y\cot x = \tan^2 x;\quad y = 2$ when $x = \frac{1}{4}\pi.$

Ans. $y = \tan x + \sqrt{2}\sin x.$

24. $\dfrac{dy}{dx}\ln x - \dfrac{y}{x} = \ln x - 1;\quad y = e + 1$ when $x = e.$

25. Find the equation of the curve whose slope at any point is equal to $x + \dfrac{1}{x} + \dfrac{y}{x}$ and which passes through the point (2,9).

Ans. $y = x^2 + 3x - 1.$

26. Find the equation of the curve whose slope at any point is equal to $y\left(y - \dfrac{2}{x}\right)$ and which passes through the point $\left(\dfrac{3}{2}, \dfrac{1}{6}\right).$

Find the general solution of the following differential equations using the indicated substitutions.

27. $x\dfrac{dy}{dx} - 1 = -\dfrac{2}{x}e^{-y}.$ Let $e^y = z.$ *Ans.* $y = \ln\left(\dfrac{1}{x} + cx\right).$

28. $x\left(1 - \dfrac{1}{y}\right)\dfrac{dy}{dx} = \dfrac{2 - y}{2 - x}.$ Let $y^2 - 2y = z.$

29. $\sin y\dfrac{dy}{dx} + \sin x\cos y = \sin x.$ Let $\cos y = z.$ $(\cos y - 1)e^{\cos x} = c.$

30. $\dfrac{dy}{dx} + \dfrac{2(y + 1)}{x + 1} = 2\sqrt{y + 1}.$ Let $\sqrt{y + 1} = z.$

31. $x\dfrac{dy}{dx} + (\ln x - 1)y = y\ln y.$ Let $\ln y = z.$ $y = xe^{cx}.$

32. $x^2\dfrac{dy}{dx} - y^2 = 0.$ Let $y^{-1} = z.$

225. Second Order Equations Reducible to First Order

Certain types of differential equations of higher order can be solved by reducing them to equivalent equations of lower order. We shall discuss two such reductions.

A. *Dependent variable absent.* If the dependent variable y is missing, a second order equation can be reduced to a first order equation by the substitution

$$\frac{dy}{dx} = p, \qquad \frac{d^2y}{dx^2} = \frac{dp}{dx}.$$

If this first order equation can be solved for p in terms of x, then an additional integration will give the required solution.

Example 1. Solve $y'y'' = 1$.

Solution: Placing $y' = p$ and $y'' = \frac{dp}{dx}$, we obtain

$$p\frac{dp}{dx} = 1; \quad \text{hence} \quad p^2 = 2x + c_1.$$

Solving for p and integrating, we find

$$p = \frac{dy}{dx} = \pm\sqrt{2x + c_1}; \quad \text{therefore} \quad y = \pm\tfrac{1}{3}(2x + c_1)^{3/2} + c_2.$$

B. *Independent variable absent.* If the independent variable x is missing, a second order equation can be reduced to a first order equation by the substitution

$$\frac{dy}{dx} = p, \qquad \frac{d^2y}{dx^2} = \frac{dp}{dy}\cdot\frac{dy}{dx} = p\frac{dp}{dy}.$$

Example 2. Solve $y'' = yy'$.

Solution: Placing $y' = p$ and $y'' = p\frac{dp}{dy}$, we obtain

$$p\frac{dp}{dy} = yp; \quad \text{hence} \quad p = \tfrac{1}{2}y^2 + C.$$

Separating variables, we have

$$dx = \frac{dy}{\tfrac{1}{2}y^2 + C}.$$

Therefore, on integrating, we find

$$x = 2c_1 \operatorname{Tan}^{-1} c_1 y + c_2,$$

where $c_1 = (2C)^{-1/2}$ and $C > 0$.

Note: If the constant C is negative, the solution of the above differential equation has the form

$$x = \frac{1}{c_1} \ln \frac{y - c_1}{y + c_1} + c_2,$$

where $c_1 = \sqrt{-2C}$.

EXERCISE 120

Find the general solution of each of the following differential equations.

1. $xy'' - y' = 0$. *Ans.* $y = c_1x^2 + c_2$.
2. $y'y'' = x$.
3. $y'' - a^2y = 0$. $y = c_1e^{ax} + c_2e^{-ax}$.
4. $y'' = y'^2 - y'$.
5. $(1 + x^2)y'' = 1 + y'^2$. $c_1^2y = c_1x - (c_1^2 + 1) \ln (1 + c_1x) + c_2$.
6. $x^2y'' = 1 + x^2$.
7. $x^2y'' = y'^2$. $y = c_1x - c_1^2 \ln (x + c_1) + c_2$.
8. $y'' - y' = e^x$.
9. $xy'' + y' = 4x$. $y = x^2 + c_1 \ln x + c_2$.
10. $y'' - 3y' + 2y = 0$.
11. $y'' + y'^2 = 1$. $y = \ln (c_1e^x + e^{-x}) + c_2$.
12. $y'' + 2yy' = 2y'$.

For the following differential equations find the particular solution which satisfies the given conditions.

13. $y'y'' = x$; $y = 0$ and $y' = 0$, when $x = 0$. *Ans.* $y = \frac{1}{2}x^2$.
14. $x^2y'' + xy' = 1$; $y = 0$ and $y' = \frac{1}{2}$, when $x = 1$.
15. $y'' + y = 0$; $y = 1$ when $x = 0$ or $\frac{1}{2}\pi$. *Ans.* $y = \sin x + \cos x$.
16. $y'' \sin x + y' \cos x = 0$; $y = 0$ and $y' = 1$, when $x = \frac{1}{2}\pi$.
17. $yy'' + y'^2 = 1$; $y = 2$ when $x = 0$ or 1. *Ans.* $y^2 = x^2 - x + 4$.
18. $(1 + x^2)y'' + 1 + y'^2 = 0$; $y = 1$ and $y' = 1$, when $x = 1$.
19. Find the equation of the circle whose differential equation is $y'' = (1 + y'^2)^{3/2}$ and which passes through the points (0,0) and (1,1). *Ans.* $(x - 1)^2 + y^2 = 1$.
20. Find the equation of the parabola whose differential equation is $yy'' + y'^2 = 0$ and which passes through the points $(-1,0)$ and $(3,4)$.
21. Solve the equations $\frac{dx}{dt} = y\sqrt{x + y}$, $\frac{dy}{dt} = x\sqrt{x + y}$, subject to the conditions that $x = 1$ and $y = 0$ when $t = 0$.
Ans. $x = 2(2 - t)^{-2} + \frac{1}{8}(2 - t)^2$, $y = 2(2 - t)^{-2} - \frac{1}{8}(2 - t)^2$.

226. Applications of First Order Differential Equations

The restrictive conditions associated with many geometrical and physical problems often necessitate the solving of differential equations.

We shall now consider a few typical examples that involve first order differential equations.

Orthogonal trajectories. A curve that intersects every member of a family of curves according to some law is called a *trajectory* of the family. If, in particular, the curve intersects every member of the family at right angles, it is called an **orthogonal trajectory** of the family.

To find the orthogonal trajectories of a family whose equation is

$$F(x,y,c) = 0, \tag{1}$$

we first find the differential equation

$$f(x,y,dy/dx) = 0 \tag{2}$$

that corresponds to (1). We observe that this equation determines the slope of the family at each point (x,y) where a curve exists. Thus it follows that the equation

$$f(x,y,-dx/dy) = 0, \tag{3}$$

will at the point (x,y) have an integral curve that is perpendicular to the corresponding curve of the family (1).

Example 1. Find the orthogonal trajectories of the family of parabolas $y^2 = ax$.

Solution: By differentiating the equation of the family, we obtain $2yy' = a$. In eliminating the constant a, we find the differential equation of the family to be $y' = y/2x$. Hence by (3) the differential equation of the orthogonal trajectories is $y' = -2x/y$. Writing this equation in the form $2x\,dx + y\,dy = 0$, we find, by integration, $2x^2 + y^2 = c$, a family of ellipses.

Rectilinear motion. Newton's second law of motion states that the rate of change of momentum of a particle is proportional to the resultant force acting on it and assumes the same direction as the force. Symbolically, this law may be written as

$$\frac{d}{dt}(mv) = \frac{W}{g}\frac{dv}{dt} = kF, \tag{4}$$

where $k = 1$, when W and F are measured in pounds, and $g = 32$ and dv/dt are given in feet per second per second.

Example 2. A body falls from rest against a resistance that is proportional to the speed at any instant. If the terminal speed of the body is 128 feet per second, find its speed after 2 seconds.

Solution: There are two forces which act on the body, namely, the weight W directed downward and the resistance kv directed upward. Hence, in accordance with (4), we have

$$\frac{W}{g}\frac{dv}{dt} = W - kv. \tag{5}$$

Since the acceleration, dv/dt, is zero when the terminal speed is reached, it follows from (5) that $W - 128k = 0$, or $k = W/128$. Thus the relation (5) may be written

$$\frac{dv}{dt} = g - \frac{gv}{128}, \qquad \text{or} \qquad \frac{dv}{128 - v} = \frac{dt}{4}.$$

By integration, we obtain

$$\ln (128 - v) = -\tfrac{1}{4}t + \ln c, \qquad \text{or} \qquad 128 - v = ce^{-t/4}.$$

Since $v = 0$ when $t = 0$, we find $c = 128$; thus from

$$v = 128(1 - e^{-t/4})$$

we obtain 50.4 feet per second as the speed of the body at the end of 2 seconds.

Chemical solutions. Solutions in which some substance is varying because of certain physical or chemical actions are usually analyzed in accordance with the following relation.

$$\left.\begin{matrix}\textit{Rate of change of}\\ \textit{substance in a volume}\end{matrix}\right\} = \left.\begin{matrix}\textit{Rate of}\\ \textit{entrance}\end{matrix}\right\} - \left.\begin{matrix}\textit{Rate of}\\ \textit{exit}\end{matrix}\right\}. \tag{6}$$

Example 3. Consider a tank that initially contains 100 gallons of a solution in which 50 pounds of salt are dissolved. Suppose that 3 gallons of brine, each gallon containing 2 pounds of salt, run into the tank each minute, and that the mixture, kept uniform by stirring, runs out at the rate of 2 gallons per minute. Find the amount of salt in the tank at time t.

Solution: Let Q denote the number of pounds of salt in the tank at time t in minutes. Since the salt concentration at time t is $Q/(100 + t)$, in accordance with (6) we have

$$\frac{dQ}{dt} = 3(2) - 2\left(\frac{Q}{100 + t}\right). \tag{7}$$

Since this relation is a linear first order equation, we have the integrating factor

$$e^{\int [2/(100+t)]dt} = e^{2 \ln (100+t)} = (100 + t)^2.$$

Hence (7) can be written in the form

$$(100 + t)^2 \frac{dQ}{dt} + 2(100 + t)Q = 6(100 + t)^2,$$

and has the general solution

$$(100 + t)^2Q = 2(100 + t)^3 + c. \tag{8}$$

Since $Q = 50$ when $t = 0$, we find $c = -1{,}500{,}000$; thus (8) can finally be expressed in the form

$$Q = 2(100 + t) - 1{,}500{,}000(100 + t)^{-2}.$$

Electric circuits. We shall consider here a circuit containing a resistance and an inductance in series with a source of electromotive force (e.m.f.). Resistance is a circuit parameter that opposes the current and causes a drop in potential given by Ohm's law, $E_R = IR$, where E, I, and R are measured in volts, amperes, and ohms, respectively. Inductance is a circuit parameter that opposes a change in current, and is analogous to inertia in mechanics. The drop in potential caused by a change in the current is given by $E_L = L\dfrac{dI}{dt}$, where t is expressed in seconds and L, called the *inductance*, is measured in henrys.

For a circuit of the preceding type a differential equation for determining the current I at time t is

$$L\frac{dI}{dt} + RI = E, \tag{9}$$

where E denotes the impressed e.m.f. in volts.

Example 4. If for equation (9) the current is initially zero, find the current at the end of t seconds.

Solution: Since (9) is a linear differential equation, an integrating factor is $(1/L)e^{Rt/L}$. Thus, by integration, we obtain

$$e^{Rt/L}I = \frac{E}{R}e^{Rt/L} + c. \tag{10}$$

Since $I = 0$ when $t = 0$, we find $c = -E/R$, and (10) may be written

$$I = \frac{E}{R} - \frac{E}{R}e^{-Rt/L}. \tag{11}$$

The term $(E/R)e^{-Rt/L}$ is called the *transient* term in formula (11) because it becomes negligibly small after a sufficient lapse of time. The *steady-state* term E/R agrees with the current expected by applying Ohm's law alone.

EXERCISE 121

1. Find the orthogonal trajectories of the family of hyperbolas $x^2 - y^2 = ay$. *Ans.* $x^3 + 3xy^2 = c$.
2. Find the orthogonal trajectories of the family of ellipses $4x^2 + y^2 = ax$.

3. Find the orthogonal trajectories of the family of curves $y = ax^5$.

Ans. $x^2 + 5y^2 = c$.

4. If $f(\theta,r,dr/d\theta) = 0$ is the differential equation of a family of curves in polar coordinates, show that $f(\theta,r, -r^2\,d\theta/dr) = 0$ is the differential equation of a family of orthogonal trajectories.

5. Prove that the differential equation of the family of trajectories which cut the integral curves of $f(x,y,y') = 0$ at an angle $\phi = \mathrm{Tan}^{-1}\,m$ is $f(x,y,[y' - m]/[1 + my']) = 0$.

6. A 16-pound weight moves in a horizontal straight line under the joint action of a constant force of 8 pounds in the direction of motion, and a resisting force whose magnitude in pounds is equal to twice the velocity in feet per second. If the body starts from rest, find its velocity and the distance traveled after $\frac{1}{4}$ second.

7. A body falls from rest. If the resistance of the air is proportional to the speed, and if the limiting speed is 160 feet per second, find the speed at the end of 5 seconds. *Ans.* 101 ft./sec.

8. A body falls from rest against a resistance that is proportional to the square root of the speed at any instant. If the terminal speed is 64 feet per second, how long will it take to attain a speed of 49 feet per second?

9. A body falls from rest against resistance proportional to the speed at any instant. If the body attains speeds of v_1 and v_2 feet per second, after 1 and 2 seconds in motion, respectively, find an expression for the limiting velocity. *Ans.* $v_1^2/(2v_1 - v_2)$.

10. A body falls against resistance proportional to the speed at any instant. If the limiting speed is 60 feet per second and the body attains half that speed in 1 second, find the initial speed.

11. A tank contains 50 gallons of water. Brine, containing 2 pounds per gallon of salt, flows into the tank at a rate of 2 gallons per minute, and the mixture, kept uniform by stirring, runs out at the same rate. How long will it take before the quantity of salt in the tank is 50 pounds?

Ans. 17.33 min.

12. A tank contains 50 gallons of water. Brine, containing 2 pounds per gallon of salt, flows into the tank at a rate of 2 gallons per minute, and the mixture, kept uniform by stirring, runs out at the rate of 1 gallon per minute. Find (*a*) how long before the quantity of salt in the tank is 100 pounds; and (*b*) the amount of salt present when the tank contains 100 gallons of brine.

13. Tank A initially holds 100 gallons of brine that contains 100 pounds of salt, and tank B holds 100 gallons of water. Two gallons of water enter A each minute, and the mixture, assumed uniform, flows from A into tank B at the same rate. If the resulting mixture, also kept uniform, runs out of B at the rate of 2 gallons per minute, how much salt is in tank B at the end of 1 hour? *Ans.* 36.1 lb.

14. A tank contains 100 gallons of brine. Three gallons of brine, each containing 2 pounds of dissolved salt, enter the tank each minute, and the mixture, assumed uniform, leaves at the rate of 2 gallons per minute. If the salt concentration in the tank is 1.6 pounds per gallon at the end of 1 hour, what was the initial concentration?

15. Air containing 20 per cent oxygen by volume passes slowly into a 5-gallon flask initially filled with pure oxygen, and the mixture of air and oxygen, assumed uniform, passes out at the same rate. How many gallons of oxygen will the flask contain after 5 gallons of air have passed into it? *Ans.* $1 + 4/e$ gal.

16. An inductance of 1 henry and a resistance of 10 ohms are connected in series with an e.m.f. of E volts. If the current is initially zero, find the current at the end of 0.1 second when (*a*) $E = 120$ volts, and (*b*) $E = 120 \sin 60t$ volts.

17. An inductance of L henrys and a resistance of 10 ohms are connected in series with an e.m.f. of 100 volts. If the current is initially zero and is equal to 9 amperes after 1 second, find L. *Ans.* $L = 4.34$.

18. An inductance of 1 henry and a resistance of 2 ohms are connected in series with a constant e.m.f. of E volts. If the current is initially zero and is equal to 10 amperes after 0.5 seconds, find E.

19. An inductance of 1 henry and a resistance of 2 ohms are connected in series with an e.m.f. of $100e^{-t}$ volts. If the current is initially zero, what is the maximum current attained? *Ans.* 25 amp.

20. A constant inductance of 1 henry and a variable resistance R are connected in series with a constant e.m.f. of E volts. If $R = 1/(1 + t)$ ohms at time t seconds and if the current is initially zero, what value of E will make the current 24 amperes after 4 seconds?

21. Radium decomposes at a rate proportional to the amount present. If the half-life is 1600 years, that is, if half of any given amount is decomposed in 1600 years, find the percentage remaining at the end of 200 years. *Ans.* 91.7%.

22. The rate at which a body cools is proportional to the difference in temperature between the body and the surrounding atmosphere. If a body in air at 0° will cool from 200° to 100° in 40 minutes, how many more minutes will it take the body to cool from 100° to 50°?

23. When an amount of money invested increases at a rate proportional to its size, it is said to be *compounded continuously*. If an amount of money invested at continuously compounded interest doubles itself in 10 years, find the amount of money at the end of t years. How long will it take to triple itself? *Ans.* 15.85 yrs.

24. Liquid is discharged from a vessel through an orifice of area B square feet at a rate given by $0.6B\sqrt{2gh}$, where h in feet is the head or height

of the surface above the center of the orifice, and $g = 32$ feet per second per second. If the head changes from 10 feet to 9 feet in the first 15 minutes, in what time will it be empty, assuming that the vessel is a vertical cylinder?

227. Linear Differential Equations of Order *n*

An equation of the form

$$a_0 \frac{d^n y}{dx^n} + a_1 \frac{d^{n-1}y}{dx^{n-1}} + \cdots + a_{n-1}\frac{dy}{dx} + a_n y = f(x), \tag{1}$$

where $a_0, a_1, \cdots, a_n$ are functions of x, and $a_0 \neq 0$, is called a **linear differential equation of order *n*.** The equation (1) is said to be **homogeneous** if $f(x) \equiv 0$ and non-homogeneous if $f(x) \not\equiv 0$.

Although the coefficients of (1) are in general functions of the variable x, in the following discussion we shall consider only those equations in which the coefficients are constants. Furthermore, we shall restrict the discussion to equations of second order, even though the methods used can be extended to include equations of higher order.

228. Homogeneous Equations with Constant Coefficients

Let us assume that the equation

$$\frac{d^2y}{dx^2} + A\frac{dy}{dx} + By = 0, \tag{1}$$

where A and B are constants, has a particular solution of the form $y = e^{mx}$. Substituting this value in (1), we obtain

$$m^2e^{mx} + Ame^{mx} + Be^{mx} = e^{mx}(m^2 + Am + B) = 0.$$

Thus, in order that e^{mx} be a solution of (1), it is necessary and sufficient that m have a value such that

$$m^2 + Am + B = 0. \tag{2}$$

Equation (2) is called the **characteristic** or **auxiliary equation** of (1). The roots of the characteristic equation determine the general solution of (1) in the following manner.

I. *Roots real and distinct.* If the characteristic equation has distinct roots m_1 and m_2, it follows that (1) has the particular solutions e^{m_1x} and e^{m_2x}; hence the general solution is

$$y = c_1e^{m_1x} + c_2e^{m_2x}.$$

Illustration 1. The equation $y'' - y' - 2y = 0$ has the characteristic equation $m^2 - m - 2 = 0$, whose roots are $m_1 = 2$ and $m_2 = -1$. Hence the general solution is $y = c_1e^{2x} + c_2e^{-x}$.

II. *Roots imaginary.* If the characteristic equation has imaginary roots $a + ib$ and $a - ib$ where $i = \sqrt{-1}$, the general solution, as in I, is

$$y = C_1e^{(a+ib)x} + C_2e^{(a-ib)x} = e^{ax}(C_1e^{ibx} + C_2e^{-ibx}). \tag{3}$$

However, by Euler's formula, we have

$$e^{ibx} = \cos bx + i \sin bx, \qquad e^{-ibx} = \cos bx - i \sin bx.$$

Hence (3) may be written in the form

$$\begin{aligned} y &= e^{ax}[C_1(\cos bx + i \sin bx) + C_2(\cos bx - i \sin bx)] \\ &= e^{ax}[(C_1 + C_2) \cos bx + i(C_1 - C_2) \sin bx]. \end{aligned}$$

Replacing the constants $C_1 + C_2$ and $i(C_1 - C_2)$ by c_1 and c_2, we obtain the general solution of (1) in the form

$$\mathbf{y = e^{ax}(c_1 \cos bx + c_2 \sin bx).} \tag{4}$$

Illustration 2. The equation $y'' - 4y' + 13y = 0$ has the characteristic equation $m^2 - 4m + 13 = 0$, whose roots are $m = 2 \pm 3i$. Since $a = 2$ and $b = 3$, by substituting in (4), we obtain the general solution $y = e^{2x}(c_1 \cos 3x + c_2 \sin 3x)$.

III. *Roots real and equal.* When the roots of the characteristic equation (2) are each equal to m, the above method of substitution gives only one solution e^{mx} where $m = -\frac{1}{2}A$. In this case, however, it can be shown that xe^{mx} is a second solution. Thus, by differentiation, we have

$$y = x\,e^{mx}, \qquad y' = e^{mx}(1 + mx), \qquad y'' = e^{mx}(2m + m^2x).$$

Substituting these values in (1) and dividing by e^{mx} gives

$$(m^2 + Am + B)x + (2m + A).$$

This expression vanishes since m satisfies (2) and is equal to $-\frac{1}{2}A$. Hence the general solution of (1) in this case is

$$\mathbf{y = c_1e^{mx} + c_2xe^{mx}.}$$

Illustration 3. The equation $y'' + 4y' + 4y = 0$ has the characteristic equation $m^2 + 4m + 4 = 0$, whose roots are -2 and -2. Hence the general solution is $y = c_1e^{-2x} + c_2xe^{-2x}$.

EXERCISE 122

Find the general solution of each of the following differential equations.

1. $y'' - 3y' + 2y = 0.$ *Ans.* $y = c_1e^x + c_2e^{2x}.$
2. $y'' + 3y' - 4y = 0.$
3. $y'' + 4y = 0.$ $y = c_1 \cos 2x + c_2 \sin 2x.$
4. $y'' - 2y' + 2y = 0.$
5. $y'' - 2y' + y = 0.$ $y = (c_1 + c_2x)e^x.$
6. $4y'' - 4y' + y = 0.$
7. $\dfrac{d^2y}{dt^2} - \dfrac{dy}{dt} - 6y = 0.$ $y = c_1e^{3t} + c_2e^{-2t}.$
8. $\dfrac{d^2s}{dt^2} - s = 0.$
9. $\dfrac{d^2x}{dt^2} - 4\dfrac{dx}{dt} + 5x = 0.$ $x = e^{2t}(c_1 \cos t + c_2 \sin t).$
10. $\dfrac{d^2r}{d\theta^2} + 6\dfrac{dr}{d\theta} + 9r = 0.$
11. $6y'' + 5y' - 6y = 0.$ *Ans.* $y = c_1e^{2x/3} + c_2e^{-3x/2}.$
12. $\dfrac{d^2s}{dt^2} = 0.$
13. $5y'' - 2y' = 0.$ $y = c_1 + c_2e^{0.4x}.$
14. $\dfrac{d^2y}{dt^2} + k^2y = 0.$
15. $y'' - 2y' - y = 0.$ *Ans.* $y = c_1e^{(1-\sqrt{2})x} + c_2e^{(1+\sqrt{2})x}.$
16. $y'' - 4y' + 7y = 0.$

For the following differential equations find the particular solution which satisfies the given conditions.

17. $y'' + 3y' + 2y = 0;$ $y = 0,$ $y' = 1,$ when $x = 0.$
 Ans. $y = e^{-x} - e^{-2x}.$
18. $y'' - 2y' - 8y = 0;$ $y = 0,$ $y' = 6,$ when $x = 0.$
19. $y'' + 9y = 0;$ $y = 1,$ $y' = -6,$ when $x = 0.$
 Ans. $y = \cos 3x - 2 \sin 3x.$
20. $y'' - 4y' + 4y = 0;$ $y = 2,$ $y' = 5,$ when $x = 0.$
21. $y'' - 2y' = 0;$ $y = 1 + e^2,$ $y' = 2e^2,$ when $x = 1.$
 Ans. $y = 1 + e^{2x}.$
22. $\dfrac{d^2r}{dt^2} + r = 0;$ $r = \sqrt{2},$ $\dfrac{dr}{dt} = 0,$ when $t = \frac{1}{4}\pi.$
23. $\dfrac{d^2y}{dt^2} + 4\dfrac{dy}{dt} + 13y = 0;$ $y = 0,$ $\dfrac{dy}{dt} = 12,$ when $t = 0.$
 Ans. $y = 4e^{-2t} \sin 3t.$
24. $\dfrac{d^2s}{dt^2} + 2\dfrac{ds}{dt} + s = 0;$ $s = -1$ when $t = 0,$ and $s = 0$ when $t = 1.$
25. $\dfrac{d^2r}{d\theta^2} - r = 0;$ $r = 0,$ $\dfrac{dr}{d\theta} = 1,$ when $\theta = 0.$ *Ans.* $r = \sinh \theta.$

229. Non-homogeneous Equations with Constant Coefficients

A general solution of a differential equation of the form

$$\frac{d^2y}{dx^2} + A\frac{dy}{dx} + By = f(x), \tag{1}$$

where A and B are constants and $f(x)$ is a function of the independent variable, can be obtained in the following manner.

1. *Find the general solution,* $y = u$, *for the homogeneous equation*

$$\frac{d^2y}{dx^2} + A\frac{dy}{dx} + By = 0. \tag{2}$$

The solution u *is called the* **complementary function** *for* (1).

2. *By trial, find a particular solution,* $y = v$, *of* (1).
3. *The general solution of* (1) *is then* $y = u + v$, *since* u *contains two independent arbitrary constants and* $(u + v)$ *satisfies* (1).

Illustration 1. For the equation $y'' - y = x$, the complementary function is $u = c_1e^x + c_2e^{-x}$ and a particular solution is $v = -x$. Hence the general solution is $y = c_1e^x + c_2e^{-x} - x$.

In general, the determination of a particular solution of (1) is quite involved and beyond the scope of the present discussion. However, for certain elementary forms of the function $f(x)$ a particular solution can be obtained by assuming an arbitrary form for v and then determining the coefficients to make it an actual solution. The following rule summarizes these trial methods.

I. *If* $y = f(x)$ *is not a solution of* (2), *then*

when	*we assume*
$f(x) = a + bx$	$v = A + Bx$
$f(x) = a + bx + cx^2$	$v = A + Bx + Cx^2$
....	....
$f(x) = ae^{bx}$	$v = Ae^{bx}$
$f(x) = a\sin cx + b\cos cx$	$v = A\sin cx + B\cos cx$

Illustration 2. If $y'' - y = x + e^{2x}$, in accordance with I we assume $v = A + Bx + Ce^{2x}$.

II. *If* $y = f(x)$ *is a solution of* (2), *we assume for* v *the above form multiplied by* x, *and all terms arising from this product by differentiation.*

Illustration 3. If $y'' + y = \sin x$, in accordance with II we assume $v = Ax\sin x + Bx\cos x$.

Note 1: The terms $C \sin x$ and $D \cos x$ are also obtained from $x \sin x$ by differentiation, but these terms are not included in v since they are solutions of the homogeneous equation.

III. *If $f(x)$ is x^n times a particular solution of (2), we assume $v = Ax f(x)$ plus all terms arising from it by differentiation.*

Illustration 4. If $y'' - y = x^2e^x$, in accordance with III we assume $v = Ax^3e^x + Bx^2e^x + Cxe^x$.

Note 2: If the characteristic equation of (2) has a repeated root, it is necessary in II and III to assume v in the form $Ax^2f(x)$ plus all terms obtainable from it by differentiation.

Illustration 5. If $y'' - 2y' + y = x^2e^x$, we assume $v = Ax^4e^x + Bx^3e^x + Cx^2e^x$.

Example 1. Solve $y'' - y = 5 + e^x$. (3)

Solution: 1. The general solution of the homogeneous equation, $y'' - y = 0$, is $u = c_1e^x + c_2e^{-x}$.

2. Since e^x is a solution of the homogeneous equation and 5 is not, for a trial solution, by I and II we assume $v = A + Bxe^x$. Differentiating,

$$v' = Be^x + Bxe^x, \qquad v'' = 2Be^x + Bxe^x,$$

and substituting in (3), we have

$$(2Be^x + Bxe^x) - (A + Bxe^x) = 5 + e^x,$$

$$2Be^x - A = 5 + e^x.$$

Equating coefficients, we find $A = -5$ and $B = \frac{1}{2}$; therefore $v = -5 + \frac{1}{2}xe^x$.

3. Thus the general solution of (3) is

$$y = u + v = c_1e^x + c_2e^{-x} - 5 + \tfrac{1}{2}xe^x.$$

Example 2. Find the particular solution of

$$\frac{d^2s}{dt^2} + \frac{ds}{dt} = 4t + 2\cos t \tag{4}$$

such that $s = 0$ and $ds/dt = 0$ when $t = 0$.

Solution: 1. The general solution of the homogeneous equation, $s'' + s' = 0$, is $s = c_1 + c_2e^{-t}$.

2. Since 4 is a solution of the homogeneous equation and $\cos t$ is not, for a trial solution, by I and III we assume $s = At^2 + Bt + C \sin t + D \cos t$. Thus

$$\frac{ds}{dt} = 2At + B + C \cos t - D \sin t,$$

$$\frac{d^2s}{dt^2} = 2A - C \sin t - D \cos t.$$

Substituting in (4), we obtain

$$2At + (2A + B) - (C + D) \sin t + (C - D) \cos t = 4t + 2 \cos t.$$

Equating coefficients gives $A = 2$, $B = -4$, $C = 1$, $D = -1$.

3. Therefore the general solution of (4) is

$$s = c_1 + c_2e^{-t} + 2t^2 - 4t + \sin t - \cos t. \tag{5}$$

To find the required particular solution we set $s = 0$ and $t = 0$ in (5), and $s' = 0$ and $t = 0$ in the derived equation

$$s' = -c_2e^{-t} + 4t - 4 + \cos t + \sin t.$$

This substitution gives

$$\begin{cases} 0 = c_1 + c_2 - 1, \\ 0 = -c_2 - 4 + 1; \end{cases} \quad \text{hence} \quad \begin{cases} c_1 = 4, \\ c_2 = -3. \end{cases}$$

Therefore the required particular solution is

$$s = 2t^2 - 4t + 4 - 3e^{-t} + \sin t - \cos t.$$

EXERCISE 123

Find the general solution of each of the following differential equations.

1. $y'' - y' - 2y = 4x$. *Ans.* $y = c_1e^{2x} + c_2e^{-x} - 2x + 1$.
2. $y'' - 4y' + 3y = e^{2x}$.
3. $y'' - 4y = x^3 + x$. $y = c_1e^{2x} + c_2e^{-2x} - \frac{1}{4}x^3 - \frac{5}{8}x$.
4. $y'' - 3y' = 9$.
5. $y'' + 2y' + y = \cos x$. $y = (c_1 + c_2x)e^{-x} + \frac{1}{2} \sin x$.
6. $y'' + y' - 6y = 6x^2 + 4e^x$.
7. $y'' + 4y = \sin 2x$. $y = c_1 \sin 2x + c_2 \cos 2x - \frac{1}{4}x \cos 2x$.
8. $y'' - 2y' + 2y = e^x$.
9. $\dfrac{d^2r}{d\theta^2} + 4\dfrac{dr}{d\theta} + 4r = \cos \theta$. $r = (c_1 + c_2\theta)e^{-2\theta} + \frac{1}{25}(4 \sin \theta + 3 \cos \theta)$.
10. $\dfrac{d^2s}{dt^2} + \dfrac{ds}{dt} - 2s = t + 1$.
11. $3y'' - y' = 2x$. $y = c_1e^{x/3} + c_2 - x^2 - 6x$.
12. $y'' - 2y' + y = e^x$.
13. $y'' + y = 1 + \sin x$. $y = c_1 \sin x + (c_2 - \frac{1}{2}x) \cos x + 1$.

14. $y'' + 3y' + 2y = 4 + e^{-x}$.

15. $y'' - 4y' + 5y = e^{2x} \sin x$. $\qquad y = e^{2x}(c_1 \sin x + c_2 \cos x - \frac{1}{2}x \cos x)$.

16. $y'' + 3y' - 4y = 50xe^x$.

17. $\dfrac{d^2x}{dt^2} - 2\dfrac{dx}{dt} = 8t$. $\qquad x = c_1e^{2t} + c_2 - 2t - 2t^2$.

18. $\dfrac{d^2y}{dt^2} + 4y = 8t \cos 2t$.

19. $\dfrac{d^2z}{dx^2} - z = x^3e^x$. $\qquad z = c_1e^{-x} + \frac{1}{8}(c_2 - 3x + 3x^2 - 2x^3 + x^4)e^x$.

20. $y'' + y = \sin^2 x$.

For the following differential equations find the particular solution which satisfies the given conditions.

21. $y'' + 2y' - 3y = 6$; $y = 0, y' = 2$, when $x = 0$. *Ans.* $y = 2e^x - 2$.

22. $y'' - 4y' + 4y = 4x$; $y = 1, y' = 2$, when $x = 0$.

23. $y'' + y = -2 \sin x$; $y = 0$ when $x = 0$ and $x = \frac{1}{2}\pi$. $\qquad y = x \cos x$.

24. $y'' - 2y' + (1 + \pi^2)y = 1 + \pi^2$; $y = 1, y' = \pi$, when $x = 0$.

25. $y'' - 4y' = 8$; $y = 0, y' = 0$, when $x = 0$. *Ans.* $y = \frac{1}{2}e^{4x} - 2x - \frac{1}{2}$.

26. $\dfrac{d^2r}{dt^2} - r = t^2 - 6$; $r = 5$ when $t = 0$, $r = e^2$ when $t = 2$.

27. $y'' + 4y = 2$; $y = 0$ when $x = 0$, $y = \frac{1}{2}$ when $x = \frac{1}{4}\pi$.

Ans. $y = \sin^2 x$.

28. $\dfrac{d^2x}{dt^2} - 2\dfrac{dx}{dt} + 2x = 2e^t \cos t$; $x = 0, \dfrac{dx}{dt} = 0$, when $t = 0$.

29. $y'' - 2y' + y = 2e^x$; $y = 0$ when $x = 1$ or -1.

Ans. $y = (x^2 - 1)e^x$.

30. $y'' - y = 4xe^x$; $y = 0, y' = 0$, when $x = \frac{1}{2}$.

230. Applications of Linear Differential Equations

Linear differential equations occur frequently in scientific work and are of basic importance in engineering. A few applications that lead to equations of second order are discussed in this article.

Simple harmonic motion. Consider a particle that moves along the x axis subject to a force whose magnitude is proportional to its distance from the origin and whose direction is toward the origin. In accordance with Newton's second law of motion, we have

$$\frac{W}{g}\frac{d^2x}{dt^2} = -kx, \tag{1}$$

which may be written

$$\frac{d^2x}{dt^2} + b^2x = 0, \qquad \text{where } b = \sqrt{\frac{kg}{W}}. \tag{2}$$

By Article **228,** the general solution of (2) is

$$x = A \sin bt + B \cos bt, \tag{3}$$

where A and B are constants of integration. By trigonometry (3) can be written in the form

$$x = A' \sin (bt + B'), \tag{4}$$

where $A' = \sqrt{A^2 + B^2}$ and $B' = \cos^{-1}(A/A') = \sin^{-1}(B/A')$.

Motion defined by a relation of the form (4) is called **simple harmonic motion,** and (2) accordingly is the differential equation of simple harmonic motion. The constant A' is called the **amplitude** of the motion and the time that is required for one oscillation, $T = 2\pi/b$, is called the **period** of the motion.

Note: If the force that acts on the particle were directed away from the origin, (2) would become $d^2x/dt^2 - b^2x = 0$, and the solution, $x = Ae^{bt} + Be^{-bt}$, would not be periodic.

Damped vibrations. Because of frictional forces most vibratory motion is not simple harmonic. In fact, if the frictional forces are sufficiently large, the motion may not oscillate at all, but simply move toward the equilibrium position. For small frictional forces, however, the vibrations will merely decrease in size as time goes on. In this case we describe the motion as that of **damped vibrations.**

Suppose that the particle that we considered in deriving (1) is also subject to a frictional force, $-K(dx/dt)$, which is proportional to and opposes the velocity. Equation (1) then becomes

$$\frac{W}{g}\frac{d^2x}{dt^2} = -kx - K\frac{dx}{dt}, \tag{5}$$

and can be written in the form

$$\frac{d^2x}{dt^2} + 2a\frac{dx}{dt} + b^2x = 0, \quad \text{where } 2a = \frac{Kg}{W} \text{ and } b = \sqrt{\frac{kg}{W}}. \tag{6}$$

When $a < b$ the general solution of (6) is

$$x = e^{-at}\left[A \sin \sqrt{b^2 - a^2}\, t + B \cos \sqrt{b^2 - a^2}\, t\right], \tag{7}$$

where A and B are constants of integration. The factor e^{-at} is called the **damping factor** and the time interval $T = 2\pi/\sqrt{b^2 - a^2}$ is called the **period.**

Illustration. The equation, $x = e^{-0.2t} \cos \pi t$, represents a damped vibration of period 2, as shown in Figure 248.

When $a > b$ the general solution of (6) is

$$x = A\,e^{(-a+\sqrt{a^2-b^2})t} + B\,e^{(-a-\sqrt{a^2-b^2})t}. \tag{8}$$

Since the signs of both exponents in (8) are negative, it is apparent that the motion approaches the limiting position $x = 0$. A vibratory system that has frictional forces of this magnitude is said to be **over-damped.** If $a = b$, the general solution of (6) is

$$x = (A + Bt)\,e^{-at},$$

and the motion is said to be **critically** damped.

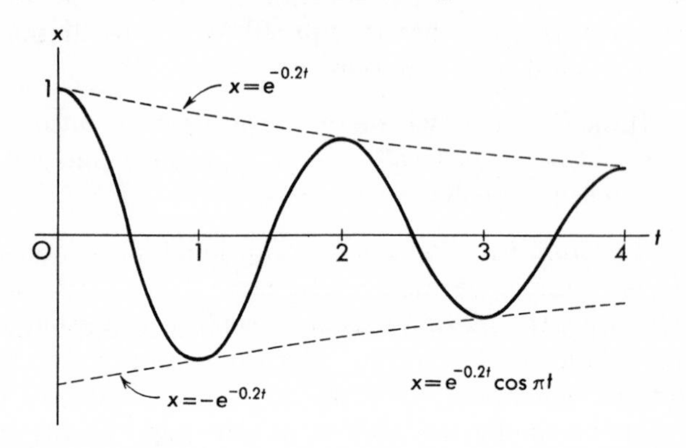

Figure 248

Forced vibrations. In addition to central restoring forces and frictional forces the motion of a particle may also be influenced by external forces which are usually periodic. In such cases we say that the particle executes forced vibrations. The following example illustrates the nature of a forced vibration.

Example 1. A one-pound weight is hanging at rest on a spring which is stretched 6 inches by the weight. Suppose that frictional losses in pounds are opposed to and equal 0.3 the speed of the weight in feet per second. If the upper end of the spring is given the motion $y = \frac{1}{2}\sin 8t$ feet, find the equation of motion of the weight.

Solution: At time t suppose that the weight and the upper end of the spring have the positions shown in Figure 249.

Since one pound stretches the spring $\frac{1}{2}$ foot, the spring constant is 2 pounds per foot. The additional stretch in the spring at time t is $x - y$ feet. Hence, by Hooke's law, the spring pulls upward on the weight with a force of $2(x - y)$ pounds. Thus, in accordance with Newton's second law of motion, we have

$$\frac{1}{g}\frac{d^2x}{dt^2} = -2(x - y) - 0.3\frac{dx}{dt}. \tag{9}$$

Taking $g = 32$ feet per second per second and substituting $\frac{1}{2}\sin 8t$ for y, the relation (9) may be written

$$\frac{d^2x}{dt^2} + 9.6\frac{dx}{dt} + 64x = 32 \sin 8t. \tag{10}$$

The general solution of (10) is

$$x = e^{-4.8t}(A \sin 6.4t + B \cos 6.4t) - \frac{5}{12}\cos 8t,$$

and by applying the boundary conditions that $x = 0$ and $dx/dt = 0$ when $t = 0$, we obtain

$$x = \frac{5}{48}e^{-4.8t}(3 \sin 6.4t + 4 \cos 6.4t) - \frac{5}{12}\cos 8t.$$

This result indicates that, after a short lapse of time, the motion of the weight is periodic with a slightly smaller amplitude than the impressed vibration.

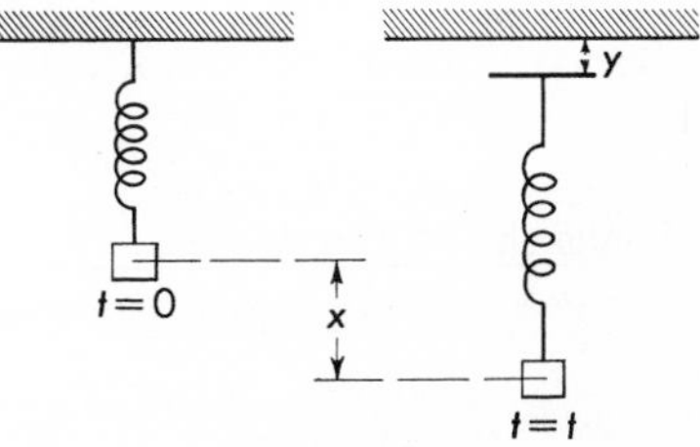

Figure 249

If the period of the impressed force is the same as that of the vibrating system, we say that the force is in **resonance** with the system. The phenomenon of resonance is of great importance in applied work. A resonant condition can cause undue stress in a mechanical system and is usually avoided for this reason. On the other hand, many acoustical and electrical problems require that a resonant condition exist.

Electric circuits. In Article **226** we considered a circuit that contained an inductance L in henrys and a resistance R in ohms in series with an e.m.f. E in volts. We shall now discuss the affect of adding a condenser to the circuit.

The charge on a condenser varies directly as the potential difference across it, so that $Q = CE_C$. If the charge Q is given in coulombs and the potential E_C in volts, the capacitance C is measured in farads. Since the current I in amperes is the rate of flow of electric charge, we also have

$$I = \frac{dQ}{dt}, \qquad \text{or} \qquad Q = \int I\,dt, \tag{11}$$

where time t is measured in seconds. Thus $E_C = (1/C) \int I\, dt$, and the charge and current for the circuit are determined at any time t by (11) and the differential equation

$$L \frac{d^2Q}{dt^2} + R \frac{dQ}{dt} + \frac{1}{C} Q = E. \tag{12}$$

Example 2. An inductance of 0.1 henry, a resistance of 7 ohms, and a capacitance of 6.4×10^{-4} farads are connected in series with an e.m.f. of 100 volts. Find equations for Q and I when the charge and current are initially zero.

Solution: Substituting the given parameters in (12), multiplying by 10, and simplifying gives

$$\frac{d^2Q}{dt^2} + 70 \frac{dQ}{dt} + 15{,}625\, Q = 1000,$$

and we easily find

$$Q = 0.064 + e^{-35t}(A \sin 120t + B \cos 120t),$$

$$I = dQ/dt = e^{-35t}[(120A - 35B) \cos 120t - (35A + 120B) \sin 120t].$$

By use of the initial conditions, $Q = 0$ and $I = 0$ when $t = 0$, we get

$$0 = 0.064 + B, \qquad 0 = 120A - 35B;$$

hence the required equations are

$$Q = 0.064 - e^{-35t}(56 \sin 120t + 192 \cos 120t)/3000,$$
$$I = (25/3)\, e^{-35t} \sin 120t.$$

These equations indicate that the current quickly dies out and that the charge just as quickly approaches a steady-state value of 0.064 coulombs, which is the value given by the formula $Q = CE$.

EXERCISE 124

1. A particle moves in simple harmonic motion in accordance with the equation $s = 3 \sin 8\pi t + 4 \cos 8\pi t$, where s and t are expressed in feet and seconds, respectively. What is the amplitude and period of its motion? *Ans.* 5 ft., 0.25 sec.
2. A damped oscillatory motion is represented by $y = 25e^{-0.1t} \sin (10t + 5)$. At what time t is the amplitude of the motion one-half the value that it has when $t = 0$?
3. A particle moves with simple harmonic motion in a straight line. When $t = 0$, the acceleration is 4 feet per second per second, the velocity is -2 feet per second, and the displacement is $s = -1$ foot. Find the amplitude and period of the motion. *Ans.* $\sqrt{2}$ ft., π sec.

4. A particle moves with simple harmonic motion on the x axis under the action of a force located at the origin. If $x = -2$ feet and $dx/dt = 6$ feet per second when $t = 0$, and if it reaches an extreme position at $x = 2\sqrt{2}$ feet, at what speed does it pass through the origin?
5. A particle moves along the x axis in accordance with the equation $\ddot{x} + 2\dot{x} + x = 0$. If it starts at $x = 2$ feet with a velocity of -4 feet per second, find the time and location of the particle when its velocity is zero. *Ans.* 2 sec., -0.27 ft.
6. A one-pound weight suspended from a spring causes an elongation of 6 inches. If the weight is released from a point 3 inches above its equilibrium position P, at what speed does it pass P?
7. A ten-pound weight is suspended by a spring which is stretched 1.5 inches by the weight. Neglecting resistance, if the weight is drawn down 1 inch below its equilibrium position and released, find the period of its motion. *Ans.* $\pi/8$ sec.
8. If a hole were bored through the center of the earth, the pull of gravity upon an object in the hole would vary directly as the distance of the object from the earth's center. Show that the motion would be simple harmonic and find the time required for an object starting from rest at one end of the hole to reach the other end. Assume that the radius of the earth is 4000 miles.
9. A weight of g pounds is suspended from a spring whose constant is 5 pounds per foot. There is a resistance in pounds equal to four times the velocity in feet per second at any instant. The weight is drawn down 4 inches below its equilibrium position and then released. Find the equation of motion. *Ans.* $x = e^{-2t}(\cos t + 2 \sin t)/3$.
10. A body is subject to damped vibrations in accordance with the equation $\ddot{x} + 2a\dot{x} + b^2x = 0$. If the period is 2 seconds and the damping factor decreases by 10% in 2 seconds, find a and b.
11. A four-pound weight suspended from a spring vibrates in accordance with the equation $\ddot{x} + 2\dot{x} + 6x = 0$ (*FPS* units). What is the magnitude of the spring constant in pounds per inch? *Ans.* $\frac{1}{16}$ lb./in.
12. A six-pound weight of specific gravity 3 stretches a spring 4 inches when immersed in water. If the weight is set in motion, and the resistance of the water is assumed to have a magnitude in pounds equal to $12/\sqrt{g}$ times the velocity in feet per second, find the period of its motion.
13. A body falls from rest in a liquid whose density is one-half that of the body. If the liquid offers resistance proportional to the velocity, and the velocity approaches a limiting value of 32 feet per second, find the distance fallen in the first second. *Ans.* 6.82 ft.
14. A one-pound weight is hanging at rest on a spring which is stretched 6 inches by the weight. If the upper end of the spring is given the

motion $y = 0.3 \sin 16t$ feet and if resistance is neglected, find the equation of motion of the weight and its maximum displacement from its equilibrium position.

15. Find the equation of motion of the weight in the preceding problem if the upper end of the spring is given the motion $y = 0.3 \sin 8t$ feet and g is taken as 32 feet per second per second. Is the motion periodic?
Ans. $x = 0.15 \sin 8t - 1.2t \cos 8t$, No.

16. An inductance of 1 henry, a resistance of 120 ohms, and a capacitance of 10^{-4} farad are connected in series with an e.m.f. of $120 \sin 100t$ volts. If the charge and current are both zero when $t = 0$, compare the magnitudes of the transient and the steady-state currents when $t = 0.01$ second.

17. A coil of inductance 1 henry and negligible resistance is connected in series with a capacitance of 10^{-6} farad and an e.m.f. of 100 volts. If the charge and current are initially zero, what is the maximum current attained by the circuit? *Ans.* 0.1 amp.

18. An inductance of 0.2 henrys, a resistance of 100 ohms, and a capacitance of 5×10^{-5} farads are connected in series with an e.m.f. of $100 \sin 400t$ volts. Find the steady-state current.

19. A cylindrical spar buoy 18 inches in diameter stands in fresh water with its axis vertical. When depressed slightly and released, the period of vibration is found to be 1.5 seconds. Find the weight of the buoy.
Ans. 201 lb.

20. A simple pendulum consists of a weight W in pounds suspended by a string of negligible weight and length L in feet. If θ in radians is the angular displacement of the string from the vertical at time t in seconds, and if resistance is neglected, show that

$$\frac{L}{g}\frac{d^2\theta}{dt^2} = -\sin\theta.$$

If the complete angle of swing 2θ is so small that $\sin\theta$ may be replaced by θ without much error, find the equation of motion when the initial conditions are $\theta = \theta_0$ and $d\theta/dt = 0$ when $t = 0$.

CHAPTER 24

Vector Analysis

231. Introduction

Elementary physical measurements fall into one of two classifications, *scalars* and *vectors*. A scalar quantity is one that is completely determined when its magnitude is known. Examples of scalars are mass, length, work, temperature, and electric charge. A vector quantity is one whose determination involves a direction as well as a magnitude. Examples of vectors are displacement, velocity, force, temperature gradient, and electric current.

A study of vector problems is a necessity in almost all scientific and engineering investigations. The development of this study has resulted in a theory, called *vector analysis*, which contains notations and concepts unique to that particular subject. It has become, in fact, a language in itself. Because of the importance of vectors, it is essential that every student of science have some familiarity with the subject.

In our discussion a scalar quantity will be represented by a number or a letter in italic type, such as x. A vector quantity will be represented by a letter in boldface type,* such as $\mathbf{V}$; and the scalar magnitude of a vector $\mathbf{V}$ will be denoted by $|\mathbf{V}|$ or by the same letter in italics, as V.

A vector is represented geometrically by a directed line segment which starts from an arbitrary initial point and is provided with an arrowhead at its terminal point to indicate its sense of direction. The length of the representative line segment is made proportional to the magnitude of the vector. Two parallel line segments of the same length and direction are said to be *equal vectors*, no matter where their initial points are located. If two parallel line segments have the same length but opposite directions, each is said to be the negative of the other. Thus, if one vector is denoted by $\mathbf{V}$, the other is denoted by $-\mathbf{V}$. A vector parallel to a second vector $\mathbf{V}$, but m times as long, is denoted by $m\mathbf{V}$.

---

* In writing vectors, many symbolisms are used to denote a vector whose magnitude is A, the most common being $\vec{A}$ and $\bar{A}$.

A *unit vector* is one whose magnitude is unity. The unit vectors of most importance are the three unit vectors, **i, j,** and **k** whose directions are the same as the directions of the positive x, y, and z axes, respectively. Rectangular axes in vector analysis must always be taken to form a *right-handed* system. That is, if the index finger of the right hand points in the direction of positive x and the middle finger toward positive y, the thumb points toward positive z.

232. Addition of Vectors

If **A** and **B** are any two vectors, and we place the initial point of **B** on the terminal point of **A,** as shown in Figure 250, the vector **R** drawn from the initial point of **A** to the terminal point of **B** is defined as the **sum** or **resultant** of A and **B**. Reversing the order of addition gives the same result, as is evident in Figure 250. Hence

$$\mathbf{A} + \mathbf{B} = \mathbf{B} + \mathbf{A},$$

and we note that *vector addition is commutative.*

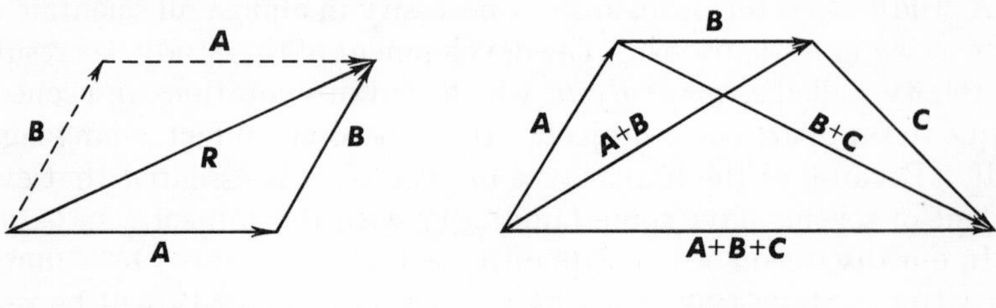

Figure 250 Figure 251

Similarly, the sum of three or more vectors is obtained by constructing a polygon (Figure 251) that has the given vectors as consecutive sides, the sum being the vector drawn from the initial point of the first vector to the terminal point of the last. It is evident in Figure 251 that *vector addition is associative,* that is,

$$(\mathbf{A} + \mathbf{B}) + \mathbf{C} = \mathbf{A} + (\mathbf{B} + \mathbf{C}).$$

Observe also that **A, B,** and **C** need not lie in a common plane, and their sum in general is represented by the diagonal of the parallelepiped formed by the three vectors.

The difference of two vectors $\mathbf{A} - \mathbf{B}$ denotes a vector which when added to **B** gives **A,** as is shown geometrically in Figure 252.

Example. Prove that the diagonals of a parallelogram bisect each other.

Solution: Let $\mathbf{A} = \overrightarrow{PQ}$ and $\mathbf{B} = \overrightarrow{PS}$ be the adjacent sides of a parallelogram as shown in Figure 253. If T is the point of intersection of the diagonals, it is apparent that $\overrightarrow{QT}$ and $\overrightarrow{PT}$ are some fractions of the vectors $\overrightarrow{QS}$ and $\overrightarrow{PR}$, respectively. Hence let $\overrightarrow{QT} = m(\mathbf{B} - \mathbf{A})$ and $\overrightarrow{PT} = n(\mathbf{A} + \mathbf{B})$. Then in triangle PQT we have

$$\mathbf{A} + m(\mathbf{B} - \mathbf{A}) = n(\mathbf{A} + \mathbf{B}),$$

or

$$(1 - m - n)\mathbf{A} + (m - n)\mathbf{B} = 0.$$

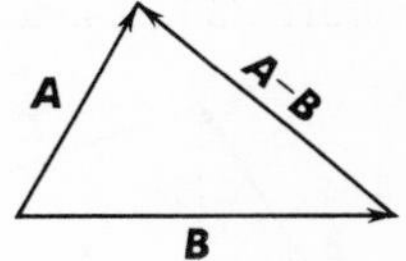

Figure 252

But since **A** and **B** have different directions, the preceding equation can hold only if

$$1 - m - n = 0 \quad \text{and} \quad m - n = 0.$$

Hence $m = \frac{1}{2}$ and $n = \frac{1}{2}$, which proves that T is the mid-point of the diagonals.

The *components* of a vector **V** can be any vectors whose sum is **V**. The components most frequently used, however, are those that are parallel to the x, y, and z axes, and that are called the **rectangular components** of the vector. If V_1, V_2, and V_3 are the projections of **V** on the x, y, and z axes, respectively, the rectangular components are $V_1\mathbf{i}$, $V_2\mathbf{j}$, and $V_3\mathbf{k}$. It is customary, however, to refer to the scalar quantities V_1, V_2, and V_3 as the components of **V**, since the subscripts are sufficient to indicate the direction of the component. Thus, if the vectors $\mathbf{A} = A_1\mathbf{i} + A_2\mathbf{j} + A_3\mathbf{k}$ and $\mathbf{B} = B_1\mathbf{i} + B_2\mathbf{j} + B_3\mathbf{k}$ are expressed in this form, we observe that their sum is

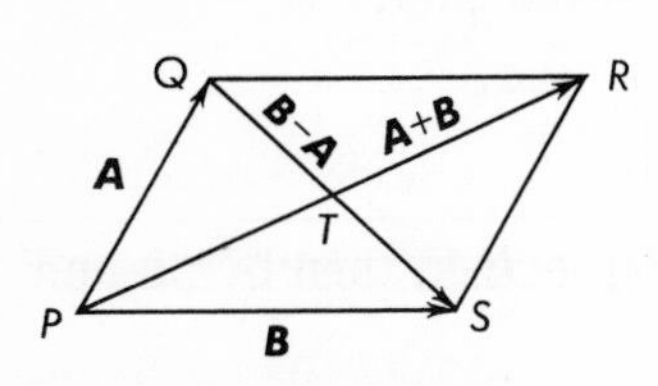

Figure 253

$$\mathbf{A} + \mathbf{B} = (A_1 + B_1)\mathbf{i} + (A_2 + B_2)\mathbf{j} + (A_3 + B_3)\mathbf{k}.$$

233. Scalar Multiplication of Vectors

Because both scalar and vector quantities are available, we define two types of products in multiplication. The product that gives a scalar is called the **scalar** or **dot product** of two vectors, and the product that gives a vector is called the **vector** or **cross product** of two vectors.

The scalar or dot product of **A** and **B** is defined as

$$\mathbf{A}\cdot\mathbf{B} = AB\cos(\mathbf{A},\mathbf{B}), \tag{1}$$

where $(\mathbf{A},\mathbf{B})$ denotes the angle between the directions of **A** and **B**.

Since $B \cos(\mathbf{A},\mathbf{B})$ is the component of **B** along **A**, we see that a dot product represents the product obtained by multiplying the magnitude of **A** by the projection of **B** upon **A**, or vice versa. Since

$$\mathbf{A}\cdot\mathbf{B} = \mathbf{B}\cdot\mathbf{A},$$

we see that *scalar multiplication is commutative.* Furthermore, in Figure 254, it is apparent that $\mathbf{A}\cdot\mathbf{B} = Ab$, $\mathbf{A}\cdot\mathbf{C} = Ac$, and $\mathbf{A}\cdot(\mathbf{B}+\mathbf{C}) = A(b+c)$; hence

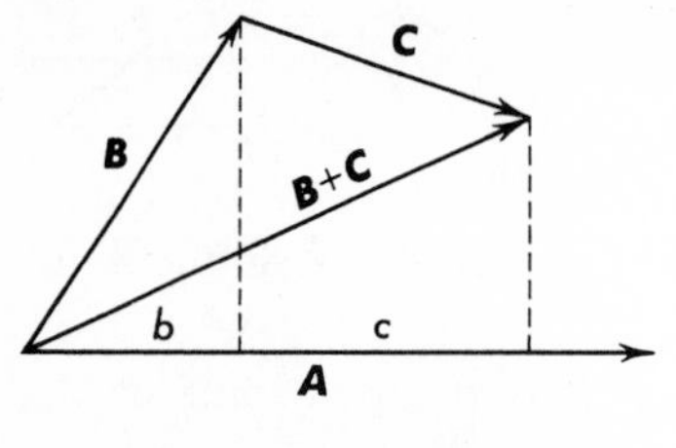

Figure 254

$$\mathbf{A}\cdot(\mathbf{B}+\mathbf{C}) = \mathbf{A}\cdot\mathbf{B} + \mathbf{A}\cdot\mathbf{C}, \quad (2)$$

which establishes the distributive law for scalar multiplication.

If **A** and **B** are perpendicular, $\cos(\mathbf{A},\mathbf{B})$ is zero, and $\mathbf{A}\cdot\mathbf{B} = 0$. Conversely, *if a scalar product is zero, then either one of the vectors is zero or the two vectors are perpendicular.* Thus from $\mathbf{A}\cdot\mathbf{B} = \mathbf{A}\cdot\mathbf{C}$ we cannot conclude that $\mathbf{B} = \mathbf{C}$, but merely that $\mathbf{A}\cdot(\mathbf{B}-\mathbf{C}) = 0$. This means that $\mathbf{B} - \mathbf{C}$ is zero or perpendicular to **A**.

For the unit vectors **i, j, k,** we have the scalar products

$$\begin{aligned} \mathbf{i}\cdot\mathbf{i} &= \mathbf{j}\cdot\mathbf{j} = \mathbf{k}\cdot\mathbf{k} = 1, \\ \mathbf{i}\cdot\mathbf{j} &= \mathbf{j}\cdot\mathbf{k} = \mathbf{k}\cdot\mathbf{i} = 0. \end{aligned} \quad (3)$$

If $\mathbf{A} = A_1\mathbf{i} + A_2\mathbf{j} + A_3\mathbf{k}$ and $\mathbf{B} = B_1\mathbf{i} + B_2\mathbf{j} + B_3\mathbf{k}$, then by (2) and (3), we find

$$\begin{aligned} \mathbf{A}\cdot\mathbf{B} &= (A_1\mathbf{i} + A_2\mathbf{j} + A_3\mathbf{k})\cdot(B_1\mathbf{i} + B_2\mathbf{j} + B_3\mathbf{k}) \\ &= A_1B_1 + A_2B_2 + A_3B_3. \end{aligned} \quad (4)$$

Illustration 1. If $\mathbf{A} = 2a\mathbf{i} - \mathbf{j} + 6\mathbf{k}$ and $\mathbf{B} = 3\mathbf{i} - a\mathbf{k}$, then

$$\mathbf{A}\cdot\mathbf{B} = (2a)(3) + (-1)(0) + (6)(-a) = 0.$$

Therefore the vectors **A** and **B** are perpendicular.

Comparing (1) and (4), we observe that the angle between two vectors **A** and **B** is determined by

$$\cos(\mathbf{A},\mathbf{B}) = \frac{A_1B_1 + A_2B_2 + A_3B_3}{AB}. \quad (5)$$

This is the same formula as that obtained in Article **178.** If $\mathbf{B} = \mathbf{A}$, it is also apparent that

$$A^2 = \mathbf{A}\cdot\mathbf{A} = A_1^2 + A_2^2 + A_3^2.$$

Illustration 2. $\mathbf{A} = \mathbf{i} \cos \alpha + \mathbf{j} \sin \alpha$ and $\mathbf{B} = \mathbf{i} \cos \beta + \mathbf{j} \sin \beta$ are unit vectors in the xy plane that make angles α and β with the positive x axis. By substitution in (5), we obtain the trigonometric formula

$$\cos (\alpha - \beta) = \cos \alpha \cos \beta + \sin \alpha \sin \beta.$$

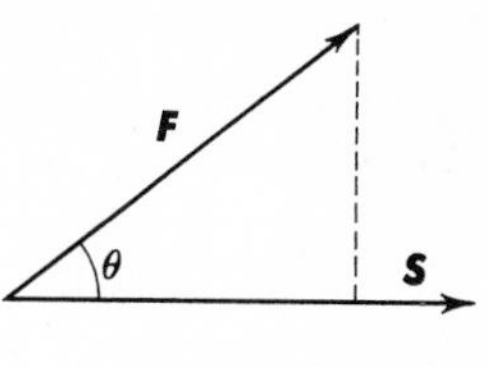

Figure 255

The simplest applied illustration of the scalar product is furnished by mechanical work. When the point of application of a force **F** undergoes a displacement represented in magnitude and direction by the vector **S** (Figure 255), the work done by the force is defined as *the product of the displacement and the component of the force in the direction of the displacement,* that is,

$$Work = SF \cos \theta = \mathbf{S} \cdot \mathbf{F}.$$

234. Vector Multiplication of Vectors

The vector or cross product of **A** and **B** is a vector $\mathbf{V} = \mathbf{A} \times \mathbf{B}$ (Figure 256) that is perpendicular to both **A** and **B**, has a magnitude

$$V = AB \sin (\mathbf{A},\mathbf{B}), \tag{1}$$

and is directed so that **A**, **B**, **V** form a right-handed system. Geometrically, we observe by this definition that the magnitude of $\mathbf{A} \times \mathbf{B}$ is equal to the area of the parallelogram that has the vectors **A** and **B** as sides.

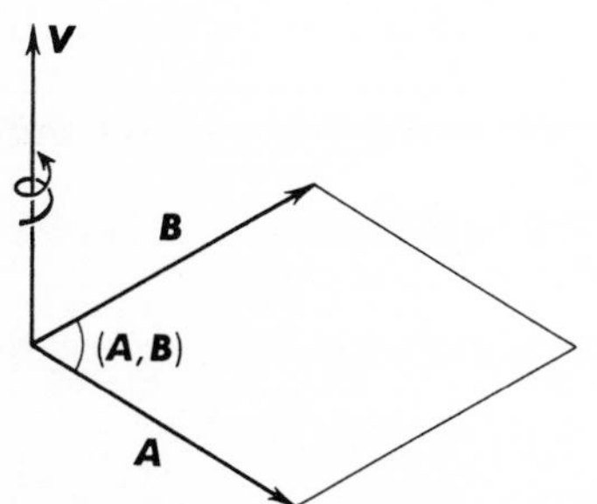

Figure 256

The product $\mathbf{B} \times \mathbf{A}$ has the same magnitude as $\mathbf{A} \times \mathbf{B}$, but the rotation that carries **B** into **A** is opposite to that which carries **A** into **B**. Thus

$$\mathbf{B} \times \mathbf{A} = -\mathbf{A} \times \mathbf{B},$$

and we find that *vector multiplication is not commutative;* hence it is important to maintain the order of vectors in a vector product.

The product $\mathbf{A} \times \mathbf{B}$ can be considered as the vector obtained by (a) projecting **B** on a plane perpendicular to **A**, (b) rotating the projection 90° in the positive direction about **A**, and (c) multiplying the resulting vector by A. Each of these operations changes a closed polygon into a closed polygon. Hence, if they are applied to the sides, **B**, **C**, $\mathbf{B} + \mathbf{C}$ of a triangle, as shown in Figure 257, the resulting vectors form the sides of a second triangle, and so we have

$$\mathbf{A} \times (\mathbf{B} + \mathbf{C}) = \mathbf{A} \times \mathbf{B} + \mathbf{A} \times \mathbf{C}. \tag{2}$$

This verifies the validity of the distributive law for vector multiplication.

If **A** and **B** are parallel vectors, it follows from (1) that

$$\mathbf{A} \times \mathbf{B} = 0.$$

Conversely, *if a vector product is zero, then either one of the vectors is zero or the two vectors are parallel.* Thus $\mathbf{A} \times \mathbf{B} = \mathbf{A} \times \mathbf{C}$ or $\mathbf{A} \times (\mathbf{B} - \mathbf{C}) = 0$ implies that $\mathbf{B} = \mathbf{C}$ or $\mathbf{B} - \mathbf{C}$ is parallel to **A**.

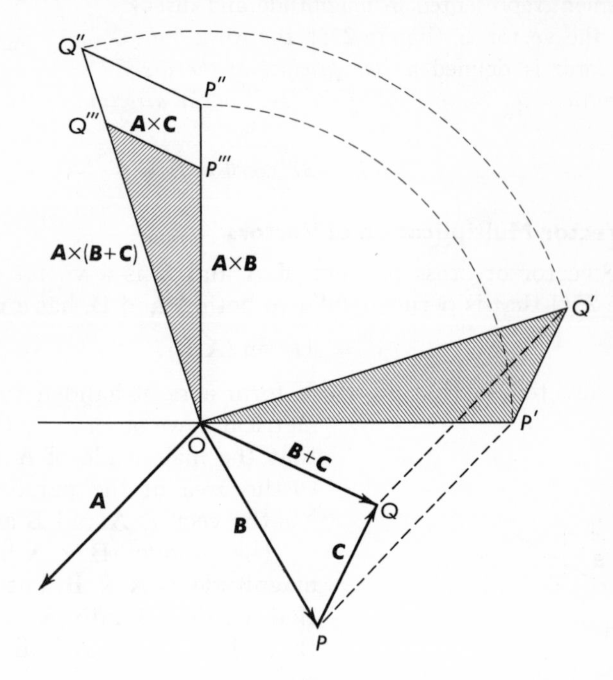

Figure 257.

For the unit vectors **i, j, k,** the definition of a vector product gives

$$\begin{aligned} \mathbf{i} \times \mathbf{i} = \mathbf{j} \times \mathbf{j} &= \mathbf{k} \times \mathbf{k} = 0, \\ \mathbf{i} \times \mathbf{j} &= -\mathbf{j} \times \mathbf{i} = \mathbf{k}, \\ \mathbf{j} \times \mathbf{k} &= -\mathbf{k} \times \mathbf{j} = \mathbf{i}, \\ \mathbf{k} \times \mathbf{i} &= -\mathbf{i} \times \mathbf{k} = \mathbf{j}. \end{aligned} \tag{3}$$

Hence, if $\mathbf{A} = A_1\mathbf{i} + A_2\mathbf{j} + A_3\mathbf{k}$ and $\mathbf{B} = B_1\mathbf{i} + B_2\mathbf{j} + B_3\mathbf{k}$, by (2) and (3) we obtain

$$\mathbf{A} \times \mathbf{B} = (A_2B_3 - A_3B_2)\mathbf{i} + (A_3B_1 - A_1B_3)\mathbf{j} + (A_1B_2 - A_2B_1)\mathbf{k},$$

a result that is more easily remembered in the determinant form

$$\mathbf{A} \times \mathbf{B} = \begin{vmatrix} \mathbf{i} & \mathbf{j} & \mathbf{k} \\ A_1 & A_2 & A_3 \\ B_1 & B_2 & B_3 \end{vmatrix}. \tag{4}$$

Illustration. The vector product of $2\mathbf{i} - \mathbf{j}$ and $\mathbf{j} - 3\mathbf{k}$ is

$$\begin{vmatrix} \mathbf{i} & \mathbf{j} & \mathbf{k} \\ 2 & -1 & 0 \\ 0 & 1 & -3 \end{vmatrix} = 3\mathbf{i} + 6\mathbf{j} + 2\mathbf{k}.$$

As an applied illustration for the use of a vector product, consider the moment M of a vector force $\mathbf{F}$ about the point O. This moment is defined as the product of the magnitude F of the force and the perpendicular distance of the line of action of $\mathbf{F}$ from O. If $\mathbf{R}$ is the vector from O to the point of application of $\mathbf{F}$, as shown in Figure 258, we obtain $M = FR \sin\theta$. Thus, if we adopt the convention that a positive moment produces a counterclockwise rotation, we may define a *moment vector* as

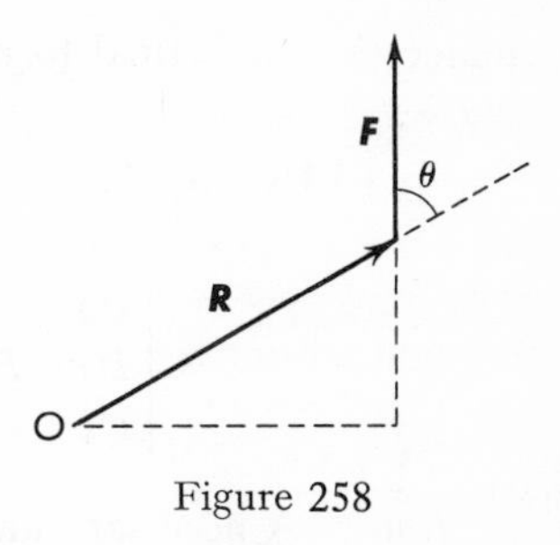

Figure 258

$$\mathbf{M} = \mathbf{R} \times \mathbf{F}.$$

235. Scalar Triple Product

The scalar product of $\mathbf{A}$ and $\mathbf{B} \times \mathbf{C}$ is denoted by

$$\mathbf{A} \cdot (\mathbf{B} \times \mathbf{C}) \qquad \text{or} \qquad \mathbf{A} \cdot \mathbf{B} \times \mathbf{C}, \tag{1}$$

and is called the *scalar triple product* of $\mathbf{A}$, $\mathbf{B}$, and $\mathbf{C}$.

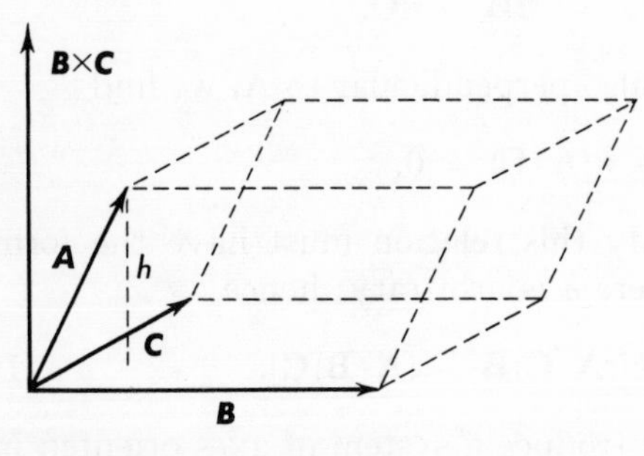

Figure 259

Consider the parallelepiped in Figure 259 which has the vectors $\mathbf{A}$, $\mathbf{B}$, and $\mathbf{C}$ as edges. The area of the base gives the magnitude of $\mathbf{B} \times \mathbf{C}$ and the altitude h is the projection of $\mathbf{A}$ on $\mathbf{B} \times \mathbf{C}$. Hence the scalar magnitude (1) gives the volume of the parallelepiped formed by the vectors $\mathbf{A}$, $\mathbf{B}$, and $\mathbf{C}$. If we consider the face formed by $\mathbf{A}$ and $\mathbf{B}$ to be the base, the volume will be given by $\mathbf{C} \cdot (\mathbf{A} \times \mathbf{B}) = (\mathbf{A} \times \mathbf{B}) \cdot \mathbf{C}$. Since this is the same volume, it is apparent that the dot and cross in a scalar triple product can be interchanged provided the order of the vectors is not altered, that is,

$$\mathbf{A}\cdot\mathbf{B}\times\mathbf{C} = \mathbf{A}\times\mathbf{B}\cdot\mathbf{C}. \tag{2}$$

For this reason, a scalar triple product is often written as $[\mathbf{ABC}]$ and called a *box product*.

From the relation (4) in the preceding article, we find

$$\mathbf{B}\times\mathbf{C} = \mathbf{i}\begin{vmatrix} B_2 & B_3 \\ C_2 & C_3 \end{vmatrix} - \mathbf{j}\begin{vmatrix} B_1 & B_3 \\ C_1 & C_3 \end{vmatrix} + \mathbf{k}\begin{vmatrix} B_1 & B_2 \\ C_1 & C_2 \end{vmatrix};$$

hence the analytical form of a box product is

$$\begin{aligned}[\mathbf{ABC}] &= A_1\begin{vmatrix} B_2 & B_3 \\ C_2 & C_3 \end{vmatrix} - A_2\begin{vmatrix} B_1 & B_3 \\ C_1 & C_3 \end{vmatrix} + A_3\begin{vmatrix} B_1 & B_2 \\ C_1 & C_2 \end{vmatrix} \\ &= \begin{vmatrix} A_1 & A_2 & A_3 \\ B_1 & B_2 & B_3 \\ C_1 & C_2 & C_3 \end{vmatrix}. \end{aligned} \tag{3}$$

Note: A necessary and sufficient condition that the vectors **A, B,** and **C** be coplanar is that the determinant in (3) be zero. Observe that this also implies that $\mathbf{C} = m\mathbf{A} + n\mathbf{B}$, where m and n are scalar numbers.

236. Vector Triple Product

The product $\mathbf{A}\times(\mathbf{B}\times\mathbf{C})$ is called a *vector triple product* of **A, B,** and **C.** It is a vector that is perpendicular to $\mathbf{B}\times\mathbf{C}$ and therefore coplanar with **B** and **C**; hence

$$\mathbf{A}\times(\mathbf{B}\times\mathbf{C}) = m\mathbf{B} + n\mathbf{C}.$$

However, since $\mathbf{A}\times(\mathbf{B}\times\mathbf{C})$ is also perpendicular to **A,** we find

$$m(\mathbf{A}\cdot\mathbf{B}) + n(\mathbf{A}\cdot\mathbf{C}) = 0.$$

All numbers m and n that satisfy this relation must have the form $m = h(\mathbf{A}\cdot\mathbf{C})$, $n = -h(\mathbf{A}\cdot\mathbf{B})$, where h is arbitrary; hence

$$\mathbf{A}\times(\mathbf{B}\times\mathbf{C}) = h[(\mathbf{A}\cdot\mathbf{C})\mathbf{B} - (\mathbf{A}\cdot\mathbf{B})\mathbf{C}]. \tag{1}$$

In order to determine h, we introduce a system of axes oriented in such a way that **i** is collinear with **B,** and **j** is coplanar with **B** and **C.** For these axes, we then have

$$\mathbf{A} = A_1\mathbf{i} + A_2\mathbf{j} + A_3\mathbf{k}, \qquad \mathbf{B} = B_1\mathbf{i}, \qquad \mathbf{C} = C_1\mathbf{i} + C_2\mathbf{j}.$$

On substituting these values in (1), we find $h = 1$. This gives us the important expansion formulas

$$\begin{aligned} \mathbf{A} \times (\mathbf{B} \times \mathbf{C}) &= (\mathbf{A} \cdot \mathbf{C})\mathbf{B} - (\mathbf{A} \cdot \mathbf{B})\mathbf{C}, \\ (\mathbf{A} \times \mathbf{B}) \times \mathbf{C} &= (\mathbf{A} \cdot \mathbf{C})\mathbf{B} - (\mathbf{B} \cdot \mathbf{C})\mathbf{A}. \end{aligned} \tag{2}$$

In comparing the relations in (2), it is evident that the operation of *vector multiplication is not associative.*

EXERCISE 125

1. Let M be the mid-point of side BC of the parallelogram $ABCD$. Prove that AM trisects the diagonal BD.
2. In triangle ABC, let M be the mid-point of AB and N the mid-point of CM. Prove that AN extended trisects BC.
3. Prove that the medians of a triangle meet at a point of trisection.
4. Let $\mathbf{A}, \mathbf{B}, \mathbf{C}, \mathbf{D}$ denote vectors from an origin to the points A, B, C, D. If $\mathbf{B} - \mathbf{A} = \mathbf{C} - \mathbf{D}$, show that $ABCD$ is a parallelogram.
5. If $\mathbf{A}$ and $\mathbf{B}$ are vectors from point P to A and B, respectively, find the vector from P to the mid-point of AB. *Ans.* $\frac{1}{2}(\mathbf{A} + \mathbf{B})$.
6. Show that the vectors $2\mathbf{i} + 4\mathbf{j} + 5\mathbf{k}$ and $\mathbf{i} + 2\mathbf{j} - 2\mathbf{k}$ are perpendicular.
7. Show that the vectors $2\mathbf{i} - \mathbf{j} + \mathbf{k}$, $\mathbf{i} - 3\mathbf{j} - 2\mathbf{k}$, and $3\mathbf{i} + 2\mathbf{j} + 5\mathbf{k}$ are coplanar.
8. Find the cosine of the angle between the vectors $\mathbf{i} + 2\mathbf{j} - 2\mathbf{k}$ and $2\mathbf{i} - \mathbf{j} - 2\mathbf{k}$.
9. Prove or disprove the following statements.
   (*a*) If $\mathbf{A} \cdot \mathbf{B} = 0$ and $\mathbf{B} \cdot \mathbf{C} = 0$, then $\mathbf{A} \cdot \mathbf{C} = 0$.
   (*b*) If $\mathbf{A} \times \mathbf{B} = 0$ and $\mathbf{B} \times \mathbf{C} = 0$, then $\mathbf{A} \times \mathbf{C} = 0$.
10. The vectors from the origin to the points A, B, and C are $\mathbf{i} + \mathbf{j}$, $3\mathbf{i} + \mathbf{k}$, and $4\mathbf{i} - 3\mathbf{j} - 4\mathbf{k}$, respectively. Show that ABC is a right triangle, and find its area.
11. Find the component of $3\mathbf{i} - 5\mathbf{j}$ along $3\mathbf{j} + 4\mathbf{k}$. *Ans.* -3.
12. Find the area of the parallelogram formed by the vectors $3\mathbf{i} + 2\mathbf{j}$ and $3\mathbf{j} - 4\mathbf{k}$.
13. Find the volume of the parallelepiped formed by the vectors $\mathbf{i} + \mathbf{j} + \mathbf{k}$, $2\mathbf{i} - \mathbf{j} - 3\mathbf{k}$, and $3\mathbf{j} - \mathbf{k}$. *Ans.* 18.
14. By computing the vector product of $\mathbf{i} \cos \alpha + \mathbf{j} \sin \alpha$ and $\mathbf{i} \cos \beta + \mathbf{j} \sin \beta$, find a formula for $\sin (\alpha - \beta)$.
15. Under what circumstances is the following statement true? If $\mathbf{A} \times \mathbf{B} = \mathbf{C}$ and $\mathbf{B} \times \mathbf{C} = \mathbf{A}$, then $\mathbf{C} \times \mathbf{A} = \mathbf{B}$.
    Ans. $\pm A = B = \pm C = 1$, or $\pm A = B = \mp C = -1$.
16. Express the sides of a triangle in the form $\mathbf{a} = \mathbf{b} - \mathbf{c}$, and derive the law of cosines by considering the scalar product

$$\mathbf{a} \cdot \mathbf{a} = (\mathbf{b} - \mathbf{c}) \cdot (\mathbf{b} - \mathbf{c}).$$

17. If **A**, **B**, **C** are vectors from an origin to the points A, B, C, and $\mathbf{C} = m\mathbf{A} + n\mathbf{B}$, show that A, B, and C are collinear when $m + n = 1$.
18. If **A**, **B**, **C** are vectors from an origin O to the points A, B, C, find the volume of the tetrahedron $OABC$.
19. By means of products express the condition that the plane through **A** and **B** be perpendicular to the plane through **C** and **D**.

    Ans. $\mathbf{A} \times \mathbf{B} \cdot \mathbf{C} \times \mathbf{D} = 0$.
20. By means of products express the condition that **A**, **B**, **C**, **D** all be parallel to a plane.
21. If **A**, **B**, **C** are vectors from an origin to the points A, B, C, show that

$$\tfrac{1}{2}|\mathbf{A} \times \mathbf{B} + \mathbf{B} \times \mathbf{C} + \mathbf{C} \times \mathbf{A}|$$

    is the area of the triangle ABC.
22. If **A**, **B**, **C**, **D** are vectors from an origin O to the points A, B, C, D, find the volume of the tetrahedron $ABCD$.
23. If **A** is a constant vector and **R** is the radius vector from the origin to the variable point (x,y,z), show that $(\mathbf{R} - \mathbf{A}) \cdot \mathbf{A} = 0$ is the equation of a plane and describe its location.

    Ans. Perpendicular to **A** at its terminus.
24. If **A** is a constant vector and **R** is the radius vector from the origin to the variable point (x,y,z), show that $(\mathbf{R} - \mathbf{A}) \cdot \mathbf{R} = 0$ is the equation of a sphere and describe its location.
25. Show that $(\mathbf{A} \times \mathbf{B}) \cdot (\mathbf{C} \times \mathbf{D}) = \begin{vmatrix} \mathbf{A} \cdot \mathbf{C} & \mathbf{B} \cdot \mathbf{C} \\ \mathbf{A} \cdot \mathbf{D} & \mathbf{B} \cdot \mathbf{D} \end{vmatrix}$. *Hint: Use* (2), Articles **235** and **236**.
26. Show that $(\mathbf{A} \times \mathbf{B}) \times (\mathbf{C} \times \mathbf{D}) = [\mathbf{ABD}]\mathbf{C} - [\mathbf{ABC}]\mathbf{D}$.
27. If $(\mathbf{A} \times \mathbf{B}) \times \mathbf{C} = \mathbf{A} \times (\mathbf{B} \times \mathbf{C})$, prove that $(\mathbf{A} \times \mathbf{C}) \times \mathbf{B} = 0$.
28. Show that $\mathbf{A} \times (\mathbf{B} \times \mathbf{C}) + \mathbf{B} \times (\mathbf{C} \times \mathbf{A}) + \mathbf{C} \times (\mathbf{A} \times \mathbf{B}) = 0$.
29. Show that $(\mathbf{A} \times \mathbf{B}) \cdot (\mathbf{B} \times \mathbf{C}) \times (\mathbf{C} \times \mathbf{A}) = [\mathbf{ABC}]^2$.
30. If a force **F** acts at a distance **R** from the origin, show that the torque T about any axis through the origin is $T = \mathbf{R} \times \mathbf{F} \cdot \mathbf{L}$, where **L** is a unit vector in the direction of the axis.
31. Prove *Schwarz's Inequality:*

$$(A_1B_1 + A_2B_2 + A_3B_3)^2 \leqq (A_1^2 + A_2^2 + A_3^2)(B_1^2 + B_2^2 + B_3^2).$$

    When does the equality hold?

    Ans. $A_1/B_1 = A_2/B_2 = A_3/B_3$.
32. If **A**, **B**, **C**, and m are constants with $\mathbf{A} \cdot \mathbf{B} \neq 0$, solve the equations $\mathbf{F} \cdot \mathbf{A} = m$ and $\mathbf{F} \times \mathbf{B} = \mathbf{C}$ for **F**. *Hint:* Cross the second equation with **A**.

237. Derivative of a Vector

If, for each value of a scalar variable t in a given domain, there corresponds a vector $\mathbf{F}$, then $\mathbf{F}$ is called a **vector function** of t and is denoted as $\mathbf{F}(t)$.

When t approaches a fixed value t_0, the vector function $\mathbf{F}(t)$ is said to approach the constant vector $\mathbf{L}$ as a limit provided the magnitude of the difference $\mathbf{F}(t) - \mathbf{L}$ approaches zero. When $\mathbf{L}$ is not zero, this means that the direction and magnitude of $\mathbf{F}(t)$ are both nearly that of $\mathbf{L}$ when t is close to t_0. When $\mathbf{L}$ is zero, the direction of $\mathbf{F}(t)$ may vary as $|\mathbf{F}(t)| \to 0$. As for scalar functions, a vector function $\mathbf{F}(t)$ is said to be *continuous* at $t = t_0$ when

$$\lim_{t \to t_0} \mathbf{F}(t) = \mathbf{F}(t_0).$$

The *derivative* of a vector function $\mathbf{F}(t)$ is defined as

$$\frac{d\mathbf{F}}{dt} = \lim_{\Delta t \to 0} \frac{\mathbf{F}(t + \Delta t) - \mathbf{F}(t)}{\Delta t},$$

and is also represented by $\mathbf{F}'(t)$. Derivatives of higher order are defined in like manner:

$$\frac{d^2\mathbf{F}}{dt^2} = \mathbf{F}''(t) = \frac{d\mathbf{F}'}{dt}, \quad \text{and so on.}$$

If $\mathbf{F}(t)$ and $\mathbf{G}(t)$ are differentiable vector functions, and $f(t)$ a differentiable scalar function, the following differentiation rules are easily obtained by using the same procedures that were used in Article **57.**

I. $$\frac{d\mathbf{C}}{dt} = 0, \quad \mathbf{C} \text{ a constant vector,}$$

II. $$\frac{d}{dt}(\mathbf{F} + \mathbf{G}) = \frac{d\mathbf{F}}{dt} + \frac{d\mathbf{G}}{dt},$$

III. $$\frac{d}{dt}(f\mathbf{F}) = f\frac{d\mathbf{F}}{dt} + \frac{df}{dt}\mathbf{F},$$

IV. $$\frac{d}{dt}(\mathbf{F} \cdot \mathbf{G}) = \mathbf{F} \cdot \frac{d\mathbf{G}}{dt} + \frac{d\mathbf{F}}{dt} \cdot \mathbf{G},$$

V. $$\frac{d}{dt}(\mathbf{F} \times \mathbf{G}) = \mathbf{F} \times \frac{d\mathbf{G}}{dt} + \frac{d\mathbf{F}}{dt} \times \mathbf{G}.$$

Since vector multiplication is not commutative, it is important to note that the *order* of the factors in V must be preserved.

The preceding formulas may be used to establish the following theorems.

Theorem 1. *A necessary and sufficient condition that a variable vector* $\mathbf{F}$ *have a constant magnitude is that*

$$\mathbf{F}\cdot\frac{d\mathbf{F}}{dt} = 0.$$

Proof: Since $F^2 = \mathbf{F}\cdot\mathbf{F}$, by use of IV we find

$$\frac{d}{dt}(\mathbf{F}\cdot\mathbf{F}) = 2\mathbf{F}\cdot\frac{d\mathbf{F}}{dt}.$$

Hence, F = constant implies $\mathbf{F}\cdot\frac{d\mathbf{F}}{dt} = 0$, and conversely.

Theorem 2. *A necessary and sufficient condition that a variable vector* $\mathbf{F}$ *always remain parallel to a fixed line is that*

$$\mathbf{F}\times\frac{d\mathbf{F}}{dt} = 0. \tag{1}$$

Proof: If $\mathbf{F} = F(t)\mathbf{u}$, where $\mathbf{u}$ is a unit vector, we have, by use of III,

$$\mathbf{F}\times\frac{d\mathbf{F}}{dt} = F\mathbf{u}\times\left(\frac{dF}{dt}\mathbf{u} + F\frac{d\mathbf{u}}{dt}\right) = F^2\,\mathbf{u}\times\frac{d\mathbf{u}}{dt}. \tag{2}$$

If $\mathbf{u}$ is constant, $d\mathbf{u}/dt = 0$, and the condition (1) follows. Conversely, since $F \neq 0$, we see in (2) that the condition (1) implies that $\mathbf{u}\times(d\mathbf{u}/dt) = 0$. However, by Theorem 1 and the fact that $\mathbf{u}$ is a unit vector, we have $\mathbf{u}\cdot(d\mathbf{u}/dt) = 0$. These two relations are contradictory unless $d\mathbf{u}/dt = 0$. Hence $\mathbf{u}$ is constant, and this means that the direction of $\mathbf{F}$ is fixed.

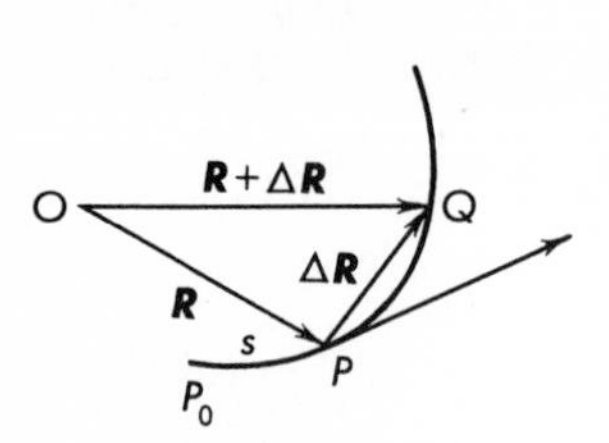

Figure 260

In Figure 260 let $\mathbf{R}$ be the vector from a fixed point O to a variable point P that moves along a curve, and let s be the distance measured along the curve from a fixed point P_0. When P moves to Q the increment $\Delta\mathbf{R}$ is the vector from P to Q, and the ratio $\Delta\mathbf{R}/\Delta s$ is a vector along the chord PQ of length

$$\left|\frac{\Delta\mathbf{R}}{\Delta s}\right| = \frac{\text{chord } PQ}{\text{arc } PQ}. \tag{3}$$

As Q approaches P, the ratio (3) approaches 1, and the line PQ approaches the tangent line at P. Hence the limit $d\mathbf{R}/ds$ represents a unit vector directed along the tangent at P.

If $\mathbf{R}(t)$ denotes the path of a particle P expressed as a function of time t, the vectors

$$\mathbf{V} = \frac{d\mathbf{R}}{dt}, \qquad \mathbf{A} = \frac{d\mathbf{V}}{dt} = \frac{d^2\mathbf{R}}{dt^2}$$

are called the **velocity** and **acceleration** of the particle, respectively. By the chain rule, we have

$$\mathbf{V} = \frac{d\mathbf{R}}{ds}\frac{ds}{dt} = v\mathbf{T}, \tag{4}$$

where $|v|$ is the speed of the particle and $\mathbf{T}$ denotes a unit vector tangent to the direction of motion.

On differentiating (4) with respect to time, we obtain

$$\mathbf{A} = \frac{dv}{dt}\mathbf{T} + v\frac{d\mathbf{T}}{dt}. \tag{5}$$

Since $\mathbf{T}$ is a unit vector an increment Δs will change $\mathbf{T}$, not in magnitude, but in direction by an amount $\Delta\mathbf{T}$. If Δs is small, the magnitude of $\Delta\mathbf{T}$ is approximately equal to the arc of a unit circle with central angle $\Delta\alpha$, this angle being the angle through which the tangent turns. Thus, in accordance with Article **96,** we find

$$\left|\frac{d\mathbf{T}}{ds}\right| = \lim_{\Delta s\to 0}\left|\frac{\Delta\mathbf{T}}{\Delta s}\right| = \lim_{\Delta s\to 0}\left|\frac{\Delta\alpha}{\Delta s}\right| = K,$$

where K denotes the curvature at P. Since $d\mathbf{T}/dt$ is perpendicular to $\mathbf{T}$ by Theorem 1, it follows that (5) may be written

$$\mathbf{A} = \frac{dv}{dt}\mathbf{T} + v\frac{d\mathbf{T}}{ds}\frac{ds}{dt} = \frac{d^2s}{dt^2}\mathbf{T} + Kv^2\mathbf{N},$$

where $\mathbf{N}$ denotes a unit vector normal to the direction of motion. These are the same relations as those obtained in Article **103** by non-vectorial methods.

238. The Gradient

In many applied problems we have occasion to deal with a scalar function of position defined at each point in a certain region of space. For example, the temperature distribution within a body represents such a function. The region throughout which this scalar property is defined is known as a *scalar field*.

Let $\phi(x,y,z)$ be a scalar function whose first derivatives are continuous in a certain region and let $\mathbf{R} = \mathbf{i}x + \mathbf{j}y + \mathbf{k}z$ be the radius vector from an origin to a variable point $P(x,y,z)$. For a small variation in x, y, and z, we find

$$d\mathbf{R} = \mathbf{i}\,dx + \mathbf{j}\,dy + \mathbf{k}\,dz, \tag{1}$$

and

$$d\phi = \frac{\partial\phi}{\partial x}\,dx + \frac{\partial\phi}{\partial y}\,dy + \frac{\partial\phi}{\partial z}\,dz. \tag{2}$$

If the variation is taken in an arbitrary direction and $ds = |d\mathbf{R}|$ denotes the distance moved, the expression

$$\frac{d\phi}{ds} = \frac{\partial\phi}{\partial x}\frac{dx}{ds} + \frac{\partial\phi}{\partial y}\frac{dy}{ds} + \frac{\partial\phi}{\partial z}\frac{dz}{ds} \tag{3}$$

is called the **directional derivative** of ϕ in the direction selected. It is clear that a scalar function has a directional derivative at P extending in every direction.

We observe that (2) may be written in the form

$$d\phi = \left(\mathbf{i}\frac{\partial\phi}{\partial x} + \mathbf{j}\frac{\partial\phi}{\partial y} + \mathbf{k}\frac{\partial\phi}{\partial z}\right)\cdot(\mathbf{i}\,dx + \mathbf{j}\,dy + \mathbf{k}\,dz)$$

$$= \left(\mathbf{i}\frac{\partial\phi}{\partial x} + \mathbf{j}\frac{\partial\phi}{\partial y} + \mathbf{k}\frac{\partial\phi}{\partial z}\right)\cdot d\mathbf{R}. \tag{4}$$

The first vector in (4), as we shall see, is of basic importance in field problems. This vector is called the **gradient** of ϕ, and it is represented by the notations grad ϕ or $\nabla\phi$; thus

$$\text{grad}\,\phi \equiv \nabla\phi = \mathbf{i}\frac{\partial\phi}{\partial x} + \mathbf{j}\frac{\partial\phi}{\partial y} + \mathbf{k}\frac{\partial\phi}{\partial z}. \tag{5}$$

The symbol ∇, called "del," can be considered to represent a symbolic vector differential operator

$$\nabla \equiv \mathbf{i}\frac{\partial}{\partial x} + \mathbf{j}\frac{\partial}{\partial y} + \mathbf{k}\frac{\partial}{\partial z}. \tag{6}$$

Illustration 1. If $\phi = R = \sqrt{x^2 + y^2 + z^2}$, then

$$\nabla\phi = \frac{\mathbf{i}x + \mathbf{j}y + \mathbf{k}z}{\sqrt{x^2 + y^2 + z^2}} = \frac{\mathbf{R}}{R}.$$

To determine the significance of a gradient, we write (3) in the form

$$\frac{d\phi}{ds} = \nabla\phi\cdot\frac{d\mathbf{R}}{ds}. \tag{7}$$

Since $d\mathbf{R}/ds$ is a vector of unit length, regardless of its direction, we see that the right side of (7) represents the component of the gradient in the direction $d\mathbf{R}$. Thus *the gradient is a vector whose component in any direction is the directional derivative in that direction.* It is also apparent in (7) that when the gradient extends in the direction of $d\mathbf{R}$ the directional derivative is maximum and has the same magnitude as the gradient.

Illustration 2. For a direction determined by $dx = dy = dz$, we have $dx/ds = dy/ds = dz/ds = 1/\sqrt{3}$. Hence the directional derivative of $\phi = xyz$ at the point $P_0(1,2,3)$ in the given direction is

$$\frac{d\phi}{ds} = \left[\frac{yz}{\sqrt{3}} + \frac{xz}{\sqrt{3}} + \frac{xy}{\sqrt{3}}\right]_0 = \frac{11}{\sqrt{3}} = 6.35,$$

whereas the directional derivative of maximum magnitude is

$$|\nabla\phi| = |\mathbf{i}yz + \mathbf{j}xz + \mathbf{k}xy|_0 = |6\mathbf{i} + 3\mathbf{j} + 2\mathbf{k}| = 7.$$

If we set the scalar point function $\phi(x,y,z)$ equal to a constant c, we get the equation of a surface on which at every point ϕ has the same value. We call this surface

$$\phi(x,y,z) = c, \tag{8}$$

a *level* or *equivalue surface* for the function ϕ. In a variation $d\mathbf{R}$ along this surface, we have

$$d\phi = \nabla\phi \cdot d\mathbf{R} = 0.$$

This means at a point P of the surface that $\nabla\phi$ is perpendicular to every vector $d\mathbf{R}$ in the surface at P. Hence *the gradient is a vector whose direction is normal to the surface* (8) *in the direction of increasing* ϕ *and whose magnitude represents the greatest rate of increase of* ϕ.

239. The Divergence

When a physical property determines a scalar at each point of a certain region in space, we have said that the region forms a *scalar field.* In like manner, if a vector is specified at each point in space, we say that the region forms a *vector field.* The velocity at each point of a fluid mass is an example of a vector field.

If $\mathbf{F}(x,y,z)$ is a vector function with components whose first derivatives are continuous in the domain of $\mathbf{F}$, the scalar

$$\begin{aligned}\nabla\cdot\mathbf{F} &= \left(\mathbf{i}\frac{\partial}{\partial x} + \mathbf{j}\frac{\partial}{\partial y} + \mathbf{k}\frac{\partial}{\partial z}\right)\cdot(\mathbf{i}F_1 + \mathbf{j}F_2 + \mathbf{k}F_3) \\ &= \frac{\partial F_1}{\partial x} + \frac{\partial F_2}{\partial y} + \frac{\partial F_3}{\partial z}\end{aligned} \tag{1}$$

is called the **divergence** of $\mathbf{F}$, and is also denoted by div $\mathbf{F}$.

Illustration. $\operatorname{div} \mathbf{R} = \nabla \cdot (\mathbf{i}x + \mathbf{j}y + \mathbf{k}z) = \frac{\partial}{\partial x}(x) + \frac{\partial}{\partial y}(y) + \frac{\partial}{\partial z}(z) = 3.$

The divergence has the following important application in hydrodynamics. Consider the flow of a fluid in a three-dimensional region. Let the magnitude of $\mathbf{V}$ denote the mass at a point P of the fluid, flowing in unit time through a unit cross-sectional area perpendicular to the direction of flow, which we take as the direction of $\mathbf{V}$. Let V_1, V_2, V_3 be the components of $\mathbf{V}$ along the coordinate axes. If we consider an elementary volume $\Delta x\, \Delta y\, \Delta z$ of the region, as shown in Figure 261, then the mass flowing into the face $PABC$ is, approximately,

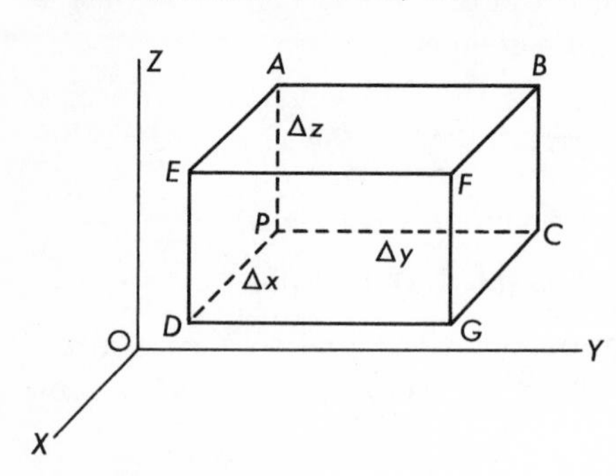

Figure 261

$$V_1\, \Delta y\, \Delta z,$$

while that flowing out of the parallel face $DEFG$ is, approximately,

$$(V_1 + \Delta V_1)\, \Delta y\, \Delta z.$$

Hence the approximate net increase of fluid in the parallelepiped due to these two faces is

$$V_1\, \Delta y\, \Delta z - (V_1 + \Delta V_1)\, \Delta y\, \Delta z = -\Delta V_1\, \Delta y\, \Delta z.$$

Similarly, the approximate net increases of fluid through the other two sets of faces is

$$-\Delta V_2\, \Delta x\, \Delta z \qquad \text{and} \qquad -\Delta V_3\, \Delta x\, \Delta y.$$

If we add these three expressions and divide by the volume $\Delta x\, \Delta y\, \Delta z$ of the parallelepiped, the total increase in mass per unit volume per unit time due to the excess of flow inward over the flow outward is found to be

$$-\frac{\Delta V_1}{\Delta x} - \frac{\Delta V_2}{\Delta y} - \frac{\Delta V_3}{\Delta z}.$$

In the limit as Δx, Δy, and Δz all approach zero, we get

$$-\frac{\partial V_1}{\partial x} - \frac{\partial V_2}{\partial y} - \frac{\partial V_3}{\partial z} = -\nabla \cdot \mathbf{V}.$$

But this is just the time rate of increase of mass density; hence

$$\frac{\partial \rho}{\partial t} = -\nabla \cdot \mathbf{V}.$$

This equation is known as the *equation of continuity*. If the fluid is incompressible $\partial\rho/\partial t = 0$; hence

$$\nabla \cdot \mathbf{V} = 0.$$

Since $-\nabla \cdot \mathbf{V}$ represents the excess of inward flow over outward flow, it is understandable that $\nabla \cdot \mathbf{V}$ represents the excess of outward flow over inward flow, or the *divergence* of the fluid.

240. The Curl or Rotation

If $\mathbf{F}(x,y,z)$ is a vector function with components whose first derivatives are continuous in the domain of $\mathbf{F}$, the vector

$$\nabla \times \mathbf{F} = \begin{vmatrix} \mathbf{i} & \mathbf{j} & \mathbf{k} \\ \dfrac{\partial}{\partial x} & \dfrac{\partial}{\partial y} & \dfrac{\partial}{\partial z} \\ F_1 & F_2 & F_3 \end{vmatrix}$$

$$= \left(\frac{\partial F_3}{\partial y} - \frac{\partial F_2}{\partial z}\right)\mathbf{i} + \left(\frac{\partial F_1}{\partial z} - \frac{\partial F_3}{\partial x}\right)\mathbf{j} + \left(\frac{\partial F_2}{\partial x} - \frac{\partial F_1}{\partial y}\right)\mathbf{k} \qquad (1)$$

is called the **curl** or **rotation** of $\mathbf{F}$, and is also denoted by curl $\mathbf{F}$ or rot $\mathbf{F}$.

Example. If $\mathbf{A}$ is a constant vector and $\mathbf{R} = \mathbf{i}x + \mathbf{j}y + \mathbf{k}z$, find $\nabla \times (\mathbf{A} \times \mathbf{R})$.

Solution: From the definition of a vector product, we have

$$\mathbf{A} \times \mathbf{R} = (A_2z - A_3y)\mathbf{i} + (A_3x - A_1z)\mathbf{j} + (A_1y - A_2x)\mathbf{k}.$$

Hence, by (1), we obtain

$$\nabla \times (\mathbf{A} \times \mathbf{R}) = \begin{vmatrix} \mathbf{i} & \mathbf{j} & \mathbf{k} \\ \dfrac{\partial}{\partial x} & \dfrac{\partial}{\partial y} & \dfrac{\partial}{\partial z} \\ A_2z - A_3y & A_3x - A_1z & A_1y - A_2x \end{vmatrix}$$

$$= 2A_1\mathbf{i} + 2A_2\mathbf{j} + 2A_3\mathbf{k} = 2\mathbf{A}.$$

The curl of a vector has a simple application in connection with rotary motion. Consider a rigid body which has an angular velocity ω about an axis that passes through an origin O fixed in the body, as shown in Figure 262. If the angular velocity is denoted by a vector $\boldsymbol{\omega}$ directed along the axis of rotation, and $\mathbf{r}$ is perpendicular to $\boldsymbol{\omega}$, it is apparent that $\boldsymbol{\omega} \times \mathbf{r}$ will denote the linear velocity $\mathbf{V}$ of the point P about the axis. Furthermore, the linear velocity may be written

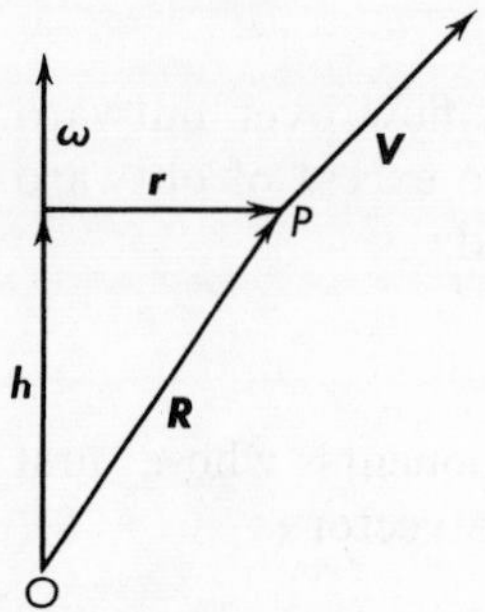

Figure 262

$$\mathbf{V} = \boldsymbol{\omega} \times \mathbf{r} = \boldsymbol{\omega} \times (\mathbf{R} - \mathbf{h}) = \boldsymbol{\omega} \times \mathbf{R}.$$

Since $\boldsymbol{\omega}$ is a constant as far as the coordinates x, y, and z are concerned, it follows from the preceding example that

$$\nabla \times \mathbf{V} = \nabla \times (\boldsymbol{\omega} \times \mathbf{R}) = 2\boldsymbol{\omega}.$$

Thus *the angular velocity of a body in rotation is equal to one-half the curl of its linear velocity.* This relation between linear and angular velocities is responsible for the use of the term *curl.*

241. Summary of Vector Differentiation

Since $\nabla\phi$ is a vector, we can compute its divergence and get the scalar

$$\nabla \cdot \nabla\phi = \left(\mathbf{i}\frac{\partial}{\partial x} + \mathbf{j}\frac{\partial}{\partial y} + \mathbf{k}\frac{\partial}{\partial z}\right) \cdot \left(\mathbf{i}\frac{\partial\phi}{\partial x} + \mathbf{j}\frac{\partial\phi}{\partial y} + \mathbf{k}\frac{\partial\phi}{\partial z}\right)$$

$$= \frac{\partial^2\phi}{\partial x^2} + \frac{\partial^2\phi}{\partial y^2} + \frac{\partial^2\phi}{\partial z^2}.$$

The operator

$$\nabla^2 = \nabla \cdot \nabla = \frac{\partial^2}{\partial x^2} + \frac{\partial^2}{\partial y^2} + \frac{\partial^2}{\partial z^2}$$

is called the *Laplacian,* since $\nabla^2\phi = 0$ gives Laplace's equation.

The vector $\nabla \times \nabla\phi$, the curl of the gradient of the scalar function ϕ, is identically zero, as is suggested by the fact that we are taking the vector product of ∇ by itself. To prove this, we expand as follows:

$$\nabla \times \nabla\phi = \begin{vmatrix} \mathbf{i} & \mathbf{j} & \mathbf{k} \\ \dfrac{\partial}{\partial x} & \dfrac{\partial}{\partial y} & \dfrac{\partial}{\partial z} \\ \dfrac{\partial\phi}{\partial x} & \dfrac{\partial\phi}{\partial y} & \dfrac{\partial\phi}{\partial z} \end{vmatrix}$$

$$= \mathbf{i}\left(\frac{\partial^2\phi}{\partial y\,\partial z} - \frac{\partial^2\phi}{\partial z\,\partial y}\right) + \mathbf{j}\left(\frac{\partial^2\phi}{\partial z\,\partial x} - \frac{\partial^2\phi}{\partial x\,\partial z}\right) + \mathbf{k}\left(\frac{\partial^2\phi}{\partial x\,\partial y} - \frac{\partial^2\phi}{\partial y\,\partial x}\right) = 0.$$

If the curl of a vector function **U** vanishes everywhere in a region D in space, **U** is said to be *irrotational* in this region. From the above expansion it is seen that if **U** is the gradient of a scalar function ϕ, then **U** is irrotational.

The scalar $\nabla\cdot\nabla\times\mathbf{F}$, the divergence of the curl of the vector function **F**, is also identically zero. For, by computing the divergence of (1) in the preceding article, we obtain

$$\nabla\cdot\nabla\times\mathbf{F} = \frac{\partial}{\partial x}\left(\frac{\partial F_3}{\partial y} - \frac{\partial F_2}{\partial z}\right) + \frac{\partial}{\partial y}\left(\frac{\partial F_1}{\partial z} - \frac{\partial F_3}{\partial x}\right) + \frac{\partial}{\partial z}\left(\frac{\partial F_2}{\partial x} - \frac{\partial F_1}{\partial y}\right) = 0.$$

If the divergence of a vector function **U** vanishes everywhere in a region D in space, **U** is said to be *solenoidal* in this region. It follows that if **U** is the curl of a vector function **F**, then **U** is solenoidal.

Other useful differentiation formulas are listed below, where ϕ denotes a scalar function of x, y, and z, and **F** and **G** are vector functions. These identities may be established by direct expansion.

$$\begin{aligned}
\nabla\cdot\phi\mathbf{F} &= \phi\nabla\cdot\mathbf{F} + \mathbf{F}\cdot\nabla\phi,\\
\nabla\times\phi\mathbf{F} &= \phi\nabla\times\mathbf{F} + \nabla\phi\times\mathbf{F},\\
\nabla\cdot\mathbf{F}\times\mathbf{G} &= \mathbf{G}\cdot\nabla\times\mathbf{F} - \mathbf{F}\cdot\nabla\times\mathbf{G},\\
\nabla\times(\mathbf{F}\times\mathbf{G}) &= \mathbf{G}\cdot\nabla\mathbf{F} - \mathbf{F}\cdot\nabla\mathbf{G} + \mathbf{F}(\nabla\cdot\mathbf{G}) - \mathbf{G}(\nabla\cdot\mathbf{F}),\\
\nabla(\mathbf{F}\cdot\mathbf{G}) &= \mathbf{F}\cdot\nabla\mathbf{G} + \mathbf{G}\cdot\nabla\mathbf{F} + \mathbf{F}\times(\nabla\times\mathbf{G}) + \mathbf{G}\times(\nabla\times\mathbf{F}),\\
\nabla\times(\nabla\times\mathbf{F}) &= \nabla(\nabla\cdot\mathbf{F}) - \nabla^2\mathbf{F}.
\end{aligned}$$

EXERCISE 126

In all of the following problems $\mathbf{R} = \mathbf{i}x + \mathbf{j}y + \mathbf{k}z$.

1. If **F** is a function of t, find the derivative of $\mathbf{F}\cdot\dfrac{d\mathbf{F}}{dt}\times\dfrac{d^2\mathbf{F}}{dt^2}$.
   Ans. $\mathbf{F}\cdot\mathbf{F}'\times\mathbf{F}'''$.
2. What is the greatest rate of increase of the function $\phi = xyz^2$ at the point (1,8,3)?
3. If **A** is a constant vector, show that $\nabla(\mathbf{A}\cdot\mathbf{R}) = \mathbf{A}$.
4. If **A** is a constant vector, show that $\nabla\cdot(\mathbf{A}\times\mathbf{F}) = -\mathbf{A}\cdot(\nabla\times\mathbf{F})$.
5. Find the divergence and curl of $\mathbf{U} = \mathbf{i}(x^2 + yz) + \mathbf{j}(y^2 + zx) + \mathbf{k}(z^2 + xy)$. *Ans.* $2(x + y + z)$, 0.
6. Find the divergence and curl of $\mathbf{U} = (\mathbf{i}x + \mathbf{j}y)/(x^2 + y^2)$.
7. For a direction determined by $dx = 2dy = -2dz$, find the directional derivative of $\phi = x^2 + y^2 + z^2$ at the point (1,2,1). *Ans.* 2.
8. Find the divergence and curl of the vector function

$$\mathbf{U} = (bz - cy)\mathbf{i} + (cx - az)\mathbf{j} + (ay - bx)\mathbf{k}.$$

9. If $\mathbf{A}$ is an arbitrary constant vector and $\mathbf{F}(t)$ is a variable vector, show that $\mathbf{A}\cdot\mathbf{F} = 0$ implies that $[\mathbf{F}\mathbf{F}'\mathbf{F}''] = 0$.
10. If f and g are scalar point functions, show that div $(\nabla f \times \nabla g) = 0$.
11. If the components of $\mathbf{F}$ are homogeneous functions of x, y, z of order n, show that $\mathbf{R}\cdot\nabla\mathbf{F} = n\mathbf{F}$.
12. At time t the vector from the origin to a moving point is

$$\mathbf{R} = \mathbf{A}\cos\omega t + \mathbf{B}\sin\omega t,$$

where $\mathbf{A}$, $\mathbf{B}$, and ω are constants. (*a*) Find the velocity $\mathbf{V}$, show that $\mathbf{R}\times\mathbf{V}$ is constant, and find its value. (*b*) Show that the acceleration is directed toward the origin and is proportional to $\mathbf{R}$.
13. If the vector $\mathbf{F}(t)$ is not parallel to a fixed line, prove that it will remain parallel to a fixed plane when $[\mathbf{F}\mathbf{F}'\mathbf{F}''] = 0$.
14. If $\mathbf{R}\times d\mathbf{R} = 0$, show that $d\mathbf{R} = m\mathbf{R}$.
15. Show that $\nabla f(x+y)\times\nabla g(x+y) = 0$ and $\nabla f(x+y)\cdot\nabla g(x-y) = 0$.
16. Show that $\nabla f(x^2 - y^2)\cdot\nabla g(xy) = 0$.
17. If $R = \sqrt{x^2+y^2+z^2}$, prove that $\nabla^2 f(R) = f''(R) + \dfrac{2}{R}f'(R)$.
18. Find a vector normal to the surface $x^2 - xy + yz = 3$ at the point $(1,2,2)$.
19. Show that (*a*) $(\mathbf{A}\times\nabla)\cdot\mathbf{R} = 0$, and (*b*) $(\mathbf{A}\times\nabla)\times\mathbf{R} = -2\mathbf{A}$.
20. Given the curve defined by $\mathbf{R} = 3\mathbf{i}\sin t + 3\mathbf{j}\cos t + 4\mathbf{k}t$, where t is a parameter, (*a*) find ds along the curve, and (*b*) find the unit tangent vector.
21. If a vector has a constant direction, prove that its curl is perpendicular to that direction.
22. A vector field is defined by $\mathbf{R}f(R)$, where $R = \sqrt{x^2+y^2+z^2}$. Determine $f(R)$ so that the field may be solenoidal.
23. Find a vector $\mathbf{F} = \mathbf{R}f(R)$ such that div $\mathbf{F} = R^m$ $(m > -3)$.

Ans. $\mathbf{R}R^m/(m+3)$.

24. If $\mathbf{A}$ is a constant unit vector, prove that

$$\text{div}\,(\mathbf{A}\cdot\mathbf{R})\mathbf{A} = 1, \qquad \text{curl}\,(\mathbf{A}\cdot\mathbf{R})\mathbf{A} = 0,$$

$$\text{div}\,(\mathbf{A}\times\mathbf{R})\times\mathbf{A} = 2, \qquad \text{curl}\,(\mathbf{A}\times\mathbf{R})\times\mathbf{A} = 0.$$

25. Show that $\nabla\ln R = \mathbf{R}/R^2$.
26. Show that $\nabla(R^n) = nR^{n-2}\mathbf{R}$.
27. Show that $\nabla\cdot(R^n\mathbf{R}) = (n+3)R^n$.
28. Show that $\nabla\times(R^n\mathbf{R}) = 0$.
29. Show that $\nabla^2 R^n = n(n+1)R^{n-2}$.
30. Prove that curl curl $\mathbf{F} = \nabla(\nabla\cdot\mathbf{F}) - (\nabla\cdot\nabla)\mathbf{F}$.
31. If $\mathbf{F} = \nabla\phi$ and div $\mathbf{F} = 0$, show that div $(\phi\mathbf{F}) = F^2$.
32. Let $\mathbf{R}$ be the radius vector from the origin to a particle P moving along a curve, and let (r,θ) be the polar coordinates of P. If $\mathbf{N}$ is a unit vector

in the direction of r increasing and $\mathbf{T}$ is a unit vector perpendicular to $\mathbf{R}$ and in the direction of θ increasing, show that

$$\frac{d\mathbf{R}}{dt} = \frac{dr}{dt}\mathbf{N} + r\frac{d\theta}{dt}\mathbf{T},$$

$$\frac{d^2\mathbf{R}}{dt^2} = \left[\frac{d^2r}{dt^2} - r\left(\frac{d\theta}{dt}\right)^2\right]\mathbf{N} + \left[r\frac{d^2\theta}{dt^2} + 2\frac{dr}{dt}\frac{d\theta}{dt}\right]\mathbf{T}.$$

33. Show that the vector

$$\mathbf{F} = \begin{cases} \mathbf{R}, & R \leqq a, \\ -a^3\nabla(1/R), & R > a, \end{cases}$$

is continuous and irrotational throughout space.

242. Line Integrals

A curve whose equations are

$$x = f(t), \qquad y = g(t), \qquad z = h(t) \tag{1}$$

is said to be a *regular arc* for a domain $t_0 \leqq t \leqq t_1$ when the functions in (1) and their first derivatives are continuous functions of t. A curve consisting of a finite number of regular arcs joined end to end, and not crossing one another, is called a **regular curve.** Since most applications involve only regular curves, we shall assume in the following discussion that all curves are regular.

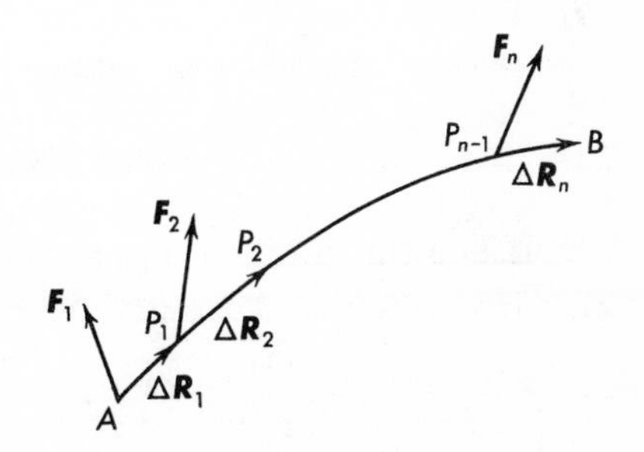

Figure 263

Let the curve AB, shown in Figure 263, be divided into n segments by the points $A = P_0$, P_1, P_2, $\cdots$, $P_n = B$, and let the chords $AP_1, P_1P_2, \cdots, P_{n-1}B$ be denoted by the vector elements $\Delta\mathbf{R}_1$, $\Delta\mathbf{R}_2$, $\cdots$, $\Delta\mathbf{R}_n$. Then, in accordance with the methods of Article **145,** we know that the sum of the magnitudes of these vector elements will approximate the length of AB. Now let $\mathbf{F}(x,y,z)$ be a vector function which is defined at each point of the curve, and has the values $\mathbf{F}_1$, $\mathbf{F}_2$, $\cdots$, $\mathbf{F}_n$ at A, P_1, $\cdots$, P_{n-1}, respectively. If the limit of the sum of the scalar products

$$\mathbf{F}_1\cdot\Delta\mathbf{R}_1 + \mathbf{F}_2\cdot\Delta\mathbf{R}_2 + \cdots + \mathbf{F}_n\cdot\Delta\mathbf{R}_n$$

exists, as $n \to \infty$ and each $|\Delta\mathbf{R}_k| \to 0$, it is denoted by

$$\int_A^B \mathbf{F}\cdot d\mathbf{R},$$

and called the **line integral** of $\mathbf{F}$ along the curve AB. Clearly, the line integral from B to A is the negative of that from A to B, and furthermore, since $d\mathbf{R} = \mathbf{i}\,dx + \mathbf{j}\,dy + \mathbf{k}\,dz$, we have

$$\int_A^B \mathbf{F}\cdot d\mathbf{R} = \int_A^B (F_1\,dx + F_2\,dy + F_3\,dz), \tag{2}$$

where the subscripts now denote the directions of the coordinate axes.

To illustrate the applied value of a line integral, we observe that if $\mathbf{F}$ represents a force acting on a moving particle, then the line integral of $\mathbf{F}$ over the path described by the particle gives the work done by the force.

Illustration. The line integral of $\mathbf{F} = \mathbf{i}y - \mathbf{j}x$ along the curve $x = t$, $y = t^2$, $z = t^3$ from (0,0,0) to (1,1,1) is

$$\int_A^B \mathbf{F}\cdot d\mathbf{R} = \int_0^1 [(y)\,dt + (-x)2t\,dt + (0)3t^2\,dt]$$

$$= \int_0^1 (t^2 - 2t^2)\,dt = -\frac{1}{3},$$

whereas the integral along the line joining the points is

$$\int_0^1 [(t)\,dt + (-t)\,dt + (0)\,dt] = 0.$$

If $\mathbf{F}$ is the gradient of a scalar point function $\phi(x,y,z)$, we have

$$F_1 = \frac{\partial\phi}{\partial x}, \qquad F_2 = \frac{\partial\phi}{\partial y}, \qquad F_3 = \frac{\partial\phi}{\partial z}$$

and

$$\int_A^B \mathbf{F}\cdot d\mathbf{R} = \int_A^B \left(\frac{\partial\phi}{\partial x}\,dx + \frac{\partial\phi}{\partial y}\,dy + \frac{\partial\phi}{\partial z}\,dz\right)$$

$$= \int_A^B d\phi = \phi_B - \phi_A.$$

In this case we see that the line integral depends solely on the end points and not at all on the path joining the points. If the curve is closed, the points A and B coincide, and $\phi_A - \phi_A$ is zero. Hence, *when* $\mathbf{F}$ *is the gradient of a scalar function, the line integral of* $\mathbf{F}$ *around a closed curve is zero.* The line integral around a closed curve is usually represented by an integral sign with a circle on it; thus

$$\oint \nabla\phi\cdot d\mathbf{R} = 0. \tag{3}$$

Conversely, *if* $\mathbf{F}(x,y,z)$ *is continuous and*

$$\oint \mathbf{F}\cdot d\mathbf{R} = 0$$

for every closed path in a three-dimensional region, there is a function $\phi(x,y,z)$ *such that* $\mathbf{F} = \nabla\phi$.

To show this, let

$$\phi(x,y,z) = \int_{P_0}^{P} \mathbf{F}\cdot d\mathbf{R}, \tag{4}$$

where P_0 is a fixed point and $P(x,y,z)$ is a variable point in the region. Since the integral around a closed path is zero, ϕ does not depend on the path from P_0 to P and hence is a function of x, y, and z. If the curve that joins P_0 and P is one for which the unit tangent $d\mathbf{R}/ds$ is continuous, we see from

$$\phi = \int_{P_0}^{P} \mathbf{F}\cdot\frac{d\mathbf{R}}{ds}\,ds,$$

that ϕ is a function of s and has the derivative

$$\frac{d\phi}{ds} = \mathbf{F}\cdot\frac{d\mathbf{R}}{ds}; \qquad \text{hence } d\phi = \mathbf{F}\cdot d\mathbf{R}.$$

We showed in Article **238**, however, that $d\phi = \nabla\phi\cdot d\mathbf{R}$; thus

$$\mathbf{F}\cdot d\mathbf{R} = \nabla\phi\cdot d\mathbf{R} \qquad \text{or} \qquad (\mathbf{F} - \nabla\phi)\cdot d\mathbf{R} = 0.$$

Since the last equation is true for all directions of $d\mathbf{R}$, the vector $\mathbf{F} - \nabla\phi$ must vanish, and we have $\mathbf{F} = \nabla\phi$.

If $\mathbf{F}(x,y,z)$ denotes a force field, we observe that the law of conservation of energy would require

$$\oint \mathbf{F}\cdot d\mathbf{R} = 0. \tag{5}$$

Hence, if a force field $\mathbf{F}$ is such that (5) holds for every closed path, we say that the field is **conservative.** In such a case the work done is independent of the path, and the quantity

$$p(x,y,z) = \int_{P}^{P_0} \mathbf{F}\cdot d\mathbf{R}$$

is called the **potential** of the vector field $\mathbf{F}$ relative to P_0. It is evident from the preceding discussion that

$$\mathbf{F} = -\nabla p,$$

that is, *in a conservative field the force is equal to the negative gradient of the potential.*

243. Surface Integrals

A portion of a surface, whose equation is

$$z = f(x,y) \tag{1}$$

and whose projection on the xy plane is the interior of a regular closed curve, is called a **regular surface element** provided that $f(x,y)$ and its first derivatives with respect to x and y are continuous functions. Since most solids in applied problems are bounded by regular surface elements, we shall assume in the following discussion that all surface elements are regular.

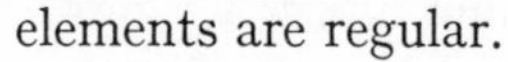

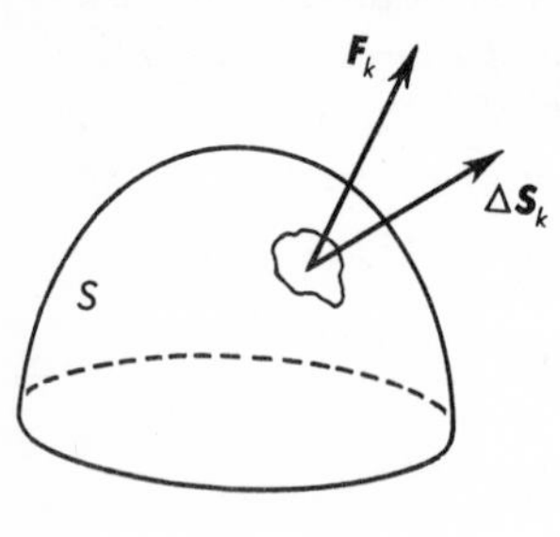

Figure 264

Let the surface S, shown in Figure 264, be divided in any manner into n parts with vector representations $\Delta\mathbf{S}_1$, $\Delta\mathbf{S}_2$, $\cdots$, $\Delta\mathbf{S}_n$, such that each vector $\Delta\mathbf{S}_k$ has a magnitude equal to the area of the kth element and a direction normal to the surface, the positive direction of a normal being arbitrary. Now let $\mathbf{F}(x,y,z)$ be a vector function which is defined at each point of the surface, and has the values $\mathbf{F}_1$, $\mathbf{F}_2$, $\cdots$, $\mathbf{F}_n$ at some point of each corresponding element. If the limit of the sum of the scalar products

$$\mathbf{F}_1\cdot\Delta\mathbf{S}_1 + \mathbf{F}_2\cdot\Delta\mathbf{S}_2 + \cdots + \mathbf{F}_n\cdot\Delta\mathbf{S}_n$$

exists, as $n \to \infty$ and the maximum dimension of each subregion $|\Delta\mathbf{S}_k|$ approaches zero, it is denoted by

$$\int_S \mathbf{F}\cdot d\mathbf{S}, \tag{2}$$

and called the **surface integral** of $\mathbf{F}$ over the surface S.

Note: In order to remove any ambiguity concerning the positive direction of a normal, the following conventions are adopted: (a) if the surface element is part of a closed surface the outward drawn normal is taken as positive; (b) if the surface element is not part of a closed surface the positive sense of describing the periphery is connected with the positive direction of the normal by a right-hand rule which states that when the fingers point in the positive direction of describing the periphery the thumb points in the positive direction of the normal.

Example. Find the surface integral of $\mathbf{F} = \mathbf{k}x$ over that part of the surface of the sphere $x^2 + y^2 + z^2 = a^2$ which lies in the first octant.

Solution: In Article **211** we found that the area of an element of surface for the sphere is

$$dS = \sqrt{1 + \left(\frac{\partial z}{dx}\right)^2 + \left(\frac{\partial z}{\partial y}\right)^2}\, dx\, dy = \frac{a}{z}\, dx\, dy. \tag{3}$$

If the positive direction on the periphery is taken as indicated in Figure 265, a unit vector **N** normal to the sphere is $\mathbf{R}/a$; hence

$$d\mathbf{S} = \frac{\mathbf{R}}{a}\left(\frac{a}{z}\, dx\, dy\right) = \frac{\mathbf{R}}{z}\, dx\, dy.$$

Therefore, by (2), we have

$$\int_S \mathbf{F}\cdot d\mathbf{S} = \iint_A \mathbf{k}x\cdot\frac{\mathbf{i}x + \mathbf{j}y + \mathbf{k}z}{z}\, dx\, dy$$
$$= \int_0^a \int_0^{\sqrt{a^2-y^2}} x\, dx\, dy = \tfrac{1}{2}\int_0^a (a^2 - y^2)\, dy = \tfrac{1}{3}a^3.$$

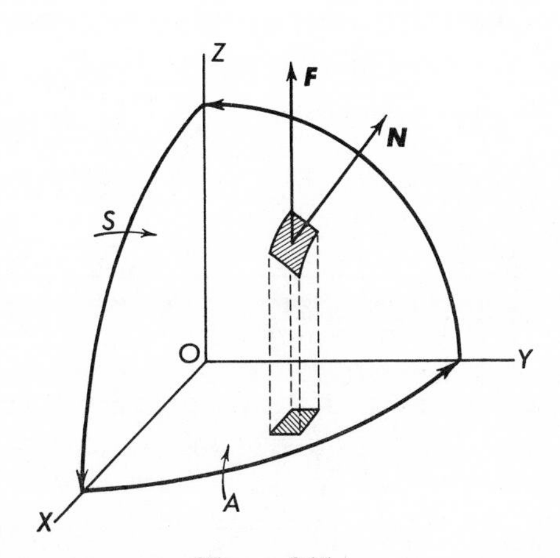

Figure 265

Observe that this result is more readily obtained by taking

$$d\mathbf{S} = \mathbf{i}\, dS_1 + \mathbf{j}\, dS_2 + \mathbf{k}\, dS_3$$
$$= \mathbf{i}\, dy\, dz + \mathbf{j}\, dz\, dx + \mathbf{k}\, dx\, dy.$$

Thus, without dependence on the formula (3), we obtain

$$\int_S \mathbf{F}\cdot d\mathbf{S} = \iint_A \mathbf{k}x\cdot(\mathbf{i}\, dy\, dz + \mathbf{j}\, dz\, dx + \mathbf{k}\, dx\, dy)$$
$$= \iint_A x\, dx\, dy.$$

The preceding remark illustrates the advantage gained in evaluating a surface integral by using the formula

$$\int_S \mathbf{F}\cdot d\mathbf{S} = \int_S (F_1\,dS_1 + F_2\,dS_2 + F_3\,dS_3).$$

If the vector field $\mathbf{F}$ represents the product of the density and the velocity of a fluid, $\mathbf{F}\cdot d\mathbf{S}$ denotes the product of the density and the volume of a prism of cross section dS and altitude equal to the component of velocity normal to the surface. Therefore $\mathbf{F}\cdot d\mathbf{S}$ represents the mass of fluid flowing through the element of surface dS in unit time, and the integral of $\mathbf{F}\cdot d\mathbf{S}$ gives the total mass flowing through the surface in unit time. This quantity is called the **flux** of $\mathbf{F}$ through the surface. A study of electric flux and magnetic flux is very important in the theory of electricity.

244. Divergence Theorem

Consider a closed region of three-dimensional space that has volume V and is bounded by regular surfaces of total area S. If the vector function $\mathbf{F}(x,y,z)$ and its first derivatives with respect to x, y, and z are continuous at all points in the interior and on the boundary of this region, it can be shown that

$$\int_V \nabla\cdot\mathbf{F}\,dV = \int_S \mathbf{F}\cdot d\mathbf{S}. \tag{1}$$

This result is usually known as the **divergence theorem,** although it is sometimes called *Gauss's theorem* in recognition of the renowned German mathematician Carl Friedrich Gauss (1777–1855).

This theorem is remarkable in the sense that it shows that if the integrand of a volume integral can be expressed as the divergence of a vector field, then the value of the integral depends only on the vectors on the surface enclosing the volume, and not at all on the vectors at interior points.

To prove the divergence theorem, we observe that

$$\int_V \nabla\cdot\mathbf{F}\,dV = \iiint_V \left\{\frac{\partial F_1}{dx} + \frac{\partial F_2}{\partial y} + \frac{\partial F_3}{\partial z}\right\} dx\,dy\,dz$$

$$= \iiint_V \frac{\partial F_1}{\partial x}\,dx\,dy\,dz + \iiint_V \frac{\partial F_2}{\partial y}\,dy\,dz\,dx + \iiint_V \frac{\partial F_3}{\partial z}\,dz\,dx\,dy.$$

We evaluate the first integral on the right by integrating partially with respect to x along a column of cross section $dy\,dz$ extending from P_1 to P_2 as shown in Figure 266,

$$\iiint_V \frac{\partial F_1}{\partial x}\,dx\,dy\,dz = \iint_{S_1} \{F_1(x_2,y,z) - F_1(x_1,y,z)\}\,dy\,dz,$$

where (x_1,y,z) and (x_2,y,z) are the coordinates of P_1 and P_2, respectively. Now at P_1, $dy\,dz = -dS_1$, and at P_2, $dy\,dz = dS_1$; hence

$$\iiint_V \frac{\partial F_1}{\partial x}\,dx\,dy\,dz = \int F_1(x_2,y,z)\,dS_1 + \int F_1(x_1,y,z)\,dS_1,$$

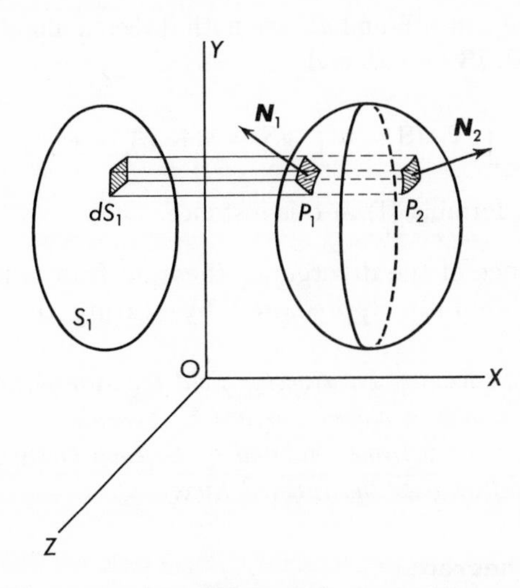

Figure 266

where the first integral is taken over the right section of the surface S and the second over the left section. Therefore

$$\iiint_V \frac{\partial F_1}{\partial x}\,dx\,dy\,dz = \int_S F_1\,dS_1, \tag{2}$$

where the surface integral is evaluated over the entire surface.

Similarly, we find

$$\iiint_V \frac{\partial F_2}{\partial y}\,dy\,dz\,dx = \int_S F_2\,dS_2, \tag{3}$$

$$\iiint_V \frac{\partial F_3}{\partial z}\,dz\,dx\,dy = \int_S F_3\,dS_3. \tag{4}$$

By adding (2), (3), and (4), we obtain

$$\int_V \nabla\cdot\mathbf{F}\,dV = \int_S (F_1\,dS_1 + F_2\,dS_2 + F_3\,dS_3) = \int_S \mathbf{F}\cdot d\mathbf{S},$$

and the theorem is proved.

Illustration. If V denotes a sphere of radius a and with center at the origin O, and $\mathbf{F} = \mathbf{i}x + \mathbf{j}y + \mathbf{k}z$, then, by Article **239**, div $\mathbf{F} = 3$, and

$$\int_V \text{div}\,\mathbf{F}\,dV = 3\int_V dV = 3(\tfrac{4}{3}\pi a^3) = 4\pi a^3.$$

On the other hand, since $\mathbf{F}$ and $d\mathbf{S}$ are both directed along the radius of the sphere, we have $\mathbf{F}\cdot d\mathbf{S} = a\,dS$ and

$$\int_S \mathbf{F}\cdot d\mathbf{S} = a\int_S dS = a(4\pi a^2) = 4\pi a^3,$$

which verifies the formula (1) in this instance.

The significance of the divergence theorem from a physical point of view can be more fully appreciated by stating the theorem in the following manner.

Divergence Theorem. *In a vector field the summation of the normal component of flux over a closed surface S is equal to the summation of the divergence over the volume enclosed by S, each being a measure of the excess of outward flux over the inward flux.*

245. Stokes's Theorem

Consider an area S which is composed of a finite number of regular two-sided surfaces, and let C denote the curve or curves that form the boundary of S. Select one side of S to be positive and let the positive direction along C be that direction in which an observer on the positive side of S must travel in order to have the area on his left. If the vector function $\mathbf{F}(x,y,z)$ and its first derivatives with respect to x, y, and z are continuous at all points of S and C, it can be shown that

$$\int_C \mathbf{F}\cdot d\mathbf{R} = \int_S \nabla\times\mathbf{F}\cdot d\mathbf{S}. \tag{1}$$

This result is attributed to the Irish mathematical physicist Sir George G. Stokes (1819–1903) and is called **Stokes's theorem.**

This theorem is remarkable in the sense that it shows that if the integrand of a surface integral can be expressed as the curl of a vector field, then the value of the integral depends only on the vectors at points on the periphery, and therefore has the same value over all surfaces which have the same periphery.

To prove Stokes's theorem, we write

$$\int_S \nabla \times \mathbf{F}\cdot d\mathbf{S} = \int_S (\nabla \times \mathbf{i}F_1 + \nabla \times \mathbf{j}F_2 + \nabla \times \mathbf{k}F_3)\cdot d\mathbf{S},$$

and consider the first term, which may be written as

$$\int_S \nabla \times \mathbf{i}F_1\cdot d\mathbf{S} = \int_S \left(\mathbf{N}\cdot\mathbf{j}\,\frac{\partial F_1}{\partial z} - \mathbf{N}\cdot\mathbf{k}\,\frac{\partial F_1}{\partial y}\right) dS, \qquad (2)$$

where $\mathbf{N}$ is a unit vector normal to the surface. To evaluate this integral, let dS be the surface element that has $dx\,dy$ for its projection on the xy plane, as shown in Figure 267; that is,

$$\mathbf{k}\cdot d\mathbf{S} = (\mathbf{N}\cdot\mathbf{k})\,dS = dx\,dy. \qquad (3)$$

At points on the surface, z is a function of x and y; hence F_1 depends only on x and y and may be written

$$F_1(x,y,z) = f(x,y).$$

The partial derivative of f with respect to y is

$$\frac{\partial f}{\partial y} = \frac{\partial F_1}{\partial y} + \frac{\partial F_1}{\partial z}\frac{\partial z}{\partial y}. \qquad (4)$$

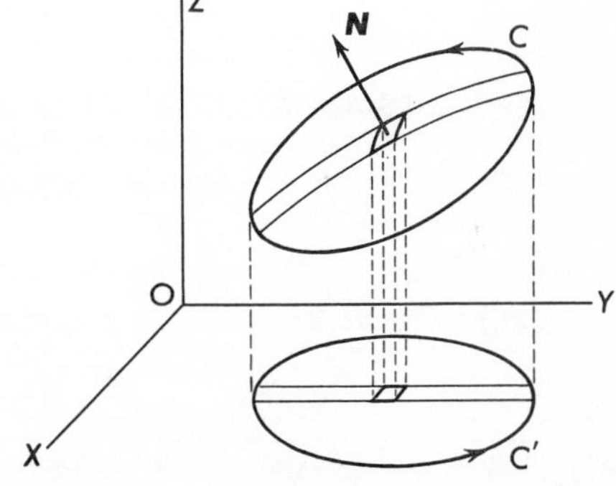

Figure 267

Likewise at points of the surface the vector $\mathbf{R} = \mathbf{i}x + \mathbf{j}y + \mathbf{k}z$ is a function of x and y only and its partial derivative with respect to y is

$$\frac{\partial \mathbf{R}}{\partial y} = \mathbf{j} + \mathbf{k}\,\frac{\partial z}{\partial y}.$$

This last vector is tangent to the curve that is cut from the surface by the plane x = constant, and therefore perpendicular to the normal $\mathbf{N}$ of the surface; thus

$$\mathbf{N}\cdot\mathbf{j} + \mathbf{N}\cdot\mathbf{k}\,\frac{\partial z}{\partial y} = 0. \qquad (5)$$

By use of the relations (3), (4), and (5), the expression (2) becomes

$$\int_S \nabla \times \mathbf{i}F_1\cdot d\mathbf{S} = -\iint \frac{\partial f}{\partial y}\,dx\,dy,$$

the integral on the right being taken over the projection of S on the xy plane. This latter integral, in iterated form, becomes

$$-\int_a^b \int_{y_1}^{y_2} \frac{\partial f}{\partial y}\, dy\, dx = -\int_a^b [f(x,y_2) - f(x,y_1)]\, dx$$

$$= \int_b^a f(x,y_2)\, dx + \int_a^b f(x,y_1)\, dx, \qquad (6)$$

where y_1 and y_2 are the lower and upper boundaries, respectively, as shown in Figure 268. Inasmuch as (6) is the definition for a line integral around the boundary C', we have

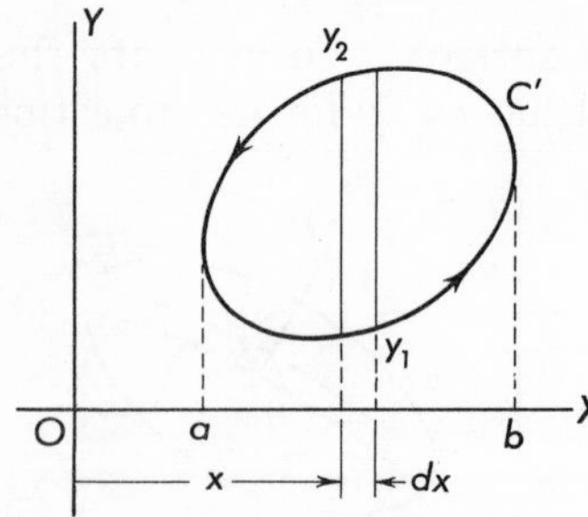

Figure 268

$$\int_S \nabla \times \mathbf{i}F_1 \cdot d\mathbf{S} = \int_{C'} f(x,y)\, dx.$$

Since the function f at the point (x,y) has the same value as the function F_1 at the point (x,y,z), and since the change in x between two points on C' is the same as the change in x between the corresponding points on C, it follows that

$$\int_{C'} f\, dx = \int_C F_1\, dx.$$

Finally, we obtain

$$\int_S \nabla \times \mathbf{i}F_1 \cdot d\mathbf{S} = \int_C F_1\, dx.$$

In a similar manner, we can show that

$$\int_S \nabla \times \mathbf{j}F_2 \cdot d\mathbf{S} = \int_C F_2\, dy,$$

$$\int_S \nabla \times \mathbf{k}F_3 \cdot d\mathbf{S} = \int_C F_3\, dz.$$

Hence, by addition, we have

$$\int_S \nabla \times \mathbf{F} \cdot d\mathbf{S} = \int_C (F_1\, dx + F_2\, dy + F_3\, dz) = \int_C \mathbf{F} \cdot d\mathbf{R},$$

and the theorem is proved.

Illustration. For the vector $\mathbf{F} = \mathbf{k}z - \mathbf{i}y$ taken over the hemisphere $z = \sqrt{a^2 - x^2 - y^2}$, we find $\nabla \times \mathbf{F} = \mathbf{k}$; hence

$$\int_S \nabla \times \mathbf{F} \cdot d\mathbf{S} = \iint_{S'} dx\, dy = \pi a^2.$$

On the other hand, for the circular boundary in the plane $z = 0$, we find

$$\int_C \mathbf{F} \cdot d\mathbf{R} = \int_C (z\, dz - y\, dx) = -\int_C y\, dx.$$

By use of the substitution $x = a \cos \theta$, $y = a \sin \theta$, we obtain

$$\int_C \mathbf{F} \cdot d\mathbf{R} = a^2 \int_0^{2\pi} \sin^2 \theta\, d\theta = \pi a^2,$$

which verifies Stokes's theorem in this instance.

246. Summary of Integration

Many integration formulas can be derived which are analogous to those already obtained; basically, however, these new formulas are merely different variations of the two formulas given in Stokes's theorem and the divergence theorem. Thus, when $f(x,y,z)$ is a scalar function and $\mathbf{F}(x,y,z)$ is a vector function, four such formulas are as follows.

$$\int_C f\, d\mathbf{R} = \int_S d\mathbf{S} \times \nabla f, \tag{1}$$

$$\int_C d\mathbf{R} \times \mathbf{F} = \int_S (d\mathbf{S} \times \nabla) \times \mathbf{F}, \tag{2}$$

$$\int_S f\, d\mathbf{S} = \int_V \nabla f\, dV, \tag{3}$$

$$\int_S d\mathbf{S} \times \mathbf{F} = \int_V \nabla \times \mathbf{F}\, dV. \tag{4}$$

In order to illustrate the connection between these formulas and the basic formulas, let us consider the relation (1). If $\mathbf{A}$ is a constant arbitrary vector, by using $f\mathbf{A}$ for the vector field in Stokes's theorem, we obtain

$$\int_C f\mathbf{A} \cdot d\mathbf{R} = \int_S (\nabla \times f\mathbf{A}) \cdot d\mathbf{S} = \int_S (\nabla f \times \mathbf{A}) \cdot d\mathbf{S}$$

$$= \int_S \mathbf{A} \cdot d\mathbf{S} \times \nabla f.$$

Since a constant factor can be taken outside the sign of integration, we have

$$\mathbf{A}\cdot\left[\int_C f\,d\mathbf{R} - \int_S d\mathbf{S}\times\nabla f\right] = 0.$$

This relation is true for all values of $\mathbf{A}$; hence the expression in the brackets must be zero, which proves (1).

To prove (4), we apply the divergence theorem to the vector $\mathbf{F}\times\mathbf{A}$, which gives

$$\int_S \mathbf{F}\times\mathbf{A}\cdot d\mathbf{S} = \int_V \nabla\cdot(\mathbf{F}\times\mathbf{A})\,dV.$$

By Article **241** this relation can be written in the form

$$\int_S \mathbf{A}\cdot d\mathbf{S}\times\mathbf{F} = \int_V \mathbf{A}\cdot\nabla\times\mathbf{F}\,dV,$$

whence

$$\mathbf{A}\cdot\left[\int_S d\mathbf{S}\times\mathbf{F} - \int_V \nabla\times\mathbf{F}\,dV\right] = 0.$$

Since this is true for all values of the constant vector $\mathbf{A}$, we conclude as before that the expression in brackets is zero.

The formulas (2) and (3) can be proved in a similar manner by using the vectors $\mathbf{F}\times\mathbf{A}$ and $f\mathbf{A}$, respectively, in Stokes's theorem and the divergence theorem.

Another theorem of considerable importance in applied problems was established by the English mathematician George Green (1783–1841). His result can be obtained by taking two scalar functions $f(x,y,z)$ and $g(x,y,z)$, and applying the divergence theorem to the vector field $f\nabla g$. Thus we find

$$\int_S f\nabla g\cdot d\mathbf{S} = \int_V \nabla\cdot(f\nabla g)\,dV$$

$$= \int_V (f\nabla^2 g + \nabla g\cdot\nabla f)\,dV. \tag{5}$$

By interchanging f and g in (5) and then subtracting the expression obtained from (5), we have the following result.

Green's Theorem. *If $f(x,y,z)$ and $g(x,y,z)$ denote two scalar potentials which, together with their first derivatives, are continuous over a volume V enclosed by a surface S, then*

$$\int_V (f\nabla^2 g - g\nabla^2 f)\,dV = \int_S (f\nabla g - g\nabla f)\cdot d\mathbf{S}.$$

EXERCISE 127

1. Show that the integral

$$\int_{(0,0)}^{(1,2)} [(3x^2 + 6xy)\,dx + (3x^2 - 4y^3)\,dy]$$

is independent of the path, and find its value. *Ans.* -9.

2. Find the value of

$$\int_{(0,0)}^{(1,2)} [(x + y)\,dx + 2xy\,dy]$$

along the paths (*a*) $y = 2x$, (*b*) $y^2 = 4x$, (*c*) $y = 0$, $x = 1$.

3. Given $\mathbf{F} = (x^2 - y^2)\mathbf{i} + 2xy\mathbf{j}$, find the value of $\oint \mathbf{F}\cdot d\mathbf{R}$ taken in a counterclockwise direction around the square bounded by the lines $x = 0$, $x = a$, $y = 0$, and $y = a$ in the xy plane. *Ans.* $2a^3$.

4. Given $\mathbf{F} = \mathbf{j}x - \mathbf{i}y$, find the value of $\int \mathbf{F}\cdot d\mathbf{R}$ from (0,0) to (4,4) along (*a*) the line $y = x$, (*b*) the parabola $y^2 = 4x$.

5. Find the value of $\oint \mathbf{T}\cdot d\mathbf{R}$ around a circle of radius a where $\mathbf{T}$ is a unit tangent vector at each point of the circle. *Ans.* $2\pi a$.

6. Show that $\oint d\mathbf{R} = 0$.

7. Show that $\oint \mathbf{R} \times d\mathbf{R}$ taken around a curve in the xy plane has a numerical value equal to twice the area enclosed by the curve.

8. Show that the function $\phi(P) = \int_{P_0}^{P} R^n\mathbf{R}\cdot d\mathbf{R}$ is independent of the path from P_0 to P, and find its value.

9. Find the vector $\mathbf{F}(x,y,z)$ such that $xyz = \int_{(0,0,0)}^{(x,y,z)} \mathbf{F}\cdot d\mathbf{R}$.

   Ans. $\mathbf{i}yz + \mathbf{j}zx + \mathbf{k}xy$.

10. If $\mathbf{F} = \mathbf{i}x^2 + \mathbf{j}2xy + \mathbf{k}(x^2 - xy)$, find the value of $\oint \mathbf{F}\cdot d\mathbf{S}$ over the surface of the cube $0 \leqq x,y,z \leqq 1$.

11. Show directly that $\int_S \mathbf{R} \times d\mathbf{S} = 0$, where S is a sphere with center at the origin. *Hint:* $\mathbf{N} = \mathbf{R}/R$.

12. Find $\int \mathbf{F}\cdot d\mathbf{S}$ for the vector $\mathbf{F} = \mathbf{i}x - \mathbf{j}y + \mathbf{k}2z$ taken over the sphere $x^2 + y^2 + (z - 1)^2 = 1$.

13. Verify Stokes's theorem for $\mathbf{F} = (2y + z)\mathbf{i} + (x - z)\mathbf{j} + (y - x)\mathbf{k}$ taken over the triangle cut from the plane $x + y + z = 1$ by the coordinate planes.

14. Compute $\oint (ax^2 + by^2 + cz^2)\,dS$ over the sphere $x^2 + y^2 + z^2 = 1$. *Hint:* Use $\mathbf{N} = \mathbf{R}$, find $\mathbf{F}$, and apply the divergence theorem.

15. Verify the divergence theorem for the vector $\mathbf{F} = \mathbf{i}x^2 + \mathbf{j}y^2 + \mathbf{k}z^2$ taken over the cube $0 \leqq x,y,z \leqq 1$.

16. If $\mathbf{F} = \mathbf{i}y - \mathbf{j}x + \mathbf{k}z^2$, find the value of $\oint \mathbf{F}\cdot d\mathbf{S}$ taken over the closed surface bounded by the planes $z = 0$, $z = 1$, and the cylinder $x^2 + y^2 = r^2$.
17. For any closed surface S in a solenoidal vector field $\mathbf{F}$, show that $\oint \mathbf{F}\cdot d\mathbf{S} = 0$.
18. For any closed curve C in an irrotational vector field $\mathbf{F}$, show that $\oint \mathbf{F}\cdot d\mathbf{R} = 0$.
19. Show that $\partial G/\partial x = \partial F/\partial y$ is a necessary and sufficient condition that $\oint (F\,dx + G\,dy) = 0$ for every closed path in the xy plane.
20. A particle is attracted toward the origin with a force that is inversely proportional to the square of its distance from the origin. Find a potential at $P(x,y,z)$.
21. Prove formula (2), Article **246.**
22. Prove formula (3), Article **246.**
23. If f and g are scalar point functions that satisfy Laplace's equation and S is a closed surface, show that $\oint_S (f\nabla g - g\nabla f)\cdot d\mathbf{S} = 0$.
24. If $\mathbf{F}$ is a vector function normal to the closed surface S at each point, and if V is the volume bounded by S, show that $\int_V \operatorname{curl} \mathbf{F}\, dV = 0$.
25. Express $\int_V \mathbf{R}\, dV$ as an integral over the surface S enclosing V.

    Ans. $\frac{1}{2}\int_S R^2\, d\mathbf{S}$.
26. Write out Green's theorem in rectangular coordinates.
27. If f is a scalar function and $\mathbf{F}$ a vector function, use Stokes's theorem to show that

$$\int_S (\nabla f \times \mathbf{F} + f\nabla \times \mathbf{F})\cdot d\mathbf{S} = \int_C f\mathbf{F}\cdot d\mathbf{R}.$$

28. Use the formula (2), Article **246,** to prove that

$$\int_S d\mathbf{S} = \tfrac{1}{2}\int_C \mathbf{R} \times d\mathbf{R}.$$

29. If f is a scalar function and $\mathbf{F}$ a vector function, use the divergence theorem to show that

$$\int_V (f\nabla\cdot\mathbf{F} + \nabla f\cdot\mathbf{F})\, dV = \int_S f(\mathbf{F}\cdot d\mathbf{S}).$$

30. If u and v are scalar functions with continuous gradients, show that

$$\int_S \nabla u \times \nabla v\cdot d\mathbf{S} = \int_C u\, dv,$$

where S is a portion of a surface bounded by a closed curve C.

31. The vector $\mathbf{F} = k\nabla(1/R)$, where R is the distance from a point O, represents an attraction that varies as $1/R^2$, the inverse square law. If S is a closed surface about O, prove that

$$\oint_S \mathbf{F}\cdot d\mathbf{S} = -4\pi k.$$

Hint: Insert a sphere of radius r around O and find the limit as $r \to 0$.

32. Apply the divergence theorem to $\mathbf{F} \times \text{curl } \mathbf{G}$ to prove that

$$\int_V (\text{curl } \mathbf{F})\cdot(\text{curl } \mathbf{G})\, dV - \int_V \mathbf{F}\cdot\text{curl curl } \mathbf{G}\, dV = \int_S \mathbf{F} \times \text{curl } \mathbf{G}\cdot d\mathbf{S}.$$

Table of Integrals

(The constant of integration is omitted)

FORMS CONTAINING $a + bu$

1. $\int (a + bu)^n \, du = \frac{(a + bu)^{n+1}}{b(n + 1)}, \quad n \neq -1.$

2. $\int \frac{du}{a + bu} = \frac{1}{b} \ln (a + bu).$

3. $\int \frac{u \, du}{a + bu} = \frac{1}{b^2} [(a + bu) - a \ln (a + bu)].$

4. $\int \frac{u^2 \, du}{a + bu} = \frac{1}{b^3} \left[\tfrac{1}{2}(a + bu)^2 - 2a(a + bu) + a^2 \ln (a + bu) \right].$

5. $\int \frac{du}{u(a + bu)} = -\frac{1}{a} \ln \frac{a + bu}{u}.$

6. $\int \frac{du}{u^2(a + bu)} = -\frac{1}{au} + \frac{b}{a^2} \ln \frac{a + bu}{u}.$

7. $\int \frac{u \, du}{(a + bu)^2} = \frac{1}{b^2} \left[\frac{a}{a + bu} + \ln (a + bu) \right].$

8. $\int \frac{u^2 \, du}{(a + bu)^2} = \frac{1}{b^3} \left[(a + bu) - \frac{a^2}{a + bu} - 2a \ln (a + bu) \right].$

9. $\int \frac{du}{u(a + bu)^2} = \frac{1}{a(a + bu)} - \frac{1}{a^2} \ln \frac{a + bu}{u}.$

10. $\int \frac{du}{u^2(a + bu)^2} = -\frac{a + 2bu}{a^2 u(a + bu)} + \frac{2b}{a^3} \ln \frac{a + bu}{u}.$

FORMS CONTAINING $\sqrt{a + bu}$

11. $\int u\sqrt{a + bu} \, du = -\frac{2(2a - 3bu)(a + bu)^{3/2}}{15b^2}.$

12. $\int u^n\sqrt{a + bu} \, du = \frac{2u^n(a + bu)^{3/2}}{b(2n + 3)} - \frac{2an}{b(2n + 3)} \int u^{n-1}\sqrt{a + bu} \, du.$

13. $\int \frac{u \, du}{\sqrt{a + bu}} = -\frac{2(2a - bu)\sqrt{a + bu}}{3b^2}.$

14. $\int \frac{u^n \, du}{\sqrt{a + bu}} = \frac{2u^n\sqrt{a + bu}}{b(2n + 1)} - \frac{2an}{b(2n + 1)} \int \frac{u^{n-1} \, du}{\sqrt{a + bu}}.$

45. $$\int \frac{\sqrt{a^2 - u^2}}{u}\,du = \sqrt{a^2 - u^2} - a \ln\left(\frac{a + \sqrt{a^2 - u^2}}{u}\right).$$

46. $$\int \frac{\sqrt{a^2 - u^2}}{u^2}\,du = -\frac{\sqrt{a^2 - u^2}}{u} - \operatorname{Sin}^{-1}\frac{u}{a}.$$

47. $$\int \frac{du}{(a^2 - u^2)^{3/2}} = \frac{u}{a^2\sqrt{a^2 - u^2}}.$$

48. $$\int \frac{u^2\,du}{(a^2 - u^2)^{3/2}} = \frac{u}{\sqrt{a^2 - u^2}} - \operatorname{Sin}^{-1}\frac{u}{a}.$$

49. $$\int \frac{du}{u(a^2 - u^2)^{3/2}} = \frac{1}{a^2\sqrt{a^2 - u^2}} - \frac{1}{a^3}\ln\left(\frac{a + \sqrt{a^2 - u^2}}{u}\right).$$

50. $$\int \frac{du}{u^2(a^2 - u^2)^{3/2}} = -\frac{\sqrt{a^2 - u^2}}{a^4u} + \frac{u}{a^4\sqrt{a^2 - u^2}}.$$

51. $$\int (a^2 - u^2)^{3/2}\,du = \tfrac{1}{4}u(a^2 - u^2)^{3/2} + \tfrac{3}{8}a^2u\sqrt{a^2 - u^2} + \tfrac{3}{8}a^4 \operatorname{Sin}^{-1}\frac{u}{a}.$$

52. $$\int \frac{(a^2 - u^2)^{3/2}}{u}\,du = \tfrac{1}{3}(a^2 - u^2)^{3/2} + a^2\sqrt{a^2 - u^2} - a^3 \ln\left(\frac{a + \sqrt{a^2 - u^2}}{u}\right).$$

TRIGONOMETRIC FORMS

53. $$\int \sin u\,du = -\cos u.$$

54. $$\int \sin^2 u\,du = \tfrac{1}{2}u - \tfrac{1}{2}\sin u \cos u.$$

55. $$\int \sin^3 u\,du = -\cos u + \tfrac{1}{3}\cos^3 u.$$

56. $$\int \sin^n u\,du = -\frac{1}{n}\sin^{n-1} u \cos u + \frac{n-1}{n}\int \sin^{n-2} u\,du.$$

57. $$\int \cos u\,du = \sin u.$$

58. $$\int \cos^2 u\,du = \tfrac{1}{2}u + \tfrac{1}{2}\sin u \cos u.$$

59. $$\int \cos^3 u\,du = \sin u - \tfrac{1}{3}\sin^3 u.$$

60. $$\int \cos^n u\,du = \frac{1}{n}\cos^{n-1} u \sin u + \frac{n-1}{n}\int \cos^{n-2} u\,du.$$

61. $\int \tan u\, du = \ln \sec u.$

62. $\int \tan^n u\, du = \dfrac{\tan^{n-1} u}{n-1} - \int \tan^{n-2} u\, du.$

63. $\int \cot u\, du = \ln \sin u.$

64. $\int \cot^n u\, du = -\dfrac{\cot^{n-1} u}{n-1} - \int \cot^{n-2} u\, du.$

65. $\int \sec u\, du = \ln (\sec u + \tan u).$

66. $\int \sec^2 u\, du = \tan u.$

67. $\int \sec^n u\, du = \dfrac{\sec^{n-2} u \tan u}{n-1} + \dfrac{n-2}{n-1}\int \sec^{n-2} u\, du.$

68. $\int \csc u\, du = \ln (\csc u - \cot u).$

69. $\int \csc^2 u\, du = -\cot u.$

70. $\int \csc^n u\, du = -\dfrac{\csc^{n-2} u \cot u}{n-1} + \dfrac{n-2}{n-1}\int \csc^{n-2} u\, du.$

71. $\int \sec u \tan u\, du = \sec u.$

72. $\int \csc u \cot u\, du = -\csc u.$

73. $\int \sin au \sin bu\, du = \dfrac{\sin (a-b)u}{2(a-b)} - \dfrac{\sin (a+b)u}{2(a+b)}.$

74. $\int \sin au \cos bu\, du = -\dfrac{\cos (a-b)u}{2(a-b)} - \dfrac{\cos (a+b)u}{2(a+b)}.$

75. $\int \cos au \cos bu\, du = \dfrac{\sin (a-b)u}{2(a-b)} + \dfrac{\sin (a+b)u}{2(a+b)}.$

76. $$\int \sin^m u \cos^n u\, du = \frac{\sin^{m+1} u \cos^{n-1} u}{m+n} + \frac{n-1}{m+n}\int \sin^m u \cos^{n-2} u\, du.$$

77. $$\int \sin^m u \cos^n u\, du = -\frac{\sin^{m-1} u \cos^{n+1} u}{m+n} + \frac{m-1}{m+n}\int \sin^{m-2} u \cos^n u\, du.$$

MISCELLANEOUS FORMS

78. $\int e^u\,du = e^u.$

79. $\int a^u\,du = \dfrac{a^u}{\ln a}.$

80. $\int ue^{au}\,du = e^{au}(au - 1)/a^2.$

81. $\int u^2e^{au}\,du = e^{au}(a^2u^2 - 2au + 2)/a^3.$

82. $\int u^n \ln u\,du = u^{n+1}\left[\dfrac{\ln u}{n+1} - \dfrac{1}{(n+1)^2}\right].$

83. $\int u \sin u\,du = \sin u - u \cos u.$

84. $\int u^2 \sin u\,du = 2u \sin u - (u^2 - 2) \cos u.$

85. $\int u \cos u\,du = \cos u + u \sin u.$

86. $\int u^2 \cos u\,du = (u^2 - 2) \sin u + 2u \cos u.$

87. $\int e^{au} \sin bu\,du = \dfrac{e^{au}(a \sin bu - b \cos bu)}{a^2 + b^2}.$

88. $\int e^{au} \cos bu\,du = \dfrac{e^{au}(a \cos bu + b \sin bu)}{a^2 + b^2}.$

89. $\int \sin^{-1} u\,du = u \sin^{-1} u + \sqrt{1 - u^2}.$

90. $\int \tan^{-1} u\,du = u \tan^{-1} u - \frac{1}{2} \ln (1 + u^2).$

91. $\int \sinh u\,du = \cosh u.$

92. $\int \cosh u\,du = \sinh u.$

93. $\int \tanh u\,du = \ln \cosh u.$

94. $\int \coth u\,du = \ln \sinh u.$

95. $\int \operatorname{sech} u\,du = 2 \operatorname{Tan}^{-1} e^u.$

96. $\int \operatorname{csch} u \, du = \ln \tanh \frac{1}{2}u.$

WALLIS' FORMULAS

97. $\int_0^{\pi/2} \sin^n x \, dx = \int_0^{\pi/2} \cos^n x \, dx$

$$= \begin{cases} \frac{1}{2}\cdot\frac{3}{4}\cdot\frac{5}{6}\cdots\frac{n-1}{n}\cdot\frac{\pi}{2}, & \text{if } n \text{ is an even integer.} \\ \frac{2}{3}\cdot\frac{4}{5}\cdot\frac{6}{7}\cdots\frac{n-1}{n}, & \text{if } n \text{ is an odd integer } > 1. \end{cases}$$

98. $\int_0^{\pi/2} \sin^m x \cos^n x \, dx$

$$= \begin{cases} \frac{2\cdot 4\cdot 6\cdots(n-1)}{(m+1)(m+3)(m+5)\cdots(m+n)}, & \text{if } n \text{ is an odd integer} > 1. \\ \frac{2\cdot 4\cdot 6\cdots(m-1)}{(n+1)(n+3)(n+5)\cdots(n+m)}, & \text{if } m \text{ is an odd integer} > 1. \\ \frac{1\cdot 3\cdots(m-1)\cdot 1\cdot 3\cdots(n-1)}{2\cdot 4\cdot 6\cdots(m+n)}\cdot\frac{\pi}{2}, & \text{if } m \text{ and } n \text{ are both even integers.} \end{cases}$$

Numerical Tables

n	n^2	$\sqrt{n}$	$\sqrt{10n}$	n^3	$\sqrt[3]{n}$	$\sqrt[3]{10n}$	$\sqrt[3]{100n}$	$1/n$
1.0	1.00	1.00000	3.16228	1.000	1.00000	2.15443	4.64159	1.00000
1.1	1.21	1.04881	3.31662	1.331	1.03228	2.22398	4.79142	.90909
1.2	1.44	1.09545	3.46410	1.728	1.06266	2.28943	4.93242	.83333
1.3	1.69	1.14018	3.60555	2.197	1.09139	2.35133	5.06580	.76923
1.4	1.96	1.18322	3.74166	2.744	1.11869	2.41014	5.19249	.71429
1.5	2.25	1.22474	3.87298	3.375	1.14471	2.46621	5.31329	.66667
1.6	2.56	1.26491	4.00000	4.096	1.16961	2.51984	5.42884	.62500
1.7	2.89	1.30384	4.12311	4.913	1.19348	2.57128	5.53966	.58824
1.8	3.24	1.34164	4.24264	5.832	1.21644	2.62074	5.64622	.55556
1.9	3.61	1.37840	4.35890	6.859	1.23856	2.66840	5.74890	.52632
2.0	4.00	1.41421	4.47214	8.000	1.25992	2.71442	5.84804	.50000
2.1	4.41	1.44914	4.58258	9.261	1.28058	2.75892	5.94392	.47619
2.2	4.84	1.48324	4.69042	10.648	1.30059	2.80204	6.03681	.45455
2.3	5.29	1.51658	4.79583	12.167	1.32001	2.84387	6.12693	.43478
2.4	5.76	1.54919	4.89898	13.824	1.33887	2.88450	6.21447	.41667
2.5	6.25	1.58114	5.00000	15.625	1.35721	2.92402	6.29961	.40000
2.6	6.76	1.61245	5.09902	17.576	1.37507	2.96250	6.38250	.38462
2.7	7.29	1.64317	5.19615	19.683	1.39248	3.00000	6.46330	.37037
2.8	7.84	1.67332	5.29150	21.952	1.40946	3.03659	6.54213	.35714
2.9	8.41	1.70294	5.38516	24.389	1.42604	3.07232	6.61911	.34483
3.0	9.00	1.73205	5.47723	27.000	1.44225	3.10723	6.69433	.33333
3.1	9.61	1.76068	5.56776	29.791	1.45810	3.14138	6.76790	.32258
3.2	10.24	1.78885	5.65685	32.768	1.47361	3.17480	6.83990	.31250
3.3	10.89	1.81659	5.74456	35.937	1.48881	3.20753	6.91042	.30303
3.4	11.56	1.84391	5.83095	39.304	1.50369	3.23961	6.97953	.29412
3.5	12.25	1.87083	5.91608	42.875	1.51829	3.27107	7.04730	.28571
3.6	12.96	1.89737	6.00000	46.656	1.53262	3.30193	7.11379	.27778
3.7	13.69	1.92354	6.08276	50.653	1.54668	3.33222	7.17905	.27027
3.8	14.44	1.94936	6.16441	54.872	1.56049	3.36198	7.24316	.26316
3.9	15.21	1.97484	6.24500	59.319	1.57406	3.39121	7.30614	.25641
4.0	16.00	2.00000	6.32456	64.000	1.58740	3.41995	7.36806	.25000
4.1	16.81	2.02485	6.40312	68.921	1.60052	3.44822	7.42896	.24390
4.2	17.64	2.04939	6.48074	74.088	1.61343	3.47603	7.48887	.23810
4.3	18.49	2.07364	6.55744	79.507	1.62613	3.50340	7.54784	.23256
4.4	19.36	2.09762	6.63325	85.184	1.63864	3.53035	7.60590	.22727
4.5	20.25	2.12132	6.70820	91.125	1.65096	3.55689	7.66309	.22222
4.6	21.16	2.14476	6.78233	97.336	1.66310	3.58305	7.71944	.21739
4.7	22.09	2.16795	6.85565	103.823	1.67507	3.60883	7.77498	.21277
4.8	23.04	2.19089	6.92820	110.592	1.68687	3.63424	7.82974	.20833
4.9	24.01	2.21359	7.00000	117.649	1.69850	3.65931	7.88374	.20408
5.0	25.00	2.23607	7.07107	125.000	1.70998	3.68403	7.93701	.20000
5.1	26.01	2.25832	7.14143	132.651	1.72130	3.70843	7.98957	.19608
5.2	27.04	2.28035	7.21110	140.608	1.73248	3.73251	8.04145	.19231
5.3	28.09	2.30217	7.28011	148.877	1.74351	3.75629	8.09267	.18868
5.4	29.16	2.32379	7.34847	157.464	1.75441	3.77976	8.14325	.18519

n	n^2	$\sqrt{n}$	$\sqrt{10n}$	n^3	$\sqrt[3]{n}$	$\sqrt[3]{10n}$	$\sqrt[3]{100n}$	$1/n$
5.5	30.25	2.34521	7.41620	166.375	1.76517	3.80295	8.19321	.18182
5.6	31.36	2.36643	7.48331	175.616	1.77581	3.82586	8.24257	.17857
5.7	32.49	2.38747	7.54983	185.193	1.78632	3.84850	8.29134	.17544
5.8	33.64	2.40832	7.61577	195.112	1.79670	3.87088	8.33955	.17241
5.9	34.81	2.42899	7.68115	205.379	1.80697	3.89300	8.38721	.16949
6.0	36.00	2.44949	7.74597	216.000	1.81712	3.91487	8.43433	.16667
6.1	37.21	2.46982	7.81025	226.981	1.82716	3.93650	8.48093	.16393
6.2	38.44	2.48998	7.87401	238.328	1.83709	3.95789	8.52702	.16129
6.3	39.69	2.50998	7.93725	250.047	1.84691	3.97906	8.57262	.15873
6.4	40.96	2.52982	8.00000	262.144	1.85664	4.00000	8.61774	.15625
6.5	42.25	2.54951	8.06226	274.625	1.86626	4.02073	8.66239	.15385
6.6	43.56	2.56905	8.12404	287.496	1.87578	4.04124	8.70659	.15152
6.7	44.89	2.58844	8.18535	300.763	1.88520	4.06155	8.75034	.14925
6.8	46.24	2.60768	8.24621	314.432	1.89454	4.08166	8.79366	.14706
6.9	47.61	2.62679	8.30662	328.509	1.90378	4.10157	8.83656	.14493
7.0	49.00	2.64575	8.36660	343.000	1.91293	4.12129	8.87904	.14286
7.1	50.41	2.66458	8.42615	357.911	1.92200	4.14082	8.92112	.14085
7.2	51.84	2.68328	8.48528	373.248	1.93098	4.16017	8.96281	.13889
7.3	53.29	2.70185	8.54400	389.017	1.93988	4.17934	9.00411	.13699
7.4	54.76	2.72029	8.60233	405.224	1.94870	4.19834	9.04504	.13514
7.5	56.25	2.73861	8.66025	421.875	1.95743	4.21716	9.08560	.13333
7.6	57.76	2.75681	8.71780	438.976	1.96610	4.23582	9.12581	.13158
7.7	59.29	2.77489	8.77496	456.533	1.97468	4.25432	9.16566	.12987
7.8	60.84	2.79285	8.83176	474.552	1.98319	4.27266	9.20516	.12821
7.9	62.41	2.81069	8.88819	493.039	1.99163	4.29084	9.24434	.12658
8.0	64.00	2.82843	8.94427	512.000	2.00000	4.30887	9.28318	.12500
8.1	65.61	2.84605	9.00000	531.441	2.00830	4.32675	9.32170	.12346
8.2	67.24	2.86356	9.05539	551.368	2.01653	4.34448	9.35990	.12195
8.3	68.89	2.88097	9.11043	571.787	2.02469	4.36207	9.39780	.12048
8.4	70.56	2.89828	9.16515	592.704	2.03279	4.37952	9.43539	.11905
8.5	72.25	2.91548	9.21954	614.125	2.04083	4.39683	9.47268	.11765
8.6	73.96	2.93258	9.27362	636.056	2.04880	4.41400	9.50969	.11628
8.7	75.69	2.94958	9.32738	658.503	2.05671	4.43105	9.54640	.11494
8.8	77.44	2.96648	9.38083	681.472	2.06456	4.44796	9.58284	.11364
8.9	79.21	2.98329	9.43398	704.969	2.07235	4.46475	9.61900	.11236
9.0	81.00	3.00000	9.48683	729.000	2.08008	4.48140	9.65489	.11111
9.1	82.81	3.01662	9.53939	753.571	2.08776	4.49794	9.69052	.10989
9.2	84.64	3.03315	9.59166	778.688	2.09538	4.51436	9.72589	.10870
9.3	86.49	3.04959	9.64365	804.357	2.10294	4.53065	9.76100	.10753
9.4	88.36	3.06594	9.69536	830.584	2.11045	4.54684	9.79586	.10638
9.5	90.25	3.08221	9.74679	857.375	2.11791	4.56290	9.83048	.10526
9.6	92.16	3.09839	9.79796	884.736	2.12532	4.57886	9.86485	.10417
9.7	94.09	3.11448	9.84886	912.673	2.13267	4.59470	9.89898	.10309
9.8	96.04	3.13050	9.89949	941.192	2.13997	4.61044	9.93288	.10204
9.9	98.01	3.14643	9.94987	970.299	2.14723	4.62607	9.96655	.10101

Use ln 10 = 2.30259 to find logarithms of numbers greater than 10 or less than 1.

N	0	1	2	3	4	5	6	7	8	9
1.0	0.0000	0100	0198	0296	0392	0488	0583	0677	0770	0862
1.1	0953	1044	1133	1222	1310	1398	1484	1570	1655	1740
1.2	1823	1906	1989	2070	2151	2231	2311	2390	2469	2546
1.3	2624	2700	2776	2852	2927	3001	3075	3148	3221	3293
1.4	3365	3436	3507	3577	3646	3716	3784	3853	3920	3988
1.5	0.4055	4121	4187	4253	4318	4383	4447	4511	4574	4637
1.6	4700	4762	4824	4886	4947	5008	5068	5128	5188	5247
1.7	5306	5365	5423	5481	5539	5596	5653	5710	5766	5822
1.8	5878	5933	5988	6043	6098	6152	6206	6259	6313	6366
1.9	6419	6471	6523	6575	6627	6678	6729	6780	6831	6881
2.0	0.6931	6981	7031	7080	7129	7178	7227	7275	7324	7372
2.1	7419	7467	7514	7561	7608	7655	7701	7747	7793	7839
2.2	7885	7930	7975	8020	8065	8109	8154	8198	8242	8286
2.3	8329	8372	8416	8459	8502	8544	8587	8629	8671	8713
2.4	8755	8796	8838	8879	8920	8961	9002	9042	9083	9123
2.5	0.9163	9203	9243	9282	9322	9361	9400	9439	9478	9517
2.6	9555	9594	9632	9670	9708	9746	9783	9821	9858	9895
2.7	9933	9969	*0006	*0043	*0080	*0116	*0152	*0188	*0225	*0260
2.8	1.0296	0332	0367	0403	0438	0473	0508	0543	0578	0613
2.9	0647	0682	0716	0750	0784	0818	0852	0886	0919	0953
3.0	1.0986	1019	1053	1086	1119	1151	1184	1217	1249	1282
3.1	1314	1346	1378	1410	1442	1474	1506	1537	1569	1600
3.2	1632	1663	1694	1725	1756	1787	1817	1848	1878	1909
3.3	1939	1969	2000	2030	2060	2090	2119	2149	2179	2208
3.4	2238	2267	2296	2326	2355	2384	2413	2442	2470	2499
3.5	1.2528	2556	2585	2613	2641	2669	2698	2726	2754	2782
3.6	2809	2837	2865	2892	2920	2947	2975	3002	3029	3056
3.7	3083	3110	3137	3164	3191	3218	3244	3271	3297	3324
3.8	3350	3376	3403	3429	3455	3481	3507	3533	3558	3584
3.9	3610	3635	3661	3686	3712	3737	3762	3788	3813	3838
4.0	1.3863	3888	3913	3938	3962	3987	4012	4036	4061	4085
4.1	4110	4134	4159	4183	4207	4231	4255	4279	4303	4327
4.2	4351	4375	4398	4422	4446	4469	4493	4516	4540	4563
4.3	4586	4609	4633	4656	4679	4702	4725	4748	4770	4793
4.4	4816	4839	4861	4884	4907	4929	4951	4974	4996	5019
4.5	1.5041	5063	5085	5107	5129	5151	5173	5195	5217	5239
4.6	5261	5282	5304	5326	5347	5369	5390	5412	5433	5454
4.7	5476	5497	5518	5539	5560	5581	5602	5623	5644	5665
4.8	5686	5707	5728	5748	5769	5790	5810	5831	5851	5872
4.9	5892	5913	5933	5953	5974	5994	6014	6034	6054	6074
5.0	1.6094	6114	6134	6154	6174	6194	6214	6233	6253	6273
5.1	6292	6312	6332	6351	6371	6390	6409	6429	6448	6467
5.2	6487	6506	6525	6544	6563	6582	6601	6620	6639	6658
5.3	6677	6696	6715	6734	6752	6771	6790	6808	6827	6845
5.4	6864	6882	6901	6919	6938	6956	6974	6993	7011	7029

Example. ln 220 = ln 2.2 + 2 ln 10 = 0.7885 + 2(2.30259) = 5.3937.

N	0	1	2	3	4	5	6	7	8	9
5.5	1.7047	7066	7084	7102	7120	7138	7156	7174	7192	7210
5.6	7228	7246	7263	7281	7299	7317	7334	7352	7370	7387
5.7	7405	7422	7440	7457	7475	7492	7509	7527	7544	7561
5.8	7579	7596	7613	7630	7647	7664	7681	7699	7716	7733
5.9	7750	7766	7783	7800	7817	7834	7851	7867	7884	7901
6.0	1.7918	7934	7951	7967	7984	8001	8017	8034	8050	8066
6.1	8083	8099	8116	8132	8148	8165	8181	8197	8213	8229
6.2	8245	8262	8278	8294	8310	8326	8342	8358	8374	8390
6.3	8405	8421	8437	8453	8469	8485	8500	8516	8532	8547
6.4	8563	8579	8594	8610	8625	8641	8656	8672	8687	8703
6.5	1.8718	8733	8749	8764	8779	8795	8810	8825	8840	8856
6.6	8871	8886	8901	8916	8931	8946	8961	8976	8991	9006
6.7	9021	9036	9051	9066	9081	9095	9110	9125	9140	9155
6.8	9169	9184	9199	9213	9228	9242	9257	9272	9286	9301
6.9	9315	9330	9344	9359	9373	9387	9402	9416	9430	9445
7.0	1.9459	9473	9488	9502	9516	9530	9544	9559	9573	9587
7.1	9601	9615	9629	9643	9657	9671	9685	9699	9713	9727
7.2	9741	9755	9769	9782	9796	9810	9824	9838	9851	9865
7.3	9879	9892	9906	9920	9933	9947	9961	9974	9988	*0001
7.4	2.0015	0028	0042	0055	0069	0082	0096	0109	0122	0136
7.5	2.0149	0162	0176	0189	0202	0215	0229	0242	0255	0268
7.6	0281	0295	0308	0321	0334	0347	0360	0373	0386	0399
7.7	0412	0425	0438	0451	0464	0477	0490	0503	0516	0528
7.8	0541	0554	0567	0580	0592	0605	0618	0631	0643	0656
7.9	0669	0681	0694	0707	0719	0732	0744	0757	0769	0782
8.0	2.0794	0807	0819	0832	0844	0857	0869	0882	0894	0906
8.1	0919	0931	0943	0956	0968	0980	0992	1005	1017	1029
8.2	1041	1054	1066	1078	1090	1102	1114	1126	1138	1150
8.3	1163	1175	1187	1199	1211	1223	1235	1247	1258	1270
8.4	1282	1294	1306	1318	1330	1342	1353	1365	1377	1389
8.5	2.1401	1412	1424	1436	1448	1459	1471	1483	1494	1506
8.6	1518	1529	1541	1552	1564	1576	1587	1599	1610	1622
8.7	1633	1645	1656	1668	1679	1691	1702	1713	1725	1736
8.8	1748	1759	1770	1782	1793	1804	1815	1827	1838	1849
8.9	1861	1872	1883	1894	1905	1917	1928	1939	1950	1961
9.0	2.1972	1983	1994	2006	2017	2028	2039	2050	2061	2072
9.1	2083	2094	2105	2116	2127	2138	2148	2159	2170	2181
9.2	2192	2203	2214	2225	2235	2246	2257	2268	2279	2289
9.3	2300	2311	2322	2332	2343	2354	2364	2375	2386	2396
9.4	2407	2418	2428	2439	2450	2460	2471	2481	2492	2502
9.5	2.2513	2523	2534	2544	2555	2565	2576	2586	2597	2607
9.6	2618	2628	2638	2649	2659	2670	2680	2690	2701	2711
9.7	2721	2732	2742	2752	2762	2773	2783	2793	2803	2814
9.8	2824	2834	2844	2854	2865	2875	2885	2895	2905	2915
9.9	2925	2935	2946	2956	2966	2976	2986	2996	3006	3016

x	e^x	e^{-x}	$\sinh x$	$\cosh x$	$\tanh x$
0	1.0000	1.0000	.00000	1.0000	.00000
0.1	1.1052	.90484	.10017	1.0050	.09967
0.2	1.2214	.81873	.20134	1.0201	.19738
0.3	1.3499	.74082	.30452	1.0453	.29131
0.4	1.4918	.67032	.41075	1.0811	.37995
0.5	1.6487	.60653	.52110	1.1276	.46212
0.6	1.8221	.54881	.63665	1.1855	.53705
0.7	2.0138	.49659	.75858	1.2552	.60437
0.8	2.2255	.44933	.88811	1.3374	.66404
0.9	2.4596	.40657	1.0265	1.4331	.71630
1.0	2.7183	.36788	1.1752	1.5431	.76159
1.1	3.0042	.33287	1.3356	1.6685	.80050
1.2	3.3201	.30119	1.5095	1.8107	.83365
1.3	3.6693	.27253	1.6984	1.9709	.86172
1.4	4.0552	.24660	1.9043	2.1509	.88535
1.5	4.4817	.22313	2.1293	2.3524	.90515
1.6	4.9530	.20190	2.3756	2.5775	.92167
1.7	5.4739	.18268	2.6456	2.8283	.93541
1.8	6.0496	.16530	2.9422	3.1075	.94681
1.9	6.6859	.14957	3.2682	3.4177	.95624
2.0	7.3891	.13534	3.6269	3.7622	.96403
2.1	8.1662	.12246	4.0219	4.1443	.97045
2.2	9.0250	.11080	4.4571	4.5679	.97574
2.3	9.9742	.10026	4.9370	5.0372	.98010
2.4	11.023	.09072	5.4662	5.5569	.98367
2.5	12.182	.08208	6.0502	6.1323	.98661
2.6	13.464	.07427	6.6947	6.7690	.98903
2.7	14.880	.06721	7.4063	7.4735	.99101
2.8	16.445	.06081	8.1919	8.2527	.99263
2.9	18.174	.05502	9.0596	9.1146	.99396
3.0	20.086	.04979	10.018	10.068	.99505
3.1	22.198	.04505	11.076	11.122	.99595
3.2	24.533	.04076	12.246	12.287	.99668
3.3	27.113	.03688	13.538	13.575	.99728
3.4	29.964	.03337	14.965	14.999	.99777
3.5	33.115	.03020	16.543	16.573	.99818
3.6	36.598	.02732	18.285	18.313	.99851
3.7	40.447	.02472	20.211	20.236	.99878
3.8	44.701	.02237	22.339	22.362	.99900
3.9	49.402	.02024	24.691	24.711	.99918
4.0	54.598	.01832	27.290	27.308	.99933
4.1	60.340	.01657	30.162	30.178	.99945
4.2	66.686	.01500	33.336	33.351	.99955
4.3	73.700	.01357	36.843	36.857	.99963
4.4	81.451	.01228	40.719	40.732	.99970
4.5	90.017	.01111	45.003	45.014	.99975
4.6	99.484	.01005	49.737	49.747	.99980
4.7	109.95	.00910	54.969	54.978	.99983
4.8	121.51	.00823	60.751	60.759	.99986
4.9	134.29	.00745	67.141	67.149	.99989
5.0	148.41	.00674	74.203	74.210	.99991

Deg.	Rad.	Sin	Cos	Tan	Cot		
0	0.0000	0.0000	1.0000	0.0000		1.5708	90
1	0.0175	0.0175	0.9998	0.0175	57.290	1.5533	89
2	0.0349	0.0349	0.9994	0.0349	28.636	1.5359	88
3	0.0524	0.0523	0.9986	0.0524	19.081	1.5184	87
4	0.0698	0.0698	0.9976	0.0699	14.301	1.5010	86
5	0.0873	0.0872	0.9962	0.0875	11.430	1.4835	85
6	0.1047	0.1045	0.9945	0.1051	9.5144	1.4661	84
7	0.1222	0.1219	0.9925	0.1228	8.1443	1.4486	83
8	0.1396	0.1392	0.9903	0.1405	7.1154	1.4312	82
9	0.1571	0.1564	0.9877	0.1584	6.3138	1.4137	81
10	0.1745	0.1736	0.9848	0.1763	5.6713	1.3963	80
11	0.1920	0.1908	0.9816	0.1944	5.1446	1.3788	79
12	0.2094	0.2079	0.9781	0.2126	4.7046	1.3614	78
13	0.2269	0.2250	0.9744	0.2309	4.3315	1.3439	77
14	0.2443	0.2419	0.9703	0.2493	4.0108	1.3265	76
15	0.2618	0.2588	0.9659	0.2679	3.7321	1.3090	75
16	0.2793	0.2756	0.9613	0.2867	3.4874	1.2915	74
17	0.2967	0.2924	0.9563	0.3057	3.2709	1.2741	73
18	0.3142	0.3090	0.9511	0.3249	3.0777	1.2566	72
19	0.3316	0.3256	0.9455	0.3443	2.9042	1.2392	71
20	0.3491	0.3420	0.9397	0.3640	2.7475	1.2217	70
21	0.3665	0.3584	0.9336	0.3839	2.6051	1.2043	69
22	0.3840	0.3746	0.9272	0.4040	2.4751	1.1868	68
23	0.4014	0.3907	0.9205	0.4245	2.3559	1.1694	67
24	0.4189	0.4067	0.9135	0.4452	2.2460	1.1519	66
25	0.4363	0.4226	0.9063	0.4663	2.1445	1.1345	65
26	0.4538	0.4384	0.8988	0.4877	2.0503	1.1170	64
27	0.4712	0.4540	0.8910	0.5095	1.9626	1.0996	63
28	0.4887	0.4695	0.8829	0.5317	1.8807	1.0821	62
29	0.5061	0.4848	0.8746	0.5543	1.8040	1.0647	61
30	0.5236	0.5000	0.8660	0.5774	1.7321	1.0472	60
31	0.5411	0.5150	0.8572	0.6009	1.6643	1.0297	59
32	0.5585	0.5299	0.8480	0.6249	1.6003	1.0123	58
33	0.5760	0.5446	0.8387	0.6494	1.5399	0.9948	57
34	0.5934	0.5592	0.8290	0.6745	1.4826	0.9774	56
35	0.6109	0.5736	0.8192	0.7002	1.4281	0.9599	55
36	0.6283	0.5878	0.8090	0.7265	1.3764	0.9425	54
37	0.6458	0.6018	0.7986	0.7536	1.3270	0.9250	53
38	0.6632	0.6157	0.7880	0.7813	1.2799	0.9076	52
39	0.6807	0.6293	0.7771	0.8098	1.2349	0.8901	51
40	0.6981	0.6428	0.7660	0.8391	1.1918	0.8727	50
41	0.7156	0.6561	0.7547	0.8693	1.1504	0.8552	49
42	0.7330	0.6691	0.7431	0.9004	1.1106	0.8378	48
43	0.7505	0.6820	0.7314	0.9325	1.0724	0.8203	47
44	0.7679	0.6947	0.7193	0.9657	1.0355	0.8029	46
45	0.7854	0.7071	0.7071	1.0000	1.0000	0.7854	45
		Cos	Sin	Cot	Tan	Rad.	Deg.

N	0	1	2	3	4	5	6	7	8	9
10	0000	0043	0086	0128	0170	0212	0253	0294	0334	0374
11	0414	0453	0492	0531	0569	0607	0645	0682	0719	0755
12	0792	0828	0864	0899	0934	0969	1004	1038	1072	1106
13	1139	1173	1206	1239	1271	1303	1335	1367	1399	1430
14	1461	1492	1523	1553	1584	1614	1644	1673	1703	1732
15	1761	1790	1818	1847	1875	1903	1931	1959	1987	2014
16	2041	2068	2095	2122	2148	2175	2201	2227	2253	2279
17	2304	2330	2355	2380	2405	2430	2455	2480	2504	2529
18	2553	2577	2601	2625	2648	2672	2695	2718	2742	2765
19	2788	2810	2833	2856	2878	2900	2923	2945	2967	2989
20	3010	3032	3054	3075	3096	3118	3139	3160	3181	3201
21	3222	3243	3263	3284	3304	3324	3345	3365	3385	3404
22	3424	3444	3464	3483	3502	3522	3541	3560	3579	3598
23	3617	3636	3655	3674	3692	3711	3729	3747	3766	3784
24	3802	3820	3838	3856	3874	3892	3909	3927	3945	3962
25	3979	3997	4014	4031	4048	4065	4082	4099	4116	4133
26	4150	4166	4183	4200	4216	4232	4249	4265	4281	4298
27	4314	4330	4346	4362	4378	4393	4409	4425	4440	4456
28	4472	4487	4502	4518	4533	4548	4564	4579	4594	4609
29	4624	4639	4654	4669	4683	4698	4713	4728	4742	4757
30	4771	4786	4800	4814	4829	4843	4857	4871	4886	4900
31	4914	4928	4942	4955	4969	4983	4997	5011	5024	5038
32	5051	5065	5079	5092	5105	5119	5132	5145	5159	5172
33	5185	5198	5211	5224	5237	5250	5263	5276	5289	5302
34	5315	5328	5340	5353	5366	5378	5391	5403	5416	5428
35	5441	5453	5465	5478	5490	5502	5514	5527	5539	5551
36	5563	5575	5587	5599	5611	5623	5635	5647	5658	5670
37	5682	5694	5705	5717	5729	5740	5752	5763	5775	5786
38	5798	5809	5821	5832	5843	5855	5866	5877	5888	5899
39	5911	5922	5933	5944	5955	5966	5977	5988	5999	6010
40	6021	6031	6042	6053	6064	6075	6085	6096	6107	6117
41	6128	6138	6149	6160	6170	6180	6191	6201	6212	6222
42	6232	6243	6253	6263	6274	6284	6294	6304	6314	6325
43	6335	6345	6355	6365	6375	6385	6395	6405	6415	6425
44	6435	6444	6454	6464	6474	6484	6493	6503	6513	6522
45	6532	6542	6551	6561	6571	6580	6590	6599	6609	6618
46	6628	6637	6646	6656	6665	6675	6684	6693	6702	6712
47	6721	6730	6739	6749	6758	6767	6776	6785	6794	6803
48	6812	6821	6830	6839	6848	6857	6866	6875	6884	6893
49	6902	6911	6920	6928	6937	6946	6955	6964	6972	6981
50	6990	6998	7007	7016	7024	7033	7042	7050	7059	7067
51	7076	7084	7093	7101	7110	7118	7126	7135	7143	7152
52	7160	7168	7177	7185	7193	7202	7210	7218	7226	7235
53	7243	7251	7259	7267	7275	7284	7292	7300	7308	7316
54	7324	7332	7340	7348	7356	7364	7372	7380	7388	7396

N	0	1	2	3	4	5	6	7	8	9
55	7404	7412	7419	7427	7435	7443	7451	7459	7466	7474
56	7482	7490	7497	7505	7513	7520	7528	7536	7543	7551
57	7559	7566	7574	7582	7589	7597	7604	7612	7619	7627
58	7634	7642	7649	7657	7664	7672	7679	7686	7694	7701
59	7709	7716	7723	7731	7738	7745	7752	7760	7767	7774
60	7782	7789	7796	7803	7810	7818	7825	7832	7839	7846
61	7853	7860	7868	7875	7882	7889	7896	7903	7910	7917
62	7924	7931	7938	7945	7952	7959	7966	7973	7980	7987
63	7993	8000	8007	8014	8021	8028	8035	8041	8048	8055
64	8062	8069	8075	8082	8089	8096	8102	8109	8116	8122
65	8129	8136	8142	8149	8156	8162	8169	8176	8182	8189
66	8195	8202	8209	8215	8222	8228	8235	8241	8248	8254
67	8261	8267	8274	8280	8287	8293	8299	8306	8312	8319
68	8325	8331	8338	8344	8351	8357	8363	8370	8376	8382
69	8388	8395	8401	8407	8414	8420	8426	8432	8439	8445
70	8451	8457	8463	8470	8476	8482	8488	8494	8500	8506
71	8513	8519	8525	8531	8537	8543	8549	8555	8561	8567
72	8573	8579	8585	8591	8597	8603	8609	8615	8621	8627
73	8633	8639	8645	8651	8657	8663	8669	8675	8681	8686
74	8692	8698	8704	8710	8716	8722	8727	8733	8739	8745
75	8751	8756	8762	8768	8774	8779	8785	8791	8797	8802
76	8808	8814	8820	8825	8831	8837	8842	8848	8854	8859
77	8865	8871	8876	8882	8887	8893	8899	8904	8910	8915
78	8921	8927	8932	8938	8943	8949	8954	8960	8965	8971
79	8976	8982	8987	8993	8998	9004	9009	9015	9020	9025
80	9031	9036	9042	9047	9053	9058	9063	9069	9074	9079
81	9085	9090	9096	9101	9106	9112	9117	9122	9128	9133
82	9138	9143	9149	9154	9159	9165	9170	9175	9180	9186
83	9191	9196	9201	9206	9212	9217	9222	9227	9232	9238
84	9243	9248	9253	9258	9263	9269	9274	9279	9284	9289
85	9294	9299	9304	9309	9315	9320	9325	9330	9335	9340
86	9345	9350	9355	9360	9365	9370	9375	9380	9385	9390
87	9395	9400	9405	9410	9415	9420	9425	9430	9435	9440
88	9445	9450	9455	9460	9465	9469	9474	9479	9484	9489
89	9494	9499	9504	9509	9513	9518	9523	9528	9533	9538
90	9542	9547	9552	9557	9562	9566	9571	9576	9581	9586
91	9590	9595	9600	9605	9609	9614	9619	9624	9628	9633
92	9638	9643	9647	9652	9657	9661	9666	9671	9675	9680
93	9685	9689	9694	9699	9703	9708	9713	9717	9722	9727
94	9731	9736	9741	9745	9750	9754	9759	9763	9768	9773
95	9777	9782	9786	9791	9795	9800	9805	9809	9814	9818
96	9823	9827	9832	9836	9841	9845	9850	9854	9859	9863
97	9868	9872	9877	9881	9886	9890	9894	9899	9903	9908
98	9912	9917	9921	9926	9930	9934	9939	9943	9948	9952
99	9956	9961	9965	9969	9974	9978	9983	9987	9991	9996

INDEX